Principles and Applications
of Water Chemistry

Principles and Applications of Water Chemistry

Edited by

SAMUEL D. FAUST
JOSEPH V. HUNTER

Department of Environmental Sciences
Rutgers University

Proceedings of the Fourth Rudolfs Research Conference
Rutgers • The State University
New Brunswick, New Jersey

JOHN WILEY & SONS, Inc.
New York • London • Sydney

Photograph Courtesy of The Bergen Evening Record Corporation

The Editors Wish to Dedicate This Volume
to the Memory of Dr. Victor K. La Mer

Preface

The application of well-known and well-established principles of chemistry to aqueous environments is, perhaps, a
relatively recent advent whereupon a new expression, a new
term, is spreading throughout the profession "water chemistry."
This "new" chemistry is receiving considerable attention in
didactic and research circles. What, then is water chemistry?
Can this term be defined? Or is it, perhaps, a variation of
an old theme?

Water chemistry has a solid foundation; namely, classical
thermo-dynamics wherein the principles are sound. On the
other hand, water chemistry is not a pure chemistry; rather,
it is an applied chemistry. This chemistry is concerned with
water and wastewater treatment, with ground and surface
waters, and with the oceans. (At this writing, the chemistry
of atmospheric waters seems a little abstract). The latter
two areas are concerned with various equilibria occurring at
the interfaces of water-air and water-solid and with interactions
occurring within the aqueous phase. As such there is little that
can be done to influence this chemistry, but much can be done
to qualitate and quantitate it. On the other hand, the chemistry
of water and wastewater treatment must be researched and
understood so that it can be influenced to provide the proper
product; namely, purer water. Since this chemistry is of more
immediate concern to mankind, it is of a more practical nature
and value. This area of water chemistry is emphasized in the
Proceedings of the Fourth Rudolfs Research Conference. (A
hint of the chemistry of natural aqueous environments in provided also). In this context, then, water chemistry does seem
to be the curiosity of the theoretician and researcher, for little
application of current knowledge has been made. This statement
seems especially true when metal corrosion products come
spewing forth from domestic water taps at the most inconvenient
times. Or when the tongue and nose respond to off-flavored
and odorous waters. This volume does not pretend to offer
solutions to everyday problems of the chemistry water and
wastewater treatment. It does, however, hope to create an

vii

awareness that chemical principles can be and should be applied to the practical technology of water and wastewater treatment.

In recent years, considerable interest has been exhibited by the pure and applied chemist to problems of chemical coagulation and flocculation, adsorption, corrosion, and aqueous metalions. Consequently, much enthusiasm has been generated by the chemical intrigue of these problems. The editors took advantage of this relatively recent enthusiasm and interest . Another of the conference's objectives, perhaps the more important one, was to bring together some of these pure and applied chemists. This is, of course, the "interdisciplinary" approach or the "cross-fertilization" concept of which we hear so often, but is so seldom practiced. No doubt, the speakers and conferree's benefited from hearing and talking with one another. It is hoped, however, that their messages, their enthusiasm, and their interest will spread to others from the twenty-three papers and discussions that are presented herein. A "critical mass" of water chemists must be developed and maintained in order to keep sharp focus on the problems of water technology.

Many people contributed to the success of the Fourth Rudolfs Research Conference. It would only prolong the length of this book to name everyone. The editors wish, however, to make special note of the excellent cooperation and competent services of Dean Westervelt Griffin and Mrs. Grace Stein of the College of Agriculture and Environmental Science. All arrangements for the conference were expertly and efficiently handled by these two. We wish to thank Rutgers, The State University, for use of the excellent physical facilities. (More precisely, we should thank the citizens of New Jersey for providing the tax money). The many graduate students, technicians, secretaries, and professors of the Department of Environmental Science should be acknowledged for their cooperation with appreciation. Financial support was provided by Research Grant No. WP860 of the Public Health Service, USDHEW, Washington, D.C. and by the Rudolfs Memorial Fund. Mrs. Betty Reagan and Mrs. John Cushing provided excellent typing services. We are indebted to John Wiley & Sons, N.Y. for their splendid cooperation in the publication of this book. Lastly, the editors are deeply indebted to the speakers and session chairmen for their contributions and patience.

New Brunswick, N. J.   Samuel D. Faust
February, 1967   Joseph V. Hunter

Welcoming Remarks

H. Heukelekian

Rutgers University

It is my privilege to open this conference by welcoming you on behalf of the Department of Environmental Sciences.

Some of you may not know why this conference is dedicated to Dr. Rudolfs. He was the first chairman of our Department who served from 1922 until 1952 when he retired. He guided the early development and subsequent growth of the Department and made numerous scientific and professional contributions.

The first of these conferences was held in 1960 and was devoted to the topic "The Principles of Colloidal Behavior and Their Application to Water Sanitation.". This was followed in 1961 with a conference which dealt with the subject of "Public Health Hazards of Microbial Pollution of Water." The third conference held in 1963 dealt with the theme of "Principles and Applications in Aquatic Microbiology." The Proceedings of these three conferences were made available to the conferees and others upon request.

You may have discerned from the themes of these past conferences certain concepts as to their objectives. There should be a rationalization and justification for adding to the long list of International, National, Regional, and State Conferences we are all tempted to attend these days and have to make decisions of selection. We may be biased but we believe that Rudolfs conferences are different, not to say unique. They are, in the first place, on a selected and restricted theme rather than being miscellaneous contributions. In this respect it is somewhat similar to the Gordon Research Conferences. The selected theme is then divided into specific topics including the theoretical and applied aspects. The outstanding authorities are invited to present these topics. The speakers are not necessarily confined to the applied scientists but are also selected from the basic disciplines. It is our feeling that we can utilize and benefit from existing concepts, developments, information and techniques, from the broad scientific areas which, unfortunately, many of us do not have the time to absorb or read in this rapid stage of scientific developments. This is the modern trend of cross-fertilization between various disciplines and the abolishing of rigid boundaries and pigeonholing and specialization of knowledge. The present conference illustrates these concepts.

Chairmen of the Sessions

M. B. Ettinger
U.S. Department of The Interior

J. Cohen
U.S. Department of The Interior

R. F. Packham
Water Research Association

A. E. Greenberg
California State Department of Health

S. Zenchelsky
Rutgers University

W. Rieman, III
Rutgers University

Contents

Henry Eyring
Edward M. Eyring
University of Utah

REACTION RATES IN SOLUTION

The simplest type of reaction rate involves a change along the reaction coordinate only with all other degrees of freedeom remaining unchanged. In this case the expression for the specific rate is:

$$k' = \frac{kT}{h} \ (1 - e^{\frac{-h\upsilon}{kT}}) \ e^{\frac{-Eo^{\ddagger}}{RT}} \tag{1-1}$$

At high temperatures the factor $(1 - e^{-h\upsilon/kT}) \to h\upsilon/kT$ and equation 1-1 takes the very simple form (1):

$$k' = \varkappa \upsilon e^{\frac{-Eo^{\ddagger}}{RT}} \tag{1-2}$$

The relaxations that occur in ordinary liquids associated with viscous flow and diffusion approximate this simple behavior. The transmission coefficient, $\varkappa$, is frequently near unity. The frequency of vibration, υ, is the degree of freedom of the reactant that passes into the reaction coordinate in the activated complex. $Eo^{\ddagger}$, R, k, h, and T are the activation energy at absolute zero, the gas constant, the Boltzmann constant, Planck's constant, and the absolute temperature respectively. For such a reaction the entropy of activation is:

1

$$\Delta S^{\ddagger} = \frac{\partial RT \ln \frac{k'h}{kT\kappa}}{\partial T} = \frac{R \partial}{\partial T}\left(T \ln\left(\frac{1}{1-e^{-h\nu/kT}} \quad e^{\frac{-E_0^{\ddagger}}{RT}}\right)\right)(1-3)$$

$$\Delta S^{\ddagger} = -R \ln (1 - e^{-h\nu/kT}) + \frac{Nh\nu}{T(e^{h\nu/kT}-1)}$$

When ν is large, $\Delta S^{\ddagger}$ approaches zero as may be seen from equation 1-3.

In another extreme type of reaction, the partition function for many degrees of freedom changes as the system passes from the initial to the activated state. This occurs in solvents with high dielectric constants, providing there is a marked change in polarity of reactants in passing from the initial to the activated state. Examples of reaction rates of all degrees of complexity can be found in the liquid state. The transmission coefficient is also an important consideration (2).

THE COLLISION THEORY APPROXIMATION.

If the collision theory applied in both directions for a reaction of the type:

$$A-B + C-D \rightleftharpoons A-C + B-D \qquad (1-4)$$

there would necessarily be almost no entropy change in the reaction. Most reactions of the type indicated by equation 1-4 involve an appreciable entropy change so that simple collision theory is inapplicable. For the collision theory to apply strictly, the three translational degrees of freedom of each molecule in the initial state must be replaced by three translational degrees, 2 rotational degrees, and a translation along the reaction coordinate in the activated complex. All other degrees of freedom must remain unchanged in passing from the initial state to the activated complex. Under these conditions the specific rate constant is (1):

$$k'_{gas} = \kappa(r_1 + r_2)^2\left[2\pi kT (m_1+m_2)/(m_1^2 m_2^2 \sigma_{12})\right]e^{\frac{-E_0^{\ddagger}}{kT}}$$
$$(1-5)$$

Here $r_1 + r_2$ is the distance between the center of the two reacting molecules in the activated state; m_1 and m_2 are the respective molecular masses and $\sigma 12$, the symmetry number, is two if the molecules are alike otherwise unity and $Eo^{\ddagger}$ is the activation energy at absolute zero. The other quantities have been defined previously. If the same reaction occurs in solution with only the same six degrees of freedom changed in passing from the initial to the activated state, the classical mechanical approximation is obtained:

$$k' \text{ solution} = k' \text{gas} \left(\frac{V_f^{\ddagger}}{V}\right)\left(\frac{V}{V_{fi}}\right)\left(\frac{V}{V_{f2}}\right) e^{-\frac{D_{AS} + D_{BS}}{2\,RT}} \frac{frl}{frg} \quad (1\text{-}6)$$

Here V_{fi} and V_f are the free volume of the ith molecule and the activated complex, respectively. V is the mean molecular volume of the solution. D_{AS} and D_{BS} are the bonds made by A with the solvent molecule and of B with the solvent molecule, respectively. The partition functions for the rotational degrees of freedom of the activated complex in the liquid and in the gas phase are frl and f_{rg}, respectively. Each of the ratios V/V_{fi} has the value r where r is the ratio of the velocity of sound in the liquid phase to its value in the gas and has a value of about 7.

The exponential factor has a value of about 10 while the last factor is apt to be of the order of 1/100 th. Thus, if the gas collision formula is used for calculating an "uncomplicated" rate of reaction in solution, the rate would be underestimated by a factor of about 10 to 100. Reactions that involve ions in polar solvents can yield a factor which varies drastically in either direction from this estimate.

SOLUTION REACTIONS INVOLVING LOW ACTIVATION ENERGIES

If there is a high probability, $\varkappa_e$, of reaction taking place whenever molecule A comes within a distance r of molecule B, it is useful to calculate the rate of such encounters. The numbers of such encounters per cc, R_e, is:

$$R_e = C_A \, \varkappa_e \, \frac{D}{\lambda} \, 4\Pi r^2 \, C_B \equiv k_e \, C_A \, C_B \quad (1\text{-}7)$$

Here C_A and C_B are the number of molecules per cc of A and B, respectively. D is the diffusion coefficient, and λ

is the distance a molecule moves as it jumps from one
molecular cage to the next. Thus C_A/λ is a concentration
gradient, $4\pi r^2$ is the surface area around a molecule B
across which the molecules A must diffuse, and $4\pi r^2 C_B$
is the total surface area for all B molecules in a cc. If
a reaction is of the type where not every collision is successful, an additional expression is required for the rate, R_C,
whenever the diffusional process ceases to be limiting.
This is:

$$R_c = k_c\, C_A\, C_B \qquad\qquad (1\text{-}8)$$

where:

$$k_c = \varkappa\, \frac{kT}{h}\, e^{-\frac{\Delta G^{\ddagger}}{RT}} \qquad\qquad (1\text{-}9)$$

The overall steady state rate at which a molecule passes
through these two successive stages leading to reaction
is then:

$$R = C_A \left[(k_e C_B)^{-1} + (k_c C_B)^{-1} \right]^{-1} = C_A C_B \frac{k_c k_e}{k_e + k_c} \quad (1\text{-}10)$$

The rate of reaction per molecule of A is, therefore, the
reciprocal of the sums of the two reactions times that
would apply if each of the two sequential steps were alone
rate limiting. The resistances to reaction are summed for
reactions in sequence the same as resistances of electrical
circuits in series. Of course, reactions in parallel add
their rates.

Thus if $k_c \gg k_e$ equation 1-7 then gives the rate of
reaction whereas if $k_c \ll k_e$ equation 1-8 then gives the rate.
When $k_c \approx k_e$ equation 1-10 is required. Some fluorescence
quenching rates are diffusion controlled in accord with
equation 1-7. Debye derived somewhat differently the rate
expression for diffusion controlled reactions several years
ago (3).

ABSOLUTE RATE THEORY (4)

It is useful to re-examine rate theory for an elementary process in the light of newer developments in liquid
theory. The activated complex is conveniently considered
as being similar to any other molecule except for a fourth

translational degree of freedom along the reaction coordinate. If $C_f^{\ddagger}$ is the concentration of activated complexes
per length δ along the reaction coordinate in equilibrium
with reactants, and $C_{\delta b}^{\ddagger}$ is the same quantity in equilibrium
with products, then the net rate of reaction, $R \equiv R_f - R_b$, is:

$$R = \tfrac{1}{2} (C_{\delta f}^{\ddagger} - C_{\delta b}^{\ddagger}) \; \frac{\bar{u}}{\delta} \; \varkappa \qquad\qquad (1\text{-}11)$$

Now $C_f^{\ddagger}$ is defined as the concentration of activated complexes per quantum state along the reaction coordinate in
equilibrium with reactants.
Then:

$$C_{\delta f}^{\ddagger} = C_f^{\ddagger} \; \frac{(2 \, \Pi \, m^{\ddagger} \, kT)^{\frac{1}{2}}}{h} \delta \qquad\qquad (1\text{-}12a)$$

Similarly:

$$C_{\delta b}^{\ddagger} = C_b^{\ddagger} \; \frac{(2 \, \Pi \, m^{\ddagger} \, kT)^{\frac{1}{2}}}{h} \delta \qquad\qquad (1\text{-}12b)$$

Since:

$$\bar{u} = \left(\frac{2 \, kT}{\Pi \, m^{\ddagger}} \right)^{\frac{1}{2}} \qquad\qquad (1\text{-}13)$$

We have:

$$R = \varkappa \; \frac{kT}{h} \; (C_f^{\ddagger} - C_b^{\ddagger}) \qquad\qquad (1\text{-}14)$$

Since activated complexes are always dilute, Boltzmann
statistics apply. Hence, the number of molecules, n_i, in
equilibrium with the number n_j is:

$$\frac{n_i}{n_j} = \frac{\exp \, (- \varepsilon_i / kT)}{\exp \, (- \varepsilon_j / kT)} \qquad\qquad (1\text{-}15)$$

or:

$$\frac{n_i}{\exp \, (- \varepsilon_i / kT)} = \frac{n_j}{\exp \, (- \varepsilon_j / kT)} = \lambda \qquad (1\text{-}16)$$

ε_i and ε_j are the respective energies of the two kinds of
molecules. λ is the absolute activity. If the states in a
system are summed, the total number of molecules, N, is:

$$N = \sum_i n_i = \lambda \sum_i \exp \, (- \varepsilon_i / kT) \qquad\qquad (1\text{-}17)$$

Since the concentration $C = N/V$, an expression can be written:

$$C = \lambda \sum_i V^{-1} \exp(-\epsilon_i/kT) \tag{1-18}$$

and:

$$\sum_i \exp(-\epsilon_i/kT) = f \tag{1-19}$$

Since f is the partition function and:

$$f/V = F \tag{1-20}$$

the partition function per unit volume, equation 1-14 can be rewritten from equations 1-18, 1-19, and 1-20 as:

$$R = \varkappa \frac{kT}{h} F^{\ddagger} (\lambda_f^{\ddagger} - \lambda_b^{\ddagger}) \tag{1-21}$$

For any equilibrium, the product of the absolute activities of the reactants equals the product of the absolute activities of the products. Thus, if:

$$A + B + \ldots \longrightarrow C^{\ddagger} + D + \ldots \longleftarrow F + G \tag{1-22}$$

Then:

$$\lambda_A \ \lambda_B \cdots = \lambda_f^{\ddagger} \ \lambda_D \cdots \tag{1-23}$$

and:

$$\lambda_F \ \lambda_G \cdots = \lambda_b^{\ddagger} \ \lambda_D \cdots \tag{1-24}$$

Rewriting equation (1-21) we have:

$$R = \varkappa \frac{kT}{h} \frac{F^{\ddagger}}{\lambda_D} \cdots (\lambda_A \ \lambda_B \cdots - \lambda_F \ \lambda_G \cdots) \tag{1-25}$$

Substances like D in equation 1-22 inhibit the rate of reaction as seen by equation 1-25. When an enzyme or catalytic surface enters into a reaction, any poison D must be desorbed from a reaction site before the activated complex can be formed. This causes the rate to be inversely proportional to the absolute activity of the poison. Since equation 1-25 is applicable to all kinds of statistics, reactions that involve condensed phases offer no difficulty in principle.

For reactions where no inhibitor D is involved and where the system follows Boltzmann statistics for all reactants we have (5):

$$R = \kappa \frac{kT}{h} F^{\ddagger} \left(\frac{C_A}{F_A} \frac{C_B}{F_B} \cdots - \frac{C_F}{F_F} \frac{C_G}{F_G} \cdots \right) \qquad (1-26)$$

Gaseous reactions ordinarily follow equation 1-26. For reactions in solution, two courses are open.

$K_f^{\ddagger}$ and $K_b^{\ddagger}$ can be defined:

$$\frac{F^{\ddagger}}{F_A \, F_B \cdots} = K_f^{\ddagger}$$

and:

$$\frac{F^{\ddagger}}{F_F \, F_G \cdots} = K_b^{\ddagger}$$

Since $K_f^{\ddagger}$ and $K_b^{\ddagger}$ behave like any equilibrium constants, we write:

$$R = \kappa \frac{kT}{h} \left(K_f^{\ddagger} C_A C_B \cdots - K_b^{\ddagger} C_F C_G \cdots \right)$$

$$R = \kappa \frac{kT}{h} \left(e^{-\frac{\Delta G_f^{\ddagger}}{RT}} C_A C_B \cdots - e^{-\frac{\Delta G_b^{\ddagger}}{RT}} C_F C_G \cdots \right)$$

$$R = \kappa \frac{kT}{h} \left(e^{-\frac{\Delta H_f^{\ddagger}}{RT}} e^{-\frac{\Delta S_f^{\ddagger}}{R}} e^{-\frac{\overline{\Delta V}_f^{\ddagger} (p-1)}{RT}} C_A C_B \cdots \right.$$

$$\left. - e^{-\frac{\Delta H_b^{\ddagger}}{RT}} e^{-\frac{\Delta S_b^{\ddagger}}{R}} e^{-\frac{\overline{\Delta V}_b^{\ddagger} (p-1)}{RT}} C_F C_G \cdots \right) \qquad (1-27)$$

Here $\Delta G^{\ddagger}$, $\Delta H^{\ddagger}$, $\Delta S^{\ddagger}$, and $\overline{\Delta V}^{\ddagger}$, are the standard free energy of activation, heat, entropy, and average volume changes in activation, respectively. The pressure in atmospheres is p.

Equation 1-27 is extremely useful for treating reaction kinetics. Experimental values found for the thermodynamic function can prove to be powerful criteria for pinpointing the reaction mechanism. However, if it is desirable to calculate the equilibrium constant from first principles, a statistical mechanical theory of the state is required in which the reaction is occurring.

Since:

$$\lambda_i = e^{\mu i / kT} = e^{\left(\frac{\partial A}{\partial n_i} \right) \frac{1}{kT}}$$

equation 1-25 can be rewritten. Here μ_i is the chemical
potential of the ith species and A is the Helmholtz free
energy. The case where there is no poison D will be treated.
It will be obvious how the equation is to be modified for
a poison:

$$R = \varkappa \frac{kT}{h} \ F^{\ddagger}\left(e^{\frac{\mu A}{kT}} \ e^{\frac{\mu B}{kT}\ldots} - e^{\frac{\mu F}{kT}} \ e^{\frac{\mu G}{kT}\ldots}\right)$$

$$R = \varkappa \frac{kT}{h} \ F^{\ddagger}\left(e^{\left(\frac{\partial A}{\partial n_A} + \frac{\partial A}{\partial n_B} + \ldots\right)\frac{1}{kT}}\right.$$

$$\left. -e^{\left(\frac{\partial A}{\partial n_f} + \frac{\partial A}{\partial n_G} + \ldots\right)\frac{1}{kT}}\right) \qquad (1\text{-}28)$$

The reaction rate problem in liquids thus is reduced to
finding the Helmholtz free energy for liquid mixtures.

THE MECHANISM OF REACTION AND ENERGY OF ACTIVATION

An atom or radical with a free valence ordinarily reacts
with a molecule with little or no activation energy providing
the reaction is exothermic. Activation energy in the reverse
endothermal direction, has a higher activation energy by an
amount equal to the heat of reaction. For example, a
deuterium atom reacts with a hydrogen molecule with an
activation energy of 8 kcal. This is a high value for this
type of reaction. When a hydrogen atom reacts with a
halogen molecule the heat of activation is more like 2 kcal.
Such reactions are exothermic. The reverse of each
exothermic reaction has an activation energy greater than
the 2 kcal. by the heat of reaction. The activation energy
for two reacting saturated molecules is typically much
higher than 2 kcal.

NATURE OF THE ACTIVATION ENERGY

Activation energy is typically the promotional energy
of electrons arising from their climb into excited states
to avoid violating the Pauli Exclusion Principle. Alterna-
tively, a marked attenuation of the weaker bond follows by
an attack of components of the weaker bond on the stronger
bond. As the molecules come close enough together to
overlap in the manner necessary to make new bonds, the
crowded condition of the electrons is alleviated whenever

possible by shifting into unoccupied orbitals. The first excited state of a hydrogen atom, however, is so high above the ground state, 9.15 v, that it is for all practical purposes inaccessible. Thus, a reaction such as:

$$D_2 + H_2 \longrightarrow H - D - D - H \longrightarrow 2\,HD \qquad (1-29)$$

can better comply with the Pauli Exclusion Principle and avoid the electronic congestion by breaking one of the hydrogen molecule bonds in passing to the activated state. There is then the possibility of a solo attack on the D_2 by one hydrogen atom or a dual attack by the two atoms approaching each side as indicated in equation 1-29. Actually the square configuration may give a slightly more stable activated complex than the four atom linear one. In any case, an activation energy which is a substantial part of the dissociation energy of one hydrogen molecule bond is to be expected for the four atom reaction mechanism. In fact, an easier 3 atom reaction pathway is available. For the equilibrium:

$$H_2 \rightleftharpoons 2H \qquad (1-30)$$

We may write:

$$\frac{(H)^2}{(H_2)} = K = e^{-\frac{\Delta H}{RT}} \, e^{\frac{\Delta S}{R}} \qquad (1-31)$$

Hence for the concentration of atoms (H) we have:

$$(H) = (H_2)^{\frac{1}{2}} \, e^{-\frac{\Delta H}{2RT}} \, e^{\frac{\Delta S}{2R}} \qquad (1-32)$$

Since the reaction:

$$H + D_2 \longrightarrow HD + H$$

has an activation energy of 8 kcal, the overall apparent activation energy is:

$$8 + \frac{102.3}{2} = 59.2 \text{ kcal} \qquad (1-34)$$

Since this is much less than the 102.3 kcal for the dissociation energy of H_2, a solo attack by one hydrogen atom on D_2 is the observed mechanism. It is not surprising that three monovalent atoms in the activated complex, which is linear, are held together by an energy equal to about one hydrogen molecule bond.

In the London approximation, the total exchange binding energy is the amount by which the three exchange integrals between pairs of atoms fail to give a closed triangle when joined together to make two 60⁰ angles. When the outside atoms are alike, on a line, and equidistant from the central atom such as in an activated complex, the exchange integral between outside atoms will be small and only slightly larger than the excess coulombic energy for a single bond. The result is that the activated state will have a total bonding energy approximately that of a single bond.

Four atoms can be joined into two pairs in three different ways. For any configuration of the four atoms, the sum of the exchange binding for each of these pairs will be called α, β, and γ, respectively. Now the overall binding for the four atoms is the vector sum of α, β, and γ when 60⁰ angles are drawn between successive vectors. In an activated state, α tends to be about equal to β with γ a little larger than the smaller of the two exchange integrals making up α. The result is, after taking account of the excess coulombic energy, that the activated state energy corresponds roughly to the strongest bond in the initial state if the reaction is in the exothermal direction.

A catalyst frequently acts by lessening the instability of an activated complex by bonding with part of the temporarily excessive number of bonding electrons in the activated state. In the absence of accessible states to alleviate the electronic pressure in an activated complex, the atoms will first break the weaker of the two bonds. Then one of the liberated atoms or radicals can make a solo attack on the stronger bond if the resultant reaction is not too endothermic. If the reaction is excessively endothermic, a two atom attack on the stronger bond will ordinarily eliminate endothermicity and will be the favored mechanism. This theory of reaction will be described as the weak bond attenuation model. The attenuation is followed by either a one atom or two atom attack on the strong bond.

These principles are illustrated by a consideration of the reactions of hydrogen with the halogens. The apparent activation energy, $E_3^{\ddagger}$, for a three atom reaction should be:

$$E_3^{\ddagger} \approx \tfrac{1}{2} D_w + 2 + E_{e3} \qquad (1\text{-}35)$$

whereas $E_4^{\pm}$ for the four atom mechanism should be:

$$E_4^{\pm} \approx D_w + 4 + E_{e4} \tag{1-36}$$

Here D_W is the dissociation energy of the weaker of two bonds entering into the reaction. Since the endothermicity, E_{e4}, of a concerted attack by the two weak bond atoms upon the strong bond is zero in all the applied cases, we have:

$$E_4^{\pm} - E_3^{\pm} = \tfrac{1}{2} D_w + 2 - E_{e3} \tag{1-37}$$

In Table I the results are recorded for reactions involving H_2 reacting with the halogens (6, 7).

TABLE I.   ACTIVATION ENERGIES FOR
HYDROGEN-HALOGEN REACTIONS

Reactants	D_w	E_{e3}	E_4		E_3	
			Calc.	Exp.	Calc.	Exp.
$H_2 + I_2$	36.2	32	40.2	40	52.1	51.5
$H_2 + Br_2$	46.1	16.1	50.1	-	41.2	40.7
$H_2 + Cl_2$	57.8	.7	61.8	-	31.6	33.5
$H_2 + F_2$	63.5	(-44.1)	67.5	-	33.8	-

There is good agreement between the calculation from our "weak bond attenuation model" and experiment in all the known cases. Substituting for E_{e3} its value:

$$E_{e3} = D_s - D_f = \tfrac{1}{2} (D_s - D_w) + \frac{\Delta H}{2}$$

into equation 1-37 gives:

$$E_4^{\pm} - E_3^{\pm} = D_w - \tfrac{1}{2} D_s - \frac{\Delta H}{2} + 2 \tag{1-38}$$

Here the heat of reaction is:

$$\Delta H = D_s + D_w - 2D_f$$

where D_f is the bond formed in the 3 atom reaction. For all isotopic reactions such as $H_2 + D_2 = 2HD$, the quantity

$E_4^{\ddagger} - E_3^{\ddagger}$ will be strongly positive since $\Delta H \approx O$ and $D_w \approx D_s$.

That the 3 atom mechanism will be preferred in all uncatalyzed isotope exchange reactions can be predicted. It is probable that every reaction which exchanges partners of two bonds can be made to go with a very low activation energy by catalysis. It becomes necessary to break one or both bonds that leave empty orbitals. This causes ions or radicals to form which are not too stably bound. Consequently, they react among themselves and leave some bonds still unbroken.

Since the preferred mechanism can be decided for a reaction in many cases because as we have seen, the activation energy can be estimated, and since the frequencies and moments of inertia ordinarily can be estimated closely from the structure of the activated complex, the rates of such reactions can be estimated a priori.

The experimentalist may ask to what extent the preceding theories of reaction kinetics apply to fast reactions in aqueous solutions that have become recently accessible to measurement by relaxation methods such as sound absorption, N.M.R., and the various temperature jump techniques. There are some comparatively rare exceptions such as the hydrolysis of SO_2 and of CO_2 for which marked differences in rates can be ascribed primarily to solute molecular structures rather than solute-solvent interactions (8). The single step reaction:

$$HSO_3^- + H^+ \underset{}{\overset{k_f}{\rightleftharpoons}} SO_2 + H_2O \qquad (1-39)$$

for which $k_f = 2 \times 10^8 \ M^{-1} \ \text{sec}^{-1}$ at 20°C, is much faster than:

$$HCO_3^- + H^+ \underset{}{\overset{k_f}{\rightleftharpoons}} CO_2 + H_2O \qquad (1-40)$$

having a forward rate constant $k_f = 5.6 \times 10^4 \ M^{-1} \ \text{sec}^{-1}$ at 25°C, apparently because in the latter reaction the bent HCO_3^- ion must form a linear CO_2 molecule whereas configuration changes in the SO_2 reaction are not as marked. At the other end of the spectrum of aqueous acid-base reactions in terms of the importance of solvent effects to the reaction mechanism is the reaction between the dianion of

2, 2-di-isopropyl malonic acid and solvent water:

$$A^{-2} + H_2O \underset{k_b}{\overset{k_f}{\rightleftharpoons}} HA^- + OH^- \qquad (1\text{-}41)$$

for which $k_f = 3.9 \ M^{-1} \ sec^{-1}$ at $25^{\circ}C$ and $k_f = 0.72 \ M^{-1} \ sec^{-1}$ at $12^{\circ}C$ (9). From this temperature dependence data and the absolute rate theory expression:

$$k_f = \frac{kT}{h} e^{-\Delta H^{\ddagger}/RT} e^{\Delta S^{\ddagger}/R} \qquad (1\text{-}42)$$

it follows that $\Delta S^{\ddagger} \approx +16$ eu. This reaction, the rate of which is said to be controlled by $\Delta S^{\ddagger}$ rather than by the more usual $\Delta H^{\ddagger}$, is one in which solvent effects are dominant. This comparatively large positive entropy of activation has been attributed to a "melting" of several water molecules from the solvation sheath of the dianion in order to attain an activated complex configuration. This notion stems from the observation that the molar entropy of fusion of water is approximately $+5$ eu (10). Calorimetric determination of heats of solution of the reactants eventually may attribute some of the trend in $\Delta S^{\ddagger}$ with various 2, 2-dialkyl substitutions of the dianion to various degrees of solvation of the reacting dianions rather than of the transition complexes (11).

While an a priori calculation of rate constants for reactions similar to reaction 1-41 in aqueous solution is not presently possible because of ignorance of the extent of solvation of the reactants as well as of the solvent and transition state structures, it is possible to make a priori calculations of quotients of rate constants in two different solvent media from absolute rate theory that are extremely useful. For instance, the quotient of the absolute rate theory specific rates for the reverse of reaction 1-41 in water and in deuterium oxide would be (12):

$$\frac{k^H}{k^D} = antilog \left(\frac{\Sigma \nu_H - \Sigma \nu_H}{12.53 \ T} \right) \qquad (1\text{-}43)$$

Where, in a first approximation, $\Sigma \nu_H$ is the sum of the stretching frequencies in the reactant state that becomes $\Sigma \nu_{H^{\ddagger}}$ in the activated complex configuration presuming all

other frequencies, including all bending modes, to be the
same in the two states. With this equation and equilibrium
constant data, it is possible to calculate secondary solvent
deuterium oxide isotope effects that permit an estimate from
the experimental effect of the primary hydrogen isotope
effect. Large primary isotope effects for the transfer of a
proton between oxygens as in reaction 1-41 indicate symmetrical transition states and, hence, quite strong bonding
of the acid proton in the monoanion (13). Here the important
point is that absolute rate theory has important applications
for the experimental reaction kineticist who is interested in
aqueous solutions even though the complexity of the solvent
medium precludes the a priori calculation of rate constants
in all but the simplest cases.

THE SIGNIFICANT STRUCTURE THEORY OF LIQUIDS (14, 15)

The thermodynamic theories of simple solids and gases
are satisfactory but liquid structure presents problems. The
liquid state is ordinarily intermediate in volume between
solid and vapor and it is also intermediate in the temperature
range in which it is stable. The volume discontinuity at
melting and the fact that the nearest neighbor distance as
revealed by X rays is almost the same for solid and liquid
indicates that the expansion is described better as arising
from vacancies than from a uniform lattice expansion.

A vacant lattice site requires the same energy for its
production as the vaporization of a molecule. In a solid the
vacancies are locked in but when enough vacancies are added
they become unlocked or are fluidized. This is the melting
process. For normal liquids this unlocking occurs when one
lattice site in eight is vacated. When a lattice site is
fluidized it moves through the liquid with much the same
velocity and ease with which molecules move in the gas phase.
Since a vacancy has the same energy of formation and entropy
as a gas molecule, a cc of vapor should contain the same
number of molecules as the number of fluidized vacancies in
a cc of liquid. Accordingly there are always just enough
molecules in a cc of saturated vapor to fill the vacancies in
a cc of liquid. Thus the only change in the mean density of
liquid and vapor is due to lattice expansion of the liquid which
follows a linear law. This explains the law of rectilinear
diameters of Cailletet and Mathias (16).

Calculation of the thermodynamic properties of any system involves knowing distribution of the normal modes. The number of moles of vacancies, n_h, in a mole E of liquid is:

$$n_h = \frac{V - V_s}{V_s} \qquad (1-44)$$

Here V is the molal volume of the liquid whereas V_s is the volume that the system would have if there were no vacancies. For simple liquids such as argon, V_s is the volume of the solid corrected for pressure and temperature changes whenever necessary. Now a vacancy in the liquid with all neighboring positions filled by molecules will act like a gas molecule. This means that three degrees of freedom of the surrounding molecules which would have been solid-like otherwise are in fact gas-like. Fortunately, it isn't necessary to specify which molecules at each instant are conferring these gas-like properties on the vacancy since their identity is changing from instant to instant. Now if a vacancy is completely surrounded by other vacancies it is without influence on the mechanical properties of the system. Since $\frac{V_s}{V}$ is the fraction of the neighboring positions which are filled by molecules this is the chance that a vacancy will be contributing gas-like properties to the system. Thus:

$$\frac{V_s}{V} n_h = \frac{V_s}{V} \frac{V - V_s}{V_s} = \frac{V - V_s}{V} = 1 - \frac{V_s}{V}$$

is the fraction of the degrees of freedom which are gas-like and the remaining fraction $\frac{V_s}{V}$ are solid-like. Thus the partition function, f^N, of N molecules of liquid can be written:

$$f_1^N = (f'_s)^{\frac{N V_s}{V}} f_g^{\frac{N V-V_s}{V}} \left(N \frac{(V - V_s)}{V} \right)! \qquad (1-45)$$

The partition function for the solid, f'_s is the usual function for a solid multiplied by a degeneracy factor:

$$1 + n \frac{V - V_s}{V_s} \exp\left(\frac{- a \, E_s \, V_s}{(V - V_s) \, RT} \right)$$

This factor is greater than one because of neighboring available vacancies. The number of these available positions is proportional to the total number of vacancies giving the factor $n \frac{(V-Vs)}{Vs}$ and the factor $e^{-\frac{a\,Es\,Vs}{(V-Vs)\,RT}}$ which is the chance a position is not occupied by some other molecule competing for the position. It is convenient and usually adequate to use for f_s the Einstein partition function for the solid:

$$f_s = \frac{e^{\,Es/RT}}{(1 - e^{\,\theta/T})^3} \tag{1-46}$$

For f_g, we have:

$$f_g = \frac{(2\,\Pi\,mkT)^{\frac{3}{2}}}{h^3} \cdot (V - Vs) \tag{1-47}$$

since $(V-Vs)$ is the maneuver space for those molecules which endow vacancies with gas-like properties. Using these relations in equation 1-45 for an argon like molecule gives:

$$f_1^N = \left(\frac{e^{\,Es/RT}}{(1 - e^{\,-\theta/T})^3} \left(1 + n\,(V-Vs) e^{\frac{-aEsVs}{(V-Vs)RT}} \right) \right)^{N\frac{Vs}{V}}$$

$$\left(\frac{(2\,\Pi\,mkT)^{\frac{3}{2}}}{h^3} \frac{eV}{N} \right)^{N\frac{V-Vs}{V}} \tag{1-48}$$

Thus an explicit expression for the Helmholtz free energy of a liquid is obtained:

$$A = kT\,\ln f_1^N \tag{1-49}$$

From equation 1-49, $\mu = \left(\frac{\partial A}{\partial N} \right)_{V, T}$ can be obtained from which reaction rates in solution can be calculated. Es, Vs, and θ are the energy of sublimation of the solid, the molal volume of the solid-like structure without vacancies, and the characteristic temperature of the solid, respectively. For simple liquids like argon the values of Es, Vs, and θ of the solid at the melting point are satisfactory. The dimensionless constants a and n are readily evaluated at the melting point where the liquids can be treated as a lattice. If Z is taken as the number of neighboring lattice positions, since the fraction $\frac{V-Vs}{V}$ are unoccupied we have at the melting point:

$$N \frac{V-Vs}{Vs} = Z \frac{V-Vs}{V} \qquad (1\text{-}50)$$

Most liquids approximate a close packed structure with empty lattice sites. Accordingly, $Z = 12$. The expansion on melting is 12% so $\frac{Vs}{V} = 1.12$. This gives $n = 10.7$ in agreement with 10.8 the value which leads to the best calculated results.

Also, at the melting point, the kinetic energy of a molecule is $\frac{3}{2}$ kT. If a molecule shares this kinetic energy between two lattice sites, it will have a kinetic energy of $\frac{1}{2}(\frac{3}{2}kT)$ per lattice site. Any molecule is in competition

with the other $(n-1)$ neighbors for a site. Since kinetic energy density is a measure of pressure, only when a molecule puts as much or more kinetic energy in a site as the $(n-1)$ competitors, will it be able to preempt the site. Thus, it can be written:

$$\left(\frac{a\ EsVs}{V-Vs}\right) = \frac{n-1}{Z}\frac{1}{2}\left(\frac{3\ kT}{2}\right) = \frac{(n-1)}{2Z}\frac{V-Vs}{V}\ Es \qquad (1\text{-}51)$$

The factor $\frac{1}{Z}$ takes care of the fact that a molecule is only moving toward a particular vacancy $\frac{1}{Z}$ th of the time. The last equality arises because the energy of melting is all potential energy and the potential energy spent in melting per molecule on vacancies must balance the kinetic energy $(\frac{3}{2}kT)$ per molceule if the system is to be stable. Substituting the known values into equation 1-51 gives $a = .0052$ as compared with the parameter .00534 chosen to fit the experiment. Significant structure theory thus leads to a satisfactory theory of the Helmholtz free energy and therefore of all the properties of simple liquids.

In reaction kinetics, it is necessary to know the activity of the reactants as well as the partition function for the activated complex. This means a theory of liquid mixtures is necessary which has been developed for binary mixtures (17).

The theory uses the methods of calculating average values
of Es, Vs,θ, a, and n which were earlier developed for
van der Waals equation with excellent results. Significant
structure theory has been developed also to calculate the
properties of liquid metals (18), of water and of molten
salts (19), as well as transport properties (20, 21). It
should be recognized, however, that an a priori calculation
of specific rates of reaction in water will still require
further developments since the varying degrees of solvation
of reactant solute species and activated complexes have not
yet been formulated.

LITERATURE CITED

1. Eyring, H., J Chem Phys, 3, 107 (1935).

2. Eyring, H., et al, Condensation and Vaporization of
   Condensed Phases in Condensation and Evaporation of
   Solids, Rutner, E., et al, Eds., Proc Intern Symp on
   Condensation and Evaporation of Solids, Gordon and
   Breach Science Publishers, New York, N.Y.,pp 3-38
   (1964).

3. Debye, P., Trans Electrochem Soc, 82, 265 (1942).

4. Eyring, H. and E.M. Eyring, Modern Chemical Kinetics,
   Reinhold Publ. Corp., New York, N.Y.,(1963).

5. Glasstone, S., et al, The Theory of Rate Processes,
   McGraw-Hill Book Co., Inc., New York, N.Y.,(1941).

6. Pauling, L., Nature of the Chemical Bond, First Ed.,
   Cornell Univ. Press, Ithaca, N.Y.,p 53 (1940).

7. Benson, S.W., The Foundations of Chemical Kinetics,
   McGraw-Hill Book Co., Inc., New York, N.Y.,p 340,
   Table XIII, 6 (1960).

8. Eigen, M., et al, Progress in Reaction Kinetics, 2,
   G. Porter, Ed., Pergamon Press, New York, N.Y.,
   pp 285-318 (1964).

9. Miles, M.H., et al, J Phys Chem, 69, 467 (1965).

10. Wynne-Jones, W. F. K. and H. Eyring, J Chem Phys, 3, 492 (1935).

11. Arnett, E. M., et al, J Am Chem Soc, 87, 1541 (1965).

12. Bigeleisen, J., J Chem Phys, 17, 675 (1949).

13. Bunton, C. A. and V. J. Shiner, Jr., J Am Chem Soc, 83, 3214 (1961).

14. Eyring, H., J Chem Phys, 4, 283 (1936); Walter, J. and H. Eyring, J Chem Phys 9, 393 (1941); Eyring, H., et al, Proc Natl Acad Sci U S, 44, 683 (1958); Eyring, H. and T. Ree, Ibid, 47, 526 (1961).

15. Eyring, H., et al, Statistical Mechanics and Dynamics, John Wiley and Sons, Inc., New York, N. Y., (1964).

16. Cailletit, L. and E. Mathias, Compt Rend Acad Sci Paris, 102, 1202 (1886); Ibid, 104, 1563 (1887).

17. Liang, K., et al, Proc Nat Acad U S, 52, 1107 (1964).

18. Carlson, C. M., et al, Proc Natl Acad Sci U S, 46, 649 (1960).

19. Carlson, C. M., et al, Proc Natl Acad Sci U S, 46, 333 (1960).

20. Ree, T. S., et al, Proc Natl Acad Sci U S, 48, 501 (1962).

21. Lin, S. H., et al, J Phys Chem, 68, 3017 (1964).

DISCUSSION

DR. VICTOR K. LA MER (Columbia University): I was very active in this field twenty-five years ago, but I've lost track in the last couple years. Could you tell me in a few words what you mean by primary and secondary kinetic effects?

DR. EYRING: It's arbitrary and, in fact, A. V. Willi, who is now at the College of Pharmacy at Columbia, makes no such distinction. Bunton and Shiner arbitrarily made this distinction, and what they meant by a secondary kinetic isotope effect was the effect stemming from all of those reactant-solvent hydrogen bonds other than those bonds involving the transferring hydrogen that reacts with the hydroxide directly.

DR. LA MER: But you don't think it is an important distinction.

DR. EYRING: It's a convenient distinction. Important probably isn't the right word, but it is a convenient distinction. It permits one to make an estimate of the importance of the two kinds of hydrogen bond.

DR. K. H. MANCY (University of Cincinnati): I would like to ask you if you care to comment on the significance of activity measurement and the role it plays in reactions which are either diffusion controlled or activation controlled. Let me put it this way, activity measurements essentially play a significant role in the understanding of the reaction kinetics which concentration measurements cannot provide.

DR. EYRING: One of the devices that we used in Eigen's laboratory in Germany for studying rates of diffusion controlled reactions was the dissociation field effect method and there one worked in solutions of such high dilution that one could speak of concentrations with safety. In other words, the activity coefficients would be essentially unity.

DR. MANCY: There are certain interferences that might make an activity coefficient more or less than unity. In this case would you think that acitivity measurements would be highly significant in a diffusion controlled reaction as contrasted with one which is activation controlled?

DR. EYRING: We take great pains to avoid situations where we are going to see significance of activity coefficients. For example, when we do our temperature jump studies of these hydrogen bonded systems we always work in solutions of tenth molar-ionic strength so that we'll not even have to think about that sort of a difficulty. What you are suggesting is that we are not doing the job as we ought to do it. It would be nice if we thought about these other difficulties too.

If reaction is diffusion controlled, the activated complex will be very like the reactants so that the activity coefficients for reactants and activated complex will be the same and thus cancel out of the rate expression. In the case of activation control where there may be an appreciable difference between the structures of the reactants and activated complex we would not expect the same degree of cancellation of activity coefficients.

DR. MANCY: I don't want to take much time, but we studied reactions which involved molecular oxygen in estuarine waters where salt water is meeting fresh water and found that the salting out effect has tremendous influence on the reaction rate which was not completely explained by accounting for changes in the activity coefficient.

DR. EYRING: On occasion when we are forced to identify one of our reactions, we will change the ionic strength to make sure that it has the right type of Brönsted dependence. But this is done as a last resort. With all these relaxation methods it's very hard to get high precision and it really takes quite high precision to see a really significant change in reaction rate constants with small changes in ionic strength. We lack the precision that you folks will be used to in working with slower reactions.

DR. ROBERT GRIEVES (Illinois Institute of Technology): For a number of years investigators have been debating back and forth the existence of the unique critical point for a single component or a multi-component system as opposed to a critical region. Will the solid-vapor theory predict a unique critical point or a narrow critical region?

DR. EYRING: It's kind of interesting to see what one does with significant structures theory. For example, from their description of liquid water they find that they can describe water at the melting point with aggregates ranging in size from 300 water molecules tied together all the way down to 30 with about equal validity. That isn't an answer directly to your question, but it suggests to you that it's an awfully broad gauge kind of a theory where you actually pump into the theory ideas that are known from elsewhere. For example, I think when they finally publish their description of water they will say that they get a best fit with 46 water molecules, the dodecahedrons that Pauling postulated long ago. But in fact it's convenient; there is a very shallow broad minimum. You don't predict a priori exact values for critical point properties. This point is worth emphasizing. It's not an a priori exact theory. It's one where you pump a lot of experimental information into your description. It's not quite like solving the Hamiltonian.

DR. HENRY EYRING (Contributed after the meeting):

In significant structure theory the molal Helmholtz free energy for the liquid, A_l , has the form:

$$A_l = \frac{V_s}{V} A_s + \frac{V-V_s}{V} A_g$$

where A_s, A_g, V_s, and V are the molal Helmholtz free energy of solid and gas, respectively, and the molal volumes of solid and liquid, respectively. Very good predictions of all properties have been obtained treating solid and liquid as ideal. To get the critical properties more exactly imperfect gas theory should be used in A_g. An exact prediction of critical properties awaits such a definitive treatment.

As Dr. Edward Eyring says calculation of the thermodynamic properties of water alone permits some latitude as to the number of molecules in the clusters which transform as a unit with rising temperature and pressure. However, if the same model is to simultaneously explain the transport properties and be reasonable in the light of what is known about clathrate structures in water solutions it is probable that the actual aggregates are not very different in size from the clusters of 46 molecules we have assumed.

J. Carrell Morris
Harvard University

KINETICS OF REACTIONS BETWEEN AQUEOUS CHLORINE AND NITROGEN COMPOUNDS

Since Weil and Morris published the kinetics and mechanism of the formation of NH_2Cl from dilute aqueous chlorine and ammonia in 1949 (1), considerable progress has been made toward a general understanding of rates and mechanisms of inorganic reactions in solution. In part, this has come about because of new investigative tools such as isotopic tracers or relaxation measurements that have made possible the acquisition of information previously inaccessible. Beyond this, however, it has become apparent that many types of inorganic reactions are amenable to the same sort of systematic treatment that earlier gave insight into the rates and mechanisms of organic reactions with the aid of concepts of nucleophilicity, electrophilicity, linear free energy relations, and generalized acidity functions.

For example, Ingold, in the preface to his book, states:

> The object of the lectures...was to point
> out that the first attempts are contempor-
> aneously being made to start the develop-
> ment of a corresponding extension in scope
> (that is, from study of static structure
> to that of dynamic mechanism) in the very
> much more diversified field of inorganic

23

chemistry, which hitherto has been
essentially restricted, as organic
chemistry used to be, to the study of
structure; and to point out, furthermore, that....to have such a guide (the
models and methods of organic chemistry)
is of some advantage in attacking the
generally more formidable problems of
mechanism that inorganic chemistry
presents. (2)

When consideration is given to reaction of a species
containing conventionally unipositive chlorine with ammonia
or one of its derivatives according to the general type equation:

$$X\text{-}Cl + R_2NH \longrightarrow ClNR_2 + H^+ + X^-$$

attention can be focused either on the electrophilic displacement
of H^+ from the nitrogen by different chlorinating agents or upon
the nucleophilic displacement of X^- by a variety of nitrogenous
compounds. The latter aspect is of principal concern in practical water chemistry with reference to relative rates of N-chlorination of the many nitrogen compounds encountered in water
supplies and waste water. Some consideration of the former
aspect is of interest also, however, for it is related to proposed
pathways of N-chlorination.

Since replacement of H^+ by Cl^+ is an electrophilic displacement, rates of N-chlorination of a given nitrogenous compound
will be expected to vary with the electrophilicity of the reacting
chlorine atom. On this basis the anticipated order of reactivity
for a number of possible donors of Cl^+ is:

$$Cl^+ > H_2OCl^+ > Cl_2 > Cl_2O > AcOCl > HOCl > ROCl >$$

$$H_2NCl > OCl^-$$

This order parallels generally the acidities of analogous
compounds with H^+ in place of Cl^+.

Little specific information for verification of this expected
order is available as yet. Action of Cl^+ and Cl_2O will probably
be observable only in essentially non-aqueous solutions, although
the relatively slow hydrolysis of Cl_2O may provide opportunity
for some study of its dilute aqueous reactivity. When Cl_2 is
dispersed in nearly neutral aqueous solutions at less than
millimolar concentration, hydrolysis to HOCl and OCl^- is so

rapid and complete that only the action of these latter species
is likely to be noted. Catalysis of N-chlorination reactions
in acid solution by chloride ion, investigated only qualitatively
so far, may proceed by way of formation of Cl_2 as chlorinating
agent. Many relatively slow N-chlorination reactions are
catalyzed by hydronium ion and by carboxylic acids. Catalysis
by H_3^+O may be due to formation of H_2^+OCl as chlorinating agent
and catalysis by carboxylic acids may occur through formation
of acyl hypochlorites. The latter process has been proposed
by Mauger and Soper for the catalytic effect of carboxylic acids
on the N-chlorination of N-methylacetamide and N-acetylglycine
(3). On the other hand, their data accord also with general
acid catalysis through formation of a protonated activated complex. Direct studies of N-chlorination by acyl hypochlorites
are needed to distinguish these possible mechanisms.

It is known that tertiary-butyl hypochlorite reacts with
ammonia to form chloramine as an intermediate in hydrazine
synthesis, but to my knowledge there is no information available
on the rate of this or similar processes. The action of alkyl
hypochlorites is also a field for fruitful investigation.

Analogy with the relative proton-donating efficiencies of
H_2O and OH^- suggests that HOCl should be a far more effective
N-chlorinating agent than OCl^-, providing the general mechanism
of the reaction is that shown by the type equation. Accordingly,
whenever the kinetic data can be explained equally well by alternate mechanisms involving HOCl or OCl^-, the former species
is to be preferred as reactant. Soper and his co-workers, who
have published many studies of N-chlorination reactions, have
quite generally considered OCl^- to be chlorinating agent; their
results, except possibly those with aromatic amides, which are
not considered in this paper, are equally interpretable in terms
of chlorination by HOCl.

Specific rates of N-chlorination with a given chlorine donor
such as HOCl, should be directly related to the nucleophilicity
of the nitrogen atom being chlorinated. Nucleophilicity toward
Cl^+ should parallel basicity toward H^+ and thus a direct relation
between basicity and rate of N-chlorination is anticipated.
Apparent steric effects, however, reduce expected basicities
of nitrogen compounds when there are multiple substituents for
the hydrogen atoms of ammonia; such effects are probably greater
for the addition of Cl^+ and may result in deviations from the
general relationship when the nitrogen is attached to more than

one bulky group.

The large specific rate of N-chlorination for nitrogenous reagents having basicities in the range of ammonia or greater also may affect the anticipated correlation. N-chlorination, in contrast to most reactions of substitution at carbon, requires little activation energy. So, when the nitrogen is strongly nucleophilic, specific rates of reaction may be limited by diffusion or molecular contacts rather than by energetics. In such circumstances, degree of nucleophilicity may have little effect.

The overall view of N-chlorination reactions in dilute aqueous solutions for interpretation of data on specific reaction systems is that they occur as S_n2 displacements of OH from HOCl by the basic forms of the nitrogeneous reactants at rates varying with the nucleophilicities of the nitrogen atoms.

Investigations of the rates and kinetics of a number of specific N-chlorination reactions have been conducted in the Engineering Laboratories of Harvard. The reactions usually have been studied in quite dilute solutions, of the order of 10^{-4}M with other conditions approaching as closely as feasible those likely to be encountered in chlorination of water supplies or waste waters. For the most part the characteristic ultra-violet adsorption bands of HOCl, OCl^-, and many N-chloro compounds have been used to follow progress of the reactions. Individual components may be readily determined in this way without alteration of the reaction mixture, but in most instances the accuracy of the determinations is limited to about 5%, partly because of overlapping of the absorption bands. Since the molar absorptivities are comparatively small, ordinarily 10^5 to 10^6 mol cm^{-2}, it is necessary to use 5- or 10- cm cells to obtain absorbance readings in the range 0.1 to 1.0.

Because the experiments were not designed specifically to assess the validity of the ideas outlined here, the results are often not complete or conclusive for them. Extension of the data for all the systems would be desirable. The available information, however, provides a basis for some attempt at correlation of the results with the proposed general mechanism.

N-CHLORINATION OF AMMONIA

Formation of NH_2Cl

Data for the reaction:

$$NH_3 + HOCl \rightarrow NH_2Cl + H_2O; \; k_1 \qquad\qquad (2\text{-}1)$$

have been published by Weil and Morris (1). The reaction was found to be second order, - first order each in total ammonia and in total hypochlorite concentration. The observed second-order rate constants vary with pH value in the range from 4 to 6 and in the range from 10 to 13 in a manner consistent either with a mechanism involving interaction between the uncharged species as shown or with one between NH_4^+ and OCl^-. Reasons for choosing the pathway in which interaction is between NH_3 and HOCl have been given.

At 25°C the second-order rate constant for reaction between the uncharged molecules is:

$$k_1 = 5.1 \times 10^6 \text{ liter mol}^{-1} \text{ sec}^{-1}; \log k_1 = 6.786$$

The general expression is:

$$k_1 = 9.7 \times 10^8 \exp (-3000/RT) \text{ liter mol}^{-1} \text{ sec}^{-1}$$

Formation of $NHCl_2$

The reaction:

$$NH_2Cl + HOCl \longrightarrow NHCl_2 + H_2O; k_2 \qquad\qquad (2-2)$$

also was studied by Weil and Morris (4). An indirect approach was necessary because of extensive decomposition when solutions containing HOCl and NH_2Cl were mixed.

Solutions of HOCl and excess NH_4^{+2} buffered at pH values near 5, where observed rates of formation of NH_2Cl and $NHCl_2$ are comparable, were mixed. Reaction was allowed to proceed until the HOCl had reacted fully. The concentrations of NH_2Cl and $NHCl_2$ were measured then and used to determined the ratio of the rate of formation of $NHCl_2$ to that of NH_2Cl. The rate constant, k_2, then could be evaluated with the aid of the known value for k_1.

Preliminary treatment of the results showed that the formation of $NHCl_2$ is, like that of NH_2Cl, a second-order reaction, -first order in each reactant. Accordingly, the equation for the distribution of products in a second-order, competitive, consecutive reaction scheme is applicable. This equation may be written in the form:

$$R_o + 2nR_m - R_m = 1 - (1 - R_o - R_m) n$$

where R_o is the ratio of initial molar concentration of total hypochlorite to twice that of initial total ammonia, R_m is the ratio of molar concentration of NH_2Cl formed to twice that of initial total ammonia, and n is the ratio of observed, rate constants for formation of $NHCl_2$ and NH_2Cl; $n = k_2/k_1$. Evaluation of n from R_o and R_m is facilitated by computer solution for n as a function R_m for fixed values of R_o. Figure 1 presents plots of results of some such computations.

In mildly acid solutions such that dissociation of HOCl is negligible the observed rate constant for formation of NH_2Cl is given by the expression:

$$k'_1 = k_1 K_a / (H^+)$$

where K_a is the acid dissociation constant of the ammonium ion. Then:

$$k'_2 = n k_1 K_a / (H^+)$$
$$= 3.5 \times 10^{-3} n / (H^+) \text{ liter mol}^{-1} \text{ sec}^{-1} \text{ at } 25^\circ C.$$

Formation of $NHCl_2$ was found to be catalyzed both by H_3O^+ and by acetic acid. At $25^\circ C$ the general expression for the observed specific rate of formation of NHCl is:

$$k'_2 = k_2 (1 + k_{2H} (H^+) + k_{2A} \left[AcOH \right])$$
$$= 3.4 \times 10^2 (1 + 5 \times 10^4 (H^+) + 2 \times 10^2 \left[AcOH \right])$$
$$\text{liter mol}^{-1} \text{ sec}^{-1}$$

No additional studies were made to assess further the generality of the acidic catalysis. The relative magnitudes of the constants, however, are in accord with concepts of general acid catalysis. Chloride also was found to catalyze the formation of $NHCl_2$, perhaps through intermediate production of Cl_2 as chlorinating agent; there has been no quantitative evaluation of this effect, however.

The rate constant for the uncatalyzed reaction at $25^\circ C$ is:

$$k_2 = 3.4 \times 10^2 \text{ liter mol}^{-1} \text{ sec}^{-1}; \log k_2 = 2.53$$

From experiments at a number of temperatures an activation energy of 7.3 kcal was determined, whence:

$$k_2 = 7.6 \times 10^7 \exp (-7300/RT) \text{ liter mol}^{-1} \text{ sec}^{-1}$$

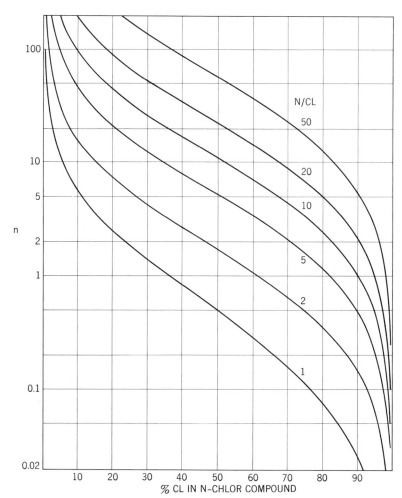

FIGURE 1   PRODUCT COMPOSITION FOR SECOND-
                ORDER CONSECUTIVE-COMPETITIVE
                FORMATION OF N-CHLOR AND N,
                N-DICHLOR COMPOUNDS. Ratio of
                specific rates of formation of N, N-dichlor
                to N-chlor compound equals $\underline{n}$.

At $25^{\circ}C$ the rate constant for formation of NH_2Cl is about 10^4 that for formation of $NHCl_2$ in accordance with the much greater nucleophilicity of NH_3; NH_2Cl is very weakly basic, its pK having been estimated as 15 (5).

Disproportionation of NH_2Cl

The disproportionation reaction:

$$2NH_2Cl \longrightarrow NHCl_2 + NH_3; k_3 \qquad\qquad (2-3)$$

can be viewed as the N-chlorination of one molecule of NH_2Cl by a second one. Thus a comparison of its rate with the rate of formation of $NHCl_2$ from HOCl and NH_3 provides an estimate of the N-chlorinating efficiency of NH_2Cl relative to that of HOCl.

Kinetic investigations of this process were conducted by Weil and Morris (6) and, more extensively, by Granstrom (7). Two mechanisms were found to be significant for the conditions investigated: pH range 4 to 6, conconcentration range 10^{-3} to 10^{-4}M, temperature range 0^0 to 40^0C. The first is a direct second-order N-chlorination by NH_2Cl which, like reaction 2-2, is catalyzed by H_3O^+ and acetic acid. The second is a slow first-order hydrolysis of NH_2Cl to HOCl and NH_3 followed by rapid reaction of the HOCl with a second molecule of NH_2Cl. The kinetics of the latter mechanism are complicated by the fact that the NH_3 hydrolyzed or otherwise present, acts as a competitor to NH_2Cl for the hydrolyzed HOCl.

By suitable choice of conditions and appropriate kinetic analysis, Granstrom was able to evaluate rate constants for both these pathways. The firect second-order mechanism at 25^0C was found to be:

$$k_3 = 5.6 \times 10^{-2} (1 + 1.3 \times 10^5 (H^+)) + 35 \left[AcOH \right])$$
$$\text{liter mol}^{-1} \text{ sec}^{-1}$$

From this:

$$k_3 = 5.6 \times 10^{-2} \text{ liter mol}^{-1} \text{ sec}^{-1}; \log k_3 = 1.25$$

Granstrom also found the general expression for the rate constant of the uncatalyzed reaction to be:

$$k_3 = 80 \exp(-4300/RT) \text{ liter mol}^{-1} \text{ sec}^{-1}$$

from experiments over the range from 7^0 to 49^0C.

The small pre-exponential factor in this equation is unusual.

It signifies a strongly negative entropy of activation; that is, the activated state is a much more ordered one than the original reaction state. Why this should be so much more the case for this particular reaction than for the others that have been considered is not immediately apparent.

Comparison of the rate constant for reaction 2-3 with that of reaction 2-2 shows that at 25°C HOCl reacts almost 10^4 times as rapidly with NH_2Cl as does NH_2Cl, in accord with the much greater electrophilicity of the HOCl. Perhaps it should be noted also that the catalytic effects of H_3O^+ and acetic acid on the two reactions are of the same order, although not identical. Granstrom's studies of reaction 2-3 indicated that the catalytic effects were entropic ones, for the catalyzed reactions had substantially the same temperature coefficients as the uncatalyzed one.

Granstrom's evaluation of the specific rate for the first-order process, equal in the absence of competing NH_3 to the rate constant for the reaction:

$$NH_2Cl + H_2O \longrightarrow HOCl + NH_3; k_4 \qquad\qquad (2\text{-}4)$$

gave, as a general expression:

$$k_4 = 8.7 \times 10^7 \exp(-17,000/RT) \sec^{-1}$$

Although matters of equilibria are beyond the scope of the present symposium, it may be noted that the ratio of this expression to that for the formation of NH_2Cl gives for the hydrolysis equilibrium of NH_2Cl:

$$K = k_4/k_1 = (HOCl)\ (NH_3)/(NH_2Cl)$$

$$= 9 \times 10^{-2} \exp(-14,000/RT) \text{ mol } l^{-1}$$

From this equation it may be computed, for example, that a pure solution of NH_2Cl at a concentration of 2.0 mg/l as Cl (2.82×10^{-5} M) will be 0.58% hydrolyzed at pH 7 and 25°C.

Formation of NCl_3

The reaction of $NHCl_2$ with HOCl to form NCl_3 has not been studied kinetically. It must be considerably slower, however, than either the formation of NH_2Cl or that of $NHCl_2$ for it seems not to form appreciably at pH values greater than 4 unless an excess of HOCl is present. Slowness of reaction would be expected, for $NHCl_2$ is not demonstrably basic, indeed it appears to echibit acid ionization much like that of organic imides with K_a about 10^{-8}.

N-CHLORINATION OF AMINES

Reactions with Methylamine

Reactions of aqueous chlorine with methylamine, analogous to the ones with ammonia, have been investigated kinetically by Weil and Morris (1).

The formation of CH_3NHCl according to the equation:

$$HOCl + CH_3NH \longrightarrow CH_3NHCl + H_2O; \quad k_5 \qquad (2-5)$$

was found to exhibit a kinetic pattern similar to that for the formation of NH_2Cl. Re-evaluation of the data of Weil and Morris, based on more accurate values for the dissociation constant of HOCl, yields a second-order rate constant at $25^\circ C$:

$$k_5 = 3.6 \times 10^8 \text{ liter mol}^{-1} \text{ sec}^{-1}; \log k_5 = 8.56$$

The re-evaluated temperature coefficient is less than that given originally with the indicated activation energy only 1.9 kcal. This yields as a general expression for the rate constant:

$$k_5 = 7.8 \times 10^9 \exp (-1900/RT) \text{ liter mol}^{-1} \text{ sec}^{-1}$$

Data on the relative specific rates of formation of CH_3NCl_2 and CH_3NHCl at $25^\circ C$ indicate that the reaction:

$$CH_3NHCl + HOCl \longrightarrow CH_3NCl_2 + H_2O; \quad k_6 \qquad (2-6)$$

is acid catlayzed like the formation of $NHCl_2$ (8). The complete expression is:

$$n = k_6'/k_5' = 1.3 \times 10^5 (H^+) (1 + 2.4 \times 10^4 (H^+)$$
$$+ 1.3 \times 10^2 \left[AcOH \right])$$

with the catalytic constants very similar to those for formation of $NHCl_2$. With $k_5' = 8.6 \times 10^{-3}/(H^+)$ in acid solutions, the value for the rate constant of reaction 2-6 at $25^\circ C$ is:

$$k_6 = 1.1 \times 10^3 \text{ liter mol}^{-1} \text{ sec}^{-1}; \log k_6 = 3.05$$

The specific rate is thus 3 to 5 times as fast the formation of $NHCl_2$ at 25°C. The temperature coefficient has not been determined.

Measurements were made also on the rate of the reaction:

$$2CH_3NHCl \longrightarrow CH_3NCl_2 + CH_3NH_2; k_7 \qquad (2-7)$$

In contrast to the disproportionation of NH_2Cl this reaction was found to be strictly second order at 25°C, pH 5, and concentration about $10^{-4}M$. Thus the hydrolytic mechanism is insignificant with these conditions. The reaction is catalyzed by H_3O^+ and acetic acid; the specific rate is nearly the same as that for the second-order disproportionation of NH_2Cl. As a general expression of the rate constant at 25°C, Weil and Morris (6) found:

$$k_7' = 4.7 \times 10^{-2} (1 + 1.5 \times 10^4 (H^+) + 2.0 \times 10^2$$

Then: $\left[AcOH \right]$ liter mol^{-1} sec^{-1}

$$k_7 = 4.7 \times 10^{-2} \text{ liter } mol^{-1} sec^{-1}; \log k_7 = 1.33$$

The temperature coefficient was not determined.

Formation of N-Chlordimethylamine

Only a monochlorinated derivative is formed with HOCl and secondary amines; so kinetic measurements tend to be more precise and their interpretation less ambiguous. Nonetheless it is here that there is some disagreement in the reported kinetic data.

Kinetic measurements on the reaction:

$$(CH_3)_2NH + HOCl \longrightarrow (CH_3)_2NCl + H_2O; k_8 \qquad (2-8)$$

have been reported by Weil and Morris (1) and also by Edmond and Soper (8). Both sets of workers found the reaction to be second order, -first order in each of the reactants, and uncatalyzed by H_3O^+ and acetic acid; the observed specific rates varied with pH in the same manner as the formation of NH_2Cl, suggesting either an interaction between OCl^- and $(CH_3)_2NH_2^+$ or between HOCl and $(CH_3)_2NH$. Edmond and Soper interpreted their data by means of the ionic reactants; Weil and Morris chose the mechanism involving neutral molecules.

The discrepancy occurs in the values of the specific rates found by the two sets of investigators. The data of Morris and Weil, recalculated as described for the methylamine reaction, yield:

$$k_8 = 3.3 \times 10^8 \text{ liter mol}^{-1} \text{ sec}^{-1}; \log k_8 = 8.52$$

at 25°C with no change within the limits of experimental error for the the temperature range 5° to 38°C. This calculated value of k_8 is the mean of values determined from experiments in acid solution at pH values 4.2 to 5.5 and in basic solution at pH values 11.5 to 13, the two sets of data being in agreement within experimental error.

Edmond and Soper's experiments were conducted in more acid solutions, pH values 2.3 to 3.5, and presumably with more concentrated reagents, although no specific values were reported. Their reaction medium had an ionic strength usually maintained at 0.2 M with chloroacetate buffer and KNO_3. The rate constant for reaction between the neutral species evaluated from Edmond and Soper's observed specific rates is:

$$k_{8s} = 5.0 \times 10^7 \text{ liter mol}^{-1} \text{ sec}^{-1}; \log k_{8s} = 7.70$$

a value only about one-seventh that obtained by Weil and Morris

A part of the difference is explained by the observation of Edmond and Soper that the reaction occurs about twice as fast in the absence of added KNO_3 as at 0.2 M ionic strength. There remains, however, still a factor of 3 to 4 between the two results.

The investigations of Friend furnish some additional information with regard to this reaction (9). Friend determined rates of formation of a number of N-chlor compounds, including N-chlordimethylamine, relative to that of NH_2Cl by a competitive method. Aqueous chlorine at a known, limited concentration was added to a buffered solution containing excess concentrations of both ammonia and the compound under investigation in an appropriate known ratio. After an interval of time sufficient for complete reaction of HOCl, the formed concentrations of NH_2Cl and other N-chlor compounds individually were determined. When the concentration of each nitrogenous compound is in molar excess of the total HOCl, as was true in Friend's experiments, the ratio of the observed specific rates for the experimental conditions is given by the expression:

$$F = k_u'/k_r' = \log(1\text{-}NCl_u/NH_u) - \log(1\text{-}NCl_r/NH_r)$$

in which $[NH]_u$ and $[NH]_r$ are the initial analytical concentrations of amine and reference ammonia, $[NCl]_u$ and $[NCl]_r$ are the resultant measured concentrations of the respective N-chlor compounds, and k'_u, k'_r are the corresponding specific rates.

To obtain the ratio of the rate constants for reaction of the neutral molecules, the fraction of the analytical concentration of each nitrogen compound in its basic form must be taken into account. The appropriate equation is:

$$k_u/k_r = k'_u/k'_r \ (K_u + [OH^-]) \div (K_r + [OH^-])$$

in which K_u and K_r are basic ionization constants for the indicated species and $[OH^-]$ is the molar concentration of $[OH]$ In strongly basic solutions, where $[OH^-]$ is much greater than K_u and K_r, the correction factor is unity; the observed ratio of specific rates is then the true ratio of rate constants. In solutions with $[OH^-]$ much less than either basic ionization constant, the correction term is simply K_u/K_r, a condition that held for Friend's results at pH 7.2 with dimethylamine and ammonia. At pH 7.2, $F = k_u/k_r = 1.2$ was found and thus $k_u/k_r = 41$ with $pK_u = 3.226$ and $pK_r = 4.745$. Calculations with the complete equation from observed ratios at pH values 8.3, 9.3, and 10.5 gave an average $k_u/k_r = 58$.

The ratio of rate constants as determined by Morris and Weil is 54, while the ratio of Edmond and Soper's value for formation of dimethylamine to that for formation of NH_2Cl is 8.2. It thus appears that the specific rate of the dimethylamine reaction determined by Weil and Morris is more consistent with other data.

REACTIONS OF OTHER AMINES

Edmond and Soper also measured the rates of reaction of hypochlorous acid with diethylamine and with dipropylamine under conditions similar to those employed for their investigation of the reaction with dimethylamine. For the reaction:

$$(C_2H_5)_2 NH = HOCl \longrightarrow (C_2H_5)_2NCl + H_2O; \ k_9 \qquad (2\text{-}9)$$

the rate constant calculated from their data is:

$$k_{9s} = 1.4 \times 10^7 \text{ liter mol}^{-1} \text{ sec}^{-1}; \ \log k_{9s} = 7.13$$

and for the reaction:

$$(C_3H_7)_2NH + HOCl \longrightarrow (C_3H_7)_2NCl + H_2O; \; k_{10} \qquad (2\text{-}10)$$

the calculated rate constant is:

$$k_{10s} = 4.3 \times 10^7 \text{ liter mol}^{-1} \text{ sec}^{-1}; \; \log k_{10s} = 7.63$$

Since these constants were determined for the same conditions as their value for reaction 2-8, they should be reliable for comparison with it, but are probably low with relation to constants determined at Harvard. This is indicated also by the results of Friend, who obtained a mean value of 23 for the rate constant for reaction 2-9 relative to that of formation of NH_2Cl. From this ratio the rate constant for diethylamine reaction is:

$$k_9 = 1.4 \times 10^8 \text{ liter mol}^{-1} \text{ sec}^{-1}; \; \log k_9 = 8.15$$

that is, about 10 times Edmond and Soper's value.

Rates of N-chlorination of a number of other amines and amino acids relative to ammonia also were determined by Friend (9). Table I presents a summary of data computed for $25^\circ C$, together with similar data from some of the systems discussed earlier that were computed from the individual rate constants. When values for log $(k_u/k_r$ are plotted as a function of pK_b, as shown in Figure 2, a rather good linear correlation is found, indicating a linear free energy relationship between base strength and rate of N-chlorination. The observed correlation is about as good as that noted on the average for Hammett plots of organic displacement reactions.

Strangely, the value showing the greatest deviation from the correlation line is that for ammonia. No rational explanation can be advanced at this time. The deviation of the value for diethylamine seems more explicable; in this instance the presence of the two bulky groups may impede somewhat the attachment of the Cl^+. The value for glycylglycine is probably in error because it is based on only two experiments and is at variance with results on glycine and glycylglycylglycine.

The slope of the correlation line is:

$$d \log F_o / d \log K_B = 0.5$$

from which:

$$k/k_o = (K_B/K_{B,o})^{0.5}$$

TABLE I   RATE CONSTANTS FOR
N-CHLORINATION RELATIVE
TO NH_3 (a)

Nitrogenous Compound	pK_o (25°C)	$F_o = k_u / k_r$		$\log F_o$
Methylamine	3.376	60	(b)	1.78
Dimethylamine	3.226	54	(b)	1.73
Diethylamine	3.067	23		1.36
Morpholine	5.30	9		0.95
Diethanolamine	5.12	9.3		0.97
Ethylaminoacetate	6.27	2.0		0.30
Glycine	4.221	22		1.34
Alanine	4.133	19		1.28
Leucine	4.256	14		1.15
-Alanine	3.765	33		1.52
Serine	4.795	6.7		0.83
Glycylglycine	5.748	0.6		-0.22
Glycylglycylglycine	6.09	2.3		0.36
Chloramide	ca 15	5.5×10^{-5}		-4.26
N-chlormethylamine	ca 13.8	1.8×10^{-4}		-3.74

(a) Based on reaction between HOCl and basic
form of N compound.
(b) Computed from individual rate constants.

where k_o and $K_{B,o}$ can refer to ammonia or to any standard
of reference. Such a relationship is anticipated, for example,
if nucleophilicity toward Cl^+ parallesl basicity and if the
transition state is midway between reactants and products.

N-CHLORINATION OF AMIDES

Because they are much less basic than amines, amides
should be N-chlorinated much less rapidly in neutral or alkaline
solutions. Experiments confirm this expectation since Friend,
in his studies with glycylglycylglycine, found that only the
amino nitrogen was chlorinated (9). Moreover, comparable
rates of formation of N-chlor, N-methylacetamide, and
N-chlordimethylamine could be obtained only a pH values 2 to
2.5 where the rate of formation of the latter compound is about
10^{-5}, its value at pH 7. A maximum estimated F_o for N-methylacetamide relative to ammonia is then 10^{-7}; the actual value

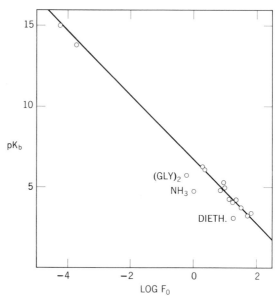

FIGURE 2   RATE OF FORMATION OF
                  N-CHLOR COMPOUND AS FUNCTION
                  OF BASE STRENGTH OF NITROGENOUS
                  REACTANT

may be much smaller, perhaps 10^{-9}, if formation of N-chlor,
N-methylacetamide is catalyzed by H_3^+O to the same extent
as formation of $NHCl_2$ or CH_3NCl_2.

Rates of N-chlorination of N-methylacetamide and
N-acetylglycine have been measured directly by Mauger and
Soper with results generally in accord with previous observations (3). Measurements were made at pH values between 3
and 9 with 10^{-3} to 10^{-2} M reactants in buffered solutions with
ionic strengths 0.1 to 0.5. Phosphate buffers were employed
from pH 6 to 9, and a number of different carboxylic acid
buffers were used in the acid region.

The reactions were found to be first order in each reactant
and to be strongly catalyzed by the acid component of the buffers.
Mauger and Soper interpreted the data to indicate preliminary
formation of an acyl hypochlorite which then acts as the direct
chlorinating agent. However, the catalytic constants for the
individual acids, including $H_2^-PO_4$ conform quite well to the

linear free energy relation (Brönsted) $k/k_o = (K_a/K_{a,o})^{0.44}$, where the K_a values are the corresponding acid dissociation constants. Thus, general acid catalysis is suggested strongly.

Against this interpretation is the failure of Mauger and Soper to observe hydronium ion catalysis. This may be simply because the effect was not sought and because almost all the experiments were conducted at pH 5 or greater, where the effect of an hydronium-ion catalysis would have been inappreciable and similar in magnitude to that found for N-chlorination of NH_2Cl and CH_3NHCl.

Full specification of the mechanism of N-chlorination of amides is difficult because of unknown effects of resonance in the amide group and ignorance of the role of the tautomeric isoamide structure, $-C(OH) - NCH_3$. Mauger and Soper have maintained that, in the absence of carboxylic acids, the N-chlorination of N-methylacetamide and N-acetylglycine occurs by reaction of $O\overset{-}{C}l$. The data are not conclusive, however, and seem equally consistent with a chlorination by HOCl. More experiments over a wider range of conditions are needed for a decision.

On the assumption that the mechanism is a direct N-chlorination by HOCl, the data of Mauger and Soper give for the reaction:

$$HOCl + CH_3CONCH_3 \longrightarrow CH_3CONCH_3 + H_2O ; k_{11} \quad (2\text{-}11)$$

with H over the left CH_3CONCH_3 and Cl over the right CH_3CONCH_3.

At $25°C$ the specific rate is:

$$k_{11} = 1.4 \times 10^{-3} (1 + 3.3 \times 10^2 [AcOH] + \dots) \text{ liter mol}^{-1} \text{ sec}^{-1}$$

Then the uncatalyzed rate constant is:

$$k_{11} = 1.4 \times 10^{-3} \text{ liter mol}^{-1} \text{ sec}^{-1}; \log k_{11} = 2.85$$

From this the value of F_o, the rate constant relative to that for ammonia, is 2.3×10^{-10}.

Reported data for the N-chlorination of N-acetylglycine are much less extensive, having been given only for acetate and phosphate solutions at pH 6. Interestingly, the uncatalyzed rate computed from the results of Mauger and Soper is considerably greater than that of N-methylacetamide and the effect of acetic acid is considerably less.

The specific rate at $25^{\circ}C$ for the process:

$$HOCl + CH_3\overset{H}{CONCH_2}COO^- \longrightarrow CH_3\overset{Cl}{CONCH_2}COO^-$$

$$+ H_2O; k_{12} \qquad\qquad (2\text{-}12)$$

computed from their data is:

$$k_{12} = 5 \times 10^{-2} (1 + 38 \left[AcOH\right]) \text{ liter mol}^{-1} \text{ sec}^{-1}$$

or:

$$k_{12} = 5 \times 10^{-2} \text{ liter mol}^{-1} \text{ sec}^{-1}; \log k_{12} = -1.3$$

giving an F_0 value equal to 8×10^{-9}.

An additional estimate of the rate of N-chlorination of amides can be obtained from Samples' work on the chlorination of urea (10). The reactions of aqueous chlorine with urea could be explained with assumptions that the reaction:

$$HOCl + NH_2CONH_2 \longrightarrow NH_2CONHCl + H_2O; k_{13} \quad (2\text{-}13)$$

is rate-determining and that subsequent rapid reactions result in total reaction of 6 molecules of aqueous chlorine for each molecule of urea. Computation from Samples' data shows that the total rate of reaction of hypochlorite at $25^{\circ}C$ and pH 7.3 is 38 liter mol^{-1} min^{-1} and gives:

$$k_{13} = 7.5 \times 10^{-2} \text{ liter mol}^{-1} \text{ sec}^{-1}; \log k_{13} = -1.12$$

for the rate of reaction of each of the two amide groups. This constant is not greatly different from that found for the rate of N-chlorination of N-acetylglycine.

In relation to Figure 2, the F_0 values for the amides are low by a factor of about 10^{-5} for their estimated pK_B values of about 14. Provided the mechanistic interpretation is not at fault, this would seem to indicate that the resonance of the amide group, which tends to place a positive charge on the amide nitrogen, has a greater effect on the rate of N-chlorination than on the basicity.

N-CHLORINATION OF SULFAMATE

For several years sulfamic acid, NH_2SO_3H, has been used as an acidifying agent and as a stabilizer for residual chlorine in swimming pools. Also, a few years ago, McCarthy found that mixed solutions of aqueous chlorine and sulfamate retained disinfecting activity far longer than solutions of aqueous chlorine alone when successive additions of sewage were made (11).

Preliminary investigation at Harvard of the likely formation of N-chlorinated derivatives of sulfamate by Hend Galal-Gorchev showed that the reactions between dilute aqueous chlorine and sulfamate are different in many ways from those of the systems considered previously. In particular, the rate of formation of a monochlorinated derivative is much slower than the reaction to form a dichlorinated compound in the pH region from 5 to 8, so that isolation of the monochlorination reaction is difficult. Moreove r, solutions containing dichlorinated sulfamate tend, in the presence of excess sulfamate, to redistribute the chlorine until the chlorine is mainly present as monochlorinated sulfamate. Both these phenomena are opposite those found for the chlorination of ammonia and methylamine, or of those known qualitatively for the chlorination of substances like acetamide and benzenesulfonamide.

General Procedures and Observations

Sulfamic acid, obtainable as a crystalline solid of sufficient purity and stability for use as a primary acidimetric standard, is a strong acid dissociated essentially completely in aqueous solution to H^+ and $NH_2^-SO_3$ for pH values greater than 2. The amide group exhibits little basic or acidic character; between pH values 2 and 13 only N-containing species of importance in solutions of sulfamic acid or simple sulfamates is the sulfamate ion $NH_2^-SO_3$. (Apparently the negative charge on the sulfonate group weakens the acid nature of the amide group in comparison with other sulfonamides, which normally have $pK_a \simeq 10$.)

Typical ultra-violet spectra of mixed solutions of aqueous chlorine and sulfamate at pH near 7 are shown in Figure 3. The spectrum for pure dichlorsulfamate, curve A is found soon after mixing when the molar ratio of chlorine to sulfamate is 2; the same spectrum is obtained with molar ratios greater than 2 after subtraction of the absorption due to excess hypochlorite. Two characteristics of importance are the absorption maximum at 298 mμ with an absorptivity in terms of chlorine molarity equal to 62 cm^{-1} and the rapidly increasing absorption with decreasing wave length below 250 mμ.

At pH 8, as shown by curves B to E of Figure 3, and at smaller pH values to about 5, dichlorsulfamate is formed predominantly even with molar ratios of chlorine to sulfamate much less than unity. From the change in f raction of dichlor-sulfamate with change in initial ratio of chlorine to sulfamate

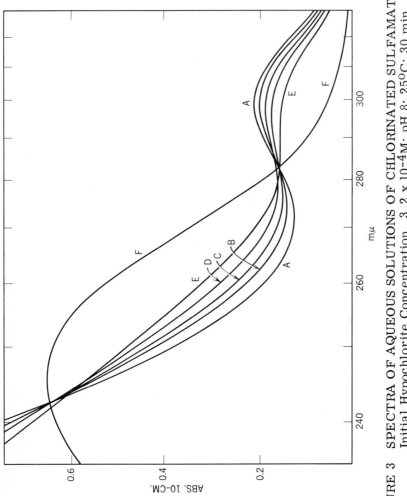

FIGURE 3   SPECTRA OF AQUEOUS SOLUTIONS OF CHLORINATED SULFAMATE
Initial Hypochlorite Concentration, 3.2 x 10⁻⁴M; pH 8; 25°C; 30 min
reaction time.   Curve A, pure N, N-dichlorsulfamate; B, N:Cl ratio 1.0;
C, N:Cl ratio 2.0; D, N:Cl ratio 5.0; E, N:Cl ratio 10.0; F, pure
N-chlorsulfamate

and from the fact that subsequent interactions are slow it may
be deduced that the chlorinated sulfamates are formed by the
sequential reactions:

$$HOCl + NH_2^-SO_3 \longrightarrow N\bar{H}ClSO_3 + H_2O; \; k_{14} \qquad (2\text{-}14)$$

$$HOCl + N\bar{H}ClSO_3 \longrightarrow N\bar{C}l_2SO_3 + H_2O; \; k_{15} \qquad (2\text{-}15)$$

as in the chlorination of ammonia and methylamine and that
the predominance of dichlorsulfamate is due to the greater
rate of reaction 2-15.

The spectrum of N-chlorsulfamate, curve F in Figure 3,
is found for reaction mixtures at pH 3 or less containing much
excess sulfamate and also for similar reactionmixtures at
greater pH values to pH 9 that have been allowed to stand until
redistribution of chlorine is complete. An absorption maximum
occurs at 247 mμ with a molar absorptivity of 196 cm^{-1}.

Small fractions of dichlorsulfamate in solutions of N-chlorsulfamate can be detected readily by comparison of the absorbance at 225 mμ with that for the isoabsorptive point at 243 mμ.
The ratio, A225/A243, is 0.632 for pure N-chlorsulfamate;
with 20% of the chlorine as dichlorsulfamate, the ratio is
already greater than unity, increasing linearly with the fraction
of chlorine as dichlorsulfamate to the value 2.58 for the pure
dichlorinated compound.

N-chlorsulfamate is acidic; titrations and spectrophotometric measurements on solutions near pH 11 have given
$K_a = 1.0 \times 10^{-11}$ at 25°C. Acid dissociation of NHClSO$_3^-$ affects
strongly the formation of dichlorsulfamate in basic solutions.
Consequently, data for pH values greater than 9.5 have not
been included in this presentation.

Dilute solutions of chlorinated sulfamate are quite stable
with respect to reduction of abailable chlorine in comparison
with solutions of many other N-chlor compounds. Decreases
of about 0.5% available chlorine per 24 hours were observed
typically for solutions predominantly dichlorsulfamate as well
as for those predominantly N-chlorsulfamate.

Rate of Formation of N-Chlorsulfamate

Direct determination of the specific rate of formation of
N-chlorsulfamate according to reaction 2-14 is complicated by
the interference of reaction 2-15. It should be possible to
evaluate the specific rate near pH 6 by direct measurement,

for the relative rate of reaction 2-15 to reaction 2-14 is great
enough in this region to make a steady-state approximation
valid. Unfortunately, rate studies at this pH were not included
in the original series of experiments.

Competitive studies similar to those of Friend, however,
have been conducted to compare the specific rate of reaction
2-14 with that for formation of N-chlordimethylamine. Use of
dimethylamine as reference reactant allowed significant
experiments to be made in quite acid solutions where k_{15} is
comparable with or less than k_{14}. Even with this technique,
results were distorted somewhat by concurrent formation of
dichlorsulfamate, the extent of which was different in the
mixed solutions with dimethylamine from that found when
separate solutions of the nitrogenous compounds were chlorinated for obtaining the reference spectra. Analytical measurements were made at 280 mμ, near an isoabsorptive point for
N-chlorsulfamate and N_1, N-dichlorsulfamate, to lessen the
effect of this interference. Corrections were made to the
apparent ratio of specific rates for estimated amounts of
reaction 2-15. Final data with somewhat greater theoretical
validity might have been obtained by a procedure involving
successive approximations, but the limited precision of the
experimental measurements did not warrant such extended
mathematical operations.

A summary of the data and the computed values of k_{14}
are shown in Table II. The values for k_{14} exhibit considerable
scatter, but there is no definite trend over the pH range 4.5
to 7, corresponding to a 300-fold change in (H^+). This con-
stancy is an indication that reaction 2-14 proceeds by the
mechanism shown, at least to the extent that the interpretation
of the formation of N-chlordimethylamine is correct. The
mean result for 25°C is:

$$k_{14} = 6.5 \times 10^2 \text{ liter mol}^{-1} \text{ sec}^{-1}; \log k_{14} = 2.81$$

This yields a value of $\log F_0$, for the specific rate relative to
that for ammonia, equal to -4.0.

The K_a value for sulfamic acid is given as 0.10, corresponding to K_B equal to 1.0×10^{-13} for sulfamate ion. There is
some evidence that undissociated sulfamic acid exists in solution
partly as a neutral molecule and partly as a zwitterion in amounts
of the same order of magnitude. Thus, it is estimated that for

TABLE II RATE OF FORMATION OF N-CHLORSULFAMATE

All experiments at 25°C with approx. 1.6×10^{-4} M aqueous chlorine; initial molar ratio of dimethylamine to chlorine, 1.6 and initial ratio of sulfamate to dimethylamine, 50.5 except as noted.

pH	$(CH_3)_2NCl$ formed (a)	k'_{14}/k'_r (b)	$k'_{14}/k_r \times 10^6$ (c)	$k_{14}/k_r \times 10^6$ (d)	$k_{14} \times 10^{-2}$ liter mol^{-1} sec^{-1}
3.93	0.028	6.9	1.0	1.0	3.3 (g)
4.48 (e)	.063	2.90	1.49	1.5	4.9 (g)
4.51	.239	5.15	2.83	2.5	8.4
4.93	.160	0.98	1.40	1.3	4.4
4.95	.116	1.48	2.23	2.1	7.0
5.00 (f)	.440	0.94	1.58	1.6	5.2
5.49	.330	0.357	1.86	1.6	5.2
6.05	.491	.170	3.22	2.3	7.5
6.60	.751	.0485	3.28	.20	6.5
7.04	.866	.0214	3.96	2.4	7.8

Mean: 6.5×10^2

(a) fraction of initial aqueous chlorine reacting to form $(CH_3)_2NCl$.
(b) observed ratio of specific rates for experimental conditions.
(c) column 3 times $(OH^-)/K_b$; $K_b = 5.9 \times 10^{-4}$.
(d) column 4 times factor $(2-D)/2$, where D is estimated fraction of chlorinated sulfamate as dichlorsulfamate (expressed as chlorine).
(e) sulfamate-dimethylamine ratio 5.95.
(f) sulfamate-dimethylamine ratio 13.2; dimethylamine-chlorine ratio 6.4.
(g) omitted from mean because fraction of $(CH_3)_2NCl$ was less than 0.10.

Formation of N, N-Dichlorsulfamate

Determinations of the relative specific rate of formation of N, N-dichlorsulfamate to that of N-chlorsulfamate have been made by measurement of the percentages of the the two compounds formed with varied, known, initial ratios of aqueous chlorine to sulfamate. This was followed by computations in accordance with the consecutive-competitive mechanism for the previously described experiments on the formation of $NHCl_2$. All measurements were made at 25°C.

The results are shown plotted logarithmically as a function of pH in Figure 4. The values at pH 6 and less appear to conform to the relation, $k'_{15}/k'_{14} = 1.0 \times 10^{-4}/(H^+)$, corresponding to the left-hand straight line in Figure 4. The indicated relation for pH greater than 7 is $k'_{15}/k'_{14} = 6 \times 10^8 (H^+)$, corresponding to the right-hand straight line.

These variations are unexplained so far. The observed relationship in the acid region is the reverse of that encountered generally with successive N-chlorination reactions, for formation of the dichlorinated derivative usually is favored more the smaller the pH. This holds, for example, with ammonia, amines like CH_3NH_2, amides like CH_3CONH_2, and even other sulfonamides like $C_6H_5SO_2NH_2$. Moreover, since the specific rate of formation of N-chlorsulfamate, as given in the previous section, does not change with pH in this region, the observed variation must be ascribed to a decrease in specific rate of formation of N, N-dichlorsulfamate with increasing (H^+) or to a specific rate proportional to (OH^-). Formation of unreactive $NH_2Cl^+SO_3^-$ with decreasing pH seems very unlikely; surely

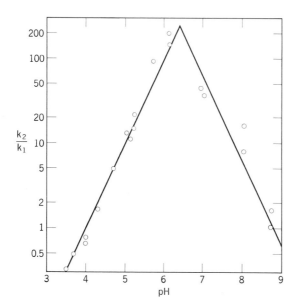

FIGURE 4   RELATIVE SPECIFIC RATE OF
                FORMATION OF N, N-DICHLORSULFAMATE
                TO N-CHLORSULFAMATE AS FUNCTION
                OF pH AT 25°C.

$NH\bar{C}lSO_3$ is not that basic. Either base catalysis of the formation of $N\bar{C}l_2SO_3$ or action of hypochlorite as chlorinating agent
for $NHClSO_3$ would account for the relationship in acid solutions,
but would create grave difficulties for interpretation of the
results in basic solutions.

The observed relative specific rates and the previously
determined value of k_{14} give for the specific rate of reaction
2-15 in acid solution:

$$k'_{15} = 6.5 \times 10^{-2}/(H^+) \ (liter \ mol^{-1})^2 \ sec^{-1}$$

but the exact process to which this quantity refers cannot be
specified at present.

The situation is even less satisfactory with regard to the
results in basic solution, for it is not even known whether the
observed drop in k'_{15}/k'_{14} with increasing pH is to be attributed
to a decrease in the numerator or an increase in the denominator
(apart from the effect of ionization of HOCl which should have

similar influence on both reactions). Intuitively the latter seems
more likely, perhaps by base catalysis of formation of $NHClSO_3$,
but this explanation makes it more difficult to account for the
results in acid solution. Acid ionization of $NHClSO_3$ to $NClSO_3^{-2}$
is too slight below pH 10 to account for the relationship.

The Redistribution Reaction
    Solutions of N, N-dichlorsulfamate when mixed with
sulfamate react according to the overall equation:

$$NCl_2SO_3^- + NH_2SO_3^- \longrightarrow 2NHClSO_3^-; \; k_{16} \qquad (2-16)$$

The reaction is quite slow in mildly acid solution near pH 5,
but increases in rate quite sharply with increase or decrease
in pH. A position of equilibrium is reached eventually.
Spectrophotometric measurements of solutions in equilibrium
at pH values from 6 to 9 give for the equilibrium constant:

$$K_{16} = \left[NHClSO_3^-\right]^2 \Big/ \left[NH_2SO_3^-\right]\left[NCl_2SO_3^-\right] = 16$$

at 25°C. This is not very different from the value of 4 expected
with a purely statistical distribution of the chlorine atoms.
Apparently, there are no great energy differences for attachment of one or two chlorine atoms to the nitrogen.
    Reaction 2-15 appears to be second order, -first order
with each reactant. Sufficiently extensive studies yet have not
been conducted however, to stipulate definitely whether a direct
interaction mechanism occurs or hydrolysis to HOCl and subsequent slow reaction with $NH_2SO_3^-$ takes place. The direct
mechanism is more probable, for the hydrolysis pathway does
not give a proper pH dependence.
    Values for the second order rate constant, k_{16}', obtained
from spectrophotometric measurements over periods up to
four days, are given in Figure 5. Each of the points for pH
values less than 7.5 is an average of two or three runs with
different ratios of sulfamate to N, N-dichlorsulfamate, ranging
from 2.6 to 50. No trend in specific rate was found as a function
of this ratio. The points for pH greater than 7.5 all are results
from single experiments, each with a ratio about 4.
    The fitted curve in Figure 5 corresponds to the equation:

$$k_{16}' = 2.0 \times 10^{-4} \left[1 + 6.5 \times 10^3 \, (H^+) + 7.7 \times 10^8 \, (OH^-)\right]$$
$$\text{liter mol}^{-1} \text{ sec}^{-1}$$

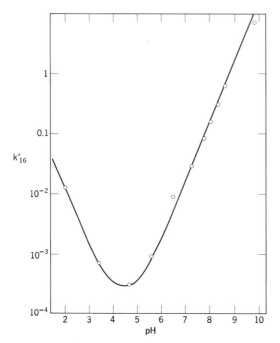

FIGURE 5   SPECIFIC RATE OF REACTION,
               $NCl_2SO_3^- + NH_2SO_3^- \longrightarrow 2NHClSO_3^-$,
               AS FUNCTION OF pH AT 25°C.

a relatiion suggestive of an acid-base catalyzed reaction. Since
the reaction ad depicted involves two negatively charged ions,
the specific rate should depend also on the ionic strength. The
data are all for ionic strengths 0. 05 to 0.1. One or two experiments at a greater ionic strength have shown an increased rate
in accord iwth expectations, but insufficient data are available
to compute k_{16} at zero ionic strength.

CONCLUSIONS
    As this survey of available data has shown, current
knowledge of the rates and mechanisms of reaction of dilute
aqueous chlorine with nitrogenous compounds is very incomplete
and scattered. Only a few systems have been studied with even
moderate thoroughness; in all instances the precision and range
of investigated conditions could be extended profitably. Data
on temperature effects are particularly scanty and must be expanded if full understanding of the nature of the reactions is to

be achieved.

It is apparent, however, from what is already known that studies on reactions of N-chlorination not only are of major practical significance for water treatment and indeed for all areas in which disinfection, bleaching, or oxidation by chlorine in aqueous solution is of concern, but that they are also of great interest for the broad field dealing with the theoretical aspects of reaction rates in solution.

The many types of nitrogenous compounds available and the wide range of properties they exhibit provide an almost limitless source for investigation of theoretical deductions. That the reactions occur in dilute aqueous solution at readily measurable rates under mild conditions makes N-chlorination processes almost unique, - apart from acid-base reactions of hydronium ion - in the opportunities they present for systematic development of aqueous solution theory. The major problems are occasional instability of the products toward oxidation-reduction and adequate methods of identification and determination.

It seems likely that continued investigations will lead to the discovery and practical development of N-chlor compounds with properties particularly adapted to special uses in disinfection, bleaching or oxidation, or to their preparation in solution under proper conditions based on a knowledge of rates and mechanisms of formation. For example, one of the major artificial sweetening agents is a salt of N-cyclohexylsulfamic acid; the possibility that the properties of its N-chlor derivative are like those of chlorinated sulfamate produces a vision, at least in a frivolously imaginative mind, of a pleasantly sweetened swimming-pool water with stabilized available chlorine.

LITERATURE CITED
1. Weil, I. and J.C. Morris, J Am Chem Soc, 71, 1664 (1949).

2. Ingol, C.K., Substitution at Elements Other Than Carbon, Fifth Weizman Memorial Lecture Series, Weizman Science Press, Jerusalem, Israel, May 1958.

3. Mauger, R.P. and F.G. Soper, J Chem Soc (London), p71 (1946).

4. Morris, J.C., et al, The Formation of Monochloramine and Dichloramine in Water Chlorination, Paper, 117th Meeting, Am Chem Soc, Detroit, Michigan, April 16-20, (1950

5. Weil, I. and J.C. Morris, J Am Chem Soc, 71, 3123 (1949).

6. Weil, I. and J.C. Morris, Kinetic Studies on the Chloramines.
   II The Disproportionation of Monchloramines, Paper,
   116th Meeting, Am Chem Soc, Atlantic City, N.J.,
   September 18-23, (1949).

7. Granstrom, M.L. The Disproportionation of Monochloramine,
   Ph.D. Thesis, Harvard University, November 30, (1954).

8. Edmond, C.R. and F.G. Soper, J Chem Soc London, p2942
   (1949).

9. Friend, A.G., Rates of N-Chlorination of Amino Acids,
   Ph.D. Thesis, Harvard University, June 1, (1954).

10. Samples, W.R., A Study on the Chlorination of Urea,
    Ph.D. Thesis, Harvard University, April (1959).

11. McCarthy, J.A., J New Eng Water Works Assoc, 74, 166
    (1960).

DISCUSSION
    DR. EYRING (University of Utah): Dr. Morris, how many
different experimental techniques are represented in taking
these data?
    DR. MORRIS: Almost all of them have been studied with
standard techniques using spectophotometric methods of
measurements. These rapid reactions can be measured in
this way because of the unfavorable equilibrium position between
the neutral molecules that are the actual reactants and the ions,
so that the concentrations of reactive species may be in the
neighborhood of ten to the minus tenth molar. That is why they
can be studied over a period of a few minutes rather than shorter
times.
    MR. G.K. SMITH (City Chemist, Frederick, Md.):
Professor, have you done any work on the formation of
nitrogen trichloride?
    DR. MORRIS: No kinetic work at all. One can only make
the qualitative statement that the formation from dichloroamine
is inherently slower than the reaction of hypochlorous acid with
monochloramine, but how much slower I don't know. The
difficulty is that dichloroamine is so unstable that one does not

have a stabilized reacting solution to start with.

DR. D. JOHNSON (University of North Carolina): You have presented some fairly complicated and some beautiful work, in my opinion, and I've done some of this work myself. It looks awfully simple the way you present it, but in the laboratory it is pretty complicated.

My question is with reference to the ammonia system and the acid and chloride catalysis. You say this work has been published?

DR. MORRIS: No, although it has been presented orally at an ACS meeting, it has never been reported in the literature except as a thesis and in government reports. This conference seemed to offer a good opportunity at least to get the fundamental figures into the literature. I hope that the studies themselves will be published in more detailed form elsewhere.

DR. JOHNSON: In this respect, how low did you have to go with pH and how high in the concentration did you have to go before you saw these complications?

DR. MORRIS: Usually with the acid catalyzed systems the catalytic constant was about ten to the fifth for hydrogen ions relative to the normal uncatalyzed reaction, so that it begins to intrude at about pH 5.

I don't know that the chloride catalysis has been quantized too well; I didn't review that data carefully in preparing this paper.

Catalytic constants for acetic acid are in the neighborhood of one hundred, so that in the neighborhood of ten to the minus two molar carboxylic-acid buffer, rates are approximately doubled.

DR. JOHNSON: In reference to the mechanism of this reaction what evidence is there that this is a simple bimolecular reaction as indicated by your diagram?

DR. MORRIS: Well, the reactions have generally been tested for orders of reaction with respect to the reactants, and usually have been found to be straight second-order reactions. For one of these reactions, the disproportionation of NH_2Cl, the kinetic order is mixed first and second order but the constant I have presented is for the second-order part of the reaction and not the complete reaction.

DR. E. CROOK (Rohm & Haas): Professor Morris, have you carried on any work with reaction of chlorinaceous compounds with polyamines? If so, what sort of reaction constants are involved? Or are you aware of any work that has been done in this area?

DR. MORRIS: Not really. The only compound studied that might be called a polyamine was urea, that has two amide groups on it. We have not worked with other polyamines at all, and I don't know of any work that has been done on them.

DR. CROOK: With polyamines would you think intuitively that you would get slower reaction rates than you would with perhaps monomeric compounds?

DR. MORRIS: If the reaction rate of diethylamine is any criterion, yes, because it looks as if steric effects might get to be important.

CHAIRMAN ETTINGER: Time for just about one more question, if there be another question.

DR. H. C. MARKS (Wallace & Tiernan): Professor Morris, the reverse reaction; namely, the hydrolysis, the reaction of hydroxyl ion with the N-chloro compound is one that is, of course, particularly important in disinfection. Would you care to comment on the question of using the data we have now on these rates formation and other data, how close we might be to significant data on hydrolysis rates that would help us in the disinfection problem?

DR. MORRIS: One hydrolysis rate has been evaluated directly, that of monochloroamine. I spoke about two mechanisms for the disproportionation of NH_2Cl. One of these involves a preliminary hydrolysis. Computations from the overall rate give quite good values for the hydrolysis rate, which can be combined with the rate of formation to give a hydrolysis constant for monochloroamine. The detailed figures are in the manuscript. The constant is 0×10^{-2}, E to the minus 14,000 over RT. The manuscript also includes some data on the percentage of hydrolysis at pH 7 with two mg/l of available chlorine; the hydrolysis is 0.58%, which is quite small.

Soper made some measurements on hydrolysis of N-chlorsulfonamides; these data are apparently quite reliable. Vapor studies on some of the more easily hydrolized materials can be carried out.

C. Fred Lee

University of Wisconsin

KINETICS OF REACTIONS BETWEEN CHLORINE AND PHENOLIC COMPOUNDS

One of the major problems associated with disinfection of water supplies by chlorination is that the organoleptic properties of the chlorinated water may be increased. This malodorous water often is produced by a reaction between chlorine and trace concentrations of organic compounds present in the water. By far the most notorious organic compounds found in water which increase the tastes and odors in the water upon chlorination are phenol and some of its homologs.

The nature of the compound or compounds which gives rise to "chlorophenolic" tastes and odors resulting from the reaction between aqueous chlorine and phenolic compounds has been investigated repeatedly (1, 2, 3, 4, 5). Little was known with certainty, however, about the chemical reactions involved in the production or destruction of chlorophenolic taste and odor until the appearance of a significant paper by Burttschell, et al (6). In this important study, the chlorophenols formed from the chlorination of phenol in dilute aqueous solutions were for the first time isolated and identified. From a knowledge of the chlorophenols, a reaction scheme was proposed, Figure 1, to account for the production

54

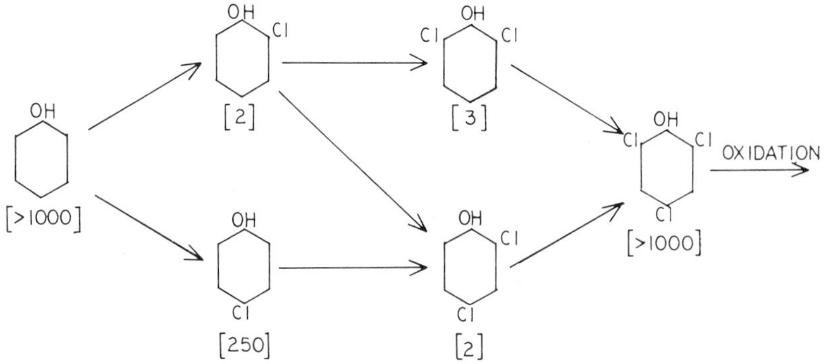

[ ] ODOR THRESHOLD CONC. MICROGRAMS PER LITER
(AFTER BURTTSCHELL ET AL)

FIGURE 1   REACTION SCHEME FOR THE
CHLORINATION OF PHENOL.

and subsequent elimination of "chlorophenolic" tastes and
odors in water supplies.

According to Burttschell, et al, the chlorination of
phenol proceeds by stepwise substitution of the 2, 4, and 6
positions of the aromatic ring (6). Initially, phenol is
chlorinated to form either 2- or 4- chlorophenol. Then 2-
chlorophenol is chlorinated to form either 2, 4- or 2, 6-
dichlorophenol while 4-chlorophenol forms 2, 4-dichlorophenol.
Both 2, 4- and 2, 6-dichlorophenol are chlorinated to form
2, 4, 6-trichlorophenol. The 2, 4, 6-trichlorophenol reacts
with aqueous chlorine to form a mixture of non-phenolic
oxidation products.

Burttschell, et al, also determined for the chlorophenols
the threshold odor concentration, i.e., the maximum
dilution at which odor can be detected by an individual with
an average olfactory sensitivity (6). These threshold odor
concentrations for each of the compounds in the reaction
scheme presented are listed also in Figure 1. The compounds
with the strongest organoleptic properties were 2-chloro-
phenol, 2, 4-dichlorophenol, and 2, 6-dichlorophenol;

these were detectable at concentrations of 2 to $3\mu g/l$. In contrast, phenol, 4-chlorophenol, and 2, 4, 6-trichlorophenol were detectable only at much higher concentrations. Consequently, it appears that 2-chlorophenol, 2, 4-, and 2, 6-dichlorophenol are the compounds primarily responsible for the "chlorophenolic" taste and odor in water supplies.

Although the investigation by Burttschell, et al (6), has contributed valuable and badly needed information about the products formed from the chlorination of phenol, it does not provide a complete picture of the way in which these products may change with time of reaction, proportions of reactants, pH, temperature, and other conditions of reaction. A thorough kinetic study of the individual reactions forming the overall pattern of chlorination was needed for these purposes. Knowledge of the changing relative importance of individual reactions, as conditions of chlorination vary, will provide the necessary data for prediction of differences in overall characteristics and for specification of optimum conditions of chlorination to minimize "chlorophenolic" taste and odor production. Consequently, determination of the kinetic properties of potential individual reactions that occur during the chlorination of phenol comprises the experimental portion of this paper.

These data have been used to compute the expected concentration of the individual chlorinated phenols as a function of time and other variables. This gives a detailed picture of the progress of the overall reaction between chlorine and phenol for the range of conditions likely to be encountered in treatment of phenol-bearing waters.

Futhermore, this information has been combined with the data on organoleptic properties of the individual chlorophenols in order to compute anticipated threshold odor values of chlorinated phenol-containing waters as a function of time and solution conditions. These final data provide a basis for prediction and selection of optimum procedures for minimizing taste and odor problems.

EXPERIMENTAL TECHNIQUES
Reagents

Stock solutions of aqueous chlorine, approximately 0.05M, were prepared by bubbling chlorine gas into chlorine-demand-free, double distilled water. These solutions were stored in "low actinic" Pyrex vessels at $5^{O}C$. Fresh solutions were prepared weekly and were standardized by iodine-thiosulfate titration using starch as an indicator (7). The concentration of aqueous chlorine remaining as a function of time of reaction was determined by the o-tolidine method (7). Absorbance was measured on a Beckman DU Spectrophotometer.

Stock solutions of phenol and each of the chlorophenols were prepared by weighing the dried compound purified by fractional distillation, and dissolving this amount in distilled water.

The pH of the reaction solution was maintained at a constant value during the course of the reaction by addition of buffers: pH 4-6, acetic acid-acetate; pH 6-8, mono- and dibasic phosphate; pH 8-10, bicarbonate-carbonate; and pH 10-12, hydroxide. All pH measurements were made on a Beckman Model G pH meter.

The reaction was conducted in the presence of added chloride, at a known ionic strength by addition of sodium perchlorate to the reaction solution.

Procedure for Kinetic Runs

All reactions were conducted in a thermostated water bath controlled to $\pm$ 0.2°C in diffuse light. The procedure for each experimental run was: to one 500-ml volumetric flask were added the desired amounts of aqueous chlorine, pH buffer, and chloride. To another 500-ml volumetric flask were added phenol or chlorophenol and perchlorate. Both flasks were placed in the water bath and allowed to come to the desired temperature. After temperature equilibrium, the contents of each flask were poured simultaneously into the reaction vessel (1 liter Pyrex reagent bottle). A stopwatch was started at the beginning of pouring. The reaction vessel was placed in the water bath; at desired time intervals an aliquot of the reaction solution was withdrawn and an analysis was made of aqueous chlorine content. At the start of each run an aliquot of the reaction solution was placed in a spectrophotometric absorption cell and a continuous record of the ultraviolet spectra was obtained on a Beckman DK-2 Ratio Recording Spectrophotometer. The infrared spectra of the reaction products were obtained for some of the reaction solutions. The chlorophenolic products were extraced by ethyl ether following the procedure

described by Burttschell, et al (6). Infrared spectra were
obtained on a Perkin Elmer Model 21 Infrared Spectrophotometer using carbon disulfide as the solvent.

EXPERIMENTAL RESULTS

The chlorination of phenol and each of the chlorophenols
conforms to a second-order rate expression in which the
rate of change of chlorine or phenolic compound is proportional to the product of the formal concentrations of aqueous
chlorine and phenolic compound. This expression in terms
of the quantities analytically measured is:

$$- \frac{dF_{Cl}}{dt} = k_{ob} \; F_{Cl} \; F_{PhOH}. \tag{3-1}$$

This equation may be integrated to yield:

$$\frac{1}{F^O_{PhOH} - F^O_{Cl}} \; \ln \; \frac{F^O_{Cl} \; F_{PhOH}}{F^O_{PhOH} \; F_{Cl}} = k_{ob} t \tag{3-2}$$

where:

F^O_{PhOH} is the initial formal concentration of phenolic
           compound

F_{PhOH} (a)   is the formal concentration of phenolic
           compound at time, t

F^O_{Cl} is the initial formal concentration of chlorine

F_{Cl} (b)   is the formal concentration of chlorine in
           an oxidation state of plus 1 at time, t

k_{ob} is the second-order rate constant in liter
           $mol^{-1} \; min^{-1}$

(a) Formal concentration of phenol is the molar sum of
     phenol or chlorophenol and phenolate or chlorophenolate.
(b) Formal concentration of aqueous chlorine is the
     molar sum of molecular chlorine, hypochlorous acid,
     and hypochlorite ion.

The rate constant, k_{ob}, was evaluated from the slope of
a plot of the left side of equation 3-2 as a function of time
for each experimental run. The constants for chlorination
of phenol and each of the chlorophenols are presented in
Table I and plotted in Figure 2.

TABLE I OBSERVED RATES OF CHLORINATION OF PHENOLIC COMPOUNDS
Temperature 25°C, $Cl^- = 10^{-3}M$, ionic strength = 0.02

pH	Phenol	2-Chlorophenol	4-Chlorophenol	2,4-Dichlorophenol	2,6-Dichlorophenol	2,4,6-Trichlorophenol
5	2.09×10^2	4.03×10^2	9.60×10^1	2.38×10^2	6.32×10^2	1.17×10^2
6	4.82×10^2	1.04×10^3	2.98×10^2	4.02×10^2	1.34×10^3	3.46×10^2
7	2.23×10^3	3.16×10^3	8.93×10^2	1.76×10^3	4.95×10^3	5.16×10^2
8	6.15×10^3	8.15×10^3	1.84×10^3	2.72×10^3	2.19×10^3	1.45×10^2
9	6.14×10^3	3.21×10^3	1.54×10^3	5.48×10^2	2.96×10^2	1.34×10^1
10	2.84×10^3	4.30×10^2	4.15×10^2	6.32×10^1	3.09×10^1	9.05×10^{-1}
11	4.73×10^2	4.60×10^1	4.70×10^1	6.37	3.12	5.44×10^{-2}
12	4.50×10^1	4.60	4.54	6.36×10^{-1}	3.15×10^{-1}	1.81×10^{-3}

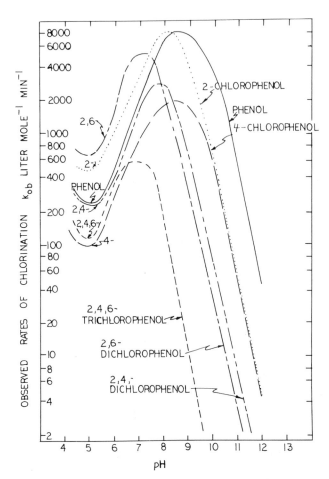

FIGURE 2   OBSERVED RATES OF CHLORINATION
OF PHENOL AND CHLOROPHENOLS,
25°C, IONIC STRENGTH 0.02, Cl^- 10^{-3}M.

The rates of chlorination of phenol in the neutral pH range
are of similar magnitude to those of the chlorophenols. Therefore, the formed chlorophenols compete for the remaining aqueous chlorine in the reaction solution. This competition causes
deviation from the second-order rate expression, equation 3-1.
To reduce this deviation and to isolate the desired reaction, it
was necessary to study the chlorination of phenol and each of
the phenolic compounds, and then use only the initial periods

of reaction to evaluate k_{ob}.

The rate constants in Figure 2 were obtained with an initial concentration of aqueous chlorine of approximately $5 \times 10^{-5} M$ and $5 \times 10^{-4} M$ for the phenolic compound. A hundred-fold dilution of these concentrations obeys the same rate expression; equation 3-1, however, great care must be exercised to remove traces of ammonia to obtain reliable results.

Examination of Figure 2 shows that chlorination of each phenolic compound has a maximum value of k_{ob} corresponding to a maximum rate of chlorination at pH 7-9. The position of the maxima shifts to lower pH values with increasing acidity of the chlorophenols. In addition, when chloride is present in the reaction solution, each system exhibits a minimum k_{ob} near pH 5. In the presence of chloride, the rates of chlorination increase rapidly with decreasing pH below pH 5. It is of interest to compare the rates of chlorination of the chlorophenols at pH 9. At this pH the dichlorophenols are chlorinated about 10 to 20 times slower than the monochlorophenols. Therefore, the chlorination of phenol in the alkaline pH range, e.g., pH 9 or greater, will result in the build-up in the reaction solution of the odorous dichlorophenols; while at pH 7-8, the odorous dichlorophenols are chlorinated at the same or at a greater rate than phenol or the monochlorophenols. The effect of pH of chlorination on distribution of chlorophenolic products and the resulting threshold odor of the reaction solution will be discussed more fully under application of the kinetic results to the chlorination of phenol-bearing water.

INTERPRETATION OF KINETIC DATA

The rates of reaction of aqueous chlorine with phenol and the chlorophenols vary enormously with pH. This is largely because of the effect of pH on acid-base equilibria which determines the concentration of the various species of hydrolyzed chlorine and phenolic compound in the reaction solution.

Soper and Smith found the variation in the rate of chlorination of phenol with pH could be explained by the hypothesis that the rate was proportional to the product of hypochlorous acid and phenolate ion concentrations (8). If equation 3-1 is expressed in terms of the activities of hypochlorous acid, HOCl, and phenolate, PhO^-, rather than the formal concentrations of chlorine and phenolic compound, a rate expression:

$$- \frac{dF_{Cl}}{dt} = k_2 \, (HOCl) \, (PhO^-) \qquad (3\text{-}3)$$

is obtained in which the rate constant, k_2, is independent of pH for the range 6-12 except for a minor acid catalysis. The data from this investigation conform to, and confirm in part, the mechanism of Soper and Smith; namely, that in the neutral or alkaline pH ranges, the chlorination of phenol and the chlorophenols proceeds by the reaction of hypochlorous acid with the phenolate or chlorophenolate. The minor deviation from the Soper and Smith mechanism found in this investigation can be attributed to an acid catalysis of this reaction.

It is of interest at this point to compare the rates of chlorination of phenol and each of the chlorophenols. As previously indicated, the pH of the maximum rate of chlorination of the phenolic compounds is related to the acidity of the phenolic compound. The more acidic compounds show a shift in the position of the maximum toward more acid pH values as seen in Figure 2. It was found that the product of the rate constant, k_2, times the acid dissociation constant for the compound under chlorination is a constant that is approximately 10^{-4}. This same relationship was found by Soper and Smith for chlorination of a variety of phenolic compounds (8). This observation may be interpreted as: those substitute groups on phenol which tend to make the substituted phenol more acidic also tend to decrease the rate of reaction of aqueous chlorine with this compound.

The rate constants, k_2, for the chlorination of phenol were found to be independent of ionic strength, concentration of pH buffering materials, and chloride concentration at pH values greater than 6. An activation energy value of 14 kcal per mole deg K was obtained for the temperature range 5 to 35°C for the uncatalyzed reaction between chlorine and phenol. This value is in the same range as commonly found for a majority of chemical reactions. An activation energy of this order of magnitude means that in the pH range 7-12, the rate of chlorination decreases by a factor of 2 for each 10°C decrease in temperature.

Below pH 6, with chloride present in the reaction solution, the equilibrium:

$$H^+ + Cl^- + HOCl \rightleftharpoons Cl_2 + H_2O \qquad (3-4)$$

is displaced far enough to the right so that a significant reaction occurs between molecular chlorine and the phenolic compound.

In reacting with aqueous chlorine, phenol and each of the chlorophenols display some tendency to undergo oxidative rupture of the benzene ring rather than substitution as was noted in infrared spectra of the reacted solutions. No attempt was made quantitatively to determine the respective fractions of oxidative rupture and substitution, but qualitatively it was found that the degree of oxidation is greater, the more highly chlorinated the phenolic reactant. The infrared data clearly show that an appreciable fraction of the reaction between aqueous chlorine and the dichlorophenols may proceed by direct oxidation rather than by substitution to the trichloro-phenol. The exact nature of these oxidation products is of little interest in this investigation since Burttschell, et al, found that these products do not contribute to the organoleptic properties of the reaction solution (6).

Measurement of the ultraviolet absorption spectra of the reaction solution yields only qualitative or, in some cases, semi-quantitative results because of the similarity of the spectra of phenol and the chlorophenols. Differences in the resulting absorption spectra were observed, however, parti-cularly between reactions conducted in the alkaline pH range and those conducted in the acid pH range. This allows some discriminatory conclusions. The ultraviolet spectra of reacting solutions in the pH range 4 to 7 during the course of the reaction exhibit marked departures from typical chlorophenolic spectra obtained in the alkaline pH range.

Atypical chlorophenolic absorption bands were obtained if the pH of chlorination was below pH 7. The maximum absorp-tion due to these bands coincides with the disappearance of aqueous chlorine from the reaction solution. After this time, the absorption due to these bands slowly decreases, and after an extended period of time, several weeks to a month, a stable absorption spectra was obtained which was very similar to that obtained if the chlorination had been conducted in more alkaline solutions. The atypical chlorophenolic absorption bands have been attributed to a long-lived reaction intermediate of undeter-mined structure. The formation of this intermediate may account for the reason why Burttschell, et al, found that atypical chlorophenolic tastes and odors were developed if the pH of chlorination was less than pH 7 (6).

CHLORINATION OF PHENOL IN THE PRESENCE OF AMMONIA

An important constituent of natural waters which has been reported to alter the kinetics of the chlorination of phenol is ammonia. Therefore, it is of interest to compare the rates of

chlorination of ammonia reported by Weil and Morris indicate
that for equal initial molar concentrations of ammonia and
phenol, pH 8, and temperature 25°C, ammonia is chlorinated
to form NH_2Cl about 1000 times faster than phenol is chlorinated
to form a monochlorophenol (9). Therefore, little chlorophenol
would be expected in the presence of excess ammonia. Burttschell,
et al, however, found that if sufficient time was allowed for the
reaction to proceed (several days to a week at water supply
concentrations) the same chlorophenols are formed when chloramine reacts with phenol as were found in a considerably shorter
period of time when chlorination of phenol was conducted in the
absence of ammonia (6).

The effect of ammonia on the rate of chlorophenol formation
in chlorinating very dilute phenol solutions may account for the
enormous concentration effects that have been reported by some
workers for this reaction. The difficulty of preparing water
free from traces of ammonia means that in experiments with
extremely dilute chlorine solutions, choramine may be formed
inadvertently. This extremely slow formation of the chlorophenols in the presence of ammonia may account for some of the
problems found in water supply practice with taste and odor
development after the water has left the treatment plant, particularly in the dead ends of the distribution systems.

APPLICATION OF RESULTS TO WATER TREATMENT

If the concentrations of each of the chlorophenols resulting
from the chlorination of phenol is known for a given initial
condition as a function of time and, if the organoleptic intensity
of each is known also, then the expected taste and odor characteristics of chlorinated phenol-containing waters can be
computed. This involves the assumption that the individual
organoleptic intensities of the chlorphenolic substances are
additive to give overall taste and odor intensities that can be
expressed as threshold odor. Computations of the expected
threshold odor for varying experimental conditions, time of
contact, relative concentrations of chlorine and phenol, pH,
and temperature permit delineation of conditions for maximal
and minimal development of objectionable organoleptic conditions and specification of conditions for chlorination of
phenol-containing waters to lessen production of noxious tastes
and odors.

Examination of reaction scheme, Figure 1, shows that a
short time after mixing chlorine and phenol, there are 8 inter-
dependent reactions occurring simultaneously. The rates

of each of these reactions have been determined in this
investigation. To compute the concentration of each of the
compounds in the reaction scheme required the integration and
simultaneous solution of 8 second-order differential equations.
These computations were made by Univac I digital computer.

Computations were performed for initial aqueous chlorine
concentrations of 1.0 mg/l and 0.2 mg/l each acting on initial
phenol concentrations of $50\mu g/l$ and $5\mu g/l$; these values were
chosen as typical of the concentrations encountered in the
treatment of water supplies. Reaction paths at pH values 7, 8,
and 9, respectively, were evaluated for each pair of reactant
concentrations.

All sets of concentrations gave similar results at a given
pH value with the major difference being the scales for concentration and time. Only the results for 1.0 mg/l chlorine and
$50 \mu g/l$ phenol are presented in Figure 3 for pH values of 7, 8,
and 9, respectively. Curves are shown for the formation and
reaction of phenol, 2-chlorophenol, 4-chlorophenol, 2,4-dichloro-
phenol, and 2,6-dichlorophenol. The concentrations of 2,4,
6-trichlorophenol or the buildup of oxidation products are not
shown since they do not contribute to the "chlorophenolic" tastes
and odors at the concentrations formed during the course of
the reaction.

At pH 7 the maximum concentrations of 2-chlorophenol,
4-chlorophenol, and 2,4-dichlorophenol are all about the same,
with each amounting to about 20% of the initial phenol concentration. For the plotted reactant concentrations, maximum
2-chlorophenol occurs after about 30 minutes, maximum
4-chlorophenol after about 50 minutes, and maximum 2,4-dichlo-
rophenol after about 80 minutes because it is formed from the
first two. At this pH, the concentration of 2,6-dichlorophenol
always remains low.

Reactions at pH 8 are more rapid as seen by comparing
the time scales of Figure 3a with 3b. The maximum concentration of 4-chlorophenol has become much less than that of
2-chlorophenol whereas 2,6-dichlorophenol has increased greatly
so that it is now greater than the maximum concentration of
4-chlorophenol. The maximum concentration of 2,4-dichloro-
phenol which now occurs after about 35 minutes is about 30%
greater than at pH 7.

Further changes in the reaction pattern are exhibited at
pH 9 as shown in Figure 3c. The overall rate of reaction is
again slower, but the peaks for the monochlorophenols are
much sharper. The peak concentration of 2-chlorophenol has

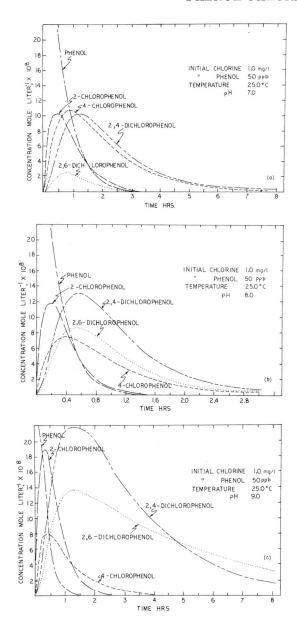

FIGURE 3   CHLORINATION OF PHENOL AND THE
                CHLOROPHENOLS FORMED AT: a. pH 7,
                b. pH 8, AND c. pH 9.

increased sharply which is about twice as great as at pH 7.
Peak concentrations of the dichlorophenols are also greater.
2, 4-Dichlorophenol concentration is more than twice as great
as at pH 7 and over 50% greater than at pH 8. The maximum
concentration of 2, 6-dichlorophenol is also about 50% greater
at pH 9 than at pH 7.

These changing concentrations and relative proportions of
chlorinated phenols as a function of time and pH will be
exhibited in changes in the intensity of the tastes and odors
produced during the process of chlorination. Since, as previously described, the compounds producing the strongest
tastes and odors are 2-chlorophenol, 2, 4-dichlorophenol, and
2, 6-dichlorophenol, it may be expected qualitatively that the
production of tastes and odors will be greater for those conditions leading to maximum total formation of these substances.

Expected Threshold Odor

The threshold odor of a water is defined as the dilution
ratio at which the odor is just detectable (7). In other words,
the threshold odor is the dilution of the water necessary to
reduce its odor to a mean perceptible level.

The threshold odor contribution of each compound of the
reaction solution was evaluated by multiplying the reciprocal
of the threshold odor concentration, Figure 1, times the computed concentration of the odorous compound. The total threshold odor of the reaction solution at any time during the course
of the reaction was obtained by adding the individual contribution
of each compound.

The assumption that the chlorophenols contribute additively
to the total organoleptic sensation and that each has the same
type of odor appears reasonable for conditions encountered in
water treatment. Even if the odors are not strictly additive,
they certainly reinforce each other, resulting in the same general
relationship between threshold odor and time as presented in
Figure 4.

Examination of Figure 4b, with an initial chlorine concentration of 1 mg/l and 50 μg/l of phenol, shows that the maximum
threshold odors are developed at pH 9, where the water is still
malodorous some 8 hours after the addition of chlorine. For
the same reaction conducted at pH 8, the threshold odors are
only 80% of the maximum of those at pH 9. Also malodorous
water is present for only about 3.5 hours at pH 8.0. At pH 7,
chlorophenolic odors develop more slowly with the maximum

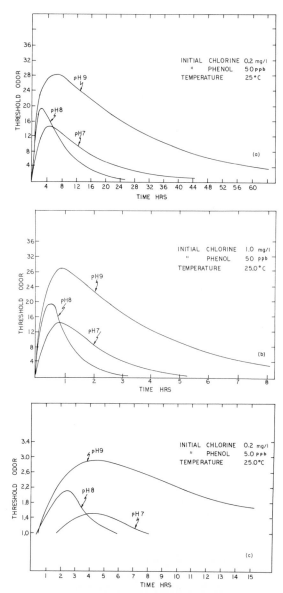

FIGURE 4   THRESHOLD ODOR FROM CHLORINATION
                OF PHENOL.(a) INITIAL CHLORINE 0.2PPM,
                INITIAL PHENOL 50 PPB.(b) INITIAL CHLORINE
                1.0PPM, INITIAL PHENOL 50 PPB, AND(c)
                INITIAL CHLORINE 0.2PPM, INITIAL PHENOL
                5.0 PPB. ALL WERE 25ºC.

occurring after about 1 hour and are about 50% at this point of
those developed at pH 9. Malodorous water, however, persists
for a longer period of time, 5.5 hours at pH 7 as compared to
3.5 hours at pH 8.

Figure 4a with an initial concentration of chlorine 0.2 mg/1
and phenol 50µg/1 and Figure 4c, 0.2 mg/1 chlorine and 5.0µg/1
phenol, show the same general relationships of threshold odor
and time of reaction as a function of pH of chlorination. Com-
praison of the results presented in Figure 4a and 4b, where the
only difference is the initial concentration of chlorine has been
reduced from 1.0 mg/1 to 0.2 mg/1 in 4a, shows that malodorous
water persists for a much greater period of time when small
amounts of chlorine are used. It was found from these and other
calculations that an increase in chlorine dose by 5-fold (0.2 to
1.0 mg/1) reduced the time necessary to obtain an odorless water
by about 8-fold. This conclusion is in accordance with water
treatment practice of using the maximum free chlorine (super-
chlorination) to carry the reaction to the odorless trichloro-
phenol and oxidation products thereby obtaining an odorless
water.

Examination of Figure 4c shows that a very small amount of
phenol, 5µg/1, may produce malodorous water which persists
for long periods of time.

It is of interest to compare the results of this computation
of threshold odors with actual measurements of threshold odor.
The results presented in Figures 4b and 4c show that the maximum threshold odor at any pH is dependent on the initial phenol
concentration. A 10-fold increase in the initial phenol concentrations (5 to 50µg/1) at pH 8 results in a 10-fold increase in the
threshold odor at the maximum (2 to 20). Ettinger and Ruchoft
found that an initial phenol concentration of 1000µg/1 at this
same pH value gave, experimentally by threshold odor measurements, a maximum threshold odor of 500 (3). By extension of
the computed results to the concentration used in this investigation, a 20-fold increase in the initial phenol concentration (50 to
1000µg/1) should result in a 20-fold increase in the maximum
threshold odor (20 to 400) which is exactly the value obtained by
Ettinger and Ruchoft. This comparison shows that three
independent investigations, Ettinger and Ruchoft (3) in 1951,
Burttschell, et al (6) in 1959, and the present investigation all
show favorable agreement.

All of the conclusions that were based on calculations
applicable to a temperature of 25°C should also be applicable

to lower temperatures, since it is reasonable to assume, based upon the temperature dependence of the rates of chlorination of phenol, the rate of the overall reaction would be reduced by a factor of 2 for each $10^{o}C$ decrease in temperature.

OPTIMUM CONDITIONS FOR CHLORINATION OF PHENOL-CONTAINING WATERS

As a result of this investigation, the optimum conditions for chlorination of phenol-containing waters may be established. The commonly accepted water works practice of using maximum free chlorine is in agreement with the conclusions of this investigation. An incremental increase in free chlorine results in a greater incremental decrease in the time of persistence of malodorous water. The water works practice of superchlorination followed by dechlorination has great merit in terms of elmination of "chlorophenolic" tastes and odors in water supplies. The large excess of free chlorine in the water insures a rapid chlorination of phenol to the odorless 2, 4, 6-trichlorophenol or oxidation products.

The breakpoint chlorination of water, as usually practiced, may not necessarily render the water free from "chlorophenolic" tastes and odors because of the slow (24-60 hours) reaction between aqueous chlorine and phenol at low concentrations of each. Free residual chlorine present in the water supply after breakpoint chlorination could still react with phenolic compounds in the water to form malodorous waters in the distribution system. The computations of the expected threshold odors for several initial conditions expected in water supply practice show that the most advantageous pH for the chlorination is between 7 and 8. If the pH of chlorination is near pH 9, much greater odors are formed which persist for longer periods of time.

The purposeful addition of ammonia to phenol-containing waters to prevent the development of malodorous water can now be explained by the relative rates of chlorination of ammonia and phenol. Ammonia is chlorinated several orders of magnitude faster than phenol, therefore, little or no chlorophenols are formed initially when a phenol-containing water is chlorinated in the presence of excess ammonia. Some of the difficulties encountered with chloramine treatment may be explained on the basis of the slow reactions between the chloramine and phenol to form chlorophenols, particularly in dead ends of the distribution system.

These results, conclusions, and recommendations apply specifically to the chlorination of phenol-bearing waters and

are not intended to be directly applicable to the chlorination
of waters which contain a variety of phenolic compounds.
From an operational point of view, the primary contribution
of this investigation is to define and show the interplay of the
important parameters which may alter the development of
"chlorophenolic" tastes and odors in water supplies.

SUMMARY AND CONCLUSIONS
     The chlorination of phenol proceeds by the stepwide sub-
stitution of the 2, 4, and 6 positions of the aromatic ring
leading to the formation of non-phenolic oxidation products.
The rate of reaction of aqueous chlorine and phenol or the
chlorophenols obeys a second-order rate expression where
the rate of reaction is proportional to the product of the
formal concentration of aqueous chlorine and phenolic compound. The rates of these reactions are highly pH dependent
with the maximum rate occurring, dependent upon the compound
being chlorinated, in the neutral or slightly alkaline pH range.
As a result of this investigation, the chlorination of phenol-
bearing waters should be conducted with the maximum possible
free chlorine in the pH range 7-8.

ACKNOWLEDGEMENTS

     This investigation was conducted under the supervision of
Professor J.C. Morris, Harvard University and was supported
in part by a Research Fellowship No. G. F. -7621-C from the
Division of Research Grants, Public Health Service and by the
Division of Engineering and Applied Physics, Harvard University.
The authors wish to acknowledge the assistance of M. Fiering
in programming the calculations made in this investigation.

———————————   ——

This paper has been published in Int. J Air Wat Poll, 6, 419
(1962). Permission granted by Pergamon Press to reprint this
paper as part of this symposium is greatly appreciated.

LITERATURE CITED
1. Adams, B.A., Water Works Eng, 33, 387 (1931).

2. Ettinger, M.B., Personal Communication.

3. Ettinger, M.B. and C.C. Ruchoft, J Am Water Works
     Assoc, 43, 561-7 (1951).

4. Ingols, R.S. and G.M. Ridenour, Water and Sewage Works, 95, 187-190 (1948).

5. Todd, A.R., J Am Water Works Assoc, 34, 1805-6 (1942).

6. Burttschell, R.H., et al, J Am Water Works Assoc, 51, 205-14 (1959).

7. Standard Methods for the Examination of Water, Sewage, and Industrial Wastes, APHA, AWWA, and FSIWA, New York, N.Y., 10th Ed. (1955).

8. Soper, F.G. and G.F. Smith, J Chem Soc London, pp 1582-91 (1926).

9. Weil, I. and J.C. Morris, J Am Chem Soc, 71, 1664-71 (1949).

DISCUSSION

PROF. LEONARD W. HOM (Sacramento State College): Do you obtain a breakpoint with the chlorination of phenolic compounds? And if so, how does this vary with pH?

DR. LEE: No, the chlorination of phenol and the chlorination of ammonia are two distinctly different systems.

DR. R. INGOLS (Georgia Tech.): Because many soft waters are chlorinated and coagulated at a pH of 6.3, will your data permit an evaluation of similar threshold value curves that you had for 7, 8, and 9?

DR. LEE: Time did not permit the discussion of the chlorination of phenol below pH 7. Burttschell, et al, found that typical chlorophenolic taste and odors do not develop when the chlorination of phenol is conducted below pH 7 (6). In my studies, I found that the ultraviolet spectrum of the reaction solution during the chlorination of phenol and the chlorophenols showed a non-chlorophenolic absorption band. This absorption band increased to a maximum at the point where free chlorine disappeared from solution. If the reaction solution is allowed to stand for a period of a week to a month, the ultraviolet absorption band slowly reverts back to a typical chlorophenolic spectrum similar to that obtained when the pH of chlorination is conducted above pH 7. These results suggest that there is an unidentified reaction intermediate formed below pH 7.

Since the chlorination of phenol below pH 7 results in non-typical chlorophenolic tastes and odor, it may be possible for water plant operators to minimize taste and odor by chlorination below pH 7.

DR. JOHNSON (University of North Carolina): In reference to your comparison between the chlorine reaction with phenol and the chloramine reaction, what kind of chloramine were you referring to here? Was this monochloramine?

DR. LEE: Yes, it was monochloramine.

MR. E. A. SIGWORTH (West Virginia Pulp and Paper Co.): I'd like to ask whether you utilized the 60°C temperature for running your threshold odor tests. And also, is there any evidence that the benzene ring is broken in chlorination?

DR. LEE: The threshold odors reported in the investigation are the result of computations based on the threshold odor concentrations reported in the literature by Burttschell, Ettinger, and others of the Taft Center. No threshold odors were measured in this investigation.

Yes, there is definite evidence of oxidative rupture of the benzene ring at each step in the reaction scheme. The degree of oxidation appears to increase as the chlorination proceeds from mono through to trichlorophenol.

MR. PIERCE (Wallace & Tiernan): Did you study preformed chlorophenols and then subsequent chlorination?

DR. LEE: This study was conducted by chlorinating phenol and each of the chlorophenols formed in this reaction. In order to evaluate the kinetics of each of these reactions, chemically pure chlorophenols were purchased and/or prepared. These phenols were mixed with chlorine under defined conditions, so that the desired reaction could be isolated from competing reactions with the products formed.

MR. PIERCE: Often you see in print the statement that if you under-chlorinate the first time, subsequent chlorination is not going to solve your taste and odor problems that are caused by chlorophenols.

DR. LEE: First, I want to emphasize that this study was restricted to the chlorination of phenol. Natural waters probably contain large number of phenolic compounds that may cause chlorophenolic tastes and odors in water supplies. Unfortunately, little is known about the nature of the phenolic compounds present in natural waters.

Based on the results of this study, I cannot see why under-chlorination should produce compounds that are more resistant to chlorination than in cases where excess chlorine is used initially.

MR. PIERCE: The indication was that there was a chloro-phenol. Once it was formed with under-chlorination it was fairly stable to subsequent chlorination. This is not borne out in your experiment.

DR. LEE: Certainly not from this work.

DR. U. WEISSENBERG (Dow Chemical Co.): What does taste threshold mean at pH 9?

DR. LEE: In all reference to taste and odors in this investigation in a strict sense, should be confined to odors alone. There is one complicating factor that should be mentioned with regard to the effect of pH on odor tensity. The pK values of the dichlorophenols are such that at pH 9 the majority of the species would be present as the anion. Normally, the threshold concentrations of salt are greater than the acid. Therefore, it is possible that the threshold odor curves for pH 9 should be less.

MR. A. A. HIRSCH (Dept. of Water and Sewerage, Shreve-port, La.): Could you make a single graphical plot which would show an operator just in which region to work, given certain initial conditions?

DR. LEE: No. We cannot do this because we do not know the specific phenolic compounds that are present in water supplies that may cause chlorophenolic odors. The chief value of this investigation is to show the operator that variations in such operating parameters as pH may minimize chlorophenolic odors. I feel that research should be initiated on the types of phenolic compounds that are actually present in the water supplies which produce chlorophenolic odors upon chlorination. Once this information is available, studies similar to our study on the chlorination of phenol should be conducted.

MR. E. BOYLE (Lower Bucks County Joint Municipal Authority, Levittown, Pa.): Do you have any information on breakdown chlorination and chlorine dioxide to remove phenols?

DR. LEE: We did do a limited amount of study on the reactions between chlorine dioxide and phenol. These studies showed that chlorine dioxide does not form the chlorophenols. The ultraviolet spectrum of the reaction solutions indicate that chlorine dioxide causes rupture of the benzene ring. Further studies are necessary to make a more effective comparison between the two compounds.

Lloyd I. Osipow

Foster D. Snell, Inc.
Subsidiary of Booz Applied Research, Inc.
New York, New York

PHYSICAL ADSORPTION
ON SOLIDS

This is a broad topic. It may include discussions on the measurement of the surface area of solids, adsorption in capillaries, multimolecular adsorption, differential and integral heats of adsorption, preferential adsorption, chromatography, dispersion and flocculation, lubrication, adhesion, ore flotation, and detergency. Plainly, time limitations permit only a brief discussion of only a few aspects of this topic.

The origin of all surface chemistry phenomena resides in the forces of attraction and repulsion between molecules, atoms, and ions. The forces acting at the surface of a solid or a liquid are merely extensions of the forces acting within the body of the material. A molecule in the center of a liquid drop is attracted equally from all sides while, at the surface, the attractive forces acting between adjacent molecules result in a net attraction into the bulk phase in a direction normal to the surface. Because of the unbalanced attraction at the surface, there is a tendency for these molecules to be pulled from the surface into the interior and for the surface to shrink to the smallest area that can enclose the liquid. The work required to expand a surface by one sq cm in opposition to these attractive forces is called the surface tension.

The above concept applies equally well to solids. Molecules in a solid surface are also in an unbalanced attractive field and possess a surface tension or a surface free energy. Whereas the surface tension of a liquid is measured easily, this is much more difficult for a solid since, to increase the surface, extraneous work must be done to deform the solid.

While surface tension is the result of attraction between like molecules, physical adsorption by solids arises from the attraction between unlike molecules. The attraction between like and unlike molecules is due to a variety of inter-molecular forces. London dispersion forces exist in all types of matter and always act as an attractive force between adjacent atoms and molecules no matter how dissimilar they are (1). Many other attractive forces depend upon the specific chemical nature of the neighboring molecules. These include dipole interactions, the hydrogen bond, and the metallic bond.

ADSORPTION AND WETTING

Wetting is one of the more important phenomenon in surface chemistry. This seemingly simple phenomenon is of cardinal importance in determining the strength of adhesive joints and of reinforced plastics. It establishes the printing and writing qualities of inks. Lubricants will wet and spread over the entire surfaces or be confined to limited working areas that depend upon built-in wetting or non-wetting properties. Ores are floated if the surrounding liquid is displaced readily by air bubbles. The dispersion of pigments in paints depends upon wetting of the individual particles by the liquid. The action of a foam breaker frequently depends upon its ability to spread on the foam. Secondary oil recovery often involves displacement of oil from sand by water. Wetting is also a factor in detergency. Water and soil repellancy depend upon non-wetting (2).

Since wetting is studied most commonly by contact angle measurements, the role of adsorption is easily overlooked. The fundamental equation of wetting, due to Young is:

$$\gamma_L \cos\theta = \gamma_{SF} - \gamma_{SL} \tag{4-1}$$

where γ_L is the surface tension of the liquid, θ is the angle of contact formed by a liquid on a solid and measured in the liquid phase, γ_{sf} is the surface tension of the solid covered with an adsorbed film in equilibrium with the liquid, and γ_{SL} is the solid-liquid interfacial tension.

It is clear that adsorption influences the wetting process through the term γ_{SF}. It may be written also:

$$\pi e = \gamma_S - \gamma_{SF} \tag{4-2}$$

and:

$$\gamma_L \cos\theta = \gamma_S - \gamma_{SL} - \pi e \tag{4-3}$$

where γ_S is the surface tension of the clean solid. πe is the equilibrium film pressure of adsorbed vapor on the solid surface. πe is equal to the decrease in the surface tension of the solid that results from adsorption of a film of vapor in equilibrium with its liquid phase.

The equilibrum film pressure, πe, can be calculated from the Gibbs adsorption equation. In the case of a solution containing the single solute:

$$\Gamma = \frac{1}{RT} \left(\frac{\partial \gamma}{\partial \ln a} \right)_T \tag{4-4}$$

where Γ is the surface excess of solute in moles per sq cm, a is the activity of the solute, γ is the surface tension of the solution, R is the gas constant, and T is the absolute temperature.

This equation also applies to the adsorption of a gas on a solid (3). At low gas pressure p, the equilibrium pressure of the gas, can be substituted for a, the activity of the solute. The amount of gas adsorbed v/V is equivalent to the surface excess, with v equal to the volume of gas adsorbed per gram of solid and V is the molar volume of the gas. Σ is the area per gram of solid. The integration of the Gibbs equation in this form is expressed by the relation:

$$\pi e = \gamma_S - \gamma_{SF} = \frac{RT}{V\Sigma} \int_0^p \frac{v}{p} \, dp \tag{4-5}$$

Figure 1 is a typical curve of experimental data obtained by Harkins (3). The film pressure, πe, may be calculated by graphic integration.

Low Energy Solids

Low energy solids such as Teflon, polyethylene, and paraffin wax readily adsorb such low energy gases as nitrogen and helium. They do not adsorb, however, high energy molecules like water or glycerine. When high energy liquids are brought into contact with low energy solids, πe is zero,

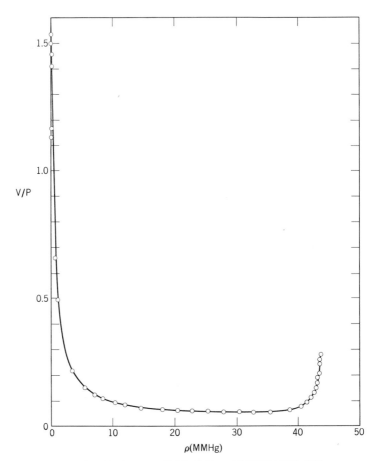

FIGURE 1   ADSORPTION OF n-HEPTANE ON
            ANATASE PLOTTED AS v/p VERSUS p (3).

and the Young equation takes a simpler form:

$$\gamma_L \cos\theta = \gamma_S - \gamma_{SL} \tag{4-6}$$

An example of a high energy liquid in contact with a low
energy solid is a drop of water on a block of paraffin wax. The
basic reason why πe is zero is that the surface tension of a low
energy material cannot be reduced by adsorption of a high energy
material. While there is an attraction between paraffin wax

molecules and water molecules, the adsorption of a water film
would serve to increase the surface free energy. In contrast,
if a liquid hydrocarbon drop was placed on a block of ice,
hydrocarbon vapor would adsorb on the surface of the ice to
lower the surface tension of the solid whereupon πe would have
a positive value.

Zisman showed that, for a homologous series of liquids on
a low energy solid, the contact angle of the liquid drops decreases
with a decrease in the surface tension of the liquid (4). This is
exemplified in Figure 2. The surface tension corresponding to
$\cos \theta = 1$ ($\theta = 0$) is the critical surface tension for wetting of the
low energy solid. All liquids with a surface tension equal to or
less than this critical value will spread on that solid. Table I
gives the critical surface tension for a number of halogenated
polyethylenes.

High Energy Solids

A variety of solid substrates, that includes metals, metal
oxides, and glasses, have surface tension values that are considerably higher than most liquids. It would be expected that
these liquids would wet all high energy solids to give zero contact angles, but this is not always the case. The most common
reason is that high energy surfaces readily adsorb contaminants
from the atmosphere which lower their surface energy. It is
particularly difficult to remove contaminants from high energy
surfaces.

There is a more fundamental reason for the non-wetting of
high energy solids by many liquids. This may be seen by
rewriting the Young equation in the form:

$$\cos \theta = \frac{\gamma_{SF} - \gamma_{SL}}{\gamma_L} \tag{4-7a}$$

For nonspreading:

$$\cos \theta < 1 \tag{4-7b}$$

then:

$$\gamma_{SF} - \gamma_{SL} < \gamma_L \tag{4-7c}$$

$$\gamma_{SF} < \gamma_{SL} + \gamma_L \tag{4-7d}$$

If the surface tension of the solid covered with an adsorbed film
in equilibrium with the liquid is less than the sum of the solid

to the surface tension of mercury.

Similarly, for water:

$$\gamma H_2O = \gamma H_2\overset{h}{O} + \gamma H_2\overset{d}{O} \qquad (4\text{-}9)$$

where $\gamma H_2\overset{h}{O}$ is the hydrogen bond contribution and $'H_2\overset{d}{O}$ is the contribution of the dispersion forces to the surface tension of water.

If water is placed over mercury, there is an interfacial tension across the region of separation of the two bulk phases. The interface is composed actually of two adjacent interfacial regions with different field forces and the interfacial tension is the sum of the tensions in each of these regions. In the interfacial region of water, the molecules are attracted toward the bulk water by intermolecular forces which produce a tension equal to the surface tension of water. There is also an attraction by mercury, acting through London dispersion forces, for water molecules in the interfacial region. Therefore, the tension in this region is a function of the difference between the surface tension of water and the London dispersion force attraction between water and mercury.

Then the tension in the region of the water interface in contact with mercury is:

$$\gamma_{H_2O} - \left(\gamma_{H_2O}^{\,d} \; \gamma_{Hg}^{\,d} \right)^{\frac{1}{2}}$$

Since the interfacial tension γH_2O, Hg is the sum of the tensions in the two layers:

$$\gamma_{H_2O, \, Hg} = {}^{\gamma}_{H_2O} + {}^{\gamma}_{Hg} - 2\left({}^{\gamma}_{H_2O}{}^{d} \; {}^{\gamma}_{Hg}{}^{d} \right)^{\frac{1}{2}} \qquad (4\text{-}10)$$

The validity of equation 4-10 was determined by measuring the interfacial tension of a number of hydrocarbons versus mercury and versus water. Since the only attraction between hydrocarbons and other atoms and molecules arises from dispersion forces, the analogous equations are:

$$\gamma_{HC, \, Hg} = {}^{\gamma}_{HC} + {}^{\gamma}_{Hg} - 2\left({}^{\gamma}_{HC}{}^{d} \; {}^{\gamma}_{Hg}{}^{d} \right)^{\frac{1}{2}} \qquad (4\text{-}11)$$

$$\gamma_{HC, \, H_2O} = {}^{\gamma}_{HC} + {}^{\gamma}_{H_2O} - 2\left({}^{\gamma}_{HC}{}^{d} \; {}^{\gamma}_{H_2O}{}^{d} \right)^{\frac{1}{2}} \qquad (4\text{-}12)$$

where HC refers to hydrocarbon.

The surface tensions of the hydrocarbons, water, and mercury are known and the dispersion force contribution to the surface tension of hydrocarbons is equal to their surface tension, $\gamma_{HC}^d = \gamma_{HC}$. Then equations 4-11 and 4-12 have only one unknown. For mercury with a surface tension of 484 dynes/cm at 20^oC, $\gamma_{Hg}^d = 200$ dynes/cm. For water with a surface tension of 72.8 dynes/cm at 20^oC, $\gamma_{H_2O}^d = 21.8$ dynes/cm. The mercury-water interfacial tension calculated from these values is 424.8 dynes/cm as compared with experimental values of 426-7 dynes/cm. This shows that the molecular interaction between mercury and water is due entirely to dispersion forces despite the high metallic bonding energy of mercury and the hydrogen bonding energy of water.

Contact Angles

For the contact angle of a liquid on a low-energy solid, where $\gamma_L > \gamma$, no adsorption occurs and $\pi e = 0$. Where the only solid-liquid interaction is due to dispersion forces, the Young equation can be expressed:

$$\cos \theta = -1 + 2 \left(\gamma_s^d \right)^{\frac{1}{2}} \left(\frac{(\gamma_L^d)^{\frac{1}{2}}}{(\gamma_L)^{\frac{1}{2}}} \right) \tag{4-13}$$

Equation 4-13 has several points of interest. It provides a convenient means for determining the dispersion force component of the surface free energy of a solid since only one contact angle measurement is needed for the determination. Also, it emphasized that only specific portions of the total surface free energy of a solid may be available for interaction with the adjacent phase. In fact where γC, the critical surface tension for the wetting of a solid has been determined with liquids having only dispersion force interactions, $\gamma C = \gamma_s d$.

Adsorption

In many studies of the physical adsorption of gases on solids, the adsorbates are nitrogen, argon, or hydrogen. Since these gases interact only by dispersion forces, the discussed relations are applied readily to these systems. When the adsorbate is in equilibrium with liquid adsorbate, Harkins has shown that (3):

$$\pi e = \gamma_s - (\gamma_L + \gamma_{SL}) \tag{4-14}$$

If we substitute:

$$\gamma_{SL} + \gamma_s + \gamma_L - 2 (\gamma_s^d \gamma_L^d)^{\frac{1}{2}} \tag{4-15}$$

$$\gamma_s^d = (\pi e + 2\gamma_L)^2 \, 2/4 \, \gamma_L^d \tag{4-16}$$

It was shown earlier that πe can be found by graphic integration of an adsorption isotherm. Values of $\gamma_s d$ obtained in adsorption

studies are in good agreement with values of γ_s^d obtained by
contact angle measurements.

Selected values for γ_s^d are shown in Table III which is a
useful guide in comparing the adsorbent properties of materials.
For example, polypropylene has the smallest γ_s^d value and is
the weakest adsorbent even for hydrocarbons. Graphite,
anatase, and stannic oxide are the strongest adsorbents shown
where interaction is due entirely to dispersion forces.

Polar Liquids

The dispersion force contribution to the surface free energy
of polar organic liquids can be determined by contact angle
measurements on solid hydrocarbons. Typical values of γ_L
and γ_L^d are shown in Table II. For many of these polar liquids,
the dispersion force interactions are much stronger than in
water and are somewhat stronger than the sum of the dipole
and hydrogen bonding interactions. Thus, glycerol and forma-
mide would be expected to adsorb more strongly on nonpolar
substrates than water.

Table IV shows the energy of water-organic liquid interactions. For all of the compounds listed, the interfacial tension
calculated by considering only dispersion force interaction at
the interface $\gamma_{1,2}^d$ is significantly greater than the observed
interfacial tension, $\gamma_{1,2}$. The excess is a measure of the energy
of interaction due to various polar interactions. Pi-bonding
interaction of the aromatic compounds with water results in an
interfacial interaction of about 15 ergs/sq cm. Organic molecules capable of hydrogen bonding have the strongest excess
interactions with water, about 40-48 ergs/sq cm. The last
column in Table IV, $2(\gamma_1^d \, \gamma_2^d)^{\frac{1}{2}}$ gives the dispersion force
interaction which is seen to be the largest single contributor
to interfacial attraction between these liquids and water.

Polar Attractions at Solid-Liquid Interfaces

Interfacial attractions between liquids and high-energy
solids are shown in Table V. The dispersion force interaction
is given as $2(\gamma_s^d \, \gamma_L^d)^{\frac{1}{2}}$. If this is the only interaction that
occurs, it is equal to the value of $\pi e + 2\gamma_L$ (from equations
4-14 and 4-15) shown in column 4. The excess, shown in
column 5, is a measure of the polar interaction.

Benzene interacts with graphite and with oxides with an
excess interaction energy over that due to dispersion force

TABLE II   VALUES OF γ_s^d OBTAINED FROM πe
MEASUREMENTS FOR ADSORBED VAPORS (a)

Adsorbent	Adsorbate	γ_s^d Ergs/Sq Cm
Polypropylene	Nitrogen	26
	Argon	28.5
Graphite	Nitrogen	123
	n-Heptane	132,115,120
Copper	n-Heptane	60
Silver	n-Heptane	74
Lead	n-Heptane	99
Tin	n-Heptane	101
Iron	n-Heptane	108
	Argon	106
	Nitrogen	89
Ferric oxide	n-Heptane	107
Anatase (TiO_2)	n-Heptane	92
	Butane	89
	Nitrogen	141
Silica	n-Heptane	78
Stannic oxide	n-Heptane	111
Barium sulfate	n-Heptane	76

(a) After Fowkes (5).

interaction of 20-25 ergs/sq cm, presumably due to pi-bonding
with these surfaces. Propanol shows a polar interaction energy
of 54-96 ergs/sq cm, while that of water is extremely high,
336-368 ergs/sq cm.

Spreading
    It was stated earlier that many pure liquids do not spread
on high-energy solids. The condition for spreading coefficient
S must be positive, where:

$$S = \gamma SF - (\gamma_L + \gamma_{SL}) \qquad (4\text{-}17)$$

In the case where solid-liquid interaction is due entirely to
dispersion forces:

$$S = 2(\gamma_s^d \gamma_L^d) - (\pi e + 2\gamma_L) \qquad (4\text{-}18)$$

TABLE III   EVALUATION OF $\gamma_L{}^d$ FOR POLAR ORGANIC
LIQUIDS FROM CONTACT ANGLE
MEASUREMENTS ON REFERENCE SOLIDS (a)

(Ergs/Sq Cm at 20°C)

	γ_L	$\gamma_L{}^d$
Tricresyl phosphate	40.9	39.2
α - Bromonaphthalene	44.6	47
Trichlorobiphenyl	45.3	44
Methylene iodide	50.8	48.5
Glycerol	63.4	37.0
Formamide	58.2	39.5
Dimethyl siloxanes	19.0	16.9
Fluorolube FCD-330	20.2	14.0

(a) After Fowkes (5).

TABLE IV   ENERGY OF WATER-ORGANIC LIQUID
INTERACTION IN EXCESS OF DISPERSION
FORCE INTERACTION (a)

(Ergs/Sq Cm at 20°C)

Liquid No. 2	γ_2	1,2	$\gamma_{1,2}{}^d$	Excess	$2\left(\gamma_1{}^d\ \gamma_2{}^d\right)^{\frac{1}{2}}$
Benzene	28.9	35	51.5	+16.5	50.2
Toluene	28.5	36.1	51.5	+15.4	50.0
Mesitylene	28.8	38.7	51.4	+12.7	50.1
Carbon tet-rachloride	26.9	45.0	51.3	+ 6.3	48.4
Carbon tet-rabromide	49.7	38.8	56.5	+ 6.8	66.0
Butryronitrile	28.1	10.4	51.3	+23.2	49.6
Aniline	42.9	5.8	53.7	+47.9	62.0
Di-n-butyl-amine	22.0	10.3	51.0	+40.7	43.8
Octanoic acid	27.5	8.5	51.3	+42.8	49.0
Cyclohexanol	32.7	3.9	51.9	+48.0	53.6

(a) After Fowkes (5).

For spreading by water, it is necessary that $\gamma_s{}^d$ be somewhat greater than 243 dynes/cm. The actual amount greater depends on the value of πe. Thus, water will not spread on many pure metal surfaces despite the high surface energy of the metals. It will spread on all metal oxides, because there is an additional interaction energy with these oxides.

SUMMARY

In this age of intensive specialization, it is too easy to forget how various phenomena are related. Thus, wetting and adsorption studies involve different experimental techniques and they are often regarded as separate disciplines. The purpose of this manuscript has been to indicate that they have the same origin in the attractive forces acting between mole-cules and that they are related by the Young equation. Recent contributions by Fowkes have made it easier to distinguish between polar and nonpolar contributions to solid-liquid inter-actions and to related adsorption data with contact angles.

TABLE V   POLAR INTERFACIAL INTERACTIONS AT SOLID-LIQUID INTERFACES (5)

Solid	Liquid	$2(\gamma_s{}^d \gamma_L{}^d)^{\frac{1}{2}}$	$\pi e + 2\gamma_L$	Excess
Graphite	n-Heptane (std)	96	96	0
	Benzene	114	134	20
Anatase	n-Heptane (std)	99	99	0
	Benzene	116	142	26
	n-Propanol	106	162	56
	Water	102	446	344
Silica	n-Heptane (std)	100	100	0
	Benzene	118	138	20
	Acetone	98	156	58
	n-Propanol	98	182	84
	Water	94	462	368
$BaSO_4$	n-Heptane (std)	99	99	0
	n-Propanol	106	202	96
	Water	102	464	362
SnO_2	n-Heptane (std)	98	98	0
	Benzene	108	134	26
	n-Propanol	98	152	54
	Water	102	438	336

LITERATURE CITED

1. London, F., Trans Faraday Soc, 33, 8-26 (1937).

2. Osipow, L.I., Surface Chemistry: Theory and Industrial
   Applications, Reinhold Publishing Corp., New York, N.Y.,
   (1962).

3. Harkins, W.D., The Physical Chemistry of Surface Films,
   Reinhold Publishing Corp., New York, N.Y., (1952).

4. Zisman, W.A., Contact Angle, Wettability and Adhesion,
   Am Chem Soc, Washington, D.C., (1964).

5. Fowkes, F.W., Ind Eng Chem, 56, 40 (1964).

ACKNOWLEDGEMENT
    The author gratefully acknowledges Dr. Philip Crispino
who read this paper at the conference.

DISCUSSION
    CHAIRMAN COHEN: Thank you, Dr. Crispino. We will
now entertain questions on Dr. Osipow's paper.
    DR. MANCY (University of Cincinnati): I'd like to ask
Dr. Crispino a question with regard to the wetting of metal
surfaces. I am interested in some studies concerning metal
surfaces and in relation to your article the wetting of pure
metal surfaces in any aqueous system is much more pronounced
than in the case where there is an anodic film, for example, an
oxide film on the metal surface. Can you comment on this and
tell me of an experimental approach to determine this difference?
    CHAIRMAN COHEN: Dr. Crispino, as you know, read the
paper of Dr. Osipow, and readers are not necessarily suppose
to know the contents. But Dr. Fowkes is in the audience near
Dr. Matijevic. I understand he can speak on this particular
subject.
    DR. FOWKES (Sprague Electric Co.): Well, as far as I
know, there is no pure metal surface that should be wet by
water. Of course, some metals will react with water to produce
an oxide film, and water will surely wet such an oxide film.
Water cannot wet any clean metal surface because the binding
forces between water and metal are weak compared with the
hydrogen bonding forces in water. Therefore, the hydrogen-
bonding forces in water tend to keep it from spreading on a clean
metal surface, and water will have a fairly high contact angle on
any pure metal.

Walter J. Weber, Jr.
University of Michigan

SORPTION FROM SOLUTION BY POROUS CARBON

The significance of surface phenomena in the natural and synthetic systems with which the water sciences are concerned has become increasingly evident through researches of the past two decades. Interfacial activity is a major factor in such water and wastewater treatment operations as aeration, aerobic and anaerobic biological processes, coagulation, disinfection, filtration, ion exchange, and sedimentation. Adsorption is perhaps the most commonly occurring and most significant of surface phenomena. That adsorptive reactions are prevalent in most natural biological, chemical, and physical processes generally is recognized today. Adsorption on solid materials such as activated carbon, activated metallic oxides, and synthetic resins is becoming a widely used operation for separation and purification of gases and solutions.

High porous carbon, activated by either thermal or chemical means, is by far the most important of adsorbents in current use. Historically, evidence of the use of charred wood for improving the palatability of drinking water is given in writings predating the Christian era. Specific recognition of the occurrence in nature of adsorptive reactions, however, may be attributed to Scheele who, in 1773, observed selective uptake

89

of certain gases from air by charcoal (1). In 1785, Lowitz
noted the adsorption of coloring matters from aqueous solution
by charcoal (2). With some understanding of the adsorptive
nature of charcoal having been gained from the observations
of Lowitz and subsequent experimenters, this material became
more widely used for treatment of private and public water
supplies.

After the initial experiments by Lowitz, there was more
than a century of application of relatively low activity charcoal
for water treatment, with little improvement in the adsorptive
properties of this material. Use of noxious gases during the
First World War, however, stimulated significant effort in
development of highly active carbons (3). In the latter part
of the 1920's and early 1930's, these active carbons were put
to large scale and successful use in a number of water treatment
facilities in Germany and throughout Europe, and at Chicago
and Cleveland (4). Today, activated carbon is used extensively
in water treatment operations in the United States. By way of
example, Jenkins, in a recent report on municipal water
facilities in communities of 25,000 or greater population, has
indicated that in 1962 just under 50% of the population in these
communities received water that had been subjected to treatment
with activated carbon for removal of taste and odor producing
substances (5). Activated carbon is also receiving consideration
and testing, and has shown much promise, for application in
advanced states of wastewater treatment (6).

Given the current and prospective significance, the present
discussion assumes the tenor of an approach to characterization
of the process of uptake of dissolved materials from solution
by activated carbon. This is based on what is now known of
the properties of the adsorbent and of variables observed to
influence the process.

CHARACTERISTICS OF CARBON

Brunauer has stated that the adsorption characteristics of
activated carbons appear to be associated with a system of
remarkably small and uniform pores (7). The most characteristic
property of activated carbon relative to adsorption is its
extremely large surface area, which is comprised mainly of
surfaces bordering inner pore spaces. The surface area of
active carbon is approximately 1,000 sq m/g. Relative to the
small geometric area of the granules or particles of the
material, this large total area requires the existence of a

considerable internal surface which can be provided only by
small capillaries. In explaining many observed relationships
associated with adsorption of materials from solution by carbon,
it is essential to consider the physical structure of this
adsorbent because the size and arrangement of the capillaries
(micropores) and channels or interstices (macropores) appear
to play a significant role in the adsorption process.

Active carbons can be prepared from a variety of raw
materials; wood, lignite, coal, bone, and nut shells. Activation, which results in the porous structure so important for
adsorption, may be accomplished by a number of methods.
Simple thermal activation by heating in a current of air is
essentially a process of destructive distillation of certain
organic constituents of the raw material. This results in a
porous carbonaceous residue. Additional activation can be
achieved in many cases by substitution of chlorine, carbon
dioxide, or steam as oxidants in place of air. Chemical
activation ordinarily is effected by treatment at elevated
temperatures with H_3PO_4, H_2SO_4, or $ZnCl_2$. Treatment with
alkali metals (na or K) has been found to increase markedly
the adsorption properties of active carbon (8).

Considerable development of the structural details of
active carbon has been derived from studies of adsorption
phenomena and from X-ray patterns (9-13). Two procedures
are common to all methods for the manufacture of active carbons.
In the first step, carbonization, the raw material is pyrolyzed
to a carbonaceous residue, yielding polynuclear aromatic
systems analogous to those of graphite. The formed graphite-
like planes, which are arranged in stacked order, are termi-
nated by functional groups - principally hydrogen and hydrocarbon
radicals. The second step, activation, is designed to develop
a porous structure in the pyrolyzed residue; approximately 50%
of the residual carbon is consumed during this step. The consumption of so much carbon during the activation indicates that
the pores are formed by the burning out or oxidation of layer
segments from stacks of graphitic planes or by the removal,
cracking, or cyclization of the less stable edge groups.
Investigations by Wolff of the structure of active carbons have
led to the description of carbon particles as consisting of large
"regions" composed of stacks of graphitic planes or groups of
such stacks (12, 13). There appears to be no systematic order
to the orientation of the graphitic layers of any one region of

the carbon particle relative to those of any other region. Wolff describes the graphitic planes as having average diameters slightly greater than 40 A^{o}. Channels through the graphitic regions and also interstices between the stacks of graphitic planes generally are considered to be the macropores with diameters of 30-100, 000 A^{o}. The micropores are fissures of approximately 10-30 A^{o} diameter within and parallel to the graphitic planes. As noted, the boundary surfaces of the micropores provide the greatest fraction of the total active area of the carbon.

Figure 1 is a simplified schematic representation of this interpretation of the structure of active carbon illustrating only one of the large particle-like regions described above. The entire particle of active carbon is composed of numerous regions similar to the one shown. A very few macropores and micropores are illustrated although the region actually is laced with many thousands of such pores.

In general, the system of macropores contributes little to the total surface area and adsorptive capacity of active carbons. A high percentage of macropore volume in an active carbon is a distinct disadvantage in many cases because of loss of density to extraneous pore volume. On the other hand, in the many instances in which intraparticle transport processes control the kinetics of uptake by porous carbon, an extensive system of larger macropores may be of considerable benefit in that full utilization of the capacity will attain more rapidly because of the relative ease and speed of transport in larger pores.

The total pore volume of an active carbon may be measured by displacement of an inert gas such as He to account for the micropore volume and by displacement of Hg to account for the macropore volume. At atmospheric pressure, however, Hg will not penetrate pores less than about 10 in diameter, hence simple Hg and He displacement measurements will not yield sufficiently accurate information regarding pore size distribution. For characterization of the distribution of micropores in active carbons, the water desorption method of Juhola and Wiig is employed often (14). This method is based on the general observation that activated carbon is not a good adsorbent of water vapor. At sufficiently high vapor pressures, water is taken up by porous carbon, but this is believed to be a result of condensation of vapor in the pre spaces and not attributable to adsorption at the surface. Hysteresis, noted upon desorption, is then attributable to the emptying of the pore spaces in which case application of the Kelvin equation to the desorption branch

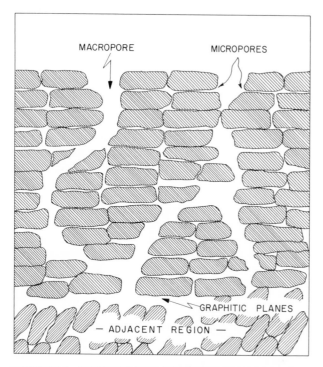

FIGURE 1 SCHEMATIC REPRESENTATION OF A
CONSTITUENT REGION OF AN ACTIVATED
CARBON PARTICLE.

of the water isotherm permits rather precise evaluation of
pore size. The Kelvin equation, which derives from free
energy relationships associated with the transfer of liquid
from solution to adsorbed phase in fine capillaries, is given as:

$$D = \frac{4\ V_m\ \cos}{RT\ \ln \frac{P}{P_o}}$$ (5-1)

in which the pore diameter is represented by D, the surface
tension by , the molar volume of water by V_m, the water-
carbon angle by , and P and P_o are the vapor pressure and
saturation vapor pressure of water, respectively. For most
measurements, the contact angle, temperature, surface
tension, and molar volume are held constant, in which case

the equation assumes the simplified form:

$$D = \frac{K}{\ln\left(\frac{P}{P_0}\right)} \qquad (5\text{-}2)$$

Thus the pore diameter is inversely proportional to the relative vapor pressure P/P_0. This permits appropriate substitution of pore diameter for P/P_0 in a plot of the water isotherm to yield reasonable information on the distribution of the micropores in the carbon. It is apparent that as the vapor pressure closely approaches the value of the saturation vapor pressure, the pore diameter rapidly approaches infinite size and the accuracy permitted by the Kelvin relationship decreases considerably. As a result, other methods must be used to measure pore diameters in excess of approximately 1, 000 A^0.

Ritter and Drake have described a method for measurement of diameters wherein the pore volume of the carbon is evacuated and Hg is forced into the carbon at different pressures (15). The volume of Hg penetrating the carbon at each pressure is noted. Under pressures of 2, 000 lbs per sq in, the mercury will penetrate pores having diameters of approximately 1, 000 A^0. The applied pressure, P then may be converted to a pore dimension by means of the capillary rise equation:

$$D = \frac{4 \gamma \cos \theta}{P} \qquad (5\text{-}3)$$

The volume of Hg penetrating the carbon is represented graphically as a function of the diameter.

MECHANISMS OF ADSORPTION BY CARBON

By way of a concise working description, active carbon is a highly porous material with a surface comprised largely of active sites at the edges of the crystalline planes of the residual solid. These active sites compete with the solvent for the solute, tending to break the solute-solvent association and establish a solute-solid association. Because sites at or near the exterior of the active carbon are most readily available for competition with the solvent for the solute, rapid initial adsorption occurs thereon. If adsorption is irreversible, subsequent competition of the solid for the solute must occur at uncovered sites on the walls of the interior pore spaces until such time as all sites become covered or until pore blockage or restriction renders the remaining uncovered sites inaccessible to the solute.

For a thermodynamically reversible adsorption process, solute
adsorbed at sites near the exterior ends of the pore channels
continually undergoes an exchange process at the surface,
alternately adsorbing at the wall and returning to the solution
within the pore space to continue net movement in the direction
of decreasing concentration toward the interior of the adsorbent.
The reversible process will continue until an equilibrium distribution of solute between solution phase and solid phase occurs,
whereupon no net change in adsorption takes place.

The porous nature of active carbon raises a question as to
whether adsorption results in monolayer or multilayer formation
or if capillary condensation occurs resulting in heavy pore
deposits of adsorbate retained by virtue of a low solvent-solute-
solid contact angle and the solute-solvent interfacial tension.
The case for the latter mechanism finds support in some results
from studies of vapor-phase sorption on active carbons, as
cited by Hansen and Hansen (16). There is, however, at least
as much evidence and support for Langmuir-type adsorption
by porous carbon (17, 18, 19). Except in cases where hysteresis
occurs or where non-Langmuir type isotherms are obtained,
Langmuirian adsorption on active carbon from solutions of low
to medium concentration is the probable primary type.

As for any adsorption process, the equilibrium position of
uptake on carbon will be determined, in part, by the frequency
of active center-solute interactions which, in turn, is largely
a function of the concentration of solute. At very low concentrations, the adsorptive capacity of carbon will not be exhausted
totally before equilibrium is achieved. In most cases, however,
the degree of utilization of adsorptive capacity rises sharply
with increasing concentration of solute to a point at which it
becomes almost constant with additional increase in concentration.
This constant utilization level is referred to as the ultimate
capacity.

A number of adsorption models has been set forth for
description of the above behavior. The two most important
representations of isothermal equilibrium behavior are the
Langmuir equation and the Brunauer, Emmett, and Teller
(BET) equation. The latter equation, which is generally applicable for multilayer adsorption, has the form:

$$X = \frac{X_m A C}{(C_s - C)\,(1 + (A-1)\,C/C_s)} \qquad (5\text{-}4)$$

where **X** is the observed capacity of the carbon, X_m the ultimate capacity, A an energy-related constant, C the concentration of solute in solution at equilibrium, and C_s the saturation concentration of solute. The Langmuir equation, for cases where adsorption leads to deposition of a single layer of solute molecules at the surface, has the form:

$$X = X_m \ bC/ \ (1 + bC) \tag{5-5}$$

where X, X_m, and C have the same significance as in the BET equation and b is the reciprocal of the equilibrium concentration at which half-coverage of the available surface is attained. The term b is thus a measure of relative adsorptive affinity.

Langmuir-type adsorption behavior often is observed for uptake of solutes by carbon from dilute solution (18). Figure 2 is a plot of typical isotherms obtained for adsorption of a sulfonated 3-dodecylbenzene by granules of carbon of three different sizes. The curves drawn through the plotted data are calculated Langmuir isotherms. The fit of the calculated curves to the experimental points indicates a good description of the observed data by this model for adsorption equilibria.

While the final position of equilibrium is of considerable import, the rate at which adsorption proceeds is of paramount significance in most practical applications of this process. There are essentially three kinetic stages occurring consecutively in the sorption of a molecule from solution by porous active carbon. First, the molecule must be transported to the exterior surface of the adsorbent. Second, neglecting the insignificant amount of adsorption taking place at the exterior surface, the molecule diffuses or is transported into and through the pore spaces of the adsorbent. Third, adsorption occurs at an active site on the surfaces bordering the inner pore spaces of the adsorbent. Rates at which interfacial tensions are lowered by surface-active materials suggest that the adsorption process itself is not likely to be rate-limiting but that a much slower process must control the overall rate of uptake by porous carbon (20). Under appropriate conditions, it is possible that transport of adsorbate to the adsorbent is the rate-limiting step. If sufficient turbulence is provided, however, it would appear that transport of the adsorbate within the porous carbon will control the overall kinetics.

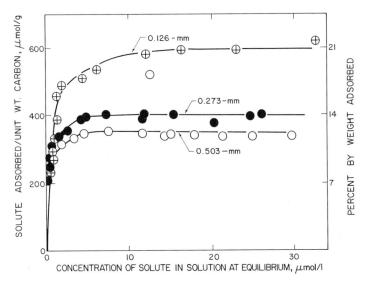

FIGURE 2   ADSORPTION ISOTHERMS - CARBON OF
            DIFFERENT PARTICLE SIZE.

In referring to intraparticle transport as the rate-limiting
step, it must be recognized that this process is not one of
simple molecular diffusion, but rather may derive from the
net action of a number of molecular forces.   For aqueous
systems typical of waters and wastewaters, the forces that
likely influence transport of the solute through the capillary
pores of carbon may be enumerated: (a) adsorption;   (b) two-
dimensional molecular association;   (c) three-dimensional
molecular assoication;   (d) electrokinetic interactions;   and
(e) molecular diffusion.   Adsorption, resulting from attractive
forces between the adsorbate and the surfaces of the capillary
walls or from repulsive forces between the former and the
aqueous solvent, serves to withdraw temporarily the adsorbate
from solution phase.   Withdrawal by adsorption retards the transfer of an individual molecule or ion of the adsorbate and, at
the same time, acts to reduce the effective cross section of
the capillary to inhibit transport of other molecules.   As noted
previously, an individual molecular species undergoes continuous exchange at surfaces encompassing the pore spaces,
alternately adsorbing at the wall and returning to the solution

within the pore to continue net movement in the direction of decreasing concentration. The detention time at the surface may be increased substantially by formation of two-dimensional molecular associations or micelles in the adsorbed film, further inhibiting free diffusion.

The total pore volume of the adsorbent is generally small relative to the volume of solution being treated, thus, the overall concentration of adsorbate contained in the pore volume may approach the critical concentration for molecular association for a given substance soon after initial contact of the adsorbent with solution. As three-dimensional micelles or associations form in the pore spaces of the adsorbent, these, rather than individual molecular species, must be transferred through the capillaries. The micelles or agglomerations of molecules, naturally, are transported more slowly than single molecules.

Electrokinetic interaction between adsorbate and adsorbent or between adsorbate and other solutes in a given system may be an important factor in intraparticle transport phenomena. Since many organic pollutants of waters and wastewaters are anionic in character and carbon surfaces are considered generally to bear net negative charges (21), some interference with the movement of such materials through the pores of activated carbon may be anticipated.

Characterization of the Rate Mechanism

It is apparent then that several possibilities exist for limitation of the rate of uptake of solute from solution by porous active carbon. Characterization of the rate-limiting step is important because the process must be described in terms of appropriate rate expressions and rate parameters.

Certain properties of the adsorbate are useful for determining the nature of the rate-controlling step. For example, if intraparticle transport determines the rate of reaction, the size and structure of an individual solute ion or molecule will affect this rate to the extent that it affects molecular mobility. It is apparent that the diameters of micropores are of molecular dimension, thus, steric influences certainly must be present for adsorption by active carbons.

A study of the variation of reaction rates with temperature permits evaluation of an activation energy and is, consequently, a further means for determining the nature of the rate-limiting reaction. Rate of adsorption is related to activation energy by:

$$k = Z \, e^{-E/RT} \tag{5-6}$$

where k is the absolute rate constant, T the absolute temperature, and Z is a temperature-independent parameter referred
to as the frequency factor. Equation 5-6 may be written also:

$$\ln k = \ln Z - \frac{E}{RT} \tag{5-7}$$

which implies a linear relationship between the logarithm of
k and $1/T$ with a slope of $-E/R$. Equation 5-7 may be written
for any two rates k_1 and k_2 corresponding to absolute temperatures T_1 and T_2, respectively. The difference is expressed:

$$\ln \frac{k_1}{k_2} = \frac{E (T_1 - T_2)}{RT_1 T_2} \tag{5-8}$$

From this relationship the activation energy, E, can be
evaluated for any adsorption system. Although direct adsorption
is an exothermic process, rate of uptake of solute by porous
carbon will be endothermic if intraparticle transport is the
rate-limiting mechanism because diffusion is an endothermic
process. Thus, rate of uptake of solute by porous carbon often
will increase with increasing temperature.

For a system in which the overall rate is controlled by
strictly adsorptive reaction, the variation of rate should be
directly proportional to the concentration of solute in solution
phase. For very simple diffusion, the rate is expected also
to be proportional to the first power of concentration. Theoretical equations for intraparticle transport, however, indicate
that the relationship between concentration and the rate of
reaction will not be one of direct proportionality (22). Since
concentration affects a number of the parameters of these
equations, it is not possible to predict an exact concentration-
rate relationship for this reaction. Qualitatively, however,
if diffusion of solute within the pores and capillaries of the
carbon limits the rate, the variation of rate with concentration
is not expected to be linear, whereas a direct proportionality
is anticipated for strictly adsorptive reactions. Thus, the
concentration dependence of the rate of reaction may be used
as a partial test of hypothesis regarding the nature of the
rate-controlling step.

Because the extent of a surface reaction such as adsorption
will vary with available surface area, adsorption rate should
exhibit a monotonic increase with some function of the inverse
of the diameter of the adsorbent particles. If the mechanism

of uptake is simply one of adsorption on specific external sites, the rate should vary reciprocally with the first power of the diameter for a given mass of adsorbent, whereas for intra-particle transport the variation should be with the reciprocal of some higher power of the diameter (22). Variation of rate with particle size is, thus, another method which may be used for characterization of the rate-limiting step for a particular adsorption system.

Approaches to characterization of intraparticle transport kinetics by separation and evaluation of component molecular diffusion parameters have been made by Edeskuty and Amundson (23), and Weber and Rumer (24). Edeskuty and Amundson evaluated the coefficient of diffusion, D, for intraparticle transport of phenol in porous active carbon using a diffusion-with-adsorption form of Fick's law based on the assumption of a linear adsorption equilibrium. Linear equilibria are attained only infrequently for adsorption on porous carbon, obtained patterns being more generally of the Langmuir or BET form (18).

The analysis of intraparticle transport kinetics by Weber and Rumer involved data for rates of adsorption in several dilute, aqueous, single-solute systems, with each system containing a linear-chain sulfonated alkylbenzene as the adsorbate and porous active carbon as the absorbent. From measurements of rate of removal of solute from bulk solution for each system and from separate measurements of adsorption isotherms, values for the corresponding coefficients of molecular diffusion were calculated by numerical integration of a conservation of diffusing mass equation which incorporated an expression for simultaneous adsorption according to the non-linear Langmuir monolayer model for adsorption. This equation has the form:

$$\frac{\partial C}{\partial t} = \frac{1}{r} \frac{\partial}{\partial r} \left(rD \frac{\partial C}{\partial r} \right) - \frac{\partial X}{\partial t} \qquad (5-9)$$

where r is a dimension along the radius of a cylindrical particle of carbon, C represents the concentration of diffusing mass at any position, r, in the cylindrical particle, X is the concentration of adsorbed solute, $X = X_m bC/(1 + bC)$, t is the time from initiation of diffusion, and D is the coefficient of molecular diffusion.

Values calculated by Weber and Rumer for coefficients of diffusion for a homologous series of sulfonated alkylbenzenes are of the order of 10^{-5} - 10^{-7} cm^2/sec. These agree with values cited in the literature for the same and similar solutes measured in aqueous solution. This accordance indicates that the diffusion with non-linear adsorption model for intraparticle transport may be valid for description of the rate-limiting process in agitated non-flow systems similar to those from which the experimental data were derived. Further, the technique permits reduction of experimental data to a common parameter to facilitate system-to-system comparisons.

FACTORS INFLUENCING ADSORPTION ON CARBON

Characterization of a specific adsorption system is given usually in terms of the nature and properties of three general components; the adsorbent, the adsorbate, and the solution or vapor phase from which adsorption takes place.

As cited previously, two important properties of the adsorbent are surface area and pore size distribution. Pore size distribution is not unrelated, of course, to surface area for in addition to playing a significant role in governing the rate of transport of adsorbed species from the exterior surfaces of the adsorbent to the interior surfaces, the size distribution of the molecular-dimension pores may determine what portion of the total surface will be finally available for the adsorption of a given solute. In other words, two carbons having different pore size distributions may exhibit identical surface areas as measured by nitorgen or even phenol adsorption, but entirely different surface areas as measured by adsorption of a high molecular weight solute such as sulfonated tetradecylbenzene. One study of adsorption of a series of normal aliphatic alcohols through heptyl alcohol on six different carbons of varying pore size indicates that adsorptive capacity does increase with pore size, indicating an increasing availability of the total surface area (25). Dubinin has presented data which give evidence for increasing capacity and increasing rate of adsorption with increasing porosity of carbon (26).

A third significant property of the adsorbent, again not unrelated to surface area, is particle size. As noted, adsorption rate should exhibit a monotonic increase with some function of the inverse of particle diameter. Variation with the reciprocal of the first power of diameter should obtain for simple adsorption

on specific external sites, variation with the reciprocal of
some higher power of diameter for an intraparticle-transport
rate control. For example, relative rate of uptake of straight-
chain sulfonated alkylbenzenes on a granular cocoanut carbon
in agitated non-flow systems has been found to vary as the
reciprocal of the square of the diameter of the granules (27).
Figure 3 is a plot of the relative rate constant for adsorption
of a branched-chain sulfonated alkylbenzene as a function of
particle size for a coal-base carbon. Again a variation with
the reciprocal of the square of the particle diameter is noted
for the non-flow system. Illustration of the effect of particle
size in a flow-through adsorption system is given in Figure 4.
This plot represents the amount of adsorption of a branched-
chain sulfonated alkylbenzene by 45 g of carbon in a 1" column
at a flow rate of 2.5 gpm/sq ft up to an arbitrary time at which
the effluent concentration was equal to 0.3 of the concentration
of solute in the influent to the column.

Adsorption capacity should vary also as the inverse of the
particle diameter. For porous materials such as activated
carbon, however, the fragmentation of large particles to form
smaller ones quite probably serves to open some tiny, sealed
channels in the carbon which then become available for adsorption.
This slightly increases the dependence of equilibrium capacity
on particle size above a simple variation with the inverse of
the diameter (18). An illustration of this effect is to be noted
in Figure 2.

Both the rate and extent of adsorption by particles of a
fixed size should vary approximately linearly with the dosage
of adsorbent over a range of doses that does not result in
great differences in the concentration of solute remaining in
bulk solution phase (18, 27). Large differences in the concentration of residual solute introduce a second variable for both
rate and capacity for adsorption. This second variable, the
concentration of the adsorbate in bulk phase, merits further
consideration and is discussed below. Data from experiments
on the uptake of sulfonated 3-dodecylbenzene by 0.200-mm
carbon at $40^{\circ}C$ in systems with carbon concentrations varied
in increments of 10 mg/l from 20 mg/l to 50 mg/l are presented
in Figure 5. It is evident from these data that the effect of
carbon concentration follows quite well the expected behavior
and that the relative rate constant remains essentially the same
over the experimental range of concentrations.

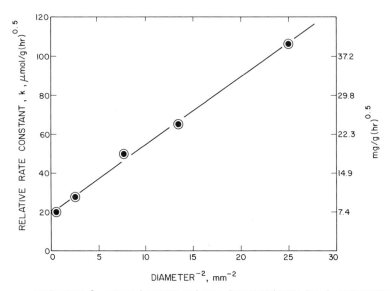

FIGURE 3   RELATIVE RATE CONSTANT AS A FUNCTION
            OF CARBON PARTICLE SIZE.

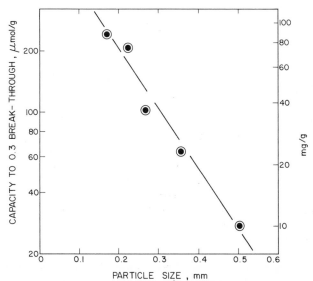

FIGURE 4   SOLUTE UPTAKE PER UNIT WEIGHT OF
            CARBON AS A FUNCTION OF PARTICLE
            SIZE IN AN ADSORPTION COLUMN.

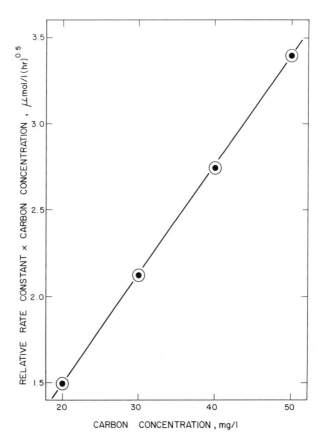

FIGURE 5   EFFECT OF CARBON CONCENTRATION
ON RATE OF ADSORPTION.

The chemical nature of the surface of carbon may in
some instances play a significant role in adsorption, particularly as regards to the relative polarities of the surface
and the solute molecules. A pure carbon surface can be
considered as non-polar, but rarely is the surface of an
active carbon pure. Rather, oxygen interacts with carbon to
produce specific active sites which render the surface slightly
polar. It has been quite well established that these active
sites behave in a fashion similar to the carboxyl, hydroxyl,
and carbonyl functional groups on high molecular weight
multi-ring aromatic compounds (28, 29, 30). The degree of

interaction of oxygen with active carbon thus establishes the so-called surface acidity of the carbon and to some extent its relative sorptive behavior with respect to acidic and basic solutes. Measurements of surface disposed oxygen have been found to correlate quite well with measurements for base (OH⁻) sorption capacities of active carbons (31).

Ash content is a commonly expressed property of active carbon, but conflicting reports have been given as to relationships between this property and adsorptive capacity. The results from one study indicate that surface area increases with decreasing ash content for a series of wood and lignite carbons (31). On the other hand, another study of adsorption of a group of aromatic acids on a series of four carbons ranging in ash content from 0.05% to 2.6% gives evidence for decreasing adsorption with decreasing ash content (32). In neither case is an explanation put forth nor does one seem immediately apparent.

Concentration of Solute

Quantitiative prediction of the variation of rate of adsorption as a function of solute concentration is difficult. If the mechanism of adsorption is one of rapid formation of an equilibrium interfacial concentration at the exterior surfaces of the adsorbent followed by slow transport of adsorbate into the carbon particles, then a simple dependence on solution concentration is not to be expected. Moreover, mathematical treatment of the intraparticle transport process does not lead to a simple algebraic relationship between external solute concentration and time of reaction even when a constant saturated external layer is maintained. Theoretical equations for intraparticle transport indicate that the concentration dependence of a diffusion-adsorption reaction will vary depending on the characteristics of the adsorption isotherm and on the fraction of the initial solute adsorbed at equilibrium (22). Thus, it appears that any observed relationship between concentration and rate of uptake for a specific system could be more than a useful relationship for correlation of data for that system within the range of observed data.

The dependence of adsorption capacity upon concentration of solute in solution phase if course is expressed, for a constant temperature and in a given system, by the adsorption isotherm. This relationship between capacity and solute concentration, as for relationships between rate and concentration, is not quantitatively general.

Although relationships between solution-phase solute concentration and adsorption rates and capacities are rather system-specific, it can be stated qualitatively that both rate and capacity will increase for positive adsorption phenomena with increasing concentration of solute in solution phase (18, 27).

Nature of the Solute

In any consideration of adsorption from solution on active carbon two facts quickly become evident; the solubility of the solute is, to a large extent, a controlling factor for adsorption equilibria while molecular geometry of the solute is a controlling factor for intraparticle transport and, consequently, for adsorption kinetics.

In general, an inverse relationship can be anticipated between the extent of adsorption of a solute and its solubility in the solvent from which adsorption occurs. This observation often is referred to as Lundelius's rule, the first of two more or less general rules which may be applied for semiquantitative prediction of the effect of the nature of a solute on its uptake from solution.

For example, adsorption of an aliphatic series of organic acids on carbon from aqueous solution increases in the order formic-acetic-propionic-butyric whereas the order is reversed for adsorption from toluene (19). In both cases, however, adsorption increases with decreasing solubility of the solute in the solvent. Another example is that for adsorption of iodine from various solvent systems on carbon. Observed ratios for adsorption from CCl_4, $CHCl_3$, and CS_2 are 1:2 : 4.5, respectively (33). These ratios are close to the inverse ratios for the solubility of iodine in the respective solvents. Similar evidence has obtained for adsorption of a series of aromatic acids on active carbon, again adsorption increasing with decreasing solubility (34). Working with a homologous series of fatty acids, acetic through n-heptylic, Hansen and Craig found that adsorption isotherms for these materials were nearly superimposable when plotted as amount adsorbed versus equilibrium concentration of solute reduced through division by the solubility of the solute, rather than simply against the equilibrium concentration of solute in solution phase (35).

The effects noted relative to solubility-adsorption relationships can be interpreted by postulating the necessity of breaking
some form of solute-solvent bond before adsorption can occur.
The greater the solubility, the stronger the solute-solvent
bond and the smaller the extent of adsorption. While numerous
examples of systems which obey Lundelius's rule can be cited,
there are also many exceptions. Thus, as for many adsorption
"rules", Lundelius's rule can be considered only as semiquantitative in nature.

In general, solubility of any organic compound in water
decreases as the length of the chain increases. This is due
to the fact that the compound becomes more hydrocarbon-like
as the number of carbon atoms becomes greater. This fact
forms the basis for the second major statement of a relationship between extent of adsorption and nature of the solute;
Traube's rule. Adsorption from aqueous solution increases
as a homologous series is ascended, largely because the
explusion of increasingly large hydrophobic molecules from
water permits an increasing number of water-water bonds to
reform.

Some observations of this effect have been mentioned
already. Another study on fatty acids in the series C_1 - C_7
and alcohols in the same series yields the same information
as well as the additional observation that the rate of variation
above C_4 is very small in both cases (36). This is due probably to the fact that above C_4, the hydrocarbon nature of the
acids and alcohols undergoes only small changes for each
additional carbon in the chain. Another study on a series of
dicarboxylic acids yielded similar results (37).

Concordant results were obtained for adsorption on active
carbon of a series of sulfonated alkylbenzenes ranging from
the unsubstituted acid up to sulfonated tetradecylbenzene (18).
These results are shown in Figure 6. A one carbon increase
at the beginning of the series produced a 50% increase in X_m
while a two carbon increase in chain length between C_6 and
C_8 produced only a net 10% increase and between C_{12} and C_{14}
the increase was only 9%.

Molecular size is of significance also as it relates to
rate of uptake of organic solutes by porous active carbon for,
if the rate is controlled by intraparticle transport forces, the
reaction generally will proceed more rapidly the smaller the
adsorbate molecule. Data plotted in Figure 7 for rates of
adsorption of a series of sulfonated alkylbenzenes of different

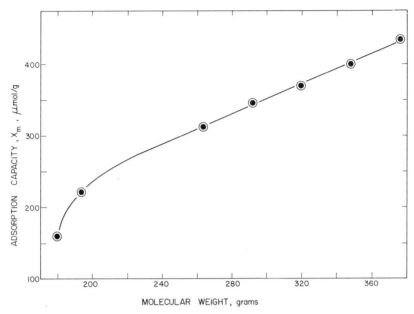

FIGURE 6   ADSORPTION CAPACITY AS A FUNCTION
            OF MOLECULAR WEIGHT.

molecular size clearly demonstrate a decrease in rate with
increasing molecular weight.

Variations in geometry of molecules seem to have much
smaller effects on equilibrium conditions than do increases
in chain length. Studies on the adsorption of three sulfonated
alkylbenzenes substituted at the 2, 3, and 6 positions on the
hydrocarbon chain, respectively, showed virtually no variations
in constants for the Langmuir equation (18). There are some
reports to the contrary, however. An investigation of the
adsorption of a series of 2, 6-dialkyl phenols from cyclohexane
indicated an eight-fold decrease in adsorption in the series
from 2, 6-dimethyl to 2, 6-di-tertbutyl phenol, a molecule
possessing very great steric hindrance (38). While this seems
a great decrease, it must be noted that these studies were run
in a hydrocarbon solvent in which the 2, 6-di-tert-butyl phenol
would be much more soluble and, therefore, less strongly
adsorbed than 2, 6-dimethyl phenol. Thus, the solubility effect
should be by far the most important in this case. The position

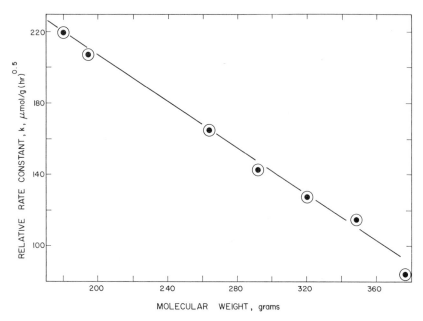

FIGURE 7   RELATIVE RATE CONSTANT AS A FUNCTION
OF MOLECULAR WEIGHT.

of substitution in hydroxy and aminobenzoic acids has been
reported as having a marked effect on adsorption on carbon,
the sequence of decreasing strength of adsorption being ortho,
para, and meta (39).

Since the controlling factor in the kinetics of adsorption
often is intraparticle transport, that molecule of a related
pair which is more compact may be adsorbed more rapidly.
Studies on linear-chain 2-, 3-, and 6- dodecylbenzenesulfonates
confirm the validity of this prediction with observed rates
decreasing in the sequence 2-3-6 (27). This observation might
be interpreted by noting that the ring of the (2-dodecyl-) isomer
is near the end of the chain which places it in a position suitable
for coiling to form a more compact molecule. The ring of the
(6-dodecyl-) isomer is attached to one of the middle carbon
atoms; a structure much less able to coil into a compact form.
The (3-dodecyl-) isomer, the structure of which is intermediate
between the other two, shows an intermediate rate. A technical
sulfonated dodecylbenzene, which would be expected to possess
a high degree of branching of the chain, gives a rate value only

about half that of the linear-chain sulfonated dodecylbenzenes; an observation in accord with this theory.

Many components of waters and wastewaters either exist as, or have the potential of existing as, ionic species. Acids such as the sulfonated alkylbenzenes, fatty acids, phenolic species, amines, and many pesticides are a few of the materials and classes of materials having the property of ionizing under appropriate conditions of pH. Because activated carbon carries a net negative surface charge (21) which is believed to be of significance for adsorption, and because many of the physical and chemical properties of a given compound undergo drastic changes upon ionization, considerable study has been devoted to comparing adsorption differences between neutral species and their conjugate ions.

The bulk of observations seems to point to the generalization that as long as the compounds are structurally simple, adsorption is at a minimum for the charged species and at a maximum for the neutral species. As the compound becomes more complex, the effect of ionization becomes of decreasing importance.

Several studies on different types of organic acids have been reported in the literature. In all cases, decreasing adsorption with increasing ionization has been observed (40-42) For example, adsorption of propionic acid on carbon is minimum in the range pH 3.5 to pH 5.5; succinic acid has been observed to have a minimum between pH 4.0 to 7.0; and caproic acid between pH 4.8 to pH 7.5 (42). One reference reports determination of the dissociation constant of lauric acid to within one percent by equating the amount of acid adsorbed with the amount of unionized acid (43). In yet another study adsorption for a series of substituted benzoic acids was found to vary inversely with the dissociation constant (44). Studies on organic bases such as nicotine (40) and substituted pyridines (45) again indicate adsorption maxima at the point of least ionization.

There are of course also those compounds which have the capacity to be both an acid and a base, the amphoteric compounds. Studies on this type of compound indicate an adsorption maximum at the isoelectric point; that pH at which both the acidic end and the basic end of the compound are ionized and the compound bears a net charge of zero (40, 46). This again accords with the general observation that adsorption is at a maximum for neutral species.

A general rule that may be applied to prediction of the effect of solute polarity on adsorption is that a polar solute will tend to prefer the phase which is more polar. In other words, a polar solute will be strongly adsorbed from a non-polar solvent by a polar adsorbent, but will much prefer a polar solvent to a non-polar adsorbent. Polarity of organic compounds is a function of charge separation within the molecule. Almost any asymmetric compound will be found to be more or less polar but several types of functional groups tend to produce fairly high polaritites in compounds   Examples of these are hydroxyl, carboxyl, nitro, nitrile, carbonyl, sulfonate, and amine. Thus ethanol, C_2H_5OH, is polar, having an incremental negative charge on the hydroxyl and a corresponding positive charge on the ethyl group. Since solvation by water involves formation of a hydrogen bond from one of the positively charged hydrogens of the water to a group bearing more or less of a negative charge along with some bonding in the reverse direction to the water oxygen, water solubility would be suspected to increase with increasing polarity. This is the case. It, therefore, follows that adsorption will decrease as polarity increases even though active carbon is a somewhat polar adsorbent.

In support of the above conjecture, a series of sugars, which are polyhyroxyl compounds of very high polarity, gives adsorption values on the order of 0. 25% of the weight of the adsorbent (47). Since most compounds of reasonable polarity give values in the range of 10 to 30% of adsorbent weight for ultimate capacity (18), it can be seen that the value for this very polar type of compound is low indeed.

Temperature

Adsorption reactions normally result in an entropy decrease, thus, the reaction must be exothermic if a decrease in free energy is to occur. Hence, as an exothermic reaction, the extent of adsorption will increase with decreasing temperature. Changes in enthalpy for adsorption are usually of the order of magnitude of those for condensation or crystallization reactions. Thus, small variations in temperature tend not to alter the extent of adsorption to a significant extent.

The change in the heat content of a system in which adsorption occurs, the total amount of heat evolved in the adsorption of a definite quantity of solute on an adsorbent, is termed the heat of adsorption, ΔH Heats of gas-phase adsorption generally are several kcal per mole but, because water is desorbed from the surface when adsorption from aqueous solution occurs, heat effects for the latter process are generally somewhat smaller than those for gas-phase adsorption.

The differential heat of adsorption may be calculated from maximum levels of adsorption at two or more different temperatures with the van't Hoff-Arrhenius equation in the form:

$$\Delta H = \frac{RT_1 T_2}{T_2 - T_1} (\ln X_{m,1} - \ln X_{m,2}) \qquad (5\text{-}10)$$

where T_1 and T_2 are the absolute temperatures of two otherwise identical systems, and X_m is, for this example, the limiting monolayer adsorption value for the Langmuir adsorption model. A plot of values for the logarithm of X_m versus the reciprocal of absolute temperature for a given system should then yield a linear trace with a slope equal to $\Delta H/RT_1 T_2$. While the temperature dependence of equilibrium capacity for adsorption is defined by the parameter ΔH, the dependence of rate of adsorption usually is expressed in terms of the activation energy, E, as discussed previously.

As cited earlier, for uptake of solute from solution by porous carbon, the process will be endothermic rather than exothermic if intraparticle transport is the rate limiting mechanism. Because diffusion is an endothermic process while adsorption is exothermic, rate of uptake of solute by porous solids often will increase with increasing temperature while for the same system the equilibrium position of adsorption or adsorption capacity will decrease with increasing temperature. Evidence for this type of behavior has been obtained from studies of the kinetics and equilibria for adsorption of sulfonated alkylbenzenes on carbon (18, 27). As illustrated in Figure 8, rate of uptake from solution was found to increase with increasing temperature in accordance with expectations for an intraparticle-transport rate control. An activation energy of 4.27 kcal/g-mole was calculated for this reaction. Ultimate capacity, however, was found to decrease with increasing temperature as illustrated in Figure 9. The value for ΔH obtained in these studies was -1.4 kcal/g-mole.

In any event, the direction of the temperature effect and values for the energy parameters, E and ΔH, are useful tools for delineating the nature of adsorption mechanisms as well as for predicting optimum conditions for operation of an adsorption process. In general, however, temperature variations normally experienced in water and wastewater treatment operations will not lead to significant variation in adsorption by carbon.

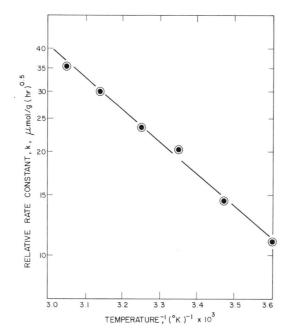

FIGURE 8   EFFECT OF TEMPERATURE ON RATE OF
            ADSORPTION ON CARBON.

Hydrogen-Ion Concentration
    The pH of a solution from which adsorption occurs, for
one or more of a number of reasons, may influence the extent
of adsorption on active carbon. Because H^+ and OH^- ions
tend to be adsorbed quite strongly, the adsorption of other
ions is influenced by the pH of the solution. Further, to the
extent to which the ionization of an acidic or basic compound
affects its adsorption, so will pH affect the adsorption in that
it governs the degree of ionization of the compound.
    In general, adsorption of typical organic pollutants from
water increases with decreasing pH. For example, experimental evidence has shown an increasing affinity with decreasing pH for the adsorption of sulfonated alkylbenzenes on
activated carbon (18, 27). In this case the effect is not likely
to be one of ionization of the compound because the effect was
observed well above the pH region of the ionization or protolysis constant for alkylbenzenesulfonic acids (pK ~ 1.5).
Rather, because the ionic species of the sulfonated alkylbenzenes are charged negatively, enhanced adsorption at a low

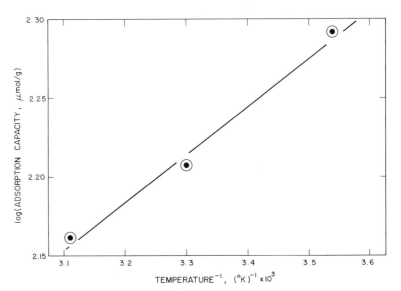

FIGURE 9   EFFECT OF TEMPERATURE ON CAPACITY
ON ADSORPTION ON CARBON.

pH may result from neutralization of negative charges at the
surface of the carbon with increasing hydrogen-ion concentration,
thereby reducing hindrance to diffusion and also making available more of the active surface of the carbon.   This effect
then would be expected to vary in degree for different carbons
because the charges at the surfaces of the carbon depend on
the composition of the raw material used for preparing the
activated carbon and on the technique of activation.

Data which show the effect of pH on adsorption in a column
of active carbon are presented in Figure 10.   The data were
obtained by passing a solution of sulfonated alkylbenzene, with
an unadjusted pH slightly below neutral, at a flow rate of
2.5 gpm/sq ft through a column containing 45 g of 0.359-mm
carbon.   When the ratio, (C/C_0), of the concentration of
solute in the effluent to that in the influent reached 0.55, the
pH of the influent was decreased instantaneously to 2.5 by
addition of concentrated H_3PO_4.   As illustrated in Figure 10,
the decrease in leakage through the column after acidification

of the influent was dramatic.

COMPETITIVE INTERACTIONS IN ADSORPTION ON CARBON
    Only in rare instances will adsorption operations with
active carbon be limited to the removal of only one solute
from solution. Natural waters and wastewaters generally
contain heterogeneous mixtures of substances which will be
adsorbed by carbon. It might be anticipated that mutual inhibition of adsorption will occur for mixed solutes. This has
been found to be the case for adsorption on carbon from bi-
solute solutions of mixed organic acids (48), and for solutions
containing both iodine and acetic acid (49). It is essential
then, for design of adsorption processes for complex systems
that appropriate consideration be given to competitive interactions which may occur between solutes contained in these
systems.
    Weber and Morris have presented experimental evidence
of competitive interactions for adsorptive removal of sulfonated
2-dodecylbenzene, dodecyl sulfate, phenol, and o- and p-
chloronitrobenzene from dilute aqueous bi-solute solutions by
porous carbon (50). The competitive effects of each adsorbate
on the rate of uptake of the other from bi-solute solutions of
phenol and sulfonated 2-dodecylbenzene are illustrated in
Table I. The relative rate parameter, k, denotes the slope
of a linear trace of the rate data for each system plotted as
the square of the quantity of adsorbate per unit weight of
adsorbent removed from the bulk solution vs. time measured
from introduction of the adsorbent to the experimental system.
A plot of the square of the quantity removed from solution vs.
time is equivalent to a plot of the quantity vs. the square root
of time; a graphical form commonly used to linearize kinetics
data for systems in which diffusion phenomena control the rate
of reaction (22). The terms $C_{0,a}$ and $C_{0,p}$ in Table I denote
the initial molar concentrations of sulfonated 2-dodecylbenzene
and phenol, respectively, and k_a' and k_p' the corresponding
relative rate parameters.
    Mutual interference between the two adsorbates is apparent
from the data presented in Table I. As the ratio $C_{0,p}/C_{0,a}$
decreases for a given value of $C_{0,p}$, the rate of adsorption
of phenol decreases. Similarly, as $C_{0,p}/C_{0,a}$ increases, to
values above 1.36, for a nearly constant $C_{0,a}$, the relative
rate parameter k_a' decreases progressively.

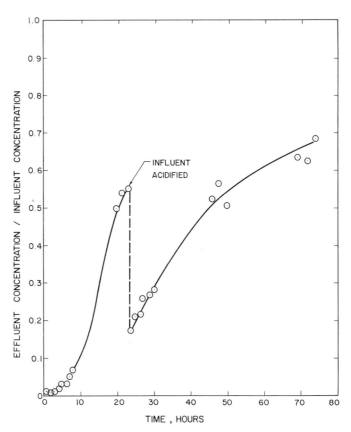

FIGURE 10   EFFECT OF ACIDIFICATION ON
             ADSORPTION IN A CARBON COLUMN.

The competitive effect of the sulfonated 2-dodecylbenzene on k'_p is obviously more pronounced than that of the phenol on k'_a. The smaller phenol molecule normally diffuses more rapidly in the capillaries of porous carbon than does the long-chain sulfonated dodecylbenzene as evidenced by the values of k'_a and k'_p in Table I for the conditions of $C_{o,p} = 0$ and $C_{o,a} = 0$, respectively. The observed reductions in k'_a and k'_p for the conditions $C_{o,p} > 0$ and $C_{o,a} > 0$, respectively, can be explained qualitatively in terms of an intraparticle-transport mechanism by the hypothesis that a large, slowly diffusing molecule, once

TABLE 1   RATES OF ADSORPTION OF PHENOL AND
         SULFONATED 2-DODECYLBENZENE FROM
         BI-SOLUTE SOLUTIONS ON 0.126-mm CARBON

$C_{o,a}$ u mol l	$C_{o,p}$ u mol l	$C_{o,p}/C_{c,a}$	k'_a $\left[(\text{u mol/g})^2/\text{hr}\right]$ x 10^{-3}	k'_p $\left[(\text{u mol/g})^2/\text{hr}\right]$ x 10^{-3}
21.9	0.0	0.0	14.2	--
0.0	29.2	∞	--	96.1
21.6	29.4	1.36	14.2	48.4
24.5	0.0	0.00	14.4	--
23.9	77.2	3.23	12.1	230.4 (a)
23.0	128.6	5.59	9.6	1322.5
0.0	129.2	∞	--	3062.5

(a) In comparing this value of k' with any other
     large difference in Co,p must be taken
     into account.

its repetitive processes of adsorption, desorption, and translational movement are initiated along the length of a capillary
of nearly molecular diameter, may essentially block most of
the cross-sectional area of the capillary. This reduces the
effective rate of transport of smaller molecules subsequently
entering the pore. The process appears to be too complex to
be described quantitatively in terms of simple diffusion or
adsorption mechanisms and can probably be represented only
by statistical models.
    Chloronitrobenzenes similarly were found to have little
effect upon the rate of adsorption of the sulfonated alkylbenzene
for $C_{o,n}/C_{o,a}$ values below 3. Depression by the surfactant
of the rate of uptake of the chloronitrobenzene, however, was,
as for phenol, appreciable. The explanation given for the
somewhat one-sided effect of the large-molecule sulfonated
alkylbenzene on rate of uptake of phenol should be equally
tenable for its effect on rate of absorption of chloronitrobenzenes.
    The same studies indicated that dodecylsulfate has a much
greater effect upon the rate of uptake of the sulfonated 2-dode-
cylbenzene than does either phenol or chloronitrobenzene. If

the previous hypothesis is accepted for rate interference; the
greater rate-depressing effect of the dodecylsulfate is to be
expected since this molecule is considerably larger than either
the phenol or chloronitrobenzene and no doubt diffuses in the
pore spaces at a rate much more comparable to that of the
sulfonated alkylbenzene.

It is of interest to note that in all of the systems studied,
the rate of uptake of each solute was decreased in the presence
of the second solute but that the sum of the rates of the two
solutes was, in each case where both were determined, greater
than the rate of adsorption of either from a single-solute
solution. The most likely explanation is an increase in 'diffusion
pressure" because of the larger total number of molecules in
the bi-solute solutions.

Although the kinetics of the removal of adsorbates by porous
carbon from dilute solution are complicated by simultaneous
diffusion-adsorption phenomena, the final positions of equilibrium attained are governed only by adsorptive forces. Thus,
competitive equilibrium interactions are subject to exact and
systematic mathematical description. In the range of concentrations studied in the previous investigation, all of the
adsorbates exhibited Langmuir-type isotherms for adsorption
from single-solute solutions on the experimental carbon (50).
It was, therefore, possible to define the extent of steady-state
adsorption as a function of the relative equilibrium concentrations
of constituent solutes according to a monolayer adsorption
model.

By letting X_i represent the amount of solute adsorbed per
gram of adsorbent for an equilibrium concentration C_i in
solution and $X_{m,i}$ the amount of solute adsorbed per gram at
concentrations corresponding to complete monolayer coverage
of the available surface, the Langmuir equation for equilibrium
adsorption of solute i from an n-solute system is:

$$X_i = \frac{X_{m,i}\, b_i\, C_i}{1 + \sum\limits_{j=1}^{n} b_j\, C_j} \tag{5-11}$$

where b_i is expressive of the energy of adsorption and corresponds to the reciprocal of that value of C_i for which half-
saturation, in the monolayer sense, of the available adsorptive
surface obtains for a pure solution of the ith solute.

Good agreement was obtained by Weber and Morris between competitive effects calculated with equation 5-11. Experimentally observed competitive effects for several bi-solute systems indicate that the inhibitive effect of one solute on the adsorption of another is predictable with considerable accuracy by a treatment based on competitive Langmuir-type adsorption (50).

While capacity of the carbon for each adsorbate in the bi-solute systems was reduced relative to its value for the respective pure solutions, it is significant that the combined capacity was greater than that for either of the pure substances alone. It thus, appears that total adsorptive capacities may be increased with mixed solutes. This observation, too, can be explained partially on the basis of the increased total concentration and the resultant effect on adsorptive capacity, as in single-solute systems. Another explanation, perhaps even more appropriate than the former because the data follow a Langmuir pattern that dictates an essentially constant value for X in the range of concentrations studied, is that the differ-ent solutes do not compete entirely for the same adsorption sites. It is quite likely that smaller molecules are able to penetrate small pores not available to large molecules. Small molecules that reach these pores then no longer must compete with excluded adsorbates for adsorption sites.

The conclusion from previous work then is that the intensity of the competitive effect of one adsorbate on another is a function of the relative as well as absolute concentrations of the two and of their relative energies of adsorption. In addition, because the rate of uptake by porous carbon appears to be controlled by the velocity of movement of adsorbate in the capillary channels between and among graphitic planes in the carbon, kinetic interactions depend to some extent on relative effective diffusivities and, consequently, on respective sizes and configurations of adsorbate molecules.

Although there is clearly a depression in rates of uptake and final extent of adsorption of the individual components of bi-solute systems, both the total rate and total steady-state capacity are enhanced in such systems. Thus, it can be concluded with reasonable confidence that not all of the adsorbates compete entirely for the same surfaces at the liquid-solid interface.

In the application of adsorption on carbon to multiple component systems account must be taken of the nature of competitive interactions. Once chemical characterization of the system has been accomplished, appropriate combinations of multiple-solute investigations such as those carried out by Weber and Morris should be useful for predicting the competitive effects of the individual materials in the complex system and for establishing process design criteria.

SUMMARY

An approach has been made in the foregoing discussion to characterization of the mechanism of adsorption by active carbon from solution and to definition of the physical and chemical factors that affect the kinetics and equilibria of the process. Adsorption on carbon appears to be a most promising method for removing a broad spectrum of pollution materials from aqueous systems.

The physical character of an active carbon, particularly as regards pore structure, is a significant factor in adsorption. In natural waters and wastewaters, the process is additionally subject to influence by a number of environmental variables and to nature of the solute system. Among such factors are: temperature; hydrogen-ion concentration; mixing or degree of turbulence; molecular structures and physico-chemical properties of the adsorbates; and competing solutes.

For any instance of adsorption on carbon, clear distinction should be made between rates of adsorption and adsorption equilibria or capacity. This is important since certain variables may tend to influence the kinetic system and not the equilibrium system or vice versa, or may actually have a different influence on each. For example, temperature increases often may increase the rate of sorptive removal of solute from solution by porous carbon - depending upon the rate-limiting step in the overall process-while decreasing the capacity for adsorption. Increased mixing or degree of turbulence usually will increase the rate of adsorption but not affect the equilibrium capacity. Increasing hydrogen ion concentration usually is found to enhance both rates and capacities for adsorption on carbon, while the presence of competing solutes has been found to affect each adversely.

Conclusions from the foregoing discussion are rather generally applicable to adsorption of organic solutes by active carbon from aqueous solution. Nonetheless, each specific system should be examined individually, for in solutions as heterogeneous as natural waters and wastewaters, unpredictable specific interactions of the numerous factors involved in this process frequently lead to unexpected results.

LITERATURE CITED
1. Ostwald, W., Klassiker der Exakten Wissenchaften, No. 58 (1894).

2. Lowitz, T., Crell's Chem Ann, 1, 211 (1786).

3. Lamb, A.B., et al, Ind Eng Chem, 11, 420 (1919)

4. Baylis, J.R., Elimination of Taste and Odor in Water, McGraw-Hill Book Co. Inc., New York, N.Y., (1935).

5. Jenkins, K.H., JAm Water Works Assoc, 55, 1485 (1963)

6. Environmental Health Series: AWTR-9, AWTR-10, AWTR-11, AWTR-12, Division of Water Supply and Pollution Control, Public Health Service, USDHEW, Washington, D.C., (1964).

7. Brunauer, S., The Adsorption of Gases and Vapors, Physical Adsorption, 1, Princeton Univ. Press, Princeton, N.J., (1943).

8. Wolff, W.F., et al, J Phys Chem, 64, 646 (1960).

9. Arnell, J.C. and W. M. Barss, Can J Research, 26A, 236 (1948).

10. Riley, H.L., Quart Rev (London), 1, 59 (1947).

11. Emmett, P.H., Chem Rev, 43, 69 (1948).

12. Wolff, W.F., J Phys Chem, 62, 829 (1958).

13. Wolff, W.F., J Phys Chem, 63, 653 (1959).

14. Juhola, A.H. and E. O. Wiig, J Am Chem Soc, 71, 2069 (1949).

15. Ritter, H.L. and L.C. Drake, Ind Eng Chem, Anal Ed, 17, 782 (1945).

16. Hansen, R. D. and R. S. Hansen, J Colloid Sci, 9, 1 (1954).

17. Morrison, J.L. and D. M. Miller, Can J Chem, 33, 330 (1955).

18. Weber, W. J., Jr. and J.C. Morris, J Sanit Eng Div Am Soc Civil Eng, 90, SA3, 79 (1 964).

19. Holmes, H.N. and J.B. McKelvey, J Phys Chem, 32, 1522 (19?

20. Nutting, G.C., et al, J Am Chem Soc., 62, 1496 (1940).

21. Bean, E.L., et al, J Am Water Works Assoc, 56, 214 (1964).

22. Crank, J., The Mathematics of Diffusion, Oxford at the Clarendon Press, London, England, (1956).

23. Edeskuty, F.J. and N.R. Amundson, Ind Eng Chem, 44, 1698 (1952).

24. Weber, W.J., Jr. and R.R. Rumer, Water Resources Res, 1, 361 (1965).

25. Chaterji, A.C. and R.D. Srivastara, J Indian Chem Soc, 28, 547 (1951).

26. Dubinin, M., Z Physik Chem, 155A, 116 (1931).

27. Weber, W.J., Jr. and J.C. Morris, J Sanit Eng Div Am Soc Civil Eng, 89, SA2, 31 (1963).

28. Garten, V.A. and D.E. Weiss, Australian J Chem, 8, 68 (1955).

29. Puri, B.R., et al, J Sci Ind Res (India), 20D, 366 (1961).

30. Rivin, D., Fourth Rubber Technology Conference, London, Livesey LTD., Shrewsbury, England, (1962).

31. Truemper, J.T., Paper Presented Before the Div of Colloid and Surface Chem, 147th Meeting ACS, Philadelphia, Pa., April 6-10, (1964).

32. Ermolenko, N.F., et al, Uch Zap Belorussk Gos Univ Ser Khim, No. 24, 70 (1955).

33. Lundelius, E.F., Kolloid-Z, 26, 145 (1920).

34. Ermolenko, N. F. and N. L. Lemets, Zh Obsch Khim, 23, 1313 (1953).

35. Hansen, R. S. and R. P. Craig, J Phys Chem, 58, 211 (1954).

36. Kzhigit, O. M., et al, J Phys Chem (USSR), 22, 107 (1948).

37. Ermolenko, N. F. and O. R. Skorokhold, Uch Zap Belorussk Gos Univ Ser Khim, No. 23, 58 (1955).

38. Wheeler, O. H. and E. M. Levy, Can J Chem, 37, 1235 (1959).

39. Zechmeister, L., Progress in Chromatography, John Wiley & Sons, Inc., New York, N. Y., (1950).

40. Andersen, A. H., Acta Pharmacol Toxicol, 3, 199 (1947).

41. Hesse, G. and O. Sauter, Naturwissenschaften, 34, 251 (1947).

42. Phelps, H. J., Proc Roy Soc (London), 13A, 17 (1931).

43. Ermolenko, N. F. and O. R. Skaraokhod, Uch Zap Belorussk Gos Univ, Ser Khim, No. 20, 165 (1954).

44. Langloid, G., Mem Serv Chim Etat Paris, 40, 83 k (1955).

45. Waksmundski, A. and J. Oscik, Ann Univ Mariae Curie-Sklodowska, Lublin-Polonia, Sec AA, 6, (1961).

46. Hesse, G. and O. Sauter, Naturwissenschaften, 34, 277 (1947).

47. Meloun, B., Listy Cukrovar, 66, 75 (1949).

48. Freundlich, H., Kapplillarchemie, 1, 4th Ed, Akademische Verlagsgesellschaft M. B. H., Leipig, Germany, (1930).

49. Schmidt, G. C., Z Physik Chem, 74, 689: Ibid, 76, 58: Ibid, 77, 641: Ibid, 78, 667: Ibid, 83, 674: Ibid, 91, 103 (1910-1917).

50. Weber, W. J., Jr. and J. C. Morris, J Am Water Works Assoc, 56, 447 (1964).

DISCUSSION

CHAIRMAN COHEN: Thank you, Dr. Weber. We'll now entertain questions on Dr. Weber's paper.

DR. ROBERT B. DEAN (R.A. Taft Sanitary Engineering Center): One possible action of carbon on adsorbed materials; namely, that of oxidation or chemical reaction, was more or less passed over in your work. I'd like your comments on the possibility that at very low concentrations, in the order of ppb, phenol may actually be oxidized on carbon surfaces. Some of this shows from work that you did for us where two isotherms were observed.

Another not unrelated fact is that the phenol number of carbon, which is measured in the ppb range, bears no relation to its surface area or its possibility to adsorb anything else whatsoever--this is some recent work just reported in Detroit. When you add to this the fact that the phenol treatment at a low cost, one suspects that perhaps it's just an oxide surface put on as a post-treatment rather than going through the extensive activation to increase surface area.

DR. WEBER: Addressing the first part of your question Dr. Dean, I would say there is certainly the possibility of oxidation of adsorbed solutes at the surface of active carbon. This can occur by the catalytic activity of certain surface impurities--as you are doubtless aware, active carbons contain a number of metallic impurities, such as iron, which can serve to promote oxidation reactions at the surface--or by the concentration of solute at the surface. Regarding agreement, or lack thereof, between the adsorption capacity represented by the phenol number for an active carbon and the Langmuir capacity term, X_m, recall that X_m represents the limiting value of adsorption for a complete monolayer coverage of available surface. I have found from my own experiences that the phenol number tends to be quite conservative and not in fact representative of the total true equilibrium capacity of a carbon, even for adsorption of phenol. However, the lack of agreement I note between the phenol number capacity and the Langmuir monolayer capacity would certainly not bespeak an oxidation or destruction of phenol at the surface, but rather an inefficient use--in determination of the phenol number--of the total available surface. Nor do I agree with your suggestion that the existence of two rather distinct types of adsorption isotherms for high and low ranges of residual concentrations

of phenol, as measured in my own work, indicates surface
oxidation of the phenol. I suggest rather that a low concentrations adsorption is limited of a monolayer coverage of available
surface sites, whereas multilayer adsorption occurs if the
concentration in solution phase is sufficiently high. Comparison
of the relative energies of adsorption of phenol in the two regions
of bulk concentration indicates that the tightness of binding of
adsorbed phenol is much higher at low concentrations, which
suggests that a certain proportion of the available sites on the
surface are quite active relative to others. As I have indicated
in the paper, it is improbable that the surface is uniform in
activity; there must be regions with differing degrees of affinity.
The influence of adsorption at the more active sites will of
course be more pronounced at low concentration because these
sites there represent a greater proportion of the total number
of available sites than they do in the multilayer region of
concentration.

DR. DEAN: That is the same thing. A little bit of phenol
is adsorbed by quite a different mechanism from the mechanism
that adsorbs the bulk of the phenol or other similar organic
molecules, and phenol number is only measuring that little
bit. It may have no relationship to anything else.

DR. WEBER: I agree that the phenol number is not
representative of the total adsorptive capacity of an active
carbon. However, I do not think that a lack of agreement
between the phenol number capacity and the Langmuir adsorption
constant, X_m, indicates anything about the possibility of oxidation
of adsorbed material at the surface. One cannot deduce this.

DR. DEAN: You can't deduce it from that, but somebody
might well study the fate of phenol in the phenol number, find
where it actually goes.

DR. WEBER: I think this would be a worthwhile study,
not only for phenol but for a number of other compounds.

CHAIRMAN COHEN: I think we have time for just one
short question, if there is one. The gentleman in the rear.

DR. G. COLACICCO (Albert Einstein College of Medicine):
Do I understand that the driving force and therefore the free
energy of adsorption of long chain compounds on carbon surfaces
is contributed primarily by the solvent-solvent interaction and
therefore by the expulsion of the hydrophobic chains from the
solvent? Have you considered the possibility that the water
involved here is the water on the carbon surface and an inter-

action in the form of a water exchange mechanism may involve the polar head of the long chain compound and the hydrated carbon surface? That is known as the first step in monolayer penetration.

DR. WEBER: That's an interesting thought. You suggest then that adsorption may occur because the polar portion of the molecule is attracted to water already adsorbed at the surface.

DR. COLACICCO: Not to the water but the polarized carbon surface. And it would exchange with and displace the water, as in a mechanism of film penetration.

DR. WEBER: I think that certainly the adsorbate must displace water adsorbed at the surface. I do not think, however, that the initial attraction of the adsorbate molecule to the surface is to the water adsorbed to the surface. I can think of no reason why the solute should be attracted from one water layer to another water layer. It's already in solution phase in the capillary. It must, however, displace water adsorbed at the surface; I agree with that.

DR. COLACICCO: Is there any exact knowledge as to the point of attachment of the adsorbate of the long chain compound on the carbon surface by the hydrophobic chain or the polar side?

DR. WEBER: Everything would lead one to believe that the attachment is to the hydrocarbon chain. I doubt that anyone has ever physically examined an adsorbed molecule at the surface and actually observed this. However, all thermodynamic evidence would indicate that the aforementioned orientation of the molecule would occur.

CHAIRMAN COHEN: Thank you very much.

Cooper H. Wayman
Colorado School of Mines

ADSORPTION ON CLAY MINERAL SURFACES

Clay minerals may have an important function in natural water systems because of their large surface area per unit weight. In effect, clay minerals may operate as adsorbents for dissolved chemicals in water. Rivers and streams having a high content of suspended solids, of which clays comprise a significant amount, may transport chemicals, biological wastes, and gases by adsorption at the clay-water interface. Clay minerals make an appreciable contribution to natural soils. Therefore, dissolved or suspended constituents in natural or wastewater infiltrating soil horizons may react with clay minerals through adsorption. Clay minerals thus perform the task of a decontamination device in both the suspended solid load of natural water and also in soil horizons.

Whether or not clays react with dissolved constituents in water, however, depends on a complex set of physico-chemical conditions. In general, the inherent nature of the clay surface and changes imposed upon this surface by the water environment must be assessed in order to evaluate the adsorption character-istics at the clay-water interface. In this paper, an attempt is made to account for the sorptive properties of clays and to indicate results obtained from various types of adsorption studies. Only the clay minerals, kaolinite, illite, and montmorillonite will be considered. It is proper that certain characteristics

127

peculiar to clay minerals must be indicated before a discussion
of adsorption.

PROPERTIES OF CLAYS

Origin
Clay minerals originate either as components in residual
bodies through weathering of a geological feature or through
the agency of hydrothermal synthesis at high temperature and
pressure. Details of their origin can be obtained from various
reviews such as that of Grim (1).

Size and Shape
Clay minerals are quite variable with respect to size
and shape. The particular environment under which clays are
formed is probably the controlling factor. Kaolinite might
range from a well-crystallized hexagonal grain to an irregular
mass displaying poor crystalline outline. Illite and montmorillonite contain poorer crystalline fabrics than kaolinte. For
the purpose of this paper, clay size is assumed not to exceed
2μ .

Physical dimensions of kaolinite flakes have been described
with surface dimensions ranging from 0.3 to 4μ, and thicknesses
from 0.05 to 2μ (1). Montmorillonite is usually much finer
grained than kaolinite with surface dimensions of 0.02 to 0.2μ
and thicknesses in the range $0.002\,\mu$. Illite usually is defined
poorly and may have surface dimensions ranging from 0.1 to
0.3μ. The shapes and dimensions mentioned above are merely
a guide. In nature, deviations from these values would be
expected.

Structure
Structure of the three clay minerals under consideration
in this paper can be described in terms of stacking between
hydrated silica and gibbsite and silica. In Figure 1, silicon
is shown in tetrahedral coordination with oxygen and aluminum
in octahedral coordination with hydroxyl. Kaolinite is a typical
two-layer clay containing one gibbsite layer and one hydrated
silica layer. A simplified sketch of kaolinite is shown in
Figure 2 (along the C-axis). As indicated, the C-axis spacing
in this structure is about $7.2 \, A^{\circ}$. The structural formula
according to Figure 2 is: $Al_4Si_4O_{10} (OH)_8$ or the chemical

formula amounts to: $Al_2 Si_2 O_5 (OH)_4$. Compared to montmorillonite, kaolinite is a non-expandable type of clay mineral.
Montmorillonite is comprised of a gibbsite layer between two
hydrated silica layers which is designated as a three-layer type.
The minimum C-axis spacing usually amounts to $9.2A^O$. The
C-spacing of montmorillonite, however, is quite variable as
a result of sorbed water between the layers (interlayer or
interlamellar water). Illite is a three-layer structure being
similar to that of muscovite, but is different in that only about
15% of Si is substituted by Al in comparison to about 25% in
muscovite. In illite, the charge deficiency due to isomorphous
replacement is compensated by K. The C-axis dimension in
illite is about $10.1A^O$.

Origin of Surface Charge

Much of the previous information suggests that clay surfaces contain a net charge deficiency which is negative. There
is also evidence, however, that the edges of clay minerals
contain positive charges. Thiessen has shown that negative
gold micelles are sorbed readily by kaolinite (2). Michaels's
studies have shown that the exchange capacity of kaolinite is
increased through the adsorption of negative polyphosphate on
positive edges (3). Schofield and Samson present data that
suggest Cl^- ion can be adsorbed on positive edges of kaolinite
(4, 5). In further support of this concept, van Olphen proposed
a dual charge in terms of the electrical double layer theory (6).
It is suggested that a negative double layer exists along the
faces (Figure 3) and that a positive double layer occurs on the
particle edge, notwithstanding the overall effect of net negative
charge (7). If this evidence is correct, the overall net negative
charge readily explains the higher cationic exchange capacity
on faces in comparison to the observed low values of anionic
exchange occurring most likely at the edges.

There are three mechanisms believed to be responsible
for charge phenomena on clay mineral surfaces. Specifically,
these mechanisms are isomorphous replacement, broken bonds,
and lattice defects.

The creation of negative charges on clay surfaces from
isomorphous replacement might occur through substitution
of Al for Si in the tetrahedral layer or by Mg for Al in the
octahedral layer. Schofield and Samson suggest that only one
Si ion out of 400 need be replaced by Al to effect an exchange
capacity of 2 meq/100 g (5). Obviously, this approach could

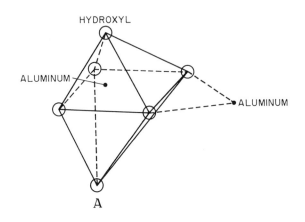

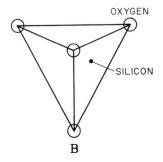

FIGURE 1   ALUMINUM IN OCTAHEDRAL COORDINATION
(A) AND SILICON IN TETRAHEDRAL
(B) COORDINATION.

not be substantiated by chemical analysis. If this mechanism
is valid, such an explanation would apply to the face of a clay
particle. Many investigators believe that this mechanism is
more germane to montmorillonite than to kaolinite with respect
to exchange capacity.

Many investigators also support the concept that broken
bonds along crystalline edges of clay platelets (parallel to the
C-axis) are also an important mechanism (1, 8, 9). Bonds may
be broken in either the tetrahedral or octahedral layer. In the
octahedral layer the situation would involve:

$$Al - O - Al - O$$

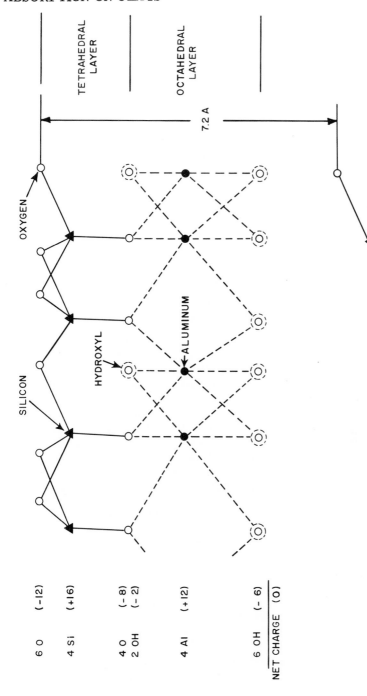

FIGURE 2   SCHEMATIC OF THE UNIT CELL OF KAOLINITE ALONG THE C-AXIS.

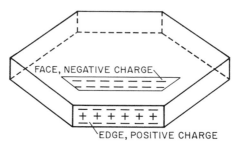

FIGURE 3   SCHEMATIC OF DUAL CHARGE ON A
                KAOLINITE PARTICLE.

If the severance is between Al and O, then a site is created with
a positive charge. If between O and Al, then the site becomes
negative as a result of the exposed oxygen (generally of an OH
ion). The same type of reasoning can be applied to the tetrahedral
layer edges wherein the bonding is:

$$Si - O - Si - O$$

In all probability, it is not unreasonable to predict that both
positive and negative sites should occur along the edge. In
water, therefore, either the Si-O or Al-O bonds tend to hydrolyze
in the formation of weak acid (Si-OH) to form Si-O bonds.
Because of the weakness of Si-OH, the hydroxyl tends to ionize
the Si-OH to $SiO^- + H^+$ This concept is most plausible under
neutral and alkaline conditions. It also explains why the exchange
capacity increases with increase in pH. Under acid conditions,
the metal to oxygen bond would tend to adsorb a hydrogen ion
and neutralize the site. In acid solution, the surface may become
positive through adsorbed hydrogen or other cations along with
the exposed cationic sites created from breaking of bonds. The
broken bond concept, however, cannot explain negative charges
in acid solution.

The most recent proposal, especially for kaolinite, is a
mechanism creating negative charges from lattice defects.
Investigators proposing this mechanism believe that an interlayer between the tetrahedral and octahedral layers (Si and Al)
is possible because of similarity in thicknesses of these layers
(10, 11). It is indicated that, if lattice defects (holes in the
lattice) were attributed to a deficit of 0.15% from Al atoms,
then a negative charge could arise. An alternative approach
suggests that, to explain the charge deficit, Al might be in a

tetrahedral coordination with oxygen rather than an octahedral coordination. It is suggested further that certain defects may be eliminated as a result of internal compensation within the lattice. If this becomes a requirement, then a significantly larger number of lattice defects must be available. Although the lattice defect theory would not be detectable by conventional X-ray techniques, this concept is not unreasonable and may pick up additional support in the future.

Surface Area, Charge Density, and Exchange Capacity
    These three parameters should be related somewhat. As surface area increases, the total charge density and exchange capacity should likewise increase. The theoretical surface area of a kaolinite plate (two faces) can be calculated from a knowledge of its unit-cell weight, Avogadro's number (the number of unit-cells in the unit-cell weight), and the surface area of a unit-cell (its crystallographic a and b dimensions). The unit-cell weight of ideal kaolinite, $Al_4 Si_4 O_{10} (OH)_8$, is 516.12 g. Hence, the surface area/g amounts to:

$$1/516 \times 6.02 \times 10^{23} \times 2 \times 2.15 \times 8.95 = 1071 \ m^2/g$$

The values for a 5.15 A^O and b = 8.95 A^O were taken from Brown (12). This calculation is based upon the one given for montmorillonite in the Na form in which a value of 750 m^2/g was obtained (13). It is significant to point out that the surface area usually measured for kaolinite by the BET method ranges from 10 to 20 m^2/g. Obviously, on a practical basis, only a small amount of its surface area is available which is limited probably by the granularity of the kaolinite. If it is desired to calculate the surface area for kaolinite available per mono-valent cation, a value of 15 m^2/g (an average value for kaolinite) can be employed. A value of 0.10 meq/g is assumed for the exchange capacity. Therefore:

$$\frac{15 \ m^2/g \times 10^{20} \ A^{o2}/m^2}{0.1 \times 6.02 \times 10^{20}} = 25 \ A^{o2}/ion$$

The same calculation for montmorillonite yields 136 A^{o2}/ion. These values represent the surface area available per monovalent ion for 1 g of clay. Thus, the ratio of the amount of area available on montmorillonite to kaolinite is about 5.4. This is a reasonable value since montmorillonite has an exchange capacity from 6 to 10 times that of kaolinite.

The surface charge density on monovalent kaolinite can be computed for a sq cm of surface area:

$$10^{16} \ A^{o2}/cm^2 \text{ x 1 electron}/25 \ A^{o2} \text{ x } 4.8 \text{ x } 10^{-10}$$

$$esu/electron = 1.92 \text{ x } 10^5 \ esu/cm^2$$

For a monovalent montmorillonite, the value is $3.5 \text{ x } 10^4 \ esu/cm^2$. Thus a monovalent ion has less freedom to move on a kaolinite surface because of the higher charge density on kaolinite as compared to montmorillonite. In theory, a monovalent ion should be held more tenaciously on kaolinite than montmorillonite. Recent studies indicate that the surface charge density on kaolinite of a dilute solution for a NaCl-phosphate buffer system ranges from 4,000 to 6,000 esu/cm^2 (14). The agreement between theory and experiment is not exact since deviations of approximately an order of magnitude are possible from the above data for kaolinite. Although the intensity of charge densities is similar, the larger surface area of montmorillonite would effect a larger total surface charge density. Thus, the relationship between surface area, exchange capacity, and surface charge density is predictable.

Based upon previous work, the surface area and exchange capacity are dependent upon the ionic character of the clay surface and its previous history. Table I shows values obtained experimentally but strict extrapolations based upon the data should be made only from a specific clay under consideration. Although these data are in proper orders of magnitude, values found in various soils and sediments would probably show deviations, that can best be explained from impurities on clay surfaces and because natural materials contain mechanical mixtures of clay minerals.

ADSORPTION

Adsorption phenomena are most readily explicable on the basis of inequities or unbalanced forces at an interface. This interface may arise among solids, liquids, or gases. In nature, clay minerals might form interfaces with either liquids or gases. For the purpose of this discussion, only the solid-liquid interface (clay mineral-liquid interface) is considered.

In the case of liquids, adsorption at the liquid-air interface is the usual example characterized by the physico-chemical property of surface tension. Surface tension of a liquid is a

TABLE I   SURFACE AREA AND EXCHANGE CAPACITY
OF SELECTED CLAY MINERALS

Mineral	Literature Cited	Surface Area m^2/g (a)	Cation Exchange Capacity meq/100 g
Georgia Kaolin	15	10 - 25	2 - 4
Natural Kaolinite	16	11	-
Kaolinite	17	20	3.5
Kaolinite	1	-	3 - 15
Fithian Illite	16	100	-
Fithian Illite	17	78	25
Illite	1	-	10 - 40
Illite	18	80 - 7	-
Montmorillonite	19	102	100
Wyoming Bentonite	19	38	101
Montmorillonite	17	109	99
Montmorillonite	1	-	80 - 150

(a) Based upon BET measurements using nitrogen.

property which enables a surface to assume a minimum area
that is caused by molecular cohesive forces. Surface molecular
forces tend to be attracted inward to the bulk of a liquid at a
greater rate than their escaping tendency at the surface. This
effect produces unbalanced forces at the interface in the form
of a contracted surface with a minimum surface area or minimum surface free energy. Thus, surface tension of a liquid
medium can be lowered through the adsorption of a surface-
active agent at the interface. The solute prefers to get out of
water and tends to migrate to the liquid-air surface to effect
an imbalance of solute concentration. The higher concentration
of solute at the surface than the bulk solution creates unbalanced
forces which are reflected by a lowering of surface tension.

Similar reasoning can be applied to the clay mineral-water
interface. Some solids contain essentially balanced forces
within themselves either as a result of primary valence bonds
and weaker (secondary van der Waals) forces. At the surface
of solids, however, forces are unbalanced and must be compensated. As indicated with clay minerals, unbalanced forces at

the surface may arise as a result of broken bonds at the surface, from lattice defects, or from isomorphous substitution within the lattice. These unbalanced surface forces may be satisfied by adsorption. Sorption is a term often employed to described the adsorption process which may consist of either weak or strong attractive forces. Physical adsorption is considered in terms of weak van der Waals forces that are associated with the condensation of liquids and contain low heat of adsorption values, usually not in excess of 10 kcal/mole.

In contrast to physical adsorption, some compounds may be adsorbed at relatively high heats of adsorption, considerably greater than 10 kcal/mole. This type of adsorption is referred to as chemical adsorption or chemisorption. These two types can be differentiated usually on the basis of a bond formed between the adsorbent and adsorbate. Chemisorption forms strong bonds in contrast to the weak bonds of physical adsorption. In certain types of reactions involving the formation of a clay-organic complex, the nature of the bond might become so intense that desorption is not possible; this type of adsorption is irreversible.

Adsorption depends, among other factors, on the strength of the surface energy of the solid. Total surface energy depends upon the product of the surface energy per unit area of the solid and the total surface area of the solid. Adsorption is most effective at high values of total surface energy. Therefore, clays serve as good sorbents in contrast to other minerals as a result of their large surface area per unit weight.

Electrical Double-Layer Concept

As indicated previously, the net charge on a clay mineral is negative. It was indicated also that along the edges of particles, sites of both negative and positive charges might exist. According to one theory it is suggested that edges, are essentially positive (6). If a net positive charge does occur at the edge, such an occurrence would be most probable under acid conditions. The positive edge could explain the relatively small exchange capacity of anions (of the order of 0.03 to 0.05 meq/g). The double layer concept will be developed from the viewpoint of a net negative charge along the plane surface of a clay particle.

When a clay particle is in a dilute solution of water, the charge density developed at the clay particle-water interface depends upon the solution environment. The first theory was given by Helmholtz in 1879 who postulated that a charged particle

behaved as a simple condenser in solution. The charge on the
mineral surface formed either the positive or negative portion
whereas the opposite charges (counter ions) in solution comprised
the other portion. Obviously, this model was over-simplified
and was improved later by Gouy (20, 21) and Chapman (22). In
this theory (Figure 4) the electrical potential, θ, developed at
the solid-liquid interface depends upon counter ions (opposite
in sign to the particle surface charge) near the surface and
also on those ions in the diffuse layer some distance X from
the surface. The diffuse double layer consists of a higher concentration of counter ions near the particle surface and both
lesser amounts of counter ions and ions of identical particle
charge at distances farther removed from the surface. As
indicated in Figure 4, the potential decreases with distance
from the surface. In this theory, as $X \longrightarrow \infty$, $\theta \longrightarrow 0$. At
$X = \infty$, the diffuse layer does not exist. The thickness of the
double layer decreases as the concentration of counter ions
and charge on the counter ions is increased. From a practical
approach, a clay particle immersed in a solution containing
both ions of similar (-) and of opposite (+) charge, the (+) ions
would tend to adsorb near the surface at which point θ is a
maximum and the (-) ions would be found in the diffuse layer
at lower values of θ. On the basis of this model, cations
would tend to be adsorbed at the clay surface and anions repelled.
If positive sites become available along the clay surface, however,
the reverse would occur. The Gouy model has certain limitations
since it considers the counter ions as point charges which, therefore, fails to take into consideration the effect of ionic size. The
theory also fails to consider specific reactions between the particle surface and the solution. Later theories are beyond the
scope of this paper.
   A knowledge of the structure and changes occurring in the
double layer is important because this is the area where adsorption and/or ion exchange take place. The double layer theory
is a very elegant approach to describe a redistribution of ions
between the bulk solution and those surrounding a charged
particle, especially in dilute solution. The exchange of Na for
Ca on a clay can be represented:

$$CaX + 2\ Na^+ \rightleftharpoons 2\ NaX + Ca^{+2} \tag{6-1}$$

where X is the exchange site. For this type of exchange,
Eriksson has shown that the amount of Na^+ ions with respect to

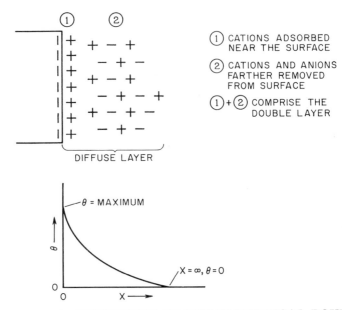

FIGURE 4   STRUCTURE OF THE ELECTRICAL DOUBLE
LAYER AROUND A CLAY PARTICLE BASED
UPON GOUY THEORY.

the total number of ions in the double layer, R, can be
expressed by (25):

$$R = \frac{[Na^+]}{[Na^+ + Ca^{+2}]} = \frac{Na^+}{2\,Z^{\frac{1}{2}}(Ca^{+2})^{\frac{1}{2}}}\, \sinh^{-1}\frac{2\,Z^{\frac{1}{2}}(Ca^{+2})^{\frac{1}{2}}}{(Na^+) + (Ca^{+2})}\,\mu \qquad (6\text{-}2)$$

where Z and μ are functions of surface charge density and surface potential between charged plates, respectively. Brackets
refer to equivalents of exchangeable ions and parentheses are
ionic concentrations in the bulk solution.

Mass Action Principle

For a system at equilibrium, the same number of ions
enter (adsorbed) the double layer as compared to the same
amount leaving (desorbed). Ion exchange is basically the same
concept except that the equilibrium is altered during exchange
either by addition or removal of ions from the double layer.

Although the law of mass action has been employed to describe ion exchange reactions, it is somewhat fictional. Actually reactants do not form products in the conventional chemical notion in ion exchange. The mass action law is employed merely to explain the transfer of ions between the diffuse double layer around a clay particle and the bulk solution. For exchange between ions of the same valence (homovalent), the reaction of K^+ replacing Na^+ is:

$$NaX + K^+ \rightleftharpoons KX + Na^+ \qquad (6\text{-}3)$$

for the expression which is:

$$K_{Na, K} = \frac{[K^+]_E \ (Na^+)_S}{[Na^+]_E \ (K^+)_S} \qquad (6\text{-}4)$$

Brackets refer to concentration (eq per weight) and parentheses are ionic activities. Some investigators employ ionic concentrations and not activities for practical considerations. This is not absolutely correct. E is the exchanger phase and S the solution phase.

For heterovalent exchange (e.g., exchange of Ca^{+2} for Na^+) by the reaction:

$$2 NaX + Ca^{+2} \rightleftharpoons CaX + 2 Na^+ \qquad (6\text{-}5)$$

for which the expression is:

$$K_{Na, Ca} = \frac{[Ca^{+2}]_E \ (Na^+)_S^2}{[Na^+]_E^2 \ (Ca^{+2})_S} \qquad (6\text{-}6)$$

K, for any ion exchange reaction, is dependent upon the mole fractions of the constituent ions involved in the exchange. Different investigators have suggested other versions of the mass action relationship (26, 27) whereas still other prefer to employ kinetic considerations (28, 29).

Donnan Equilibrium

Many investigators employ the Donnan concept in ion exchange studies, because it has some very desirable properties. It can be distinguished from the Gouy double layer theory because a knowledge of the structure of the particle is not required. It is also possible to describe the behavior of both anions and cations with this concept. With a clay-electrolyte system, the Donnan equilibrium (at constant temperature and pressure) involves the adsorption or exchange of counter ions on the clay surface, at which the concentration of counter ions is greater than at distances removed from the surface. In effect, there is an unequal distribution of ions within the clay-electrolyte that contains cations and anions, the Donnan equilibrium is expressed in terms of an ion product equation. For any electrolyte, $R_A M_B$, the Donnan equilibrium is expressed:

$$(R)_E^A \cdot (M)_E^B = (R)_S^A \cdot (M)_S^B \tag{6-7}$$

or by rearrangement:

$$\left[\frac{(R)_E}{(R)_S} \right]^{1/A} = \left[\frac{(M)_S}{(M)_E} \right]^{1/B} \tag{6-8}$$

Thus, if $\overset{+}{Na}$ was to replace Ca^{+2} on a clay, the relation would be:

$$\frac{(\overset{+}{Na})_E}{(\overset{+}{Na})_S} = \frac{(Ca^{+2})_E^{\frac{1}{2}}}{(Ca^{+2})_S^{\frac{1}{2}}} \tag{6-9}$$

or:

$$K_{Ca,\,Na} = \frac{(\overset{+}{Na})_E^2 \;\; (Ca^{+2})_S}{(\overset{+}{Na})_S^2 \;\; (Ca^{+2})_E} \tag{6-10}$$

where the ions in parentheses represent activities.

If activities are replaced by the products of the concentrations and activity coefficients, then equation 6-10 becomes:

$$K_{Ca,\,Na} = \frac{\left[\overset{+}{Na} \right]_E^2 \cdot \gamma^2 \, \overset{+}{Na}_E \cdot \left[Ca^{+2} \right]_S \cdot \gamma_{Ca}^{+2}{}_S}{\left[\overset{+}{Na} \right]_S^2 \cdot \gamma^2 \, \overset{+}{Na}_S \cdot \left[Ca^{+2} \right]_E \cdot \gamma_{Ca}^{+2}{}_E} \tag{6-11}$$

This equation, however, is oversimplified and suffers from thermodynamic unsoundness because of the inability to determine a value for the activity coefficient, γ_E, in the exchanger phase. If this equation was employed and a value of $K > 1$ obtained, $\overset{+}{Na}$ would be strongly adsorbed than Ca^{+2} and would easily replace Ca^{+2}; if $K = 1$, both ions are adsorbed with equal strength; if

K<1, then $\overset{+}{Na}$ would have difficulty in replacing Ca^{+2}. Similar relationships for anions could be used through the considerations developed from equations 6-8 through 6-11 providing the necessary conditions are satisfied.

Activity of the Solid Phase

The above formulae have been employed with the tacit assumption that the activity of the solid phase (clay exchange site) is unity. Previous studies suggest that this concept should be questioned. In certain studies on reactions of feldspar surfaces, it was suggested that K-feldspar behaves like a dissolved molecular species similar to dissolved ions (30). Under these conditions, the solid displays an apparent activity and its concentration would involve a function of its surface area ranging from low values (low surface area) to high values (high surface area). The regular solution theory has been employed also to signify the importance of the solid phase (31). If monovalent ions were exchanged on a hydrogen-clay, the equilibrium constant $K_{H,M}$ can be expressed:

$$K_{H,M} = \frac{\left[\overset{+}{H}\right](MX)}{\left[\overset{+}{M}\right](HX)} \exp\left\{\frac{W_{HM}}{RT}(1 - 2N_{HX})\right\} \qquad (6\text{-}12)$$

Brackets represent aqueous ion activities and parentheses concentrations in the binary solid-solution on the clay. W_{HM} is a constant for a specific clay and specific type of exchange. N_{HX} is the mole fraction of H-clay remaining at any stage of exchange. The equilibrium constants may vary from 2 to 4 orders of magnitude if regular solution theory is considered in comparison to unit activity.

Another problem indirectly involving the solid phase is the nature of the exchange site. Truesdell has presented an interesting model with respect to divalent selectivity on the clay surface (32). In this model, it is assumed that -1 sites may be crowded together more closely from sites separated by 20 A^O to those separated by only 5 A^O. For -1 sites separated at less than 5 A^O, divalent cations were adsorbed 10^{10} times greater than monovalent cations. The distinction, however, is made that divalent cations are preferred at -1 sites and not at -2 sites (pairs of -1 sites).

The solid phase (exchange site), therefore, would seem to deserve more attention than it has been given previously.

Negative Adsorption

If an ionic salt is placed in contact with a dry clay, there seems to be an apparent increase in concentration of the anion in solution. This effect was explained previously by assumption that a thin water layer formed on clays decreased the water volume or increased the salt concentration. This model has no physical interpretation. It is believed now that negative adsorption (increase in anions in solution) can be explained from either the Donnan equilibrium or the Gouy theory. In either theory, the anions are repelled, producing an unequal distribution in the diffuse double layer. Negative adsorption can be overcome through charge reversal by lowering the pH, by phosphate addition, etc.

Factors Influencing Adsorption

The probability that adsorption or ion exchange may occur is influenced by a number of variables. Properties of the adsorbing ion are no doubt most important. Those ions which tend to have the same hydrated ionic radii as a hole in the hexagonal cavities of the oxygen layer would tend to be replaced by ion exchange with difficulty. K^+, NH_4^+, and H_3O^+ have almost ideal properties with respect to fitting into ion holes in the clay lattice and for this reason are adsorbed strongly. There seems to be a gross difference of opinion with respect to the hydrated ionic radii and its influence on adsorption. Some investigators attribute ease of adsorption and difficulty of replacement to those ions showing the lowest degree of hydration (33). This concept explains why Li^+ has a small tendency to replace other cations on clays. Other investigators, however, believe that Na^+, H^+, K^+, and the trivalent ions, are not hydrated in clay-water systems (34). This concept would tend to contradict that requiring hydration as a control. The actual effect of ionic size cannot be separated from its charge regardless of hydration. It seems probable that ions which can be adsorbed most readily depend upon the charge size ratio. Maximum adsorption should occur at high charge and small ionic size, i.e., when this ratio is large. In dilute solution, it is generally observed that ionic replacement follows the series monovalent < divalent < trivalent. This series is supported by the Schulze-Hardy rule which indicated that flocculation values and, therefore, adsorption occurs most readily in the ratio M^{+3}: M^{+2} $M^{+3}:M^{+2}:M^+$ as 1000: 100:1. Thus, it takes only 0.001 the concentration of a trivalent in comparison to a monovalent ion to effect flocculation.

The conventional lyotropic or Hofmeister series often is quoted to show relative replacing power for negative surfaces:

$$\text{Li} < \text{Na} < \text{K} < \text{NH}_4 < \text{Rb} < \text{Cs} < \text{H} < \text{Mg} < \text{Ca} < \text{Sr} < \text{Ca}$$

and for positive surfaces:

$$\text{CNS} < \text{I} < \text{NO}_3 < \text{Br} < \text{Cl}$$

Hydrogen tends to function as a divalent or trivalent cation. This effect is explained most readily on the basis that a hydrogen clay is unstable and degrades into a H-Al clay (38). The Al-chemistry in clay-water systems is a subject in itself and is beyond the scope of this paper. If Al becomes hydrated on a clay surface, it can sterically hinder (occlude) some sites from adsorption.

If the mass action law is assumed and activities are employed, adsorption should increase as ionic activity increases for any specified ionic salt in solution.

Impurities on clay surfaces are the rule and not the exception. Thus, the peculiar adsorption of a clay would depend somewhat upon the type and amount of impurities. Two of the most common impurities on clays are hydrated iron and hydrated alumina. These hydrated species are significant because of the influence on surface charge. If $\overset{+}{\text{H}}$ or $\overset{-}{\text{OH}}$ ions are potential determining, then those sites on the clay surface containing such compounds may become amphoteric with the acidic or basic nature of the site being pH dependent. Recent work has shown that the charge on hydrated iron depends upon charge transfer of complex species such as Fe(OH)_2 and FeO_2^- (35). Both species are pH dependent. The pH at which hydrated iron reverses its charge from (+) to (-) is 8.5 (35) or 6.7 (36). The situation for hydrated alumina is much more complex. The nature of the surface complex of hydrated alumina depends on pH.

The point at which hydrated alumina reverses its charge (Zero Point of Charge, ZPC) is not known accurately. Van Schuylenborgh and Saüger give values for the ZPC of hydrated alumina that range from 2.2 to 5.6 (37). Little significance can be attached to these values because a definite knowledge of the Al-surface complex is required to predict the nature of the charge. It seems apparent, however, that some form of hydrated alumina on a clay surface is charged positively somewhat below a pH value of 5. At this point, it is also of interest to indicate the pH at which the surface charge of kaolinite becomes reversed. It is assumed that if such a charge reversal may occur, it is associated with the net negative effect on the faces and any negative character associated along the edge. The true zero point of charge of kaolinite has not been determined as yet.

Perhaps the greatest difficulty in the determination of the ZPC is the instability of the kaolinite surface. It has been suggested that the ZPC of kaolinite lies below a pH of 4 (10). Values of the ZPC of kaolinite and bentonite have been reported at pH values of 3.4 and $<$ 3, respectively (39). With respect to the difficulty in determining the ZPC of kaolinite, Wayman and Robertson have shown that the surface is unstable (40). Figure 5 shows that a Na-clay essentially is flocculated in the pH range 2.0 to 4.0. There are, however, apparent inconsistencies with the surface as reflected by a series of dispersion-flocculation maneuvers. At low pH values (2 to 4), the Na-clay (Figure 5) probably has degraded into a H-Al clay. Figure 6 shows that Al at low pH is removed continuously from the kaolinite surface with time. In this particular experiment, Na-kaolinite was equilibrated with distilled water at pH of 2; aluminon method was employed to determine Al in these determinations (41). Because of this continuous change in the kaolinite surface at low pH and the subsequent reaction of Al, determination of the true ZPC is questionable.

Aluminum can react with water, most likely through some combination with the hydronium ion (H_3^+O), to form a range of Al-hydrolysate polymers. Figure 7 shows a series of possible hydrolysate polymers with Al in a 6-fold coordination. This series indicates that the low pH form is a hydrated trivalent Al ion. With subsequent deprotonation (loss of H^+) the structure may change to the aluminate ion in alkaline solution. The stability of any species is pH dependent. It is uncertain which specific form is stable at a specified pH. Matijevic, et al, suggest that the hydrated trivalent species is most probable species shown at pH 4 (42). Between pH 4 and 7, hydrolysis of a tetravalent species is suggested. With respect to hydrolysis of Al on clay surfaces, an excellent analysis is given by Frink whose research supports the view that the hydrated trivalent species is most likely in acid solution (43). For additional considerations on Al hydrolysis, other recent research can be examined (44, 45). The effects of impurities and pH manifest a profound influence on the nature of clay surfaces. In acid

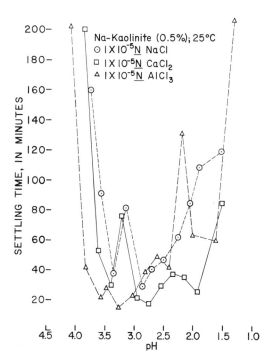

FIGURE 5   FLOCCULATION CHARACTERISTICS OF
            Na-KAOLINITE AT VARIOUS VALUES OF pH.

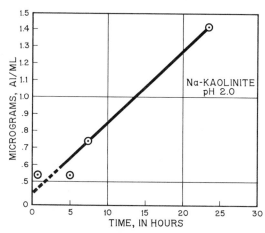

FIGURE 6   DISSOLUTION OF ALUMINUM FROM
            Na-KAOLINITE AT pH 2.0.

solution, impurities on Fe and Al compounds are charged positively. In addition, kaolinite probably is charged positively in acid solution as a result of the formation of some form of hydrated aluminum on the clay surface. Although the specific pH value for charge reversal on kaolinite is not known exactly, evidence seems to show that kaolinite presents some positive character and should be a better anionic than cationic adsorber at low values of pH.

The polarity of the adsorbate also may exert some influence on adsorption. Many nonionic and organic molecules behave as dipoles with centers of positive and negative charges. Water is a most important polar molecule and for this reason is adsorbed readily by clays. With respect to montmorillonite, water can be replaced by polar organic compounds (46, 47). This replacement probably depends upon the differences in dipole moments between water and the replacing substances and also upon the nature of the complex formed on the clay surface. The following contain some types of polar groups which might be adsorbed on clay surfaces: -OH, -COOH, -CHO, -CN, -CONH$_2$, -NH$_2$, -NHCN$_3$, -SH, -NCS, -COR, -COOM, -COOR, -NO$_2$, -CH = CH$_2$, -C ≡ CH.

There are, no doubt, many other factors that may influence adsorption on clay surfaces, but a more definitive treatment is not within the scope of this paper.

Empirical Relationships

Scientists usually prefer to fit experimental data to curves that may be explained adequately. This consideration has not been overlooked with adsorption on clays. The Freundlich and Langmuir isotherms seem to be the conventional methods of plotting adsorption data. Both isotherms were developed originally for gas reactions on solid surfaces. Later modifications and usage indicate that these isotherms adequately describe adsorption or exchange of ions in solution on clay surfaces. The Freundlich equation is expressed:

$$x/m = k \, p^{1/n} \tag{6-13}$$

x/m is the amount (μg, mg) of ion adsorbed at equilibrium per g of clay, p is the amount of ion remaining in solution at equilibrium, and k and n are constants. If the log x/m is plotted against log p, a straight line is obtained with a slope of 1/n and an intercept on the ordinate of log k at log p = 0, i.e., p = 1.

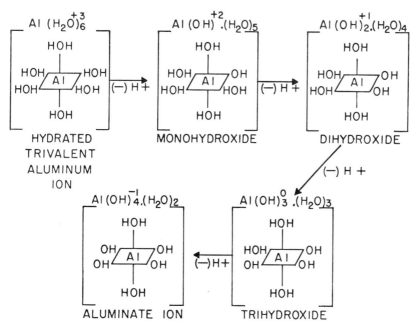

FIGURE 7   POSSIBLE FORMS OF Al-HYDROLYSATE
POLYMERS WITH DEPROTONATION.

Equation 6-13 is parabolic in form and for this reason cannot
be used to predict the ultimate adsorption (adsorption maximum).
The equation, however, can be employed with success at concentrations not exceeding one another by one to two orders of
magnitude.

The Langmuir equation can be expressed (48):

$$\frac{y}{p} = \frac{a}{1 + bp} \tag{6-14}$$

or by rearrangement:

$$p/y = \frac{1}{a} + \frac{b}{a} \, p \tag{6-15}$$

Thus, a plot of p/y against p yields a straight line. In this
equation, p is the equilibrium ionic concentration, y is the
amount of ion adsorbed per unit weight, and a and b are constants. Because of the hyperbolic nature of equation 6-15, it

can be used to express ultimate adsorption at any concentration.
Hence, this equation might be preferred over the Freundlich.
The Langmuir isotherm is based upon a monomolecular layer
of coverage. For adsorption at several monolayers of coverage
(multilayer adsorption), an equation of the Brunauer, Emmett,
and Teller (BET) type would be preferred. Although equation
6-15 quantifies adsorption more completely and gives some
measure of the type of molecular adsorption, many investigators
seem to prefer equation 6-13.

SPECIFIC TYPES OF ADSORPTION

Adsorption of inorganic ions on clays has been considered
in the previous sections and will not be considered here. Except
when forming inorganic ionic complexes ($CuOH^+$, $CuCl^+$, $ZnOH^+$,
etc.), adsorption of small inorganic ions can be predicted from
the lyotropic series for cations and, in some cases, anions.
If inorganic complex ions form in solution and adsorb on the clay
surface, the surface charge may be reversed (- to +).

Water

It has been known for some time that clays sorb various
amounts of water which has a natural tendency to condense on
clay surfaces because of the water dipole and also of the large
surface area of clays and their peculiar structure, especially
montmorillonite. Figure 8 gives some indication of the variation
of water uptake as a function of the partial pressure of water
vapor (49). These data suggest that desorption is essentially
complete with kaolinite and less complete with illite and montmorillonite. The most extreme situation is shown by montmorillonite. It can be deduced that water is adsorbed by weak bonding forces on kaolinite and becomes more strongly bonded in
montmorillonite. The essential difference is the character of
the bond that probably results from the interlayer bonding in
montmorillonite and not in the other two clays. Therefore,
hysteresis is lacking on kaolinite. Careful studies on water
vapor sorption of kaolinite suggest that water is not desorbed
completely and the particular amount of hysteresis depends on
the homoionic character of the clay and the previous history of
the clay surface (the degree of hydration) (50). It is proposed
that the manner in which water vapor is adsorbed should be
expressed as an energy difference: U-A, where U is the hydration energy and A is specific adsorption. The difference, U-A,
is a function of the partial vapor pressure of water. If the

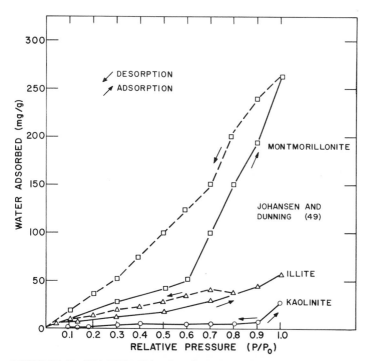

FIGURE 8   WATER VAPOR ADSORPTION AND
DESORPTION ON VARIOUS CLAYS.

difference is less than zero, it is assumed that water is retained
only by weak van der Waals forces and no hysteresis occurs.
If the difference becomes positive, then specific adsorption
occurs and hysteresis develops. Hysteresis would occur most
likely for ions that become strongly hydrated.

The nature of the adsorbed water film on clays is understood incompletely. Available data indicate that on Na-mont-
morillonite, the density of water rapidly increases above that
of liquid water for water contents less than 0.5 g water/g clay
(51). The density is less than that of liquid water in the range
0.5 to 6.5 g water/g clay. Beyond this sorption, the adsorbed
water has characteristics similar to liquid water. Current
concepts attribute the nature of adsorbed water to either a
solid-like substance or to a two-dimensional liquid. In a recent
paper, it is shown on the basis of entropy, that the thermodynamic
nature of water on Li-kaolinite exceeds that of liquid water only

during the initial stage of adsorption (52). At less than a
monolayer of coverage, the entropy becomes less than that of
liquid water. The change is attributed to dissolution of Li^+
ions in the liquid film. Thus, the character of a water film
no doubt depends, as indicated, on many variables.

In general, water may be sorbed from less than a monolayer to ten or more monolayers. The particular amount of
adsorption would be dependent upon the activity of water and
type of clay. Because of the high water uptake by montmorillonite
in the interlayer space, lattice expansions up to 70 A^O are not
uncommon (53). If the concentration of an electrolyte is
increased, an interlayer spacing of as much as 120 A^O has been
observed (53).

The remainder of this paper will be concerned with specific
applications of adsorption on clays. Although other considerations will be indicated, specific applications will refer to organic
molecular adsorption and water pollution.

Surfactants

The adsorption of surfactants (surface-active agents) on
clays deserves attention due to two specific considerations.
Clays may act as adsorbents for the removal of surfactants in
wastewater which infiltrate the subsurface soil and also as an
adsorbent for transport as a suspended sediment in surface
waters. Surfactants also have another application with respect
to waterproofing that is concerned with the artificial alteration
of natural material from a hydrophilic (water-attracting) to a
hydrophobic (water-repelling) type of surface. Through the
agency of a hydrophobic surface, surfactants may increase the
rate of infiltration of water through soil or prevent water from
entering soil with each case dependent upon permeability.

A considerable amount of research has been reported on
the adsorption of ABS (alkylbenzenesulfonate), the most important surfactant in detergents, on clay minerals (17, 54-56). In
these studies, clay minerals were equilibrated under various
conditions with radio-tagged (S^{35}) ABS. The clay mineral was
heteroionic; the type which would be expected under natural
conditions. Figure 9 shows that chain length influences the
amount of ABS removed by clays. At pH 4, the C_{15} alkyl chain
ABS is removed to a greater extent than the C_{12} ABS. It is
significant to indicate that the amount of anions like ABS
retained on clays is low. For the conditions specified, the
three clays seem to have similar adsorption capacities. At

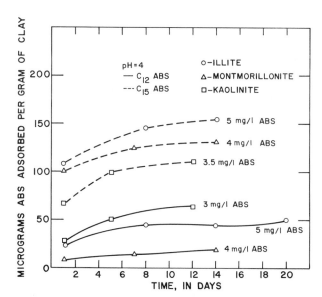

FIGURE 9   ADSORPTION OF ABS ON VARIOUS CLAYS
WITH VARIABLE CHAIN LENGTH .

pH 4, the adsorption capacity is a maximum; as pH is increased,
all the clays showed lower adsorption capacity. Figure 10 shows
a Freundlich isotherm for clays and other natural minerals.
These data indicate that adsorption increases with ABS concentration. The results for illite and montmorillonite do not fit this
type of isotherm as well as kaolinite. This uncertainty may be
attributed to the differences in structure of the three clays or
to the inability to fit certain mineral to the Freundlich isotherm.
Natural materials have very low adsorption capacity for ABS.
For the range of concentration (1 to 10 mg/l) to be anticipated
in natural or wastewater, the adsorption capacity ranges from
25 to 2000 mg/g. For similar conditions, activated charcoal
and colloidal alumina (activated) show adsorption capacities
of synthetic materials in comparison to natural clays is no doubt
a function of the larger surface areas of synthetics and also as
reflected by their peculiar internal structure.

Another application of surfactant sorption on clays has
been shown for the adsorption of 4-tert-butylpyrocatechol (TBC)
on kaolinite and montmorillonite (57). TBC (probably a nonionic
substance) can alter the surface properties of clays from

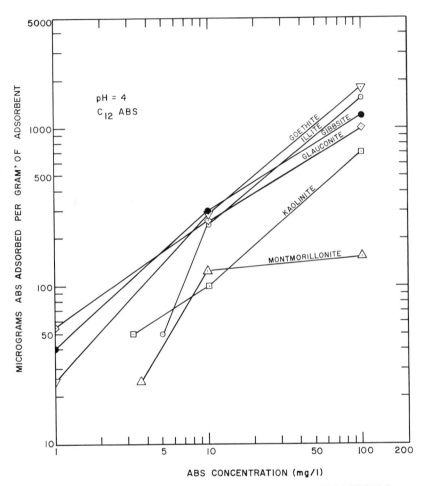

FIGURE 10   FREUNDLICH ADSORPTION ISOTHERM
OF ABS ON VARIOUS MINERALS.

hydrophilic to hydrophobic if applied in the concentration range
100 to 1000 mg/l.   Figure 11 shows the adsorption capacities
for TBX on various homoionic clays.   The rate of adsorption
tends to be rapid in the beginning and then becomes much
slower.   The suggested mechanism for this type of adsorption
involves the formation of a surface complex (chemical sorption)
with exchangeable Al on the clay surface.   This model may

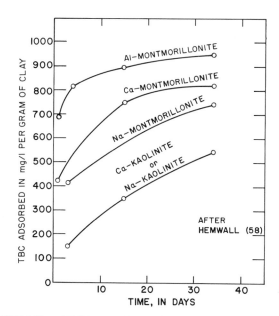

FIGURE 11   ADSORPTION OF TBC ON KAOLINITE
AND MONTMORILLONITE.

explain the much higher adsorption capacity with the Al-clay
than with other ionic forms. It is suggested also that TBC
should be adsorbed more intensely in acid solution because
Al would tend to dissolve more readily under these conditions.

Polyelectrolytes and Coagulation

Synthetic polyelectrolytes are becoming quite prominent
as coagulant aids in the flocculation of suspended solids. Long-
chain polymers have been employed for a number of coagulation
problems. LaMer, et al, studied the effects of polyelectrolytes
on flocculation of phosphate slimes (58, 59). Polymers have
been employed also to flocculate colloids in metallurgical
operations (60) and also to stabilize colloids (61). The exact
mechanism controlling the reactions between polymers and
clay surfaces is somewhat uncertain. Several possibilities
have been suggested; such as, hydrogen bonding, displacement
of water, and ionic interactions with edges of clay.

In order to determine specific effects of reactions
between polyelectrolytes and clay surfaces, a study was

undertaken on the adsorption of hydrolyzed polyacrylonitrile (HPAN) on kaolinite (62). The specific polymer employed was Na-polyacrylate labelled with C^{14} with the approximate formula:

$$\left(\begin{array}{c} -C^{14} \ H \ - \ C^{14} \ H_2- \\ | \\ COONa \end{array} \right)_X$$

where $X = 60,000$. In this particular system (clay-HPAN), many factors were found to influence adsorption. Figure 12 shows that a Langmuir type of adsorption isotherm is obeyed for a limited range of equilibrium concentrations (1 - 6 mg). The maximum amount of adsorption is 1.5 meq/100 g and 2.6 meq/100 g for Na-kaolinite and H-kaolinite, respectively. Adsorption increases in the direction of decreasing zeta potential: $Th^{+4} > Ca^{+2} > Ba^{+2} > \overset{+}{H} > \overset{+}{NH_4} > \overset{+}{K} > \overset{+}{Na}$. With respect to sorbed anions, adsorption is increased in the direction of electronegativity: $\underset{-}{F} > \underset{-}{OH} > H_2PO_4 > Cl >$ $CH_3 \ COO > NO_3$. This is a lyotropic series for correlation purposes. As expected, adsorption increases with an increase in concentration of electrolyte and also with a decrease in pH. Adsorption is decreased, however, by dissolution of Al from the lattice. Apparently this is a steric effect producing a lowering in the number of exchange sites available to HPAN. The suggested adsorption mechanism may be attributed to formation of ionic bonds between the ionized carboxylate (CH_3 COO) of HPAN and unsatisfied valence bonds of exposed lattice Al and base exchange salts on the kaolinite surface.
       Although limited data are available on polyelectrolyte-clay mineral interactions, this field seems to be very fruitful and should stimulate research efforts in wastewater treatment.

Protein-Enzyme Clay Reactions
       Because of the increase in discharge of refractory organic compounds to water systems from wastewater treatment plants, a provocative question may arise with respect to the effect of clay minerals on the biodegradation process. Biodegradation depends, among other things, on oxidation and hydrolysis reactions. If certain of the component entities on an organic molecule are blocked by sorption reactions, it seems reasonable to predict that biological decomposition should be retarded in the presence of clays. Contrariwise,

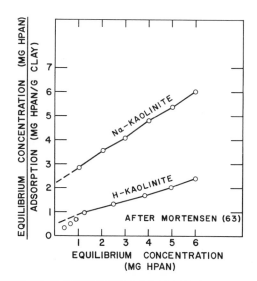

FIGURE 12   LANGMUIR ADSORPTION ISOTHERM OF
HPAN ON KAOLINITE .

adsorption sites on clay minerals may catalyze biological
degradation. Some of the earlier investigators have reached
opposing views. Waksman attributed an enhanced formation
of humus to intense biological activity in the presence of
clay (63). Mattson, however, suggested a decrease in biode-
composition of proteins in the presence of clays (64). Later workers
suggest that enzyme hydrolysis of protein surfaces depends upon
the particular clay involved (65). With kaolinite, protein hydrolysis
is not hindered sufficiently. Adsorption on montmorillonite,
especially between the interlayers, blocks hydrolysis and retards
decomposition as a result of orientation and inaccessibility of the
active groups.
    The actual mechanisms involved in biodecomposition are
no doubt complex and depend on the properties of both the clay
and the adsorbate. In a recent paper, the nature of adsorption
and complexes formed on montmorillonite by reactions with
proteins, enzymes, and antibiotics found in soils was studied (66).
    With respect to protein-montmorillonite complexes, both
the nature of the complex and the amount of protein present
influence microbial activity. Figure 13 shows that the protein-

montmorillonite complex (A) is very stable and quite resistant
to decomposition in comparison to a mixture of protein and
clay (B) and to the protein alone (C). For this particular
system, there seems to be unequivocal evidence that protein
decomposition is inhibited by complex formation with montmorillonite. Data show that the amount of protein-clay complex
decomposition increases with increase in per cent protein
(10-55%). At low concentrations of protein, it is found that the
complex is a monolayer; at higher concentrations, multilayer
complexes form. In monolayers, only about 20% of the protein
complex is decomposed. In multilayer complexes, much larger
amounts can be degraded as reflected in collapse of C-spacings
from 30A$^{\circ}$ to 12A$^{\circ}$. It is concluded that the stronger retention
of proteins in monolayers results from combined coulombic and
van der Waals forces postulated previously (67).

The complex between the enzyme (urease) and montmorillonite was compared to that of kaolinite. Montmorillonite
definitely inactivates enzymatic activity. The activity of urease
adsorbed on H-montmorillonite amounts to about one -half the
activity of urease adsorbed on H-kaolinite. With respect to
enzyme-clay complexes, an additional factor must be considered.
During breakdown of the complex, ammonia is released which
increases the pH. Because of this change in pH, coulombic
attractive forces may be lowered which weaken the bond between
the clay and the enzyme producing a desorption phenomenon.

Clay-organic complexes, therefore, may be significant
in studies related to biodegradation. The types of observations
predictable from previous work would tend to indicate that each
clay-organic complex reaction may present its own peculiar
set of conditions. Based upon limited data, it might be suggested
that organic compounds tending to sorb between montmorillonite
interlayers become resistant to decomposition. Hence, the
concept indicating that montmorillonite suppresses biodegradation seems valid. Because biodegradation will become increasingly more important, future studies should not overlook the
influence that clay minerals may contribute.
Pesticides

Because of Rachel Carson's "Silent Spring" much
enthusiasm has developed on pest control chemicals. Studies
are now under way on biodegradation of pesticides, but studies
related to the effect of clay on biodegradation do not seem to
be stressed. For a good review on the sorption of organic
pesticides on soils, the paper of Bailey and White should be

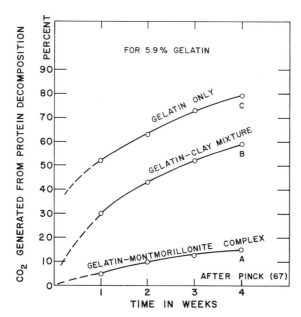

FIGURE 13 RATES OF DECOMPOSITION OF THE
PROTEIN (GELATIN) UNDER VARIOUS
CONDITIONS.

examined (68).

Most of the work to date has been concentrated on herbicides. In a recent paper, it was shown that the herbicides, Monuron ($C_9H_{11}ClN_2O$) and Diuron ($C_9H_{10}Cl_2N_2O$), are sorbed weakly by soils (69). Clays in these soils consisted of essentially kaolinite and montmorillonite. The Freundlich isotherm for Monuron ranges from 1 to 50 mg/g of soil for the concentration range 1 to 100 mg/l. Recent work by Faust and Aly suggest that clays have little tendency to adsorb 2,4-D (70). Their data show that the relative adsorption capacities of kaolinite, illite, and bentonite for the Na salt of 2,4-D are 38, 29, and 25 ug/g of clay, respectively. The adsorption of 2,4-D on clays also has been investigated by Frissel and Bolt (71). These investigators also show that adsorption of the 2,4-D anion is low. In the pH range 4-7, it is suggested that 2,4-D adsorbs on positive sites on illite, whereas this type of site was not suggested for kaolinite and montmorillonite. Based upon other studies, however, there seems to be evidence that positive sites are present on kaolinite, especially in acid solution. Enhanced adsorption below pH 4 is attributed to formation of the unionized 2, 4-D molecule at this pH.

Thus, limited data show that herbicides have little tendency to adsorb on clays. Unfortunately, a generalized statement cannot be given as a result of dearth of data available. It would seem highly desirable to obtain adsorption data on clays for the organo-phosphates and halogenated hydrocarbons.

Bacteria

In the field of wastewater treatment, the relation among bacterial activity, dissolved solids, and suspended solids is unknown. It would seem fruitful to obtain data on the adsorption characteristics of bacteria on clay surfaces. If bacteria do sorb and form complexes with clays, the numbers of bacteria available for oxidation of organic compounds might be reduced. Because bacterial cell walls are comprised of proteinaceous material, it is possible that bacterial cells could be attached to clay surfaces through the formation of protein-clay complexes. Possibly the only study with respect to bacteria-clay reactions is that of Lahav wherein it was shown that adsorption depends on pH, ionic strength, and type of electrolyte in solution (72). Since it can be inferred that bacteria are charged negatively at pH 7, there would be little chance of bacteria adsorbing on clays, other than at positive "edge" sites. At lower pH values, however, adsorption should increase because of the increased positive character of the clay. An important factor also might involve the change in the nature of bacterial surfaces with change in pH. Bacterial cell wall-clay reactions apparently have been overlooked and should give a rewarding return to future research.

ADSORPTION FORCES

Up to this point, little discussion has been given to the nature of the binding forces between clay surface and the adsorbate. The strength of a bond essentially is determined by the surface charge density, but the nature of the substance to be adsorbed also contributes to the overall force. From available data, the surface charge density of some clay minerals are very similar; kaolinite 2. 0 . ( ), illite 1. 7 . ($_2$), and montmorillonite 1. 4 . ( ), where ( ) is 10^3 meq/m^2 (73). Thus, for a given ion involving only physical attraction, the bonds

are similar, but increase in strength in the direction kaolinite
$>$ illite $>$ montmorillonite. For physical adsorption, the
combined effects of both coulombic attraction and van der Waals
molecular interactions would be involved. With the double
layer theory, both forces would be involved. With the double
layer theory, both forces would be operative in the vicinity
where counter ions are attracted most strongly (that is, where
θ is a maximum) At distances farther removed from the
surface, where θ becomes reduced, the attractive forces are
a lesser intensity. These considerations would apply to all
clay minerals, but additional forces are involved for adsorption
at the interlayer spaces in montmorillonite.

The conventional view regarding forces between the
adsorbate and montmorillonite has relied heavily upon van der
Waals interaction distances. The unexpanded lattice distance
of montmorillonite is considered to amount to the distance
between oxygen ion planes ($6.6A^{\circ}$) plus the van der Waals
interaction of oxygen ($2 \times 1.4A^{\circ}$). This convention gives an
unexpanded lattice of montmorillonite equivalent to $9.4A^{\circ}$. To
predict the interlayer interaction, the measured expanded
lattice after complex formation with montmorillonite was
determined from which the unexpanded value was substracted.
With a knowledge of the van der Waals radii of the saturating
molecule, it was possible to calculate the number of monolayers
formed between the interlayers. Although the model for van
der Waals bonding forces may be correct, actual measurements
show that the C-spacing is lower by about 0.4 to $1.0A^{\circ}$ as
compared to calculations based upon van der Waals radii.
This model presumably would explain physical adsorption, but
some compounds probably adsorb with the formation of a
chemical bond. If this occurs, then adsorption would be intense
and the adsorbed entity would probably be difficult to replace.
Physical adsorptive forces explain why water can readily be
replaced by stronger and more polar substances in the interlayer.

There are other considerations with respect to montmorillonite complexes also, but the interested reader can refer to
a recent review (74).

SUMMARY

Adsorption on clay minerals is an involved subject. It is
important because clays may play a role in either holding
potential contaminants from entering underground water (by
soil-water reactions) and also by acting as vehicles for the
transport of contaminants in open water courses (surface water).

This paper surveys some of the available literature. An attempt was made to describe some of the properties of clays to account for their sorptive properties and to give actual examples of adsorption of various solutes on clays. The field of wastewater chemistry has been emphasized.

ACKNOWLEDGEMENT
Dr. Cooper H. Wayman was a Research Chemist with the U.S. Geological Survey, Denver, Colorado when this manuscript was prepared. Publication, therefore, was authorized by Director, U.S. Geological Survey, Washington, D.C

LITERATURE CITED
1. Grim, R.E., Clay Mineralogy, McGraw Hill Book Co., New York, N.Y. (1953).

2. Thiessen, P.A., Elektrochem, 48, 675 (1942).

3. Michaels, A.L., Ind Eng Chem, 50, 6 (1948).

4. Schofield, R.K. and H.R. Samson, Clay Minerals Bull, 2, 9 (1953).

5. Schofield, R.K. and H.R. Samson, Discussions Faraday Soc, 18, 135 (1954).

6. van Olphen, H., J Colloid Sci, 19, 313 (1964).

7. van Olphen, H., Rec Trav Chim, 69, 1308, 1313 (1950).

8. Marshall, C.E., Colloid Chemistry of the Silicate Minerals, Academic Press Inc., New York, N.Y., p 50 (1949).

9. Iler, R.K., Colloid Chemistry of Silica and Silicates, Cornell Univ Press, Ithaca, N.Y., p 259 (1955).

10. Street, N. and A.S. Buchanan, Australian J Chem, 9, 450 (1956).

11. Hunter, R.J. and A.E. Alexander, J Colloid Sci. 18, 820 (1963).

12. Brown, G., Ed., The X-ray Identification and Crystal

Structures of Clay Minerals, Mineralogical Society
(Clay Minerals Group), London, England, p 100 (1961).

13. van Olphe, H., An Introduction to Clay Colloid Chemistry,
Interscience Publishers, New York, N.Y., p 244 (1963).

14. Hunter, R.J. and A.E. Alexander, J Colloid Sci, 18,
833 (1963).

15. Murray, H.H. and S.C. Lyons, Clays Clay Minerals,
Proc Nat Conf, 8, 12 (1960).

16. Olsen, H.W., Clays Clay Minerals, Proc Nat Conf, 11,
134 (1962).

17. Wayman, C.H., Proc Intern Clay Conf (Stockholm, Sweden),
1, 330 (1963).

18. Nelson, R.A. and S.B. Hendricks, Soil Sci, 56, 285 (1941).

19. Aylmore, L.A.G. and J.P. Quirk, Clays Clay Minerals,
Proc Nat Conf, 11, 108 (1962).

20. Gouy, G., Ann Phys (Paris), Serie 4, 9, 457 (1910).

21. Gouy, G., Ann Phys (Paris), Serie 9, 7, 129 (1917).

22. Chapman, D.L., Phil Mag, 25, 6, 475 (1913).

23. Stern, O., Elektrochem, 30, 508 (1924).

24. Grahame, D.C., Chem Rev, 41, 441 (1947).

25. Eriksson, E., Soil Sci, 74, 103 (1952).

26. Vanselow, A.P., Soil Sci, 33, 95 (1932).

27. Krishnamoorthy, C. and R. Overstreet, Soil Sci, 69,
41 (1949).

28. Jenny, H., J Phys Chem, 40, 501 (1936).

29. Magistad, O.C., et al, Soil Sci, 57, 371 (1944).

30. Garrels, R. M. and P. Howard, Clays Clay Minerals, Proc Nat Conf, 2, 68 (1959).

31. Christ, C. L. and A. H. Truesdell, Abstracts of Annual Meeting of Geol Soc Am, p 32A (1963).

32. Truesdell, A. H., Abstracts of Annual Meeting of Geol Soc Am, p 170A (1963).

33. Weigener, G. and H. Jenny, Kolloid-Z, 43, 268 (1927).

34. Hendricks, S. B., J Am Chem Soc, 62, 1457 (1940).

35. DeBruyn, P. L. and G. E. Agar, 50th Anniversary Vol., Ed., D. W. Fuerstenau, SIMME, New York, N. Y., p 180 (1962).

36. Iwasaki, I., Report of Investigation No. 5593, U.S. Bureau of Mines (1960).

37. Van Schuylenborgh, J. and A. M. H. Sauger, Rec, 68, 999 (1949).

38. Schofield, R. K., J Soil Sci, 1, 1 (1950).

39. Iwasaki, I., Trans SIME, 223, 97 (1962).

40. Wayman, C. H. and J. B. Robertson, Abstracts of Annual Meeting Geol Soc Am, p 218 (1964).

41. Craft, C. H. and G. R. Makepeace, Ind Eng Chem, Anal Ed, 17, 206, 306 (1954).

42. Matijevic, E., et al, J Phys Chem, 65, 826 (1961).

43. Frink, C. R., Reactions of the Aluminum Ion in Aqueous Solutions and Clay Suspension, Univ Microfilms No. 61-1427, 156 (1963).

44. Hsu, P. H. and T. F. Bates, Mineralog Mag, 33, 749 (1964).

45. Brosset, C., Acta Chem Scand, 8 1917 (1954).

46. Bradley, W. F. , J Am Chem Soc, 67, 975 (1945).

47. MacEwan, D. M. C. , J Soc Chem Ind (London), 65, 298 (1946).

48. Langmuir, I. , J Am Chem Soc, 40, 1361 (1918).

49. Johansen, R. T. and H. N. Dunning, Clays Clay Minerals, Proc Nat Conf, 2, 249 (1959).

50. Martin, R. T. , Clays Clay Minerals, Proc Nat Conf, 2, 259 (1959).

51. Martin, R. T. , Clays Clay Minerals, Proc Nat Conf, 9, 28 (1956).

52. Kohl, R. A. , J Colloid Sci, 19, 699 (1964).

53. Norrish, K. , Discussions Faraday Soc, No. 18, p 120 (1954).

54. Wayman, C. H. , et al, U.S. Geol Surv Prof Paper 450-E, 179 (1963).

55. Wayman, C. H. , et al, U.S. Geol Surv Prof Paper 475-B, 213 (1963).

56. Wayman, C. H. , et al, U.S. Geol Surv Prof Paper 475-C, 221 (1963).

57. Hemwall, J. R. , Proc Intern Clay Minerals Conf (Stockholm, Sweden), 1, 319 (1963).

58. LaMer, V. K. , et al, J Colloid Sci, 12, 566 (1957).

59. LaMer, V. K. and R. H. Smellie, Clays Clay Minerals, Proc Nat Conf, 1, 295 (1962).

60. Wadworth, M. E. and I. B. Cutler, J Metals, 58, 1092 (1956).

61. Ruehrwein, R. A. and S. W. Ward, Soil Sci, 73, 483 (1952).

62. Mortensen, J. L. , Clays Clay Minerals, Proc Nat Conf, 11, 530 (1962).

63. Waksman, S.A., Humus, Origin, Chemical Composition and Importance in Nature, Williams and Wilkins Co., Baltimore, Md., (1936).

64. Mattson, S., Soil Sci, 23, 41 (1932).

65. Ensminger, L.E. and J.E. Gieseking, Soil Sci, 53, 205 (1942).

66. Pinck, L.A., Clays Clay Minerals, Proc Nat Conf, 11, 520 (1962).

67. Hendricks, S.B., J Phys Chem, 45, 65 (1941).

68. Bailey, G.W. and J.L. White, J Agr Food Chem, 12, 324 (1964).

69. Yuen, Q.H. and H.W. Hilton, J Agr Food Chem, 10, 386 (1962).

70. Faust, S.D. and O.M. Aly, J Amer Water Works Assoc, 56, 267 (1964)

71. Frissel, M.J. and G.H. Bolt, Soil Sci, 94, 284 (1962).

72. Lahav, N., Plant and Soil, 17, 2, 191 (1962).

73. Green-Kelly, R., Clay Minerals Bull, 27, 1 (1962).

74. Brindley, G.W. and R.W. Hoffmann, Clays Clay Minerals, Proc Nat Conf, 11, 546 (1962).

DISCUSSION
CHAIRMAN COHEN: Thank you Dr. Wayman. Are there any questions?
DR. T. W. HEALY (University of California):
Dr. Wayman, the inability that you experienced of locating a zero point of charge for kaolinite from a coagulation experiments has concerned us also. We find that the answer lies in the various mutual coagulation effects that occur in kaolinite dispersions. Using a more general Derjaguin-Landau-Verwey-Overbeek treatment we have been able recently in our laboratories to predict the sort of behavior you have obtained for the coagulation of kaolinite as a function of pH. Your experimental data

with the two minima and a maximum in between, fits the theory very well and it is expected therefore that you cannot locate a single unique ZPC.

DR. WAYMAN: Well,–the other thing I think that bothered me on this particular type of system is that as one lowers pH, the surface of kaolinite is continuously changing and if one could actually define or count for a ZPC it would be an undefined surface.

DR HEALY: The fact is that there are really two surfaces. It is as if you had, for example, two oxides in the dispersion. Suppose you had, instead of kaolinite platelets, just a mixture of silica and alumina particles. At any given pH between the zero points of charges of these two minerals the silica will be charged oppositely to the alumina and you will get a coagulation effect. So that in fact with kaolinite there are regions of pH for which the face and the edge are charged oppositely and you get mutual coagulation. You also observe coagulation at pH values where the face and edge charges are reduced to zero.

DR. WAYMAN: That analogy gives us confidence in these application studies.

DR. DEAN (R.A. Taft Sanitary Engineering Center): I'd like to tie together this work with some work on carbon we were doing. We found a substantial breakthrough of organic matter through carbon columns closely correlated with the presence of colloids. I don't know how much of the colloids was merely colloidal clay, because some of your numbers indicate that clay probably doesn't carry an awful lot of organic matter through. But there is no question that colloids were carrying a lot of organic matter right through carbon columns and there was no colloid adsorption whatsoever. So this was in part a comment on the previous paper as well as on this.

I would like to ask if you have indications on less pure systems as to how much organic matter can be associated with clay?

DR. WAYMAN: No, I can't cite you any figures, but I'm sure there is quite a bit of information available in the literature. We do know that organic constituents are readily adsorbed on clays, especially montmorillonite.

CHAIRMAN COHEN: Dr. Packham, I think, is in the audience and has made some determinations on that.

DR. PACKHAM (Water Research Association): In a study of the nature of material constituting turbidity in river water we isolated samples using a continuous high speed centrifuge. Analysis of the solids by wet oxidation and by ignition procedures indicated an average organic content in the region of 20 to 30%.

It would be difficult to say, however, what proportion of this represented organic matter adsorbed onto clay in contrast to algae and minute particles of plant detritus.

We have shown in a number of cases that the contribution of such organic matter to the COD of a river water is small as evidenced by an insignificant reduction of COD after centrifugation or diatomaceous earth filtration.

DR. COLACICCO (Albert Einstein College of Medicine): With reference to the cationic character of the clays, as in the van Olphen model, I wonder if in place of the change of coordination of the Al in the lattice or the lattice defects one could postulate that the long contact of generally anionic clays with salts of heavy metals, as of Al and Fe, may cause an increased adsorption of these ions. This is possible as they are known to be adsorbed much more strongly than other counterions and result in a charge inversion. I notice, by experience with monolayers of long chain compounds and electrokinetic measurements on micelles, that as you increase the concentration of $CaCl_2$ you invert the charge of the micelle air/water and oil/water interfaces from negative to positive. When this occurs the new micelle or the new interface exhibits cationic behavior. I wonder if there is evidence in either direction to indicate whether the positive charge in the van Olphen model is change of coordination of the metal ion, or is a charge derived from adsorbed aluminum in the double layer.

DR. WAYMAN: I think van Olphen's model is mainly one on double layer without any specific charge. I think mainly he is talking about the dual charge on the edge of the clay and this, of course, is dependent on pH. However, I believe it has nothing to do whatsoever with lattice defects.

CHAIRMAN COHEN: I think we have time for just one more question.

DR. G. STOTZKY (Kitchawan Research Laboratory, Brooklyn Botanic Garden): In your initial slide, the last topic under adsorption phenomena was bacteria. As you didn't mention this in your discussion and as the Chairman has given you a few more minutes, would you comment on this, please?

DR. WAYMAN: I cut that short. There has been very little work done on bacteria, and for two reasons I think this is one of the fields in which we need more work. Number one, in the activated sludge system we certainly have a problem with any clays or colloids formed and this would involve certain problems of biodegradation. The interesting effect here is that

both bacteria and clay are approximately the same size, and
that at pH 7 they also have the same charge, so there are many
interesting colloid chemistry problems here with respect to
adsorption of bacteria on clay surfaces.

CHAIRMAN COHEN: I think we can stand one more question.

DR. E. MATIJEVIC (Clarkson College): You had a diagram
on Al species. Does this apply to Al species in solution, or do
you visualize this as changing in hydroxylation of an Al built into
the clay?

DR. WAYMAN: I think it could apply to either. In other
words, I see no reason why you couldn't have Al dissolve from
the surface of the clay and then reacting or hydrolyzing as
compared to having the same type of Al on a clay surface.

DR. MATIJEVIC: Well, this is where I disagree with you
because if it is in solution I think it is now in general agreement
that hydrolyzed monomers do not exist and any model based upon
the assumption of monomers would be doubtful. This may have
important consequences with regard to adsorption and all kinds
of effects involving Al. So I think that's passe' as far as our
knowledge on Al species is concerned.

DR. WAYMAN: How could you actually differentiate these
species?

DR. MATIJEVIC: There are quite a few methods in the
literature. I don't want to give a lecture on it now, but we know
that the species are really polymerized and monomers are
non-existent.

CHAIRMAN COHEN: Give a colloid chemist an inch and
he will take a foot.

DR. V. K. LAMER: Our friend Matijevic is correct,
but he is stealing my thunder.

E. Gus Fruh
University of Texas

G. Fred Lee
University of Wisconsin

SORPTION OF CESIUM
ON STRATIFIED MICA

The intelligent management of our water resources requires an understanding of the chemistry of pollutants in the aquatic environment. Numerous studies have shown that the chemistry of many pollutants, e.g., radioactive wastes, pesticides, and other organic compounds in natural waters is controlled by sorption reactions with suspended and deposited particulate matter.

At this time, despite recent research advances, the effects of many variables on the rate and extent of sorption of these pollutants are not well understood, and for the most part, only qualitative interpretation can be made. The purpose of this investigation was to develop a rational mathematical model that would be useful in correlating some of the many variables that effect sorption in the aquatic environment.

The equations to be presented in this model are neither necessarily definitive nor final descriptions of the various sorption phenomena. The fit of the equations to the data obtained in the studied system is not intended to be an application of a specific mechanism to the occurrence.

SORPTION MODEL

Uninhibited Sorption

As a basis for the theoretical development to be presented, it is assumed that the sorbate in solution becomes bound to the sorbent in such a manner that an "activated intermediate" is formed. The concentration of this "intermediate" is assumed to rise quickly to a steady value. The "activated intermediate" once formed undergoes internal reaction or rearrangement so that the sorbate occupies a site on the sorbent. The substance or element originally on the site is released in some manner and enters the solution. The sorption scheme is:

$$B + S \underset{-1}{\overset{1}{\rightleftharpoons}} X \overset{2}{\longrightarrow} S + A \qquad (7\text{-}1)$$

when:

B = sorbate
A = substance originally occupying the site
S = sorbent
X = "activated intermediate"

The total amount of sorbent, S_T, is constant throughout the reaction period, for its sites contain A and/or B or are part of the "activated intermediate":

$$S_T = S + X \qquad (7\text{-}2)$$

The kinetic equations for the four variables are:

$$dX/dt = k_1 BS - k_{-1}X - k_2 X \qquad (7\text{-}3)$$

$$dS/dt = -k_1 BS + k_{-1}X + k_2 X \qquad (7\text{-}4)$$

$$dB/dt = -k_1 BS + k_{-1}X \qquad (7\text{-}5)$$

$$dA/dt = k_2 X \qquad (7\text{-}6)$$

It is assumed that the amount of B in the "activated intermediate" X is insignificant compared to the quantity of B remaining in the solution.

By a steady state treatment (1, 2), v, the rate of sorbate B's disappearance from solution can be defined as:

$$v = -dB/dt = k_2 X = k_2 S_T B/(B + K_1) \qquad (7\text{-}7)$$

when:

$$K_1 = (k_{-1} + k_2)/k_1 \tag{7-8}$$

A qualitative inspection of equation 7-7 indicates that if B were quite small, any variation in B would have little effect on the denominator $(B + K_1)$. Therefore, at low concentrations of B, an approximate linear relationship with slope $k_2 S_T/K_1$ will result if v was plotted vs. B. At very large values of B, the presence of K_1 in the denominator has little effect on $(B + K_1)$. Thus, at large concentrations of B, v approaches a value independent of B and the curve approaches a straight line whose height above the abcissa is $k_2 S_T$. This will be defined as the maximum or saturating velocity V as shown in Figure 1.

A better graphical technique would be to use the reciprocal of equation 7-7:

$$v = VB/(B + K_1) \tag{7-7a}$$

and:

$$1/v = (B/VB) + (K_1/VB) = 1/V + (K_1/V)(1/B) \tag{7-7b}$$

The graphical analysis of equation 7-7b is shown in Figure 2.

However, if significant quantities of B are bound to the "activated intermediate" X:

$$B_T = B + X \tag{7-9}$$

when:

  B_T = total sorbate concentration at any time
  B = unbound sorbate still in solution
  X = sorbate bound to the "activated intermediate"

The sorption scheme and kinetic equations previously derived for the basic case remain the same.

Differentiation of equation 7-9 leads to:

$$dB_T/dt = dB/dt + dX/dt \tag{7-10}$$

At steady state, $dX/dt = 0$, and:

$$dB_T/dt = dB/dt \tag{7-11}$$

Thus, it will make no difference, as far as rate measurements are concerned, whether the analytical method measures the change in total sorbate or the sorbate remaining in solution.

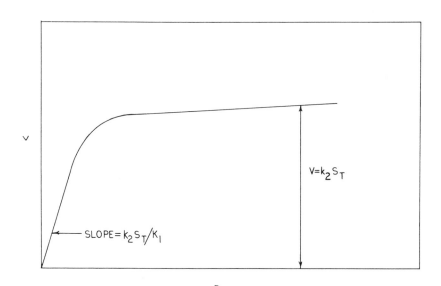

SLOPE=$k_2 S_T/K_1$

$V=k_2 S_T$

B

FIGURE 1   SORBATE UPTAKE RATE VS. SORBATE
                   REMAINING IN SOLUTION.

Substituting equations 7-2 and 7-9 into equation 7-3 when
X is at steady state results in:

$$(S_T - X) = K_1 X/(B_T - X) \qquad (7-12)$$

A qualitative inspection of equation 7-12 indicates that when
$B_T >>> X$, $K_1 X/(B_T - x) \simeq 0$. Consequently, $(S_T - X) \simeq 0$,
and $S_T \simeq X$. Thus, if a saturating concentration of sorbate
B_T was used, all of the sorbent S_T would be bound in the
"activated intermediate" X. Therefore, $v = k_2 X$, and $V = k_2 S_T$.
The relative rate of sorption, r, would be:

$$r = v/V = k_2 X/k_2 S_T = X/S_T \qquad (7-13)$$

and:

$$r S_T = X \qquad (7-13a)$$

Substituting equation 7-13a into equation 7-12 results in:

$$B_T = r S_T + K_1 r/(1 - r) \qquad (7-14)$$

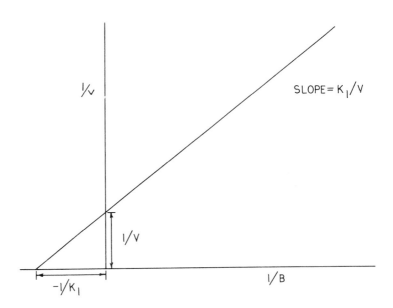

FIGURE 2   RECIPROCAL PLOT OF SORBATE UPTAKE
RATE VS. SORBATE REMAINING IN
SOLUTION.

However, graphing equation 7-14 would be difficult because as
r approaches 1, the term $r/(1 - r)$ approaches infinity. Therefore, let:

$$u = r/(1 - r) \qquad (7-15)$$

Consequently, equation 7-14 becomes:

$$B_T = S_T u/(1 + u) + K_1 u \qquad (7-16)$$

Equation 7-16 is graphed in Figure 3.

If, as derived previously, an insignificant fraction of sorbate B was bound to the "activated intermediate" X than
equation 7-7a would result:

$$v = VB/(B + K_1) \qquad (7-7a)$$

Again introducing the relative rate:

$$r = v/V = VB/V(B + K_1) = B/(B + K_1) \qquad (7-17)$$

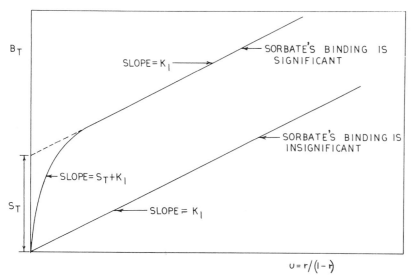

FIGURE 3   METHOD OF DISTINGUISHING THE
SIGNIFICANCE OF SORBATE BINDING.

Rearranging:

$$B = K_1 r/(1 - r)$$ (7-17a)

Letting $u = r/(1 - r)$ and plotting equation 7-17a on Figure 3,
it can be readily shown that this graphical technique can distinguish whether or not a significant quantity of B is bound to
the "activated intermediate" X.

Inhibition
        Sorption can be greatly affected by the addition of chemical
elements or substances to the sorbate suspension. These
additives can produce inhibitory or activating effects by interacting with the sorbent, with the sorbate, or with other substances
already present in the suspension.
        In the simple case under consideration in this study, an
inhibitor can prevent binding of the sorbate to the sorbent by
combining with the sorbent to form another "activated intermediate" or by increasing the potential energy required by the
"activated intermediate" to rearrange. General inhibition will

be the term used if both types of inhibition are operating. If
the inhibitor only competes for the sorption site, it will be
called specific S-type inhibition. If the inhibitor only increases
the energy needed for the "activated intermediate" to internally
rearrange, it will be called specific X-type inhibition. Complete
inhibition will be the case in which the inhibitor completely
inactivates the sorbent. If the inhibitor only modifies the uptake
characteristics of the sorbent, it will be called partial inhibition.

SIGNIFICANT FRACTION OF INHIBITOR BOUND IN THE "ACTIVATED INTERMEDIATE"

Complete General Inhibition
    The following equations describe the sorption scheme:

$$B + S \underset{-1}{\overset{1}{\rightleftharpoons}} X \overset{2}{\longrightarrow} S + A \qquad (7\text{-}1)$$

$$I + S \underset{-3}{\overset{3}{\rightleftharpoons}} S_i \qquad (7\text{-}18)$$

$$I + X \underset{-4}{\overset{4}{\rightleftharpoons}} X_i \qquad (7\text{-}19)$$

For complete inhibition, X_i and S_i are assumed incapable
of further interaction. Then the equations for the sorbent and
inhibitor are:

$$S_T = S + X + S_i + X_i \qquad (7\text{-}20)$$

$$I_T = I + S_i + X_i \qquad (7\text{-}21)$$

The kinetic equations for these variables are:

$$dS/dt = -k_1 SB + k_{-1} X + k_2 X - k_3 IS + k_{-3} S_i \qquad (7\text{-}22)$$

$$dX/dt = k_1 SB - k_{-1} X - k_2 X - k_4 XI + k_{-4} X_i \qquad (7\text{-}23)$$

$$dB/dt = -k_1 SB + k_{-1} X \qquad (7\text{-}24)$$

$$dA/dt = k_2 X \qquad (7\text{-}25)$$

$$dI/dt = -k_3 SI + k_{-3} S_i - k_4 XI + k_{-4} X_i \qquad (7\text{-}26)$$

$$dS_i/dt = k_3SI - k_{-3}S_i \tag{7-27}$$

$$dX_i/dt = k_4XI - k_{-4}X_i \tag{7-28}$$

As written in this scheme, the "activated intermediates" S_i and X_i are involved in only their own separate reactions. Thus, it can be assumed that both these compounds are in an equilibrium process, where:

$$S_i = SI/K_3 \tag{7-18a}$$

and:

$$X_i = XI/k_4 \tag{7-19a}$$

The inhibited sorption rate, $\underline{v}$, after X has reached the steady state, is:

$$\underline{v} = k_2X = k_2\left\{ -(a - db) + \left[(a - db)^2 - 4abS_T/2ab\right]^{1/2}\right\} \tag{7-29}$$

when:

$$a = 1 + K_1/B \tag{7-30}$$

$$b = K_1/BK_3 + 1/K_4 \tag{7-31}$$

$$d = S_T - I_T \tag{7-32}$$

   A qualitative inspection of equation 7-29 reveals that if $I_T = 0$, $d = S_T$, and $(a - db) = (a - bS_T)$. By multiplying out the terms under the radical, finding their square root, and combining terms in the numerator:

$$\underline{v} = k_2 2bS_T/2ab = k_2S_T/a = k_2S_T/(1 + K_1/B) = v, \tag{7-29a}$$

which is the uninhibited rate expressed in equation 7-7. If $I_T \gg B$, then $(a - bd) \simeq bI_T$. Therefore, v approaches 0.

   In most experimental situations, one desires to determine how much inhibition occurs with a specific amount of inhibitor present. If the uptake rate with inhibitor present is $\underline{v} = k_2X$, and without inhibitor present is $v = k_2S_T/a$, the fractional inhibition is defined as:

$$i = \frac{\text{(rate without inhibitor) - (rate with inhibitor)}}{\text{(rate without inhibitor)}} \tag{7-33}$$

$$i = (k_2 S_T/a - k_2 X)/(k_2 S_T/a)$$

$$i = 1 - aX/S_T \qquad (7-34)$$

Assuming that the "activated intermediates" have reached the steady state, the kinetic and material balance equations can be rearranged so that X, S, and I are expressed in terms of i:

$$I_T = iS_T + (a/b) \left[i/(1 - i) \right] \qquad (7-35)$$

The term a/b is related to the sorbate concentration:

$$a/b = \frac{1 + K_1/B}{K_1/BK_3 + 1/K_4} = \frac{B + K_1}{K_1/K_3 + B/K_4} \qquad (7-36)$$

The term $i/(1 - i)$ is the fractional inhibited sorption rate divided by the fractional uninhibited sorption rate. Equation 7-35 is used to find the degree of inhibition $i/(1 - i)$ which occurs when a given quantity of inhibitor I_T is added to a suspension with sorbent S_T and sorbate B.

Equation 7-36 relates a/b to B. Figure 4 shows that as B approaches 0, a/b approaches K_3. Also as B approaches ∞. a/b approaches K_4. Thus, a/b will increase if $K_3 < K_4$, will remain constant if $K_3 = K_4$, or will decrease if $K_3 > K_4$.

Thus, to obtain a particular degree of inhibition $i/(1 - i)$ for a certain quantity of sorbent, it can be inferred from equation 7-35 and Figure 4 that increasing B would require a greater quantity of I_T if $K_3 < K_4$, or I prevented binding more than internal rearrangement. If the opposite occurred, $K_4 < K_3$, and increasing B requires less I to obtain a particular degree of inhibition for the same quantity of S_T.

Complete Specific Inhibition

Specific inhibition is defined as either of the two extremes of general inhibition. If the inhibitor prevents only binding, and not internal rearrangement, $K_4 = \infty$, and equation 7-36 becomes:

$$a/b = \frac{B + K_1}{K_1/K_3 + B/K_4} = \frac{B + K_1}{K_1/K_3 + 0}$$

$$a/b = K_3 (1 + B/K_1) \qquad (7-36a)$$

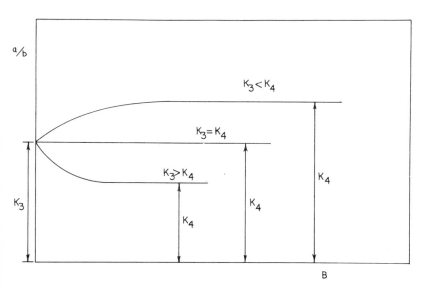

FIGURE 4   QUALITATIVE INTERPRETATION OF
                      EQUATION 7-36.

Thus, increasing B increases a/b, which causes an increase
in the amount of inhibitor necessary to obtain the given degree
of inhibition $1/(1 - i)$ shown in equation 7-35. If I effects only
internal rearrangement, $K_3 = \infty$, and equation 7-36 becomes:

$$a/b = \frac{B + K_1}{K_1/K_3 + B/K_4} = \frac{B + K_1}{0 + B/K_4}$$

$$a/b = K_4 (1 + K_1/B) \qquad\qquad (7\text{-}36b)$$

Thus, increasing B decreases a/b, which naturally decreases
the quantity of I necessary to acquire a given degree of inhibition
in equation 7-35.

INSIGNIFICANT QUANTITY OF INHIBITOR BOUND TO THE
ACTIVATED INTERMEDIATE

Complete Inhibition
      The sorption scheme and kinetic equations remain the same.
However, because the amount of inhibitor bound to the "activated
intermediates" is insignificant compared to the quantity of inhibitor

still in the solution, the inhibitor balance of equation 7-21 can
be omitted. Assuming that X has reached the steady state,
substitution of equations 7-27, 7-28, and 7-23 into equation
7-20, the sorbent balance equation results in:

$$X = S_T B / \left[B \left(1 + I/K_4\right) + K_1 \left(1 + I/K_3\right) \right] \qquad (7\text{-}37)$$

The rate of disappearance of B would be:

$$\underline{v} = k_2 X = k_2 S_T B / \left[B \left(1 + I/K_4\right) + K_1 \left(1 + I/K_3\right) \right] \qquad (7\text{-}38)$$

Inverting equation 7-38 gives the reciprocal equation which is
plotted in Figure 5.

$$1/\underline{v} = \left[K_1 \left(1 + I/K_3\right) /B + \left(1 + I/K_4\right) \right] /k_2 S_T \qquad (7\text{-}39)$$

Thus, if general inhibition occurs, the slope $(K_1/V) \left(1 + I/K_3\right)$
and the intercept $(1/V) \left(1 + I/K_4\right)$ of equation 7-39 will change.
If addition of I prevents only binding, $K_4 = \infty$, and the intercept
of equation 7-39 will be the same as the uninhibited control, no
matter how great the quantity of I. The slope will increase with
increasing I. This type of inhibition is depicted in Figure 5 as
specific S-type inhibition. If I prevents only internal rearrangement of the "activated intermediate", $K_3 = \infty$. The slope of
equation 7-39 would be the same as the uninhibited control, but
the intercept would differ. This is depicted in Figure 5 as
specific X-type inhibition.

To distinguish whether or not a significant quantity of I_T
was bound to the "activated intermediate" equation 7-38 is
divided by B to give:

$$\underline{v} = k_2 S_T / \left[\left(1 + I/K_4\right) + \left(K_1/B\right) \left(1 + I/K_3\right) \right] \qquad (7\text{-}40)$$

Rearranging:

$$\underline{v} = k_2 S_T / \left[\left(1 + K_1/B\right) + I \left(K_1/BK_3 + I/K_4\right) \right] \qquad (7\text{-}40a)$$

or:

$$\underline{v} = k_2 S_T / (a + bI) \qquad (7\text{-}40b)$$

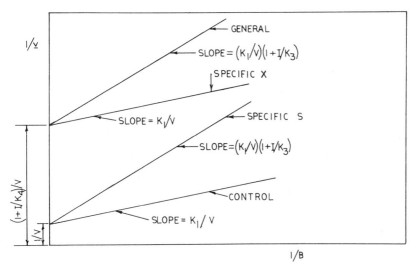

FIGURE 5   RECIPROCAL PLOTS OF COMPLETE
             INHIBITION PATTERNS.

The definition of i is:

$$i = \frac{\text{(uninhibited rate)} - \text{(inhibited rate)}}{\text{(uninhibited rate)}} \qquad (7\text{-}33)$$

therefore:

$$i = \left\{ (k_2 S_T/a) - \left[k_2 S_T/(a - bI) \right] \right\} / (k_2 S_T/a) \qquad (7\text{-}41)$$

Rearranging:

$$I = (a/b) \left[i/(1 - i) \right] \qquad (7\text{-}42)$$

Figure 6 shows that a graphical analysis can distinguish
when a significant quantity of inhibitor was bound to the sorbent
as:

$$I_T = iS_T + (a/b) \left[i/(1 - i) \right] \qquad (7\text{-}35)$$

and when an insignificant quantity of inhibitor was bound to the
sorbent as:

$$I = (a/b) \left[i/(1 - i) \right] \qquad (7\text{-}42)$$

Comparison of the two equations shows that only the iS_T term differs due to the two original assumptions. Thus, the iS_T term can be assumed equal to the quantity of inhibitor bound to the "activated intermediates", and $(a/b)\left[i/(1 - i)\right]$ indicates the quantity of inhibitor remaining in the solution.

Partial Inhibition by Mutual Displacement

In the previous section, it was assumed that S_i and X_i, once formed, could no longer participate in the sorption scheme. However, it is possible that B and I can mutually replace one another on the sorbent. If inhibition did occur in such a manner the sorption scheme could be represented by the following equation

$$B + S \underset{-1}{\overset{1}{\rightleftharpoons}} X \overset{2}{\longrightarrow} S + A \qquad (7\text{-}1)$$

$$I + S \underset{-3}{\overset{3}{\rightleftharpoons}} S_i \qquad (7\text{-}18)$$

and:

$$S_i + B \underset{-5}{\overset{5}{\rightleftharpoons}} X + I \qquad (7\text{-}43)$$

The sorbent balance equation would again be:

$$S_T = S + S_i + X \qquad (7\text{-}44)$$

It will be assumed that the quantity of I bound to the "activated intermediates" is insignificant compared to the quantity of inhibitor remaining in solution. The kinetic equations are:

$$dS/dt = -k_1SB + k_1X + k_2X - k_3SI + k_{-3}S_i - k_5S_iB + k_{-5}XI \quad (7\text{-}4$$

$$dX/dt = k_1SB - k_{-1}X - k_2X + k_5S_iB - k_{-5}XI \qquad (7\text{-}46)$$

$$dB/dt = -k_1SB + k_{-1}X - k_5S_iB + k_{-5}XI \qquad (7\text{-}47)$$

$$dA/dt = k_2X \qquad (7\text{-}48)$$

$$dS_i/dt = k_3SI = k_{-3}S_i - k_5S_iB + k_{-5}XI \qquad (7\text{-}49)$$

In the following analysis, it is assumed that equation 7-18 is in

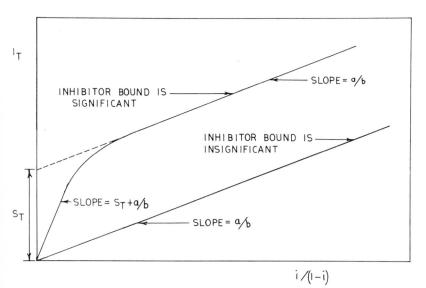

FIGURE 6   METHOD OF DISTINGUISHING THE
             SIGNIFICANCE OF INHIBITOR BINDING.

in equilibrium.
Thus:

$$S_i = SI/K_3 \qquad\qquad (7\text{-}50)$$

for this particular sorption scheme. Substituting equation 7-50
for S_i in equation 7-46 with X at steady state results in:

$$S = X\,(k_{-1} + k_2 + k_{-5}I)\,/B\,(k_1 + k_5I/K_3) = X/Be \qquad (7\text{-}51)$$

when:

$$e = (k_1 + k_5I/K_3)/(k_{-1} + k_2 + k_{-5}I) \qquad\qquad (7\text{-}52)$$

Substitution for S and S_i in equation 7-44 when X has reached the
steady state leads to:

$$X = S_T Be/(1 + I/K_3 + Be) \qquad\qquad (7\text{-}53)$$

By similar algebraic manipulation:

$$\underline{v} = k_2 X$$

and:

$$\underline{v} = k_2 S_T Be / (1 + I/K_3 + Be) \qquad (7\text{-}54)$$

A qualitative inspection of equation 7-54 reveals that if $I \gg B$, $e \simeq k_5/k_{-5}K_3$ in equation 7-52 and I/K_3 would be the dominant term in the denominator of equation 7-54. Thus, $\underline{v} \simeq 0$. If $B \gg I$:

$$\underline{v} \simeq k_2 S_T Be/Be \simeq k_2 S_T \simeq V$$

V is the maximum sorption rate with no inhibitor present.

$$1/\underline{v} = (1/V) \left[(1 + I/K_3) \, (1/e) \, (1/B) + 1 \right] \qquad (7\text{-}55)$$

A plot of equation 7-55 in Figure 7 shows that it is linear. The intercept is $1/V$, which is independent of I and always the same as the control. The slopes of the equation increase with increasing I. This is similar to the results expressed in Figure 5 for the complete specific S case.

To distinguish the two types of inhibition, the slopes of $1/\underline{v}$ vs. $1/B$ graphed in Figure 7 are used. The slope would be:

$$y = (1/V) \, (1 + I/K_3) \, (1/e) \qquad (7\text{-}56)$$

$$y = (1/V) \, (1 + I/K_3) \, (k_1 + k_2 + k_{-5}I)/(k_1 + k_5 I/K_3) \qquad (7\text{-}56a)$$

Consider y as a function of I. At the initial portion of the curve, I is very small. Expanding the denominator through use of the binomial theorem and discarding all powers of I greater than 1:

$$y = (1/V) \left\{ K_1 + I \left[k_{-5}K_3 + K_1 \, (k_1 - k_5) \right] /k_1 K_3 \right\} \qquad (7\text{-}56b)$$

The equation is linear with slope:

$$Z_i = \left[k_{-5}K_3 + K_1 \, (k_1 - k_5) \right] /k_1 K_3 V \qquad (7\text{-}56c)$$

and intercept:

$$T_i = K_1/V \qquad (7\text{-}56d)$$

As I becomes very large, equation 7-56a becomes:

$$y = (1/V) \, (K_5 I + K_5 K_3 + K_i k_1/k_5) \qquad (7\text{-}56e)$$

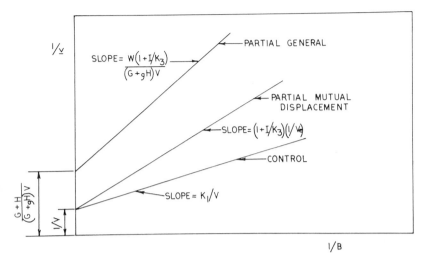

FIGURE 7   RECIPROCAL PLOTS OF PARTIAL
              INHIBITION PATTERNS.

The slope of this linear equation is:

$$Z_f = K_5/V \qquad\qquad (7\text{-}56f)$$

and the intercept is:

$$T_f = (K_5K_3 + K_1k_1/k_5)/V \qquad\qquad (7\text{-}56g)$$

To determine the type of resulting curve, the initial slope
is subtracted from the final slope:

$$Z_f - Z_i = (K_5K_3 - K_1)(k_1 - k_5)/k_1K_3V \qquad\qquad (7\text{-}57)$$

Thus, the graph of y vs. I bends upward if $(K_5K_3 - K_1)$ and
$(k_1 - k_5)$ are of the same sign, and downward if the terms are
of opposite sign. However, the graphs of y vs. I can be linear
if $K_3K_5 = K_1$ or $k_1 = k_5$. If the slope of equation 7-39 for the
specific S-type inhibition was plotted vs. I it would also be
linear as shown in Figure 8.

To have a means to distinguish these special cases of
partial inhibition from the complete specific S-type inhibition,
it should be recalled that for specific S-type inhibition, $K_4 = \infty$,
and:

$$I = (a/b)\left[i/(1 - i) \right] \qquad\qquad (7\text{-}42)$$

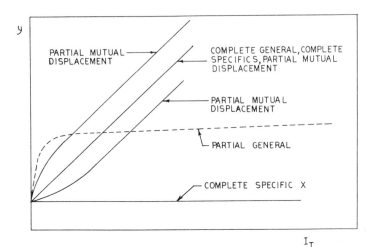

FIGURE 8   SLOPES OF FIGURES 5 AND 7 VS.
              INHIBITOR CONCENTRATION.

$$I = \frac{(1 + K_1/B)}{(K_1/BK_3 + 1/K_4)} \left[\frac{i}{(1 - i)}\right]$$

$$I = K_3(B + K_1)/K_1 \left[i/(1 - i)\right] \qquad (7-42a)$$

Thus the equation is linear, passes through the origin, and the slope increases proportionally to B, as shown in Figure 9.

For the partial inhibition by mutual displacement:

$$i = (v - \underline{v})/v = 1 - \underline{v}/v \qquad (7-33)$$

Substituting equations 7-54 and 7-7 for $\underline{v}$ and v, respectively, results in:

$$i/(1 - i) = \left[(1 + I/K_3)/e - K_1\right]/(B + K_1) \qquad (7-58)$$

For small values of I, the denominator can be expanded through use of the binomial theorem. Cancelling all powers of I greater than 1, and rearranging:

$$I = \frac{k_1 K_3(B + K_1)}{k_{-5}K_3 + K_1(k_1 - k_5)} \left[i/(1 - i)\right] \qquad (7-58a)$$

This linear equation passes through the origin and has a slope $K_1K_3(B + K_1)/\left[k_{-5}K_3 + K_1(k_1 - k_5)\right]$. When I becomes very large, equation 7-58 becomes:

$$I = \left[(B + K_1)/K_5\right]\left[i/(1 - i)\right] - \frac{\left[k_{-5}K_3 + K_1(k_1 - k_5)\right]}{k_{-5}} \quad (7\text{-}58b)$$

This linear relationship has a slope $(B + K_1)/K_5$. Thus, increasing B would increase the slope of the line. To obtain the intercept on the $k/(1 - i)$ axis, let $I = 0$. Hence:

$$i/(1 - i) = \left[k_{-5}K_3 + K_1(k_1 - k_5)\right]/k_5(B + K_1) \quad (7\text{-}58c)$$

To obtain the intercept on the I axis, let $i/(1 - i) = 0$ in equation 7-58b. Thus:

$$I = -\left[k_{-5}K_3 + K_1(k_1 - k_5)\right]/k_{-5} \quad (7\text{-}58d)$$

This negative intercept is independent of B. Hence. if the partial mutual displacement type inhibition was operating, the final linear portion of the relationship between I and $i/(1 - i)$ when extrapolated should pass through the same negative point on the I axis no matter what the concentration of B was. The relationship is shown in Figure 9.

Partial Inhibition - General
      The general partial inhibition case follows the subsequent sorption scheme:

$$B + S \underset{-1}{\overset{1}{\rightleftarrows}} X \overset{2}{\longrightarrow} S + A \quad (7\text{-}1)$$

$$I + S \underset{-3}{\overset{3}{\rightleftarrows}} S_i \quad (7\text{-}18)$$

$$I + X \underset{-4}{\overset{4}{\rightleftarrows}} X_i \quad (7\text{-}19)$$

$$B + S \underset{-6}{\overset{6}{\rightleftarrows}} X_i \quad (7\text{-}59)$$

$$X_i \overset{7}{\longrightarrow} S_i + A \quad (7\text{-}60)$$

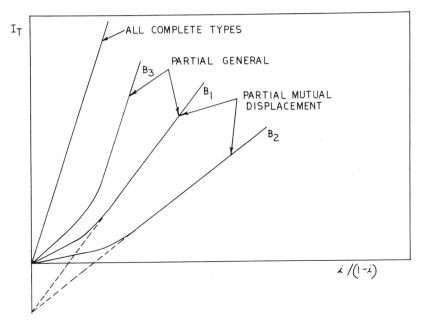

FIGURE 9   DEGREE OF INHIBITION OF SORBATE
            UPTAKE AS A FUNCTION OF SORBATE
            CONCENTRATION B.

The sorbent equation is again:

$$S_T = S + X + S_i + X_i \tag{7-20}$$

It is assumed that the quantity of inhibitor bound to the "activated
intermediates" is insignificant compared to the quantity of inhibitor remaining in solution.   The kinetic equations are:

$$dS/dt = -k_1 SB + k_{-1} X + k_2 X - k_3 IS + k_{-3} S_i \tag{7-61}$$

$$dX/dt = k_1 SB - k_{-1} X - k_2 X - k_4 XI + k_{-4} X_i \tag{7-62}$$

$$dB/dt = -k_1 SB + k_{-1} X - k_6 S_i B + k_{-6} S_i \tag{7-63}$$

$$dA/dt = k_2 X + k_7 X_i \tag{7-64}$$

$$dI/dt = -k_3 SI + k_{-3} S_i - k_4 XI + k_{-4} X_i \tag{7-65}$$

$$dS_i/dt = k_3SI - k_{-3}S_i - k_6S_iB + k_{-6}X_i + k_7X_i \qquad (7\text{-}66)$$

and:

$$dX_i/dt = k_4XI - k_{-4}X_i + k_6S_iB - k_{-6}X_i - k_7X_i \qquad (7\text{-}67)$$

It is assumed that equation 7-18 is an equilibrium process. Hence:

$$S_i = SI/K_3 \qquad (7\text{-}68)$$

Equation 7-20 becomes:

$$S_T = S + X + S_i + X_i = (1 + I/K_3) S + X + X_i \qquad (7\text{-}69)$$

Assuming that X and X_i have reached the steady state, substitution of equations 7-68 and 7-69 into equations 7-62 and 7-67 and solution by determinants results in:

$$\underline{v} = k_2X + k_7X_i \qquad (7\text{-}70)$$

$$\underline{v} = k_2S_TB(G + gH)/\left[W(1 + I/K_3) + B(G + H)\right] \qquad (7\text{-}70a)$$

when:

$$G = k_1(k_{-4} + k_{-6} + k_7) + k_{-4}k_6I/K_3 \qquad (7\text{-}70b)$$

$$H = (k_{-1} + k_2 + k_4I)(k_6I)/K_3 + k_1k_5I \qquad (7\text{-}70c)$$

$$W = (k_{-4} + k_{-6} + k_7)(k_{-1} + k_2) + (k_{-6} + k_7)k_4I \qquad (7\text{-}70d)$$

and:

$$g = k_7/k_2 \qquad (7\text{-}70e)$$

A qualitative inspection of equation 7-70a reveals that saturating the sorbent with B does not restore the uninhibited maximum sorption rate $V = k_2S_T$. If $B \gg I$, equation 7-70a becomes:

$$\underline{V} \simeq k_2S_tB(G + gH)/B(G + H) \simeq V(G + gH)/(G + H) \qquad (7\text{-}70f)$$

The other characteristic feature of general partial inhibition is that the sorption rate never drops to zero no matter how much is added. If $I \gg B$, equation 7-70a becomes:

$$\underline{v} \simeq k_2 S_T g B k_6 / (k_{-6} + k_7 + k_6 B)$$

$$\underline{v} \simeq k_7 S_T B / (K_6 + B) \qquad (7\text{-}70g)$$

when:

$$K_6 = (k_{-6} + k_7)/k_6 \qquad (7\text{-}70h)$$

Thus, $\underline{v}$ does not equal 0 unless $k_7 = 0$, in which case complete inhibition would occur.

The reciprocal form of equation 7-70a is:

$$1/\underline{v} = (1/V) \left[\frac{G + H}{G + gH} + \frac{W(1 + I/K_3)}{B(G + gH)} \right] \qquad (7\text{-}71)$$

The relationship between $1/v$ and $1/B$ in equation 7-71 is linear. The intercept and slope of this equation behave quite differently than those of the other inhibition types. The intercept of equation 7-71 is:

$$T = (G + H)/V(G + gH) \qquad (7\text{-}71a)$$

For $I = 0$, $T = 1/V$. For large values of I, T approaches $1/gV$. The slope of equation 7-71 is:

$$y = W(1 + I/K_3)/V(G + gH) \qquad (7\text{-}71b)$$

For $I = 0$, $y = K_1/V$. For large values of I, y approaches $K_6 gV$. Equation 7-71b is plotted in Figure 8 to indicate how graphical analyses can easily distinguish the inhibition types.

APPLICATION OF MODEL

To evaluate this sorption model, data were required from experiments in which the sorbate and inhibitor concentrations were varied over a wide range. Wahlberg and Fishman studied the effects of four different cations on the 12 hour sorption of Cs by five different "pure" layer-silicate clays (3). In all cases, the cationic inhibitor was the same as the clay's saturating ion. However, no experiments were conducted in which the inhibitory cations were absent.

Jacobs and Tamura investigated the effect of various Rb concentrations on the 65 hour sorption of Cs by a "mixed" clay (4, 5). They also conducted a few studies using cations other than Rb.

Analysis of the data obtained in these investigations followed the equations derived for this model for equilibrium conditions (2). However, to properly evaluate this model, it was thought that sorption results should be obtained at various sorption times. In this manner, the data obtained within the first few minutes of the sorption reaction could be fitted to the proper equations in the model and the inhibition characteristics indicated could be compared to the actual pattern of results obtained at later times.

It was obvious also that a sorbent should be tested which exhibited complex sorption phenomena, such as lattice collapse and edge fixation. The clay chosen was saturated with Ca, K, or Na so as to obtain a sorbent with different sorption characteristics. The results presented here are only for the Ca-clay.

MATERIALS, ANALYTICAL METHODS, AND PROCEDURES

The sorbent used in this investigation was a stratified mica-vermiculite clay. It was extracted from a "Colorado granite" soil using the H_2O_2 treatment described by Jackson (6). The particle size range was from 50-177 μ . A 1N sodium acetate at pH 5 was used to destroy the carbonates and remove the exchangeable divalent cations (7). To extract the usually non-exchangeable interlayer "native" K and to expand the lattice, the clay was leached for two weeks with a 0.067 N sodium tetraphenyl boron + 1N NaCl solution. The K-precipitate was removed following washing with 0.5N NaCl-acetone solution (8, 9, 10). To remove any remaining salts and to aid in making active some slowly expanding vermiculite layers, the clay was washed with a solution of 1N sodium acetate at pH 7.0 (7). The sorption sites were saturated with Ca using three washings with 1N calcium acetate and one washing with 1N $CaCl_2$. All solutions were at pH 7.0. The clay was leached repeatedly with 80% acetone until a negative test for Cl^- resulted. The clay was dried in a 70°C oven for a few minutes. It was placed then in a dessicator above a saturated $Na_2SO_4 \cdot 10 H_2O$ solution. The dessicator was placed in a 0°C temperature control room until used. The clay's cation exchange capacity was 83 meq/100 g.

Cesium was chosen as the sorbate because: it is present in nature in only minute amounts; it is the most electropositive of all the alkalis; and it would be expected to readily take part in sorptions reactions, but not in side reactions, such as complex reactions. Moreover, Cs salts dissolve completely in water and dilute acids so that a Cs-137 tracer could be used to measure Cs sorption by the rapid and reliable method of gamma spectroscopy. Although trace quantities of Cs are sorbed by glassware and filter paper (11), Finston and Kinsely report that the addition of approximately 1 mg of Cs carrier per ml was sufficient to stabilize a solution for a six-month period (12). This was substantiated in preliminary experiments (2).

Furthermore, Cs would be expected to collapse the opened lattices of the Ca-saturated clay (3, 13, 14). Such "trapping" phenomena would insure the irreversibility of the sorption reaction. X-ray diffraction analyses were conducted frequently to relate the cationic inhibition of Cs sorption to the lattice structure of the clay. All samples reported in this paper in a sealed enclosure of known humidity. With the diffractometer a current of air of known humidity was passed over the sample.

Operating conditions were set up based on screening experiments described elsewhere (15). A temperature controlled water bath shaker was used with an agitation rate of 120 cycles/min, stroke length of 1" and temperature of $20 \pm 0.5^{O}C$. Five-hundredth g of clay were weighted, added to 50-ml water (distilled water re-distilled in an all-glass apparatus) and placed overnight in a $20^{O}C$ room. The Cs solution, leaching solution, and clay suspension were allowed to equilibrate in the $20^{O}C$ water bath. Fifty-ml of the desired Cs solution were added to the clay suspension and the suspension agitated for the predetermined time. The clay was filtered from the suspension using a Millipore membrane 4.5 cm diameter, and 0.45μ pore size.

Preliminary experiments with this particular clay showed that the Cs sorption was significantly effected by the clay's lattice structure (15). X-ray diffraction patterns, cation exchange capacity analyses, and leaching tests with various cations substantiated the collapse of the lattice structure and the "trapping" of the Cs within. Cesium concentration and sorption time were two of the main factors effecting the sorption characteristics of the clay. Agitation rate, pH in the range of 4 to 9, and temperature ranging from 20 to $40^{O}C$ were significant variables, but were controlled best at the values previously indicated.

EXPERIMENTAL RESULTS

Uninhibited Cesium Sorption

The quantities of Cs sorbed by the Ca-saturated clay for a wide range of initial Cs concentrations and sorption times are presented in Figure 10. This graph shows that almost 100% was sorbed after 73 hours when the initial [Cs] was 7.5×10^{-4} meq/100

However, as the initial $[Cs]$ was increased, the % Cs sorbed
decreased so that, at an initial $[Cs]$ of 7.5 x 10^{-2} meq/100-ml,
only 26.5% was sorbed after 726 hours reaction time. For all
Cs concentrations studied, the majority of the Cs ultimately
sorbed was "taken up" by the sorbent within the first few minutes
of contact. Following this, the Cs sorption pattern was that of a
slowly but distinctly upward rising plateau. In all cases there
was doubt whether equilibrium actually occurred.

Due to non-equilibrium conditions within the first few minutes of the reactions, it would be expected that these data would
show the greatest variability. To determine the statistical
reliability of the data, a number of these initial runs was
repeated at various Cs concentrations. In Table I the average
initial sorption values and their ranges are listed to give an
idea of the variability of the data. The standard deviations and
coefficients of variation are presented to relate the variability
of the data to the mean values presented in the graph. It can
be seen that the variability increased as the Cs concentration
approached the clay's exchange capacity and the competition
for sorption sites increased.

Table II correlated the "irreversible" trapping phenomena
and the $[Cs]$-sorption time interaction by X-ray diffraction
patterns. The two major peaks at all times were at the 14.7A^O
vermiculite spacing and at the 10.1A^O mica spacing. There was
a number of random minor peaks between the two major peaks,
which varied somewhat with the treatment to which the clay
was subjected. The peak ratio is intended to be an indicator of
the cesium's collapse of the vermiculite layers to mica. Although
not quantitative because Cs can be sorbed by preferred sites on
the mica's surface, the peak ratio does show that "trapping" was
occurring to validate the assumed irreversibility of the second
step within the sorption scheme for the wide range of Cs concentrations used.

The term v, the initial rate of Cs sorption, was estimated
from the difference of Cs concentrations in the solution between
0 and 1.5 min reaction time. Because of the large quantity of
Cs sorbed, the Cs remaining in the solution after 1.5 min rather
than the initial $[Cs]$ was used to define B.

The data from Table I are plotted in Figure 11. The resulting linear relationship can be described by:

$$1/v = 1/V + (K_1/V) (1/B)$$
(7-7b)

TABLE I   STATISTICAL COMPUTATIONS FOR INITIAL CESIUM SORPTION

Initial $[Cs]$ meq/100-ml	# Experiments	Mean Initial Sorption meq/100-ml	(meq/100-ml) Min	Max	Standard Deviation	Coefficient of Variation
7.5×10^{-4}	5	5.23×10^{-4}	5.04×10^{-4}	5.48×10^{-4}	0.165	3.16%
15.0×10^{-4}	4	10.55×10^{-4}	10.1×10^{-4}	11.1×10^{-4}	0.33	3.13%
7.5×10^{-3}	4	3.62×10^{-3}	3.33×10^{-3}	4.0×10^{-3}	0.25	6.83%
7.5×10^{-2}	4	1.17×10^{-2}	0.91×10^{-2}	1.33×10^{-2}	0.156	13.3%

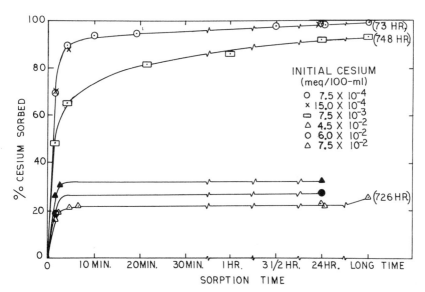

FIGURE 10   PER CENT CESIUM SORBED BY Ca-CLAY
AS A FUNCTION OF INITIAL[CESIUM]AND
SORPTION TIME.

From this result it can be assumed that the quantity of Cs
bound to the "activated intermediate" was insignificant.

Calcium Inhibition of Cesium Sorption
    The quantities of Cs sorbed as a function of initial[Cs],
sorption time, and initial[Ca]are presented in Table II.
Figure 12 compares some of the data in Table III to that in
Figure 10 in which Ca was not present. The quantity of Cs
sorbed decreased with increasing [Ca] at all sorption times.
However, the quantity of Cs inhibited was much greater at
the beginning of the experiment than after 24 hours or longer
sorption time. This clearly would be the pattern expected for
a partial-type inhibition.
    In Figure 13, the reciprocal of the quantity of Cs sorbed
within 1.5 min is plotted vs. the reciprocal of the [Cs]remaining
in the solution. The linear relationships in Figure 13 increase
with increasing [Ca] , but all have a common intercept on the
$1/v$ axis.
    Such a linear reciprocal plot with common intercept can
be interpreted from the model to be the complete S-type

TABLE II   EFFECT OF CESIUM SORPTION ON
THE CLAY'S LATTICE STRUCTURE

Sample	Chemical Treatment	Peak Ratio $(14.7A^\circ/10.1A^\circ)$
1	Ca-clay	4.2, 4.1
2	#1 + 7.5×10^{-4} meq/100-ml Cs for 1 min	3.3
3	#1 + 7.5×10^{-4} meq/100-ml Cs for 10 min	3.5
4	#1 + 7.5×10^{-4} meq/100-ml Cs for 24 hr	2.6
5	#1 + 7.5×10^{-3} meq/100-ml Cs for 1 min	2.9
6	#1 + 7.5×10^{-3} meq/100-ml Cs for 11 min	2.5
7	#1 + 7.5×10^{-3} meq/100-ml Cs for 24 hr	1.9
8	#1 + 3.0×10^{-2} meq/100-ml Cs for 1 min	1.6
9	#1 + 3.0×10^{-2} meq/100-ml Cs for 11 min	0.8
10	#1 + 3.0×10^{-2} meq/100-ml Cs for 24 hr	0.5
11	#1 + 7.5×10^{-2} meq/100-ml Cs for 1 min	1.0
12	#1 + 7.5×10^{-2} meq/100-ml Cs for 11 min	0.8
13	#1 + 7.5×10^{-2} meq/100-ml Cs for 24 hr	0.6, 0.5

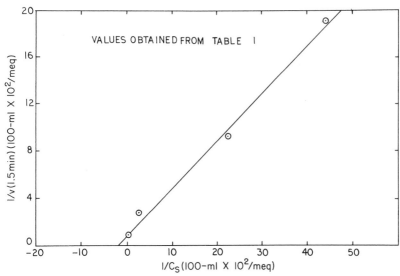

FIGURE 11   RECIPROCAL PLOT OF CESIUM
              SORPTION BY Ca-CLAY.

inhibition as depicted in Figure 5 or the partial mutual displacement inhibition depicted in Figure 7. To distinguish between
the two types, the slopes y of the linear relationships in Figure 13
were plotted in Figure 14 vs. the initial [Ca] . The resulting
curvilinear relationship can be represented by two linear seg-
ments intercepting the y axis at 6.25×10^{-1} and 4×10^{-1} (1.5 min),
respectively. Figure 14 clearly follows the pattern developed in
the model for partial mutual displacement inhibition as shown
in Figure 8.

To further substantiate that the model can distinguish the
various inhibition types from one another, the initial Ca concentrations were plotted in Figure 15 vs. the degree of inhibition
i/(1 - i) obtained for the various Cs concentrations in solutions.
Figure 15 shows that the final linear portions of the curves when
extrapolated intercepted the ordinate axis at the same negative
point. However, all the curves do start at the origin. The
results presented follow the pattern derived in the model for
the partial mutual displacement.

Figure 15 also shows that, at the highest [Cs], Cs sorption
was least inhibited, but not proportionately. In fact at concentrations of 10^{-4} and 10^{-5} meq/100-ml the difference in degree

TABLE III   CESIUM SORPTION WITH CALCIUM
             INHIBITOR PRESENT

Initial [Cs] meq/100-ml	Initial [Ca] meq/100-ml	Sorption Time hr - min	Cs Sorbed meq/100-ml
7.5×10^{-4}	5.0×10^{-3}	0-1.5	4.97×10^{-4}
7.5×10^{-4}	5.0×10^{-3}	0-20.25	7.15×10^{-4}
7.5×10^{-4}	5.0×10^{-3}	3-39	7.38×10^{-4}
7.5×10^{-4}	5.0×10^{-3}	24-0	7.40×10^{-4}
7.5×10^{-4}	1.0×10^{-1}	0-1.5	3.84×10^{-4}
7.5×10^{-4}	2.0×10^{-1}	0-1.5	3.14×10^{-4}
7.5×10^{-4}	2.0×10^{-1}	0-1.5	3.41×10^{-4}
7.5×10^{-4}	2.0×10^{-1}	0-4.5	4.65×10^{-4}
7.5×10^{-4}	2.0×10^{-1}	24-22.5	7.10×10^{-4}
7.5×10^{-4}	5.0×10^{-1}	0-1.5	2.31×10^{-4}
7.5×10^{-4}	5.0×10^{-1}	0-23.5	5.28×10^{-4}
7.5×10^{-4}	5.0×10^{-1}	5-0	6.37×10^{-4}
7.5×10^{-4}	5.0×10^{-1}	24-0	6.57×10^{-4}
7.5×10^{-4}	5.0×10^{-1}	124-0	6.80×10^{-4}
7.5×10^{-4}	5.0×10^{-1}	525-0	7.17×10^{-4}
15.0×10^{-4}	1.0×10^{-1}	0-1.5	6.85×10^{-4}
15.0×10^{-4}	1.0×10^{-1}	0-1.5	6.95×10^{-4}
15.0×10^{-4}	1.0×10^{-1}	24-0	14.8×10^{-4}
15.0×10^{-4}	2.0×10^{-1}	0-1.5	6.48×10^{-4}
15.0×10^{-4}	2.0×10^{-1}	0-1.5	6.81×10^{-4}
15.0×10^{-4}	2.0×10^{-1}	24-0	14.6×10^{-4}

TABLE III - cont'd

15.0×10^{-4}	5.0×10^{-1}	$0-1.5$	4.35×10^{-4}
7.5×10^{-3}	5.0×10^{-3}	$0-1.5$	3.15×10^{-3}
7.5×10^{-3}	5.0×10^{-3}	$0-21$	5.95×10^{-3}
7.5×10^{-3}	5.0×10^{-3}	$24-0$	6.62×10^{-3}
7.5×10^{-3}	1.0×10^{-1}	$0-1.5$	2.63×10^{-3}
7.5×10^{-3}	2.0×10^{-1}	$0-1.5$	2.23×10^{-3}
7.5×10^{-3}	2.0×10^{-1}	$0-1.5$	2.11×10^{-3}
7.5×10^{-3}	2.0×10^{-1}	$0-4.5$	3.37×10^{-3}
7.5×10^{-3}	2.0×10^{-1}	$24-0$	6.22×10^{-3}
7.5×10^{-3}	5.0×10^{-1}	$0-1.5$	1.76×10^{-3}
7.5×10^{-3}	5.0×10^{-1}	$0-21.0$	4.3×10^{-3}
7.5×10^{-3}	5.0×10^{-1}	$24-0$	5.37×10^{-3}
7.5×10^{-2}	5.0×10^{-1}	$0-1.5$	0.78×10^{-2}
7.5×10^{-2}	5.0×10^{-1}	$0-6$	1.34×10^{-2}
7.5×10^{-2}	5.0×10^{-1}	$48-0$	1.23×10^{-2}
7.5×10^{-2}	5.0×10^{-1}	$737-0$	1.95×10^{-2}

of inhibition becomes small. Thus, for dilute Cs concentrations, it can be expected that the degree of Cs inhibition will be approximately the same if the inhibitor concentration remains the same. This result is similar to the theory involved in K_d method of correlation (3).

Table IV shows the X-ray diffraction data obtained during Ca inhibition of Cs sorption. Comparison of Tables II and IV shows that the Ca did interfere with the normal time dependent Cs collapse of the lattice structure.

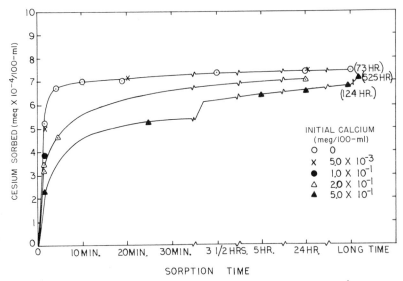

FIGURE 12   CESIUM SORBED FROM A 7.5 x 10^{-4} meq/
100-ml SOLUTION BY Ca-CLAY AS A
FUNCTION OF INITIAL CALCIUM AND
SORPTION TIME.

Sodium Inhibition of Cesium Sorption
    In the following experiment, three different cations were
involved. Table V presents the quantities of Cs sorbed by the
Ca-saturated clay as a function of initial [Cs], sorption time,
and initial [Na]. Figure 16 shows the quantities of Cs sorbed
for an initial [Cs] of 7.5 x 10^{-4} meq/100-ml and [Na] of 0 to 1
meq/100-ml. An increase in [Na] decreased the Cs sorption
within the first few minutes of the experiment, but at the end
of 24 hours reaction time the amount of Cs sorbed was approximately the same as the quantity of Cs sorbed with no Na present.
    The reciprocal plot of the data in Table V for the Na inhi-
bition of Cs sorption by the Ca-saturated clay is presented in
Figure 17. The slopes of the resulting straight lines increase
with increasing [Na] and all pass through a common intercept.
Therefore, it can be assumed that the quantity of Na bound in
the "activated intermediate" was insignificant. Similar to the
previously described Ca analysis, the slopes of the lines in

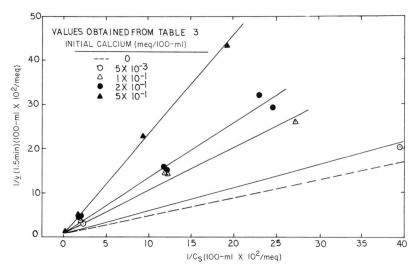

FIGURE 13   RECIPROCAL PLOT OF CALCIUM
             INHIBITION OF CESIUM SORPTION
             BY Ca-CLAY.

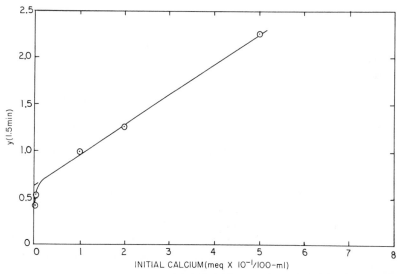

FIGURE 14   SLOPES OF FIGURE 13 VS. INITIAL[CALCIUM].

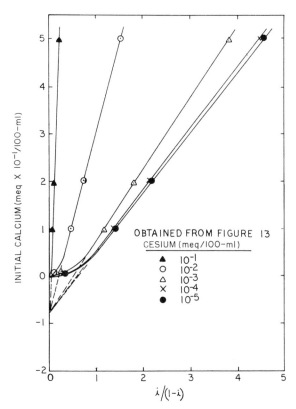

FIGURE 15   DEGREE OF CALCIUM INHIBITION OF
             CESIUM SORPTION BY Ca-CLAY.

Figure 17 were plotted in Figure 18 vs. the initial $\boxed{\text{Na}}$.
The resulting curve can be represented by linear sections.
Such a pattern is indicated by the model as the partial mutual
displacement inhibition type.

Figure 19 shows a plot of the initial [Na] vs. the degree
of inhibition i/ (1 - i) as a function of the [Cs] remaining in the
solution. When the final linear portions of these curves were
extrapolated, they all intercepted the ordinate axis at the same
negative point. All the curves start at the origin. The Cs
sorption was least inhibited at the highest [Cs], but approached
a limit as the [Cs] became dilute. Results presented in Figure 19
are representative of the pattern developed in the model for
partial mutual displacement inhibition.

TABLE IV EFFECT OF CALCIUM ON LATTICE COLLAPSE BY CESIUM

Sample	Chemical Treatment	Peak Ratio $14.7A°/10.1A°$
1	Ca-Clay	4.4
2	#1 + 7.5 x 10^{-4} Cs meq/100-ml and 5.0 x 10^{-3} Ca meq/100-ml for 1 min	3.25
3	#1 + 7.5 x 10^{-4} Cs meq/100-ml and 5.0 x 10^{-3} Ca meq/100-ml for 24 hr	2.2
4	#1 + 7.5 x 10^{-4} Cs meq/100-ml and 5.0 x 10^{-1} Ca meq/100-ml for 1 min	3.25
5	#1 + 7.5 x 10^{-4} Cs meq/100-ml and 5.0 x 10^{-1} Ca meq/100-ml for 24 hr	2.3
6	#1 + 7.5 x 10^{-3} Cs meq/100-ml and 5.0 x 10^{-1} Ca meq/100-ml for 1 min	3.45
7	#1 + 7.5 x 10^{-3} Cs meq/100-ml and 5.0 x 10^{-1} Ca meq/100-ml for 24 hr	2.4
8	#1 + 7.5 x 10^{-2} Cs meq/100-ml and 5.0 x 10^{-1} Ca meq/100-ml for 1 min	0.96
9	#1 + 7.5 x 10^{-2} Cs meq/100-ml and 5.0 x 10^{-1} Ca meq/100-ml for 24 hr	0.92

TABLE V CESIUM SORPTION WITH SODIUM INHIBITOR PRESENT

Initial [Cs] meq/100-ml	Initial [Na] meq/100-ml	Sorption Time hr - min	Cs Sorbed meq/100-ml
7.5×10^{-4}	0.5	0-1.5	4.6×10^{-4}
7.5×10^{-4}	0.5	0-4.5	6.24×10^{-4}
7.5×10^{-4}	0.5	24-0	7.35×10^{-4}
7.5×10^{-4}	1.0	0-1.5	4.27×10^{-4}
7.5×10^{-4}	1.0	0-4.0	5.65×10^{-4}
7.5×10^{-4}	1.0	24-30	7.37×10^{-4}
15.0×10^{-4}	0.5	0-1.5	9.13×10^{-4}
15.0×10^{-4}	0.5	0-4.5	12.10×10^{-4}
15.0×10^{-4}	0.5	24-0	14.80×10^{-4}
15.0×10^{-4}	1.0	0-1.5	8.1×10^{-4}
15.0×10^{-4}	1.0	0-4.5	11.62×10^{-4}
15.0×10^{-4}	1.0	27-30	14.7×10^{-4}
7.5×10^{-2}	0.5	0-1.5	1.02×10^{-2}
7.5×10^{-2}	0.5	0-4	1.22×10^{-2}
7.5×10^{-2}	0.5	24-0	1.46×10^{-2}
7.5×10^{-2}	1.0	0-1.5	1.06×10^{-2}
7.5×10^{-2}	1.0	0-4.5	1.30×10^{-2}
7.5×10^{-2}	1.0	27-0	1.64×10^{-2}

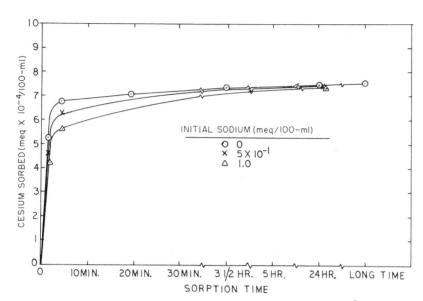

FIGURE 16   CESIUM SORBED FROM A 7.5 x 10⁻⁴ meq/100-ml
SOLUTION BY Ca-CLAY AS A FUNCTION OF
INITIAL [SODIUM] AND SORPTION TIME.

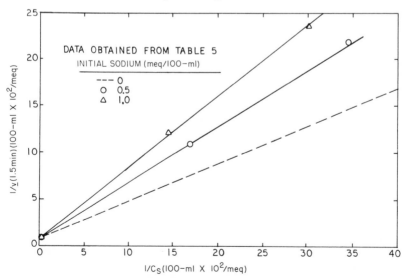

FIGURE 17   RECIPROCAL PLOT OF SODIUM INHIBITION
OF CESIUM SORPTION BY Ca-CLAY.

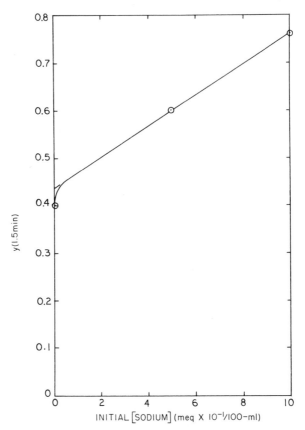

FIGURE 18   SLOPES OF FIGURE 17 VS. INITIAL SODIUM.

Comparison of the X-ray diffraction patterns of Table VI with those of Table II shows that Na did not interfere with the normal lattice collapse caused by Cs. No distinct peak occurred in the X-ray diffraction pattern at the normal $12A^O$ spacing associated with a Na-mica.

Potassium Inhibition of Cesium Sorption
Table VII lists the quantities of Cs sorbed for the various initial Cs and K concentrations and sorption time. Figure 20 demonstrates the effect of $[K]$ on the decrease in Cs sorption when the initial $[Cs]$ was 7.5×10^{-3} meq/100-ml. Furthermore, the quantity of Cs inhibited only slightly decreased with increased sorption time.

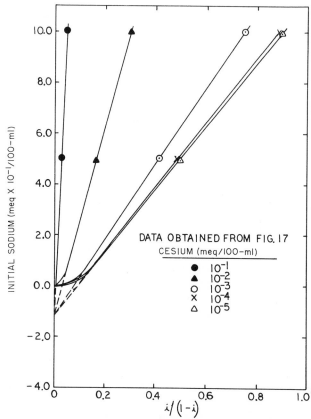

FIGURE 19   DEGREE OF SODIUM INHIBITION OF
CESIUM SORPTION BY Ca-CLAY.

Comparison of the X-ray diffraction patterns obtained with
and without K present as seen in Tables II and VIII shows that K
increased the rate of lattice collapse. This agrees with the data
presented by Tamura and Jacobs on lattice collapse of clays by
alkali metals (11, 12).

The reciprocal plot of the data in Table VII for K inhibition
of Cs sorption by the Ca clay is presented in Figure 21. A
comparison of Figure 21 with Figures 13 and 17 shows that K is
a more effective inhibitor than Ca or Na. Figure 22 shows that
a linear relationship exists between the slopes of the reciprocal

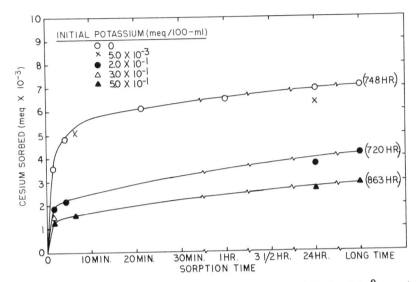

FIGURE 20   CESIUM SORPTION FROM A 7.5 x 10^{-3}meq/
100-ml SOLUTION BY Ca-CLAY AS A
FUNCTION OF INITIAL [POTASSIUM] AND
SORPTION TIME.

plot of Figure 21 and initial K present. As indicated by
equation 7-39, though a linear relationship usually indicates
complete inhibition, it could in special cases be a partial
mutual displacement type. To distinguish these two inhibition
types, the initial K was plotted in Figure 23 vs. the degree of
inhibition $i/(1 - i)$ as a function of initial Cs. All the results
are linear and pass through the origin. Only the complete
S-type inhibition would follow the pattern developed in the
model for Figures 21, 22, and 23.

DISCUSSION
    Because environmental conditions are so diversified, it is
apparent that a single simple equation cannot be developed
which would be unifyingly applicable to all sorption phenomena.
However, in the proposed sorption model simple equations
describing the various patterns of possible sorption results
can easily be added to the system. Although this paper describes
only three basic patterns of sorption results obtained when
other solutes are present in the solution, a similar approach

TABLE VI   EFFECT OF SODIUM ON LATTICE
COLLAPSE BY CESIUM

Sample	Chemical Treatment	Peak Ratio $14.7A^o/10.2A^o$
1	Ca-Clay	4.1
2	#1 + 7.5 x 10^{-4} Cs meq/100-ml and 0.5 meq/100-ml Na for 1 min	3.1
3	#1 + 7.5 x 10^{-4} Cs meq/100-ml and 0.5 meq/100-ml Na for 23 hr	3.5
4	#1 + 7.5 x 10^{-3} Cs meq/100-ml and 0.5 meq/100-ml Na for 1 min	2.8
5	#1 + 7.5 x 10^{-3} Cs meq/100-ml and 0.5 meq/100-ml Na for 24 hr	1.8
6	#1 + 7.5 x 10^{-2} Cs meq/100-ml and 0.5 meq/100-ml Na for 1 min	0.7
7	#1 + 7.5 x 10^{-2} Cs meq/100-ml and 0.5 meq/100-ml Na for 24 hr	0.55

can be used to obtain graphical analyses which distinguish between such variables as pH, temperature, increase in solids, and complexing agents.

In the complete general type inhibition, the inhibitor can unite with the sorption site or the "activated intermediate" to form other intermediates which are incapable of further reaction. The maximum uninhibited sorption rate is not restored with inhibitor present no matter how great the sorbate concentration is. However, at dilute sorbate concentrations a sufficiently high inhibitor concentration could cause the sorption rate of the sorbate to approach zero.

In the general partial type inhibition it is assumed that the formed "inhibitory intermediates" are capable in some modified way of further reaction. In this case the maximum uninhibited sorption rate cannot be restored by saturating concentrations of sorbate if an inhibitor is present. However, at dilute sorbate concentrations, the sorption rate will not drop to zero no matter how much inhibitor is present in the suspension.

In the partial mutual displacement type inhibition it is assumed that the sorbate can replace the inhibitor occupying the

TABLE VII   POTASSIUM INHIBITION OF CESIUM SORPTION

Initial [Cs] meq/100-ml	Initial [K] meq/100-ml	Sorption Time hr - min	Cs Sorbed meq/100-ml
7.5×10^{-4}	5.0×10^{-3}	0-1.5	5.18×10^{-4}
7.5×10^{-4}	5.0×10^{-3}	0-4.5	6.76×10^{-4}
7.5×10^{-4}	5.0×10^{-3}	25-30	7.45×10^{-4}
7.5×10^{-4}	2.0×10^{-1}	0-1.5	2.13×10^{-4}
7.5×10^{-4}	2.0×10^{-1}	0-4.5	2.80×10^{-4}
7.5×10^{-4}	2.0×10^{-1}	24-0	5.21×10^{-4}
7.5×10^{-4}	2.0×10^{-1}	719-0	5.82×10^{-4}
7.5×10^{-4}	3.0×10^{-1}	0-1.5	1.84×10^{-4}
7.5×10^{-4}	5.0×10^{-1}	0-1.5	1.27×10^{-4}
7.5×10^{-4}	5.0×10^{-1}	0-4.5	1.89×10^{-4}
7.5×10^{-4}	5.0×10^{-1}	24-20	3.66×10^{-4}
7.5×10^{-4}	5.0×10^{-1}	696-0	3.80×10^{-4}
15.0×10^{-4}	2.0×10^{-1}	0-1.5	4.48×10^{-4}
15.0×10^{-4}	2.0×10^{-1}	0-1.5	4.55×10^{-4}
15.0×10^{-4}	2.0×10^{-1}	24-0	10.25×10^{-4}
15.0×10^{-4}	3.0×10^{-1}	0-1.5	3.84×10^{-4}
15.0×10^{-4}	3.0×10^{-1}	0-1.5	3.38×10^{-4}
15.0×10^{-4}	3.0×10^{-1}	24-0	8.72×10^{-4}
15.0×10^{-4}	5.0×10^{-1}	0-1.5	2.25×10^{-4}
7.5×10^{-3}	5.0×10^{-3}	0-1.5	3.45×10^{-3}
7.5×10^{-3}	5.0×10^{-3}	0-6.5	5.13×10^{-3}

TABLE VII - cont'd

7.5×10^{-3}	5.0×10^{-3}	23-20	6.38×10^{-3}
7.5×10^{-3}	2.0×10^{-1}	0-1.5	1.91×10^{-3}
7.5×10^{-3}	2.0×10^{-1}	0-4.5	2.18×10^{-3}
7.5×10^{-3}	2.0×10^{-1}	24-0	3.75×10^{-3}
7.5×10^{-3}	2.0×10^{-1}	720-0	4.20×10^{-3}
7.5×10^{-3}	3.0×10^{-1}	0-1.5	1.47×10^{-3}
7.5×10^{-3}	3.0×10^{-1}	0-1.5	1.40×10^{-3}
7.5×10^{-3}	5.0×10^{-1}	0-1.5	1.43×10^{-3}
7.5×10^{-3}	5.0×10^{-1}	0-1.5	1.27×10^{-3}
7.5×10^{-3}	5.0×10^{-1}	0-6	1.61×10^{-3}
7.5×10^{-3}	5.0×10^{-1}	24-0	2.65×10^{-3}
7.5×10^{-3}	5.0×10^{-1}	863-0	2.86×10^{-3}
7.5×10^{-2}	3.0×10^{-1}	0-1.5	0.57×10^{-2}
7.5×10^{-2}	3.0×10^{-1}	0-1.5	0.51×10^{-2} (a)
7.5×10^{-2}	5.0×10^{-1}	0-4.5	0.68×10^{-2}

(a) Approximate result because of malfunction
    of instrument.

sorption site. Thus, the maximum sorption rate can be restored
at saturating concentrations of sorbate even though a good deal
of inhibitor is present in the solution. However, the sorption
rate can approach zero when the sorbate concentration is dilute
and saturating inhibitor concentrations are present.

The inhibition patterns were limited to those situations in
which there probably would be direct competition for the sorption
sites. With no other solutes present in solution, the sorption of
Cs was rapid. Within a short time the sorption rate rapidly
decreased as the Cs sorbed approached a quasi-equilibrium

TABLE VIII   EFFECT OF POTASSIUM ON LATTICE
COLLAPSE BY CESIUM

Sample	Chemical Treatment	Peak Ratio $14.7A^\circ/10.2A^\circ$
1	Ca-Clay	4.1
2	#1 + 7.5 x 10^{-4} Cs meq/100-ml and 5.0 x 10^{-1} meq/100-ml K for 1 min	1.42
3	#1 + 7.5 x 10^{-4} Cs meq/100-ml and 5.0 x 10^{-1} meq/100-ml K for 11 min	1.4
4	#1 + 7.5 x 10^{-3} Cs meq/100-ml and 5.0 x 10^{-1} meq/100-ml K for 24 hr	1.47
5	#1 + 7.5 x 10^{-3} Cs meq/100-ml and 5.0 x 10^{-1} meq/100-ml K for 1 min	1.6
6	#1 + 7.5 x 10^{-3} Cs meq/100-ml and 5.0 x 10^{-1} meq/100-ml K for 11 min	1.04
7	#1 + 7.5 x 10^{-3} Cs meq/100-ml and 5.0 x 10^{-1} meq/100-ml K for 24 hr	1.05
8	#1 + 7.5 x 10^{-2} Cs meq/100-ml and 5.0 x 10^{-1} meq/100-ml K for 1 min	0.70
9	#1 + 7.5 x 10^{-2} Cs meq/100-ml and 5.0 x 10^{-1} meq/100-ml K for 11 min	0.85
10	#1 + 7.5 x 10^{-2} Cs meq/100-ml and 5.0 x 10^{-1} meq/100-ml K for 24 hr	0.70

condition. A linear relationship resulted from the reciprocal plot of the Cs sorbed within 1.5 min and its concentration remaining in solution. X-ray diffraction patterns showed a definite interaction between [Cs] and sorption time during the clay's lattice collapse.

Addition of Na to the suspension decreased Cs sorption within the first few minutes, but after 24 hours the quantity of Cs sorbed was approximately the same as the experiments in which Na was absent. X-ray diffraction patterns showed that Na had an insignificant effect on the time dependent lattice collapse by the Cs.

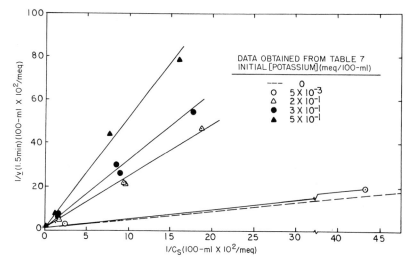

FIGURE 21   RECIPROCAL PLOT OF POTASSIUM
INHIBITION OF CESIUM SORPTION
BY Ca-Clay.

Calcium was a more effective inhibitory cation than Na.
However, as the sorption time increased the quantity of Cs
inhibited decreased. Although after 700 hours reaction time
the Cs sorbed did not reach the same level as when Ca was
absent, it was obvious that equilibrium had not been reached.
X-ray diffraction patterns showed that at high Ca concentrations,
the lattice collapse due to Cs was delayed.

Application of the graphical analyses developed in the model
also indicated that Cs, although inhibited by Na and Ca, was able
to displace these cations from the sorption sites.

Potassium was a more effective inhibitory cation than
either Ca or Na. The quantity of Cs inhibited was approximately
the same at all sorption times. This would be the trend of
results expected if complete inhibition was occurring. Application of the various graphical analyses derived in the model for
complete S-type inhibition showed that the experimental data
fitted the equations adequately. X-ray diffraction patterns
showed that addition of K to the suspension increased the rate
of the lattice collapse of the clay.

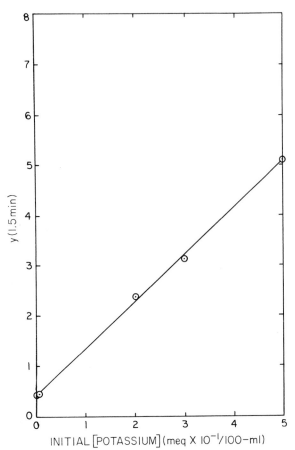

FIGURE 22   SLOPES OF FIGURE 21 VS. INITIAL
POTASSIUM.

ACKNOWLEDGEMENT

The authors wish to acknowledge the support of this investigation by a U S Public Health Service Pre-doctoral Fellowship 1-F1-WP-16455. The University of Wisconsin Research Committee and U S Public Health Service's training grant 5T1-WP-22-03 also contributed support. Thanks are also extended to Drs. S. W. Bailey, R. B. Corey, and D. E. Spyridakis for their advice and assistance.

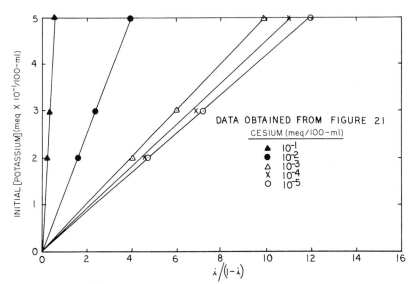

FIGURE 23   DEGREE OF POTASSIUM INHIBITION OF
CESIUM SORPTION BY Ca-CLAY.

LITERATURE CITED
1. Reiner, J.M., Behavior of Enzyme System, Burgess Publ
   Co., Minneapolis, Minn., (1959).

2. Fruh, E.G., Cesium Sorption by Hydrobiotite, PhD Thesis,
   University of Wisconsin, Madison, Wis., (1965).

3. Wahlberg, J. and M. Fishman, U S Geol Survey Bulletin 1140-A,
   (1962).

4. Jacobs, D.G., Health Phys, 4, 157 (1960).

5. Tamura, T. and D.G. Jacobs, Health Phys, 2, 391 (1960).

6. Jackson, M.L., Soil Chemical Analysis - Advanced Course,
   Dept of Soils, University of Wisconsin, Madison, Wis., (1956).

7. Jackson, M.L., Soil Chemical Analysis, Prentice-Hall Inc.,
   Englewood Cliffs, N.J., (1958).

8. Scott, A. D., et al, Soil Sci Soc Am Proc, 23, 191 (1960).

9. Scott, A. D. and M. G. Reed, Soil Sci Soc Am Proc, 26, 41 (1962).

10. Reed, M. G. and A. D. Scott, Soil Sci Soc Am Proc, 26, 437 (1962).

11. Granstrom, M. L. and B. Kahn, J Phys Chem, 59, 408 (1955).

12. Finston, H. L. and M. T. Kinsely, The Radiochemistry of Cesium, Subcommittee on Radio chemistry, National Academy of Sciences, Office of Technical Services, Dept of Commerce, Washington, D.C., (1961).

13. Barshad, I., Am Mineralogist, 33, 655 (1948).

14. Jacobs, D. G. and T. Tamura, The Mechanism of Ion Fixation Using Radioisotope Techniques, 7th Inter Cong Soil Sci, II, 206, Madison, Wis., (1960).

15. Fruh, E. G. and G. F. Lee, (In Press).

DISCUSSION
    DR. ZENCHELSKY: Thank you, Dr. Fruh. Are there any questions for Dr. Fruh?
    DR. KRISHNASWAMIENGAR KESHAVAN (University of Maine): This is not a question but a comment, that your model was very similar to the Michaelis-Menton model of enzyme-substrate reaction. In fact, the reciprocal plot is the same as the Lineweaver-Burk plot. It was very interesting to note that.
    DR. FRUH: This sorption scheme is quite similar to the models used in the enzyme and industrial catalysis fields. Enzymes are catalysts which are secreted by living organisms. Thus, enzyme-substrate reactions are surface reactions.
    The sorption scheme presented here is, however, not analogous to the Michaelis-Menton equation, which is the most well-known model used in the enzyme field. The Michaelis-Menton equation is based on the assumption that the process is at equilibrium and that the rate of the forward reaction is equal to that of the backward reaction. Analogous to the enzyme model presented in Reiner's textbook, this clay sorption scheme is based on the assumption that the reaction has reached steady state, $dX/dt = 0$.

DR. J. B. ANDELMAN (University of Pittsburgh): Have you considered the diffusion process through the unstirred liquid film at the mineral-solution interface and attempted to control it in your experiments?

DR. FRUH: Yes. We attempted to limit the effect of this factor on the quantity of Cs sorbed. For the two different Cs concentrations, we varied the agitation rate which is related to the thickness of the liquid film surrounding the clay particle. At all agitation rates tested above 100 strokes/min the per cent Cs sorbed did not increase. For practical reasons 120 strokes/min was the agitation rate used in all the experiments described.

DR. ANDELMAN: But have you considered the different diffusion processes as being rate-determining in your scheme?

DR. FRUH: No. The sorption schemes presented were not intended to be mechanistic models. The purpose of these sorption schemes was to correlate sorption data collected in the laboratory and eventually in the environment.

MR. E. A . JENNE (U S Geological Survey): Did you check the reversibility of the Cs sorption? If so, you should be able to comment upon your model, because your partially displacable vs. total inhibition should be a function of reversibility of the sorption reaction.

DR. FRUH: We used leaching solutions containing one normal concentration of various cations. The literature review indicated that such cations as Ca and Mg could leach the sorbed Cs by re-opening the clay lattice. Leaching with ammonium and K would be expected to complete the collapse of the clay lattice. At the higher Cs concentrations, with no cationic inhibitors present, approximately the same quantity of sorbed Cs was leached using Mg and ammonium solutions. At the lower Cs concentrations, the Mg leached more sorbed Cs than the ammonium and the quantity leached decreased with increased sorption time.

When other cations were competing with the Cs for sorption sites, only one normal ammonium solutions were used for leaching. Approximately 10 to 30% of the sorbed Cs was leached from the clay depending on the [Cs], the sorption time, the cationic inhibitor used, and the concentration of the inhibitor. In nearly every case the percent of the sorbed Cs which was leachable decreased with increased sorption time.

Experiments were conducted also using K - saturated clay. These were not reported in the paper. The clay was completely collapsed because of the K. The Cs sorbed did not cause further collapse and was probably sorbed on the mica edges. Approximately 50% of the sorbed Cs was leached under these conditions.

MR. JENNE: Have you checked this on anything other than vermiculite, any other clays?

DR. FRUH: In the laboratory experiments we used only vermiculite. We did compare data obtained by other investigators to check the applicability of the sorption scheme to different experimental conditions. The clays were montmorillonite, kaolinite, and illite. Data were available also for a mixed clay. The data adequately fitted the sorption scheme developed for two sites.

DR. ZENCHELSKY: Any further questions or discussion?

MR. JENNE: Did you obtain your X-ray diffraction patterns in the wet stage so as to avoid collapse of the vermiculite due to dehydration?

DR. FRUH: Yes, the X-ray diffraction patterns presented were obtained in the wet state.

MR. JENNE: These data are for the wet stage?

DR. FRUH: I did them in both states.

DR. J. J. MORGAN (California Institute of Technology): I am not so sure that you discussed this. I was absent for the first ten minutes of your paper. You did indicate later that you considered pH. Were you going to discuss that at some further time? Would you say how you controlled the pH or what sort of techniques you found suitable?

We are doing something similar to this, and find that pH is a problem because of CO_2 exchange.

DR. FRUH: By varying the pH at various Cs concentrations we found that optimum Cs sorption occurred in the range of pH 6 to 8. The pH of the clay suspension was approximately 7. Thus, in all the experiments, pH was left uncontrolled and usually did not change during the reaction. The changes when they did occur were slight.

M. Bier
Frederick C. Cooper
University of Arizona

ELECTRICAL PHENOMENA AT SURFACES

One of the guiding concepts of the organizers of the Rudolfs Conference is to stimulate an interdisciplinary approach to the problems of water and wastewater chemistry. This is most fortunate, because only from this point of view can we hope to contribute to the Conference, as we are conditioned by our biochemical background.

As such, the most striking observation in the water field is the relatively recent, but widespread interest in electrophoresis and zeta potential as a means of study of colloid stability, flocculation, filtration, etc. That electrokinetics in colloidal systems is not a negligible force can be documented best by quoting from the opening paragraph of the book by Klinkenberg and Van der Minne (1):

> Early in 1954 a large tank in Shell's refinery at Pernis exploded 40 minutes after the start of a blending operation in which a tops-naphtha mixture was being pumped into straight-run naphtha. The fire was quickly brought under control and the salvaged contents transferred to

217

```
           another tank. On the following day a
           second attempt was made to blend these
           materials and again an explosion occurred
           40 minutes after starting the pumps. This
           striking and unusual coincidence could
           only be explained by the assumption that
           both explosions had been caused by static
           electricity.
```

The recent emergence of interest is mainly the result of the pioneering work of Black and his co-workers (2, 3, 4) and of Riddick (5, 6). In these studies they have shown that raw waters contain microscopically visible colloids which characteristically possess high electrophoretic mobilities according to Black or high zeta potentials according to Riddick. On addition of alum or other coagulating agents, the electrophoretic mobility is found to decrease tending to zero at optimum coagulating proportions. Charge reversal may occur also. For example, a typical curve relating coagulability and electrophoretic mobility, as reported by Black and co-workers (7), is presented in Figure 1. Removal of organic color from water coincides with zero electrophoretic mobility with the coagulation effected by ferric sulfate. On the basis of such findings, hope was entertained that the complex art of water treatment through coagulation finally could be reduced to an exact science where the measurement of a single parameter; namely, the electrophoretic mobility or zeta potential, would suffice to predict the correct dosage of coagulant for best water treatment.

It is obvious, however, that the considerations relating electrokinetic characteristics of a colloid and its stability apply only to hydrophobic colloids. Hydrophilic colloids are by definition soluble also at their isoelectric point, and therefore may not be coagulable over any and all ranges of zeta potential or electrophoretic mobility. It should be emphasized that some of the most troublesome problems in water purification may arise from such hydrophilic colloids; the best examples of which are the detergents. Many other pollutants in domestic sewage are hydrophilic in nature as, for example, proteins. It would be only fair to assume that with increasing reuse of water, the proportion of hydrophilic to hydrophobic colloids will be constantly on the increase and give rise to the more difficult purification problems.

More surprising, exceptions to the aforementioned behavior were found even in hydrophobic colloids. As a typical example, Figure 2 taken from as yet unpublished data of Matijevic and Stryk

shows the electrophoretic mobility of an aged AgI sol in presence
of various amounts of $Al_2(SO_4)_3$ as a function of pH (8). It can
be seen that this typical hydrophobic colloid has an isoelectric
point of about pH 4.5 to 4.8, but the coagulation range indicated
by the shaded area bears no relation whatever to the electrophoretic mobility and shows strong dependence on $Al_2(SO_4)_3$
concentration. For explanation of these data, referral is made
to the forthcoming publication of the authors (8), but obviously
their findings are in apparent contrast with those of Black.

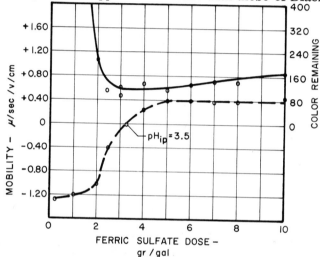

FIGURE 1   EFFECT OF FERRIC SULFATE DOSE ON
              COAGULATION OF A COLORED WATER.
              (After Black, et al, 7).

The relation between colloid stability and electrokinetic
potentials has been established firmly since the classical days
of colloid chemistry (9), and has received exhaustive treatment
in the well known treatise of Verwey and Overbeek (10). In view
of the contradictions just noted, the practical applicability of the
classical theories may be questioned. Whatever the final reply
to this question may be, the work of Black and Riddick has been
most useful in arousing the interest of the profession in electrokinetic phenomena.

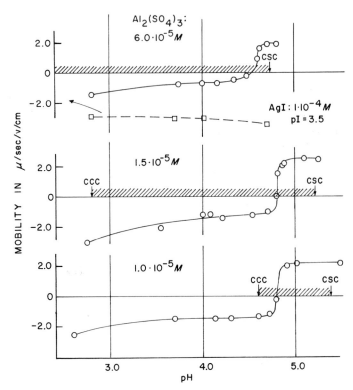

FIGURE 2   MOBILITIES OF AN AGED AgI SOL IN
              PRESENCE OF VARIOUS CONCENTRATIONS
              OF $Al_2(SO_4)_3$ AS A FUNCTION OF pH.
              Squares denote the mobilities of the same
              sol in absence of $Al_2(SO_4)_3$. Hatching
              represents the coagulation range. Critical
              coagulation concentration (ccc) and critical
              stabilization concentration (csc) are indicated
              also. (After Matijevic and Stryker, 8).

ELECTRIC POTENTIALS
     All the theories in this field are based on the fact that on
every boundary between two phases, complex surface phenomena
occur that are related to molecular interactions and give rise
to electric potentials. This happens even if the two phases are
metal and vacuum. In colloidal systems that are characterized
by their extreme ratio of surface to volume, surface phenomena
assume exceptional importance. In many instances they may

have a greater bearing on the behavior of the system than even
the chemical nature of the colloid itself.

While a number of electric potentials can be defined, only
those arising in solution need to be considered; the thermodynamic
or Galvani potential, and the zeta or electrokinetic potential. The
first is to be found, for example, between two solutions having
a common ion at different concentrations and is calculated by the
well-known Nernst equation:

$$E = \text{constant} + \frac{RT}{z_i F} \ln c_i \qquad (8\text{-}1)$$

where z_i and c_i stand for the valence and concentration of the
common ion, the potential-determining ion. It is measured
usually in concentration cells of which a familiar modification
is the measurement of the pH by means of the glass electrode.
These measurements are done under static equilibrium conditions
and give relatively easily interpretable information concerning
the potentials of ions arising from their charge. In colloid
chemistry these potentials are of importance in Donnan equilibria.

The electrokinetic or zeta potential must be taken into
consideration in dynamic measurements when there is a movement of the ion with respect to the bulk of the solution. The
difference between static and dynamic conditions arises because
of the hydration of every charged particle; the adsorbed part
of the solvent migrating with the particle as a single kinetic unit.
The slipping or frictional boundary of the ion, therefore, will
not coincide with its physical surface whether the latter can be
defined or not. At the same time, there is an electrostatic field
surrounding the particle, caused by its charge, which decays to
zero at some distance from it. As the whole solution is electrically neutral by definition, it is obvious that there is an increased
concentration of oppositely charged ions in the immediate neighborhood of the particle. While each ion is a point source of charge,
a spatial averaging is possible. The zeta potential is the potential
of this field at the distance from the particle corresponding to its
slipping boundary as shown in Figure 3 (9). It is this distribution
of potentials surrounding the charged particle which is treated in
the well known theories of the electrical double layer. Figure 4
illustrates the various possible shapes of the potential curves
and distribution of ions as quoted by Overbeek (11).

There are several methods for measuring zeta potentials,
all based on the four basic electrokinetic phenomena:

a. Electrophoresis: imposed electrical field causes

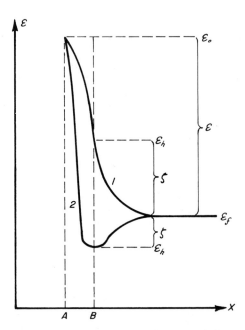

FIGURE 3   SCHEMATIC PRESENTATION OF THE
ELECTRICAL DOUBLE LAYER.
ξ - electrical potential, x - distance
from an arbitrary point inside the solid
phase, A - boundary between solid and
liquid phase, B - frictional boundary
between the phases, ξ - zeta or electrokinetic potential. Lines 1 and 2 illustrate
possible potential curves. (After Freundlich, 9).

migration of particles.
   b. Electroosmosis: imposed electrical field causes
migration of solvent.
   c. Sedimentation potential: arises from an imposed
movement of charged particles.
   d. Streaming potential: arises from an imposed movement
of solvent through capillaries.
   Electrophoresis is employed most often. In all water
experiments, direct microscopic observation of the migrating
particles in an electric field has been employed. Streaming
potential measurements may be more advantageous, if the
filtration characteristics of the floc are to be studied. To relate

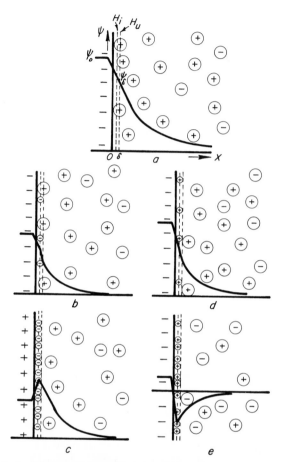

FIGURE 4 DISTRIBUTION OF IONS AND POTENTIALS
IN THE DOUBLE LAYER.
a - no specific adsorption, b - specific
adsorption of anions, c - strong specific
adsorption of anions, d- specific adsorption of cations. (After Overbeek and
Lijklema, 11).

the electrophoretic migration velocity with zeta potential, the
equations of Helmholtz-Smoluchowski, Henry, and Debye-
Hückel are applied, depending on particle size, as shown in

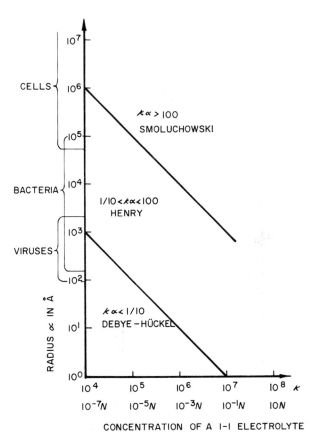

FIGURE 5   REGIONS OF APPLICABILITY OF EQUATIONS
             OF SMOLUCHOWSKI, HENRY, AND DEBYE-
             HÜCKEL AS A FUNCTION OF PARTICLE
             SIZE AND ELECTROLYTE CONCENTRATION.
             (After Brinton and Lauffer, 12).

Figure 5 (12). In practice, these calculations are fraught with
uncertainties, particularly with regard to the shape of the particle
namely, the overall shape as well as actual radius of curvature of
localized elements of its surface (12). For example, with many
proteins, the qualitative agreement between electrophoretic veloci
and charge of the protein is obtained easily as illustrated in Figur
(13). The quantitative agreement with theory was poor, however,

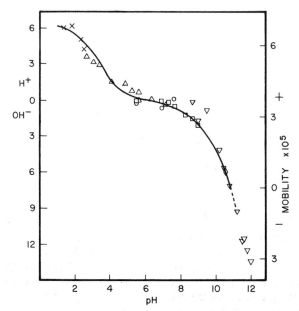

FIGURE 6   COMPARISON OF ELECTROPHORETIC
            MOBILITIES AND DISSOCIATION CURVES
            OF TRYPSIN. Solid line - dissociation
            curve, points - electrophoretic mobilities.
            (After Duke, et al, 13).

and serious discrepancies were reported (14). If there are no
theoretical needs of dealing with zeta potentials, these calculations are best avoided, and reporting of electrophoretic mobilities
is preferred since it is the actual parameter which is measured.

Without going into the complex theories of the electrical
double layer, several points ought to be considered:

a. It is relatively immaterial if the original charge of the
particle is due to dissociation of ionizable groups of the colloid
itself, as for example, with proteins and polyelectrolytes, or
if it is caused by adsorption of low molecular weight ions, as is
typically the case with many oil emulsions. This is of consideration in water treatment because, while there are Al ions, actual
charge may be altered by adsorption (15).

b. The effective radius of the electrostatic field is influenced
greatly by the overall ionic concentration. For water and

symmetrical monovalent electrolytes, the thickness of the double layer can be given as approximately 10 Å for 0.1 M, 100 Å for 10^{-3} M and 1000 Å for 10^{-5} M solutions (11). This radius is influenced relatively little by the size of the colloid.

    c. The zeta potential is strongly dependent on the radius of the particle: the ratio of zeta potential at ionic strength I = 0.02 to that at ionic strength I = 0 is 0.90 for Na ions, with a radius of 2.6 Å, and is only 0.50 for a protein with molecular weight of about 35,000 and radius of 22 Å (16). In raw waters with their usual low electrolyte concentration, the zeta potential of large particles will be influenced strongly, therefore, by relatively minor changes in ionic strength.

    d. The fields are by no means small: a potential drop of 20 m across a distance of 10 Å, corresponds to a field of 200,000 v/cm.

    All difficulties notwithstanding, the theories relating to electr potentials in colloid solutions are understood relatively well. Why, then, is there a conflict as illustrated in the first two figures? The problems arise because we deal with electrochemical phenomena, and not with purely electrical ones. An electric potential can be defined as the amount of work necessary to transfer a given charge from one point to the other, and should be independent of the materi carrying the charge. Obviously, however, the work of transporting H ions into the immediate neighborhood of a colloid will be quite different from that required in transporting Na ions or even more complex ones. Chemical work, in addition to electrical, will be necessary to change the immediate surrounding of the Na or H ions. It is because of such considerations that the notion of electro-chemical potential was introduced, as the sum of chemical and electrical potentials, but the exact separation of these two entities is impossible (11, 17). In other words, to understand the complexity of phenomena that occur during coagulation, flocculation, filtration, etc., not only must electrical phenomena be considered, but also the chemistry involved. Steric factors, conformation between sur-faces or reacting colloids, van der Waals forces, hydrogen bond-ing, or even formation of chemical bonds should be taken into consideration as mutually interacting parameters.

    A clear parallel can be drawn with the evolution of thought in the field of protein chemistry. The fact that proteins carry ioni-zable groups and as a result large electrostatic charges, is one of their most obvious charactristics. For this reason, it was believed at first that these forces are the most important in determining the stability, behavior, and tertiary structure of soluble proteins (18).

Hydrogen bonding was the second factor taken into consideration. Complete satisfaction of all possible hydrogen bonding was assumed in the well-known Pauling-Corey model of protein helix (19). Pauling was also the first to take into account the exact steric requirements derived from Corey's x-ray diffraction determinations of bond lengths, angles between bonds, and limits to free rotation. Such generalized considerations based on broad concepts, while very useful, failed to provide the answer to the structure of even a single soluble protein. This can be obtained only through the final determination of the exact chemical structure of individual proteins, i.e., amino acid sequence, coupled with x-ray determinations of the overall structure, and specific studies of configuration of proteins through a variety of highly refined methods, mainly optical in nature (20). It will be a long time before such a mass of information will be available for the complex colloidal structures occurring in water chemistry.

APPLICATIONS OF ELECTROPHORESIS

Continuing these considerations from the vantage point of biochemists not directly familiar with all the intricate problems of water chemistry, we could add that electrophoresis has been most fruitful in biological sciences for a variety of reasons. In the field of water chemistry only a very small area of possible applications has been explored. Briefly summarizing, the main areas of application of electrophoresis are:

a. Providing information that concerns the charge, zeta potential, and isoelectric point of colloids. This is the area explored by Black, Riddick, and others (2-8, 21, 22) but is of relatively little importance in protein chemistry.

b. Providing means of identification of individual components in a complex colloid mixture. This is the main usefulness of electrophoresis in protein chemistry. It arises from the fact that there are very few means of differentiating between complex colloids of similar structure. Other methods already have been used (23, 24), but electrophoresis could be an additional valuable tool. It should be emphasized, however, that this is possible only if the electrophoretic measurements are conducted in a well defined and buffered medium. The veronal buffer for many years was practically the exclusive medium for serum analysis. It could be suggested that the same approach be taken in the field of water chemistry, and that attempts should be made to classify

the colloids present in various waters by means of their electrophoretic mobility. This would necessitate formulating a typical
and easily reproducible standard water composition, in terms of
its ionic constituents. All electrophoretic data on water colloids
characteristically present rather high average electrophoretic
mobilities of the colloids. We believe that this is not due to any
actual similarities among the measured colloids, and is rather
a reflection of the low ionic content of most waters. But mainly,
without working in a well defined water medium, the data collected
in one laboratory are of little if any value to other laboratories,
where different ionic composition may prevail. The Petroleum
Institute of America has contributed significantly to water chemistr
by providing samples of well defined clay materials. It is suggeste
that electrophoresis should be used as a means of providing equally
well-defined water samples.

     c. Providing means of study of interacting macromolecular
systems (25, 26). It has been mentioned that the relation between
zeta potential and colloid stability does not apply to hydrophilic
colloids. While hydrophobic colloids may coagulate near their
isoelectric point; hydrophilic systems, to the contrary, will react
mainly at maximum charge. Polyelectrolytes, finding increased
use in water treatment, are typical examples of hydrophilic colloids
The electrophoretic behavior of protein-detergent mixtures has
been studied by several authors (14). Maximum interaction has
been found where the protein carries the greatest charge to that
of the detergent, but opposite in sign.

     d. Preparative electrophoresis: In the biological area,
electrophoresis is employed frequently for preparation of purified
colloid fractions. Our own work has been mainly concerned with
preparative applications of electrophoresis to water problems as
indicated below.

WATER PURIFICATION BY LARGE SCALE ELECTROPHORESIS

     Let us briefly describe the preparative electrophoretic metho
that was employed since it is quite different from the microscope
method used in the analytical work. In its essentials, forced-flow
electrophoresis (27, 28) is illustrated best by means of the schemati
presentation in Figure 7. An electrophoretic cell is defined by
means of two membranes, A and A', that are separated into an
input half-cell and output cell by means of filter B. The membrane
and filters are held in position by means of appropriate spacers.
These spacers are much thinner than shown with their dimensions
being 2.25" x 6" x 0.070". The membranes are the usual dialyzing

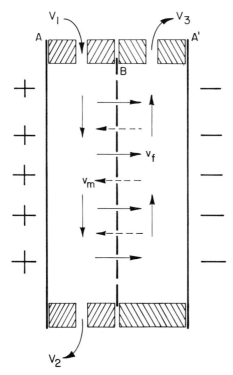

FIGURE 7   SCHEMATIC DIAGRAM OF A FORCED-FLOW
             ELECTROPHORESIS CELL. A, A' - membranes,
             B - filter, V_1 - raw water inflow, V_2 - waste
             outflow, V_3 - purified water outflow, solid
             arrows - direction of flow of water, broken
             arrows - direction of electrophoretic migration.

membranes such as Visking or cellophane. A variety of non-
metallic filters can be employed, including filter paper, micro-
porous plastic battery separators, or even Millipore filters. The
essential difference between membranes and filters is that the
membranes allow free passage of electrolytes, but do not allow
free flow of water, or diffusion of colloids. The filter allows
passage of most colloids and free flow of water. A direct current
electrical field is established across the cell by means of electrodes
external to the cell assembly.
    Raw water is fed continuously through the top inlet V_1 and

is separated into two streams, part of which is collected from the opposite end, V_2, of the input spacer, while the remainder is forced through the filter and collected from the outlet V_3. The direction of the flow of liquid through the cell and filter is indicated by solid arrows. At the same time the imposed electrical field causes a migration of the electrically charged colloids in a direction opposite to the flow of the liquid through the filter. This electrophoretic migration is indicated by the broken arrow in the diagram. If the linear migration velocity V_m is equal to or bigger than the linear rate of flow of the liquid V_f the passage of colloids through the filter is prevented effectively. Thus the apparent effect of the electrical field is to modify the properties of the filter which becomes a retentive for electrically charged colloids, while at the same time allowing an easy and free flow of the solvent. Colloid retained by the filter normally are not allowed to accumulate in the cell, but are eliminated through the liquid collected from the bottom outlet of the apparatus.

The same apparatus can be used also as a simple filtering device if the water carries coarsely suspended materials or supracolloids; such as, clay, algae, and gelatinous precipitates which would tend to clog the filter. Most of these materials carry large negative charges and their deposition on the filter will be prevented by the same process as outlined above. As a result clogging is prevented and continuous filtration can be maintained even with most troublesome suspensions. In some cases actual deposition of the coarse material occurs at the membrane opposite to the filter and cleaning may be effectuated through periodic rapid reversals of the polarity of the current.

For those familar with paper electrophoresis, an obvious analogy can be drawn; in normal paper electrophoresis separations are made within the plane of the paper. In forced-flow electrophoresis, the separation is made perpendicularly to the plane of the filter. Therefore, high rates of flow are obtained as the whole filtering surface is utilized. On the other hand, only two fractions are obtained; a colloid free fraction which has passed through the filter and a colloid enriched fraction which has been retained. The apparatus is also similar to that used in electrodialysis for desalting of saline waters. The essential difference is that in electrodialysis, ion exchange membranes are employed, while the present method a combination of semipermeable membranes and filters is used. In addition, true electrophoretic transport of colloids is involved rather than electrodialysis.

In practice a multicell apparatus is used. The arrangement

of electrodes and cell components is illustrated in Figure 8
which shows the alternate sequence of membranes and filters
and input and output spacers. A complete laboratory apparatus
is shown in Figure 9 where the console houses the power supply,
pump speed controls, and refrigeration equipment. The latter
is used only in biological experiments and is not necessary in
the work reported here.

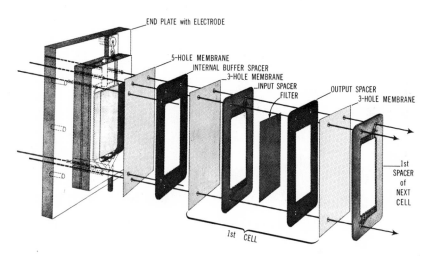

FIGURE 8   EXPANDED VIEW OF A FORCED-FLOW
              ELECTROPHORESIS CELL ASSEMBLY.

As the process yields two streams, one colloid free, the
other colloid enriched, it can be used for two purposes: (a) large
scale purification of water, and (b) concentration of colloids for
further analysis. Both applications have been explored. On the
analytical side our main efforts were to devise a simple procedure
for routine monitoring of virus pollution in water. To this effect
bacteriophages specific for E. coli were used as models of viral
pollution. Due to the specialized nature of this work, details will
not be discussed (29). The same procedure, however, can be
used for the collection of bacteria, algae, and other suspended
matter from raw waters.
      Of our work on large scale purification of water by means
of forced-flow electrophoresis, only the most illustrative data
dealing with the following water samples are presented (30, 31):

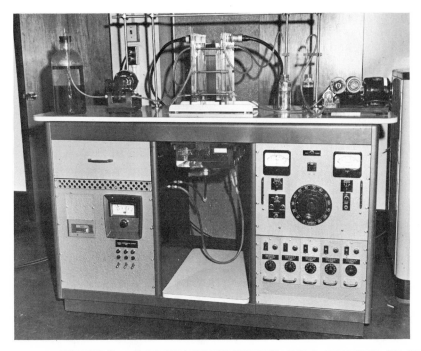

FIGURE 9   LABORATORY MODEL OF A FORCED-FLOW
ELECTROPHORESIS APPARATUS.

a. Flood runoff characteristic of this region, high in silt
and clay and low in organic pollutants.

b. Precipitation collected in asphalted catchment areas.
Such water has little or no silt but is colored highly due to water
soluble phenolic extractants from the asphalt emulsion. The
samples were provided by Kitt Peak National Astronomical
Observatory and by the Water Conservation Laboratory, USDA,
in Phoenix, Arizona.

c. The effluent from the Pima County Sanitary District
sewage stabilization pond is particularly rich in green algae
primarily of the Euglenoid group.

d. Artifically prepared solutions of various phenolics and
detergents.

Flood waters were collected from several of the local
intermittent streams shortly after summer storms and from
retention basins. The silt load was as high as 1500 mg/l and

electrophoretic treatment was effective in removing all visible
turbidity. The treatment was less effective for dissolved solids
with their concentration decreasing by only about 50%. Typical
results comparing the raw water and the electrophoretically
prepared product are presented in Figure 10. An electric field
of 30 v/cm was applied and the flow rate of the product stream
was 120 ml/min/sq ft.

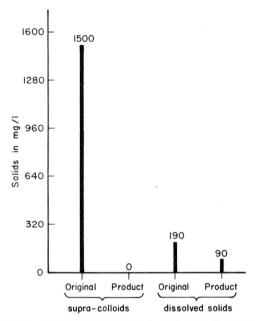

FIGURE 10   ELECTROPHORETIC REMOVAL OF
              SUSPENDED AND DISSOLVED SOLIDS FROM
              FLOOD RUNOFF. (After Cooper, 30).

Similar results were obtained on the treatment of the
effluent from the sewage stabilization pond. The complete
removal of algae depends on the type of filter. With filters
of a porosity of $5\,\mu$, complete removal was obtained at flow
rates of 50 ml/min/sq ft, but if this was increased to, for
example, 300 ml/min/sq ft, up to 20 to 30% of the algae are
found in the processed matter. Millipore filters of 0.45 μ
porosity assure complete retention of all algae and can be used

continuously without clogging at flow rates of up to 170 ml/min/ sq ft.

The anticlogging effect of the electrical current is shown in Figure 11. The solid line shows a progressively decreasing flow rate between points a and b when no current is applied and the recovery of filter performance between points b and c when an electrical field of 40 v/cm is applied. Cleaning and clogging cycles can be repeated several times which extends

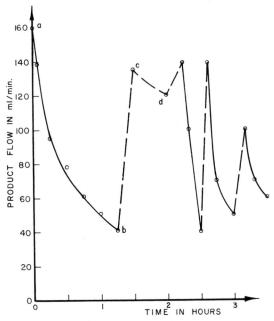

FIGURE 11   ELECTROPHORETIC REGENERATION OF MILLIPORE FILTERS FOR THE FILTRATION OF ALGAE FROM A SEWAGE STABILIZATION POND EFFLUENT. Solid line - no voltage applied, broken line - voltage applied. (After Cooper, 30).

the life of the filter. The illustrated data were obtained using a Dacron supported Millipore filter, $0.45\,\mu$. Repeated tests have shown, however, that best results are obtained with a continuous application of an electrical current of intermediate range rather

than with periodic cleaning of filters with high electrical fields
or other cyclic applications of current. Each off-current cycle
results in progressive deterioration of the filter, but even
without deterioration, most efficient utilization of electrical
power is obtained on continuous application of the field.
  An entirely different application of the method illustrates
the removal of organic pollution from the water collected in
asphalted catchment areas and which is free from supra-colloids.
Ultraviolet adsorption at 260 mμ was taken as a measure of
phenolic content. Figure 12 shows that simple filtration through
either Millipore or ESB-Reeves filters results only in a small
decrease of the ultraviolet adsorption. Upon electrophoresis,
complete removal of all detectable adsorption is obtained at a
low rate of 10 ml/min and even at 10 times higher flows, 85%
of the colloids is removed. These data were obtained with a
five-cell laboratory apparatus. A flow rate of 100 ml/min
corresponds to one of 240 ml/min/sq ft when referred to unit
filter surface area. The simultaneous concentration of the
colloid in the waste effluent is also shown. Greater concentration can be obtained if the ratio of processed stream to waste
stream is altered, but for theoretical reasons a 1:1 ratio was
employed. The concentrated waste stream can be utilized for
isolation of colloids. The sample used in this experiment was
obtained from the Kitt Peak National Astronomical Observatory
which relies on its catchment area as the sole source of potable
water. Work at the USDA laboratory in Phoenix, Arizona, has
shown that asphalted catchment areas are a practical means of
harvesting water in the rain-poor Southwest. The colloids
cannot be coagulated by alum even at high dosages. Charcoal
adsorption filters became effective at Kitt Peak only after
prolonged leaching of the asphalt. As will be shown later,
electrophoresis is particularly economical for the treatment
of such water because of its exceedingly low electrical conductance.
  One of the most troublesome problems in current water
treatment is the removal of detergents. Electrophoresis can
be used for this purpose. Figure 13 shows the residual ABS
remaining in an artificially prepared mixture containing originally
50 mg/l of detergent in tap water. Comparing data for 90%
removal, it can be seen that there is a nearly linear dependence
between applied voltage and obtainable rate of flow. The overall
flow rates are, however, very low.
  While our study has shown that electrophoresis is feasible
and can be applied to a variety of water sources, the economy of

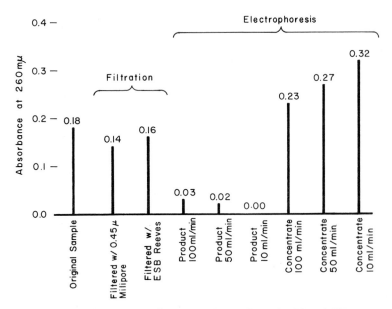

FIGURE 12   COMPARISON OF FILTRATION AND
              ELECTROPHORETIC TREATMENT OF
              A COLORED WATER SAMPLE. (After
              Cooper, 30).

the process depends mainly on two factors: (a) electrical
conductance of the raw water, and (b) type of pollutant to be
eliminated. The electrical conductivity is the more important
of the two as illustrated in Table I. Most economical is the
application to Kitt Peak water because of its low original conductance since it is essentially rain water. Least economical
is the application to secondary sewage effluents because of
their well-known high salinity. While electrophoresis was
primarily designed for removal of colloids, data in column 3
show that there is substantial desalting of the processed water.
If desalting is the primary objective, electrodialysis would
give considerably higher efficiency. This study has been conducted with a small laboratory-scale model, only 5 cells, which
has an inherent power efficiency of only 30%. This efficiency is
a function of the number of cells used in parallel, and with any
large scale apparatus it could easily be increased to 90%.

This work is believed to be the first attempt to apply
electrophoresis directly to large scale water purification.

TABLE I
COST ESTIMATE FOR WATER TREATMENT BY ELECTROPHORESIS (30)

Water Sample	Specific Conductance of		Rate	Power	Estimated Cost 1,000 gal (a)	
	Raw Water	Finished Product			Model	Scale-Up
	μmhos	μmhos	ml/min/sq ft	KW-hr/1,000 gal	$	$
Silt Separation (flood runoff)	250	67	120	62	1.24	0.41
Algae Separation (sewage effluent)	1,100	450	170	162	3.24	1.08
Color Removal (Kitt Peak)	64	15	24 (b) 240 (b)	12 1.2	0.24 0.03	0.08 0.01
ABS Removal	540	100	24	94	1.86	0.62

(a) Cost of electrical power estimated at $0.02 per KW-hr. The laboratory apparatus used in this study had an inherent 30% power efficiency, which could be increased to 90% in scale-ups.

(b) Two flow rates are quoted, giving 100% and 85% color removal, respectively. (See Figure 12).

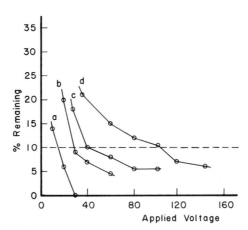

FIGURE 13   ELECTROPHORETIC REMOVAL OF ABS
             FROM TAP WATER.   Flow rates: a, b,
             c, d = 6, 12, 18, and 24 ml/min/sq ft,
             respectively. (After Cooper, 30).

There are no theoretical reasons why it could not be applied on
an equally large scale with other electrochemical processes;
such as, electrodialysis, electrolysis, or electrodeposition.
The only reason was the unavailability of adequate equipment.
Our work has shown that forced-flow electrophoresis is indeed
applicable and that it has overcome this most immediate difficulty.
Large scale experiments are needed to prove its feasibility from
a practical point of view.   The most important question yet
unanswered, is the longevity of an assembly under field conditions.
The method suffers from the shortcomings common to all "frame
and membrane" processes; namely, the relative cumbersomeness
and high cost of the equipment.   It has a theoretically appealing
justification; while other methods of water treatment are based
on reducation in zeta potential, within limits discussed earlier,
electrophoresis directly utilizes the prevailing high potentials
on colloid surfaces for their removal.

ACKNOWLEDGEMENTS
        This work has been supported in part by Research Grant
WP-00516 of the Public Health Service, USDHEW.   The authors
wish to acknowledge the helpful advice and interest of Quentin
M. Mees, Professor of Civil Engineering at the University of
Arizona, and the technical assistance of Grover Bruckner.

LITERATURE CITED

1. Klinkenberg, A. and J.L. Van der Minne, Electrostatics in the Petroleum Industry, Elsevier Publishing Co. Inc., Amsterdam, Holland, (1958).

2. Pilipovich, J.B., et al, J Am Water Works Assoc, 50, 1467 (1958).

3. Black, A.P., J Am Water Works Assoc, 52, 492 (1960).

4. Black, A.P. and S.A. Hannah, J Am Water Works Assoc, 53, 438 (1961).

5. Riddick, T.M., Chem Eng, 68, 121 (1961); Ibid, 68, 141 (1961).

6. Riddick, T.M., J Am Water Works Assoc, 53, 1007 (1961).

7. Black, A.P., et al, J Am Water Works Assoc, 55, 1347 (1963).

8. Matijevic, E. and L.J. Stryker, J Colloid Sci (In press).

9. Freundlich, H., Kapillarchemie, 4th Ed, Akademische Verlagsgesellschaft, Leipzig, (1930).

10. Verwey, E.J.W. and J.Th.G. Overbeek, Theory of the Stability of Lyophobic Colloids, Elsevier Publishing Co. Inc., Amsterdam, Holland, (1948).

11. Overbeek, J.Th.G. and J. Lijklema, Electric Potentials in Colloidal Systems in Electrophoresis (Bier, Ed) Academic Press Inc., New York, N.Y., (1959).

12. Brinton, C.S. and M.A. Lauffer, The Electrophoresis of Viruses Bacteria, and Cells, and the Microscope Method of Electrophoresis in Electrophoresis (Bier, Ed.), Academic Press, Inc., New York, N.Y., (1959).

13. Duke, J.A., et al, Arch Biochem Biophys, 40, 424 (1952).

14. Brown, R.A. and S.N. Timasheff, Applications of Moving Boundary Electrophoresis to Protein Systems in Electrophoresis, (Bier, Ed), Academic Press, Inc., New York, N.Y., (1959).

15. Matijevic, E. , et al, J Phys Chem, 65, 826 (1961).

16. Abramson, H.A., et al, Electrophoresis of Proteins, Reinhold Publishers, New York, N.Y.,(1942).

17. Guggenheim, E.A., J Phys Chem, 33, 842 (1929); Ibid, 34, 1540 (1930).

18. Loeb, J., Proteins and the Theory of Colloidal Behavior, 2nd Ed, McGraw Hill,Inc., New York, N.Y.,(1924).

19. Pauling, L. and R.B. Corey, Proc Natl Acad Sci U S, 37, 241 (1951).

20. Scherago, H.A., Protein Structure, Academic Press,Inc., New York, N.Y.,(1961).

21. Faust, S.D. and M.C. Manger, Water and Sewage Works 111, (1964).

22. Jorden, R.M, J Am Water Works Assoc, 55, 771 (1963).

23. Black, A.P. and R.F. Christman, J Am Water Works Assoc, 55, 753 (1963).

24. Bunch, R.L., et al, J Water Poll Control Fed, 33, 122 (1961).

25. Gilbert, G.A. and R.C. Ll, Jenkins, Nature,177, 853 (1956); Proc Roy Soc (London) A253, 420 (1959).

26. Longsworth, L.G., Moving Boundary Electrophoresis-- Theory in Electrophoresis (Bier, Ed),Academic Press,Inc., New York, N.Y.,(1959).

27. Bier, M., Preparative Electrophoresis Without Supporting Media in Electrophoresis (Bier, Ed),Academic Press,Inc., New York, N.Y.,(1959).

28. Bier, M., Electrical Filtering Process and Device, US Pat, 3,079,318 (1963).

29. Bier, M., et al, Trans of Symposium on Transmission of Viruses by the Water Route, (In press).

30. Cooper, F. C., Water Purification by Forced-Flow Electro-
    phoresis, Thesis, University of Arizona, (1964).

31. Cooper, F. C., et al, J Sanit Eng Div Am Soc Civil Eng,
    SA6, 13 (1965).

DISCUSSION:
    CHAIRMAN PACKHAM: Professor LaMer
    DR. BIER: I was hoping you had left the city.
    DR. LAMER (Columbia University): After those very
laudatory statements about my talk, perhaps I shouldn't say
anything, but I heard one or two things that I'd like to correct.
I understood you to say that you disagreed with me on one point,
that I did not use the electrochemical potentials.
    DR. BIER: No, no, that you did use it, but I just wanted
to say this was pointed out by Guggenheim already long ago,
but it was neglected very strongly afterwards.
    DR. LAMER: My objection now is that your dates are
wrong. Guggenheim's papers were published in J Phys Chem in
1929.
    DR. BIER: I'm sorry.
    DR. LAMER: When I was in Brönsted's laboratory in 1923,
he was impressing upon me at that time with the dictum that one
cannot measure individual ion activity coefficients by strict
thermodynamic methods. The assumption of MacInnes (1920)
that the coefficients of K^+ and Cl^- are equal, which perhaps is
very nearly true, is nevertheless not generally applicable. You
will find this point discussed in the fine print of Lewis and
Randall's "Thermodynamics."
    Guggenheim came to Brönsted's laboratory five years
later. Brönsted's ideas were published in J Phys Chem in 1929,
and are in substantial agreement, including the electrochemical
potential, with Guggenheim's. However, we should recognize
that these ideas of the electrochemical potential and the general
problem of junction potentials were foreshadowed very much
earlier in a clear but very concise paragraph in Gibbs (1875).
    I would like to tighten up a little bit the scientific language
you are using. Gibbs defined the electric potential as the work
necessary to transfer a unit charge from one medium to another.
The chemical potential, μ, involves the chemical work (RT ln C_1/C_2)
necessary to transfer a neutral molecule from medium 1 to
medium 2. The electrochemical potential involves the sum of
the chemical and the electrical works involved when an ion

carrying the electric charge is transferred.

Now, what is the zeta potential? It is the potential one observes when an electrolyte is <u>forced to flow</u> through a capillary or conversely by applying a <u>potential difference</u> to an electrolyte in a capillary and observing the movement of the ions (electrophoretic mobility). The two methods are equivalent and one can be calculated from the other by the symmetry equations for steady states given by Onsager (1931).

In my opinion a zeta potential does not exist until one starts moving the ions by an impressed pressure or an impressed electrostatic potential. On the other hand, the chemical potential and the electrochemical potential exist at all times under static conditions.

DR. BIER: The latter are thermodynamic potentials.

DR. LAMER: Yes. On the other hand, the zeta potential is an <u>electrokinetic</u> potential. When the ions in two adjacent <u>layers of liquid are</u> forced to move past one another, an electric potential difference can be measured. A correct definition of zeta potential involves the electrical work necessary to bring a unit of change from the surface of slip between the two layers to some other arbitrary point of reference in the solution. The surface of slip is an elusive quantity which cannot be easily placed geometrically.

In the Helmholtz-Smoluchowski elementary treatment of this operation one gets a simple formula connecting the calculated zeta potential and the measured electrophoretic mobility. It is only necessary to multiply the mobility by a factor, approximately 13 depending upon the temperature, to convert mobilities to zeta potentials. The factor 13 contains dimensional units which convert velocities, usually expressed as μ /sec/v/cm to electric potentials, which involve ergs and unit charges.

If one reads the J Am Water Works Assoc he will find that the zeta potential is the <u>electric charge on the particle.</u> These statements have been made repeatedly over the past decade to the present time by several authors. I object strenuously to the impression given. It is bad physics. The zeta potential cannot be the electric charge because the units of potential involve work and are not the same as electrostatic charge. What these authors mean to say is that under comparable conditions, and there are many conditions to be specified, the zeta potential can be taken as a <u>measure</u> of the charge, which is something quite different.

As long as the multiplicative factor 13 remains constant

all is well. However, if you examine the recent writings of
Henry, of Overbeek and others, we find this simplicity is not
true. The factor depends not only on temperature but upon
ionic strength and other factors. It can vary by as much as
2 fold. Until we have a complete and correct theory connecting
electrophoretic mobility and zeta potential, it is impossible to
reverse the calculation and get a reliable value for the charge
on the particle simply from the mobility. It is for these reasons
that I feel strongly that no good scientific purpose is served by
converting mobilities into zeta potentials until the more complicated connecting equations have been verified.

Of course, if you have something to sell, zeta potential
is a much better advertising catch word than is electrophoretic
mobility. The natives are mystified and admire with great awe
the black box which gives the results on the dials.

We ought not to deceive ourselves. We should measure
electrophoretic mobility and report our results in these units.
Instead of multiplying by the factor 13, we can achieve the same
result graphically by extending the ordinate by a factor 13. This
above shows that much of the recent "hullabaloo" about zeta
potentials is meaningless. (Editor's note, we are in complete
agreement with these statements!)

DR. BIER: This is the thermodynamic.

DR. LAMER: And Gibbs is, of course, absolutely right.
Well now, you start moving these two liquids, and then you do
produce a potential you measure, and it is the work necessary
to bring a charge from the surface of slip up to the other point
of reference.

DR. BIER: This is what I wanted to say.

DR. LAMER: I want to say I think you have presented
this matter very well. There is a correlation between zeta
potential (or mobility) and colloid stability. As you go through
the zero point of mobility then we find a close correlation. Away
from the zero point I don't know whose formula we should use
for calculating zeta potential. Maybe you can tell me. Henry
or Overbeek?

DR. BIER: The question, what is the surface geometry?

DR. LAMER: I have never studied it. Suppose you change
the viscosity of this flowing system, you change your surface
of slip, the Lamb correction and all of those other complicating
factors so the zeta potential has a different value.

DR. BIER: But even with proteins where we know well
the shape and where we know the disassociation and so on,

nobody has obtained good correlation, mathematical correlation.

DR. LAMER: I'm glad we're quite agreed on electrochemical potentials.

CHAIRMAN PACKHAM: If I may just interject here. It's very difficult for me to remain an impartial chairman during this session. I think that some of the arguments that have been put up against the use of zeta potential as opposed to electrophoretic mobility are justified, electrophoretic mobility is a measured quantity and to convert it to zeta potential it is inadequate merely to multiply it by a factor; some corrections have to be considered. These corrections are not always significant but where they are, the zeta potential will enable a more meaningful interpretation of the data than electrophoretic mobility which is an uncorrected quantity. Of course, if the corrections are not applied then zeta potential is equally misleading.

I think there is possibly time for one more question. I should say that our four papers this morning deal with various aspects of the same subject, and I think there will be opportunity for people to interject their comments in the discussions of some of the other papers if there is not time now.

DR. BIER: May I first answer a little bit your comment before the next question, and this is that I believe very strongly that the usefulness of the zeta potential to water chemistry would be tremendously advanced if some kind of a computer program could be established for the zeta potential, concentration of colloids and whatnot, all in one formula to help in the standardization of water. The electrophoretic mobility is only one measurement, and we need far more than this in order to correlate it. But the conversion to zeta potential does not obviate all the difficulties of using electrophoretic mobility at all.

MR. R. A. BAKER (Mellon Inst.): For the sake of the water operators, I'd like to point out that although we all enjoy this argument about the electrophoretic state, I think we are going to scare away many practical people. As you said yourself, somebody has to prove whether this is applicable in the field. We decided to set aside the arguments that have been going on particularly regarding terminology, and actually go out and use some commercial equipment in the field. Some of you know this.

If you now bring in a computer with all these formulas and I'd love to have this by the way, we are really going to discourage operating people. Some will never try it.

Recently we had the privilege of working with one of the

large water treating plants in Philadelphia. This work has been published. We did this specifically to demonstrate that there is a great value. There are representatives here from Philadelphia Water Department who can verify the fact that significant advantages have been gained on a daily cost basis, I think something of the order of $70.00 a day, by using "zeta potential." Now, you can call it anything you want, but there is practical benefit and while those of us in the laboratories are arguing, let's not frighten people out of doing something that can save money and give them better quality water in the interim.

DR. BIER: I was talking to the Washington operators instead of the men at Philadelphia, who told me it applies very well in summer, but not in the winter. This is the problem.

CHAIRMAN PACKHAM: I think it can very clearly be shown that in some cases it does not apply, and in other cases it applies very well.

Victor K. LaMer
Columbia University

COAGULATION VERSUS THE FLOCCULATION OF COLLOIDAL DISPERSIONS BY HIGH POLYMERS (POLYELECTROLYTES)

This report summarized the salient features of 14 years research on the Flocculation of Colloidal Dispersions by Polyelectrolytes by the writer and his associates. Emphasis upon the application and interpretation of the results of the research upon presently accepted theories of water purification by the alum process will be presented.

Since the demand for uranium was critical in 1950, the AEC was investigating all possible sources of supply. It was found that Florida phosphate rocks contained (usually) 0.01 to 0.1% uranium in the smaller particles (about 1 to 10 μ) that were washed away in the grinding process for preparation of fertilizer. The dispersions, often referred to as slimes, had to be stored in large artificial lakes to avoid contamination of rivers. They would neither settle nor filter sufficiently rapidly for clarification. A dewatering process was needed so that the chemical engineers could proceed with chemical digestions of the solid material and thus win U_2O_3.

The fine particles consist of varying amounts of typical clays, such as montmorillonite, kaolinite, and gibbsite, depending upon the source in addition to tricalcium phosphate types of crystals. These phosphate rock dispersions accordingly vary in their behavior between that of typical hydrophilic colloids,

246

exemplified by starches and proteins and the typical hydrophobic
colloids, such as gold or AgI sols.

COLLOIDAL STABILITY

A hydrophilic colloid like gelatin disperses spontaneously
in water and consequently is thermodynamically stable. Stability
is due primarily to chemical interactions between the hydroxyl
group of the colloidal particle and the water, which can be loosely
characterized as hydration or in general as solvation. Accordingly,
stable sols of a very high number count of particles, often reaching 10^{15} to 10^{18} particles/cm^3, can be prepared. This is true
of proteins, starches, synthetic macromolecules, or polyelectrolytes in general. These sols, which are rather insensitive to
salt additions, follow a Hofmeister series with respect to
stability. Differences between ions in the Hofmeister series
arise from specific chemical (hydrating) properties and are
not due to the charges on the ions.

By contrast, the hydrophobic sol represents an unstable
state, which, in some cases, is stabilized as a metastable state
for long periods of time by the presence of electric charges on
the particle. These quasi stable sols are sensitive to additions
of neutral salts with stability determined primarily by electric
charges on the ion of opposite sign to that of the colloid particle.
This electrical interaction may depend upon valence of the
ion of opposite sign to a power as high as the sixth (6th) but
depends only very slightly upon the specific chemical nature
of the ion of the same sign or to the valence of its electric
charge (Schulze-Hardy rule). An electrically charged clay
surface contains hydroxyl groups, oriented upon a matrix of
Si, Ca, and Al and is, therefore, somewhat hydrophilic.

Collisions between colloidal particles obey the Smoluchowski
coagulation law which is a bimolecular collision law governed
by diffusion of the particles toward one another in accordance
with Fick's law (1). In the case of aersols, the particles are
almost always electrically uncharged in a medium (air) of
dielectric constant unity. Herein, the Smoluchowski law sets
the upper limit in particle number, for the stability of an aerosol,
at about 10^7 particles/cm^3.

Possession of charges of the same sign on particles of a
hydrosol lowers the likelihood of fruitful collisions leading to
coagulation, but this factor is partly offset by the high dielectric
constant of water (88 to 78 at 0° to 25^oC). More particulary,

the surrounding atmosphere of other ions of both sign in the solvent more or less effectively screens the high electrostatic potential generated by the centrally located highly charged colloid particle. It is, therefore, not particularly surprising that in many cases, for example, the monodispersed sulfur hydrosols, the particle number of a hydrophobic sol cannot exceed $10^8/cm^3$ if the sol is to remain stable over any reasonable period of time (44).

The stability of a hydrophobic sol cannot be determined by any simple set of electrostatic or thermodynamic parameters alone but must involve time factors. Coagulation is a kinetic process involving the transition of a quasi-stable phase to two more stable phases.

DOUBLE LAYER THEORIES

By the middle 1940's it had become obvious to this writer that the problem of stability of hydrophobic colloids is conditioned by the basic physical pictures and principles of the Debye-Hückel theory of simple electrolytes, such as the diffuse ionic atmosphere, it's characteristic distance $1/\kappa$, and a time averaged electrostatic potential which determines the thermodynamic and electrokinetic behavior of the ions. It seemed that it only remained to incorporate Brønsted's theory of reaction velocity with the Debye equations, modified, of course, to apply to colloidal systems, to achieve a theory of colloidal stability which should be as successful as the Brønsted-Debye equations had proven to be in explaining the kinetics of reactions of simple ions (45, 46, 47).

Modifications of the Debye-Hückel theory of electrolytes required to make it applicable to colloidal sols, however, have posed unsurmountable problems. These have not been solved to date at least in useful terms.

Although the Debye-Hückel theory of simple electrolytes furnishes an illuminating guide for considering problems of colloidal behavior, the essential difficulty is mathematical in that the three dimensional Poisson-Boltzman cannot be solved in closed form. In Debye's treatment of electrolytes only the linear term in the expansion of the exponential is retained. Equations derived from this abridged, linear form of the Poisson-Boltzman equation meet Onsager's criterion of exact integratabilty. The Debye-Hückel theory has proven to be singularly successful in treating low valence (1, 2, 3 charges) electrolytes when the product of the charges of opposite sign

$(Z_1 Z_2)$ is less than 5 in a high dielectric medium like water (2, 3, 5, 6, 7).

Debye and Hückel, and Brønsted and LaMer, in producing experimental evidence for validity of the theory, emphasized that these criteria required that $ZE\Psi/kt \ll 1$ (of the order of 0.01) and that $\kappa a < 1$. $1/\kappa$ is the thickness of the spherical ionic atmosphere at which the time averaged potential Ψ generated by the central ion of charge ZE is reduced to $1/\varrho$ th$=$ $\dfrac{1}{1.2718}$ of its value at the surface of the ion of radius r. Here "a" represents the ratio of radius of the ion to the distance $1/\kappa$. These criteria require that the spherical ion atmosphere be highly dilute and therefore diffuse (3).

Gronwall obtained a general solution of the three dimensional Poisson-Boltzman equation that was developed as an infinite series in ascending powers of $1/D$. Numerical tables were computed by LaMer and Sandved through the 5th approximation for symmetrical electrolytes and through the 3rd approximation in the unsymmetric case (4).

The extended theory of Gronwall, LaMer, and Sandved gave excellent agreement with the emf measurements for the symmetrical (2-2) electrolytes, $MgSO_4$ and $CdSO_4$, over the range 0.0001 M to 0.01 M. The data are fitted by the physically reasonable value of the parameter, "a" = 3.64 A^O in both cases (5, 6, 7). The only adjustable parameter, "a" has the physical meaning of the distance of closest approach of the centers of the ions. The extended theory resolved the paradox of negative values of "a" resulting from application of the simple Debye-Hückel theory. While these agreements represented a triumph for Gronwall, LaMer, and Sandved's treatment in extending the range of validity of the Debye-Hückel theory to somewhat higher valence types, the results were still restricted to dilute solutions.

Bjerrum avoided a mathematical solution of the complete Poisson-Boltzman equation by introducing the concept of ion pairs as a means of correcting for the neglected higher terms in the Debye-Hückel treatment (8). The ion pair represents incomplete dissociation arising solely from electrostatic interaction. The association of high valence ions of opposite sign into ion-pairs is assumed to follow the law of mass action, whereby an association constant K' involving the parameter "a" is employed.

The ascending power series in Gronwall's solution, although convergent does not converge rapidly enough for more extreme cases than those cited for Mg SO_4 and Cd SO_4 to be useful. On the other hand, Bjerrum's integral, Q, is more flexible since it collects all of the corrections attributable to "a" and other factors by burying them in the constant K'. The two treatments give results in good agreement with each other for those ranges of concentration where they can be compared, and hence are to be considered equivalent. Bjerrium's procedure has been mentioned, since it offers a somewhat more realistic (i.e., a less mathematical) physical picture of the situation that exists when a hydrophobic particle picture of the situation that exists when a hydrophobic particle of high charge is immersed in an atmosphere of simple ions, for example, Na Cl. Such colloids should be treated as highly unsymmetric electrolytes.

Owing to the tremendous attractive forces created by a highly charged colloid particle, elementary calculations on either Gronwall, LaMer, and Sandved's theory or Bjerrum's theory show that an overwhelming fraction of the ions sign opposite to that of the particle will be tightly bound on the surface, thus neutralizing considerably, but not entirely, the initial charges on the particle. The binding of these ions consequently reduces the effective net charge. The unbound fraction of ions remaining outside this layer form a spherical ion atmosphere so diffuse that it can be approximated by the Debye-Hückel theory. In other words, κ , when computed on the basis of the ions remaining unbound, is applicable. Otherwise the calculation yields ridiculous values when computed on the basis of the total number of ions given by analysis or synthesis of the sol. This point is often completely overlooked or ignored.

In 1924, Stern advanced the idea of such a bound layer, but quite properly also ascribes its existence to forces other than the monopole coulombic forces pictured above (9). At close distances, of the order of 10^{-7} to 10^{-8} cm, the chemical forces of interaction, which are of a specific nature, become more dominant than the long range coulombic forces. Chemical forces obey a law depending upon the inverse 6th to 8th power of distance of separation; hence, they are able to overwhelm the coulombic forces which decay more slowly as the inverse square of the distance. At larger distances, chemical forces are of no importance.

When chemical forces are involved, the binding process is called adsorption, more strictly chemi-adsorption in contrast

to what can be called electrostatic adsorption. It will not be
profitable at present to assess how much of the Stern layer
results from specific chemical binding or from electrostatic
binding. The important points are that ions of the Stern layer
are not free kinetically and hence cannot contribute to properties such as freezing point lowering or conductivity. For
an ion to be classified as free it must have a kinetic energy
greater than $\frac{1}{2}$ kt per degree of freedom. Secondly, adsorption
can be treated by a Langmuir isotherm (42, 48).

The literature from 1926 to 1940 contained many attempts
to explain colloid behavior on the basis of the simple Debye
theory, but without any success. In 1939-40 Derjaguin recognized
the futility of using the linear approximation of the spherical
Poisson-Boltzman equation for colloids (10). Since this three
dimensional equation cannot be solved in simple closed form,
the use of a two-dimensional flat plate model with a one dimensional atmosphere was proposed as a simpler approximation
for the correct model of spheres with surrounding three dimensional but overlapping atmospheres.

Many years ago, Gouy (11) and Chapman (12) replaced the
layer of bound ions in the Helmholtz (13) picture of the double
layer on a flat plate by the concept of a diffuse double layer.
They obtained simple formulas in terms of the hyperbolic sine
of $Z \, e \, \Psi \, x/kt$ for the decrease in the potential Ψ as a function
of the distance x from the surface of the plate into the region
of the one-dimensional (distance x) atmosphere of ions. Whether
or not two such flat plates, when separated by a small distance
would experience an attraction or a repulsion was a debatable
question for the next 30 years. Finally, Derjaguin and Landau
proved in 1939-40 that the resulting electrostatic interaction
forces would be repulsive (14). This finding makes sense. By
combining equations for this repulsive double layer potential
with those for the so-called Hamaker attractive forces, which
constitutes a refinement of the Van der Waals attractive force
following Landau's recognition that they arise from quantum
dispersion, a balance occurs between the repulsive potential
(1st order electrostatic, or coulombic in origin) of the double
layer. These are much higher order forces in respect to decay
with distance. Verwey and Overbeek, independently of Derjaguin
and Landau, made many calculations on the same basis, which
are to be found in their well known monograph (15).

It can now be said that the Derjaguin-Landau and Verwey Overbeek theories based on the flat plate double layer picture as a simplification and an approximation to the more physically acceptable three dimensional model of Debye, and therefore more tractable mathematically does explain the major problems of stability of hydrophobic colloids and their coagulation following the addition of simple electrolytes. They do not explain flocculation due to long chain polyelectrolytes.

When some of the recently presented double layer calculations are examined, some paradoxes and inconsistencies are encountered that merit comment. For example, Sawyer and Rehfeld in treating charged polymeric lattices and association colloids, calculate and use values of $E \Psi / kt = 40$ and of $\varkappa a = 30$ (16). It is incorrect and misleading for these authors to say that they are employing the Debye-Huckel theory of simple electrolytes for these high values violate flagrantly the restrictions placed upon the Debye-Huckel treatment. The explanation lies in the fact that the double layer theory used by the authors is applicable only to flat plates. This model becomes unrealistic when applied to spherical particles surrounded by a spherical atmosphere of ions.

In passing to the flat plate model, one dimension is lost. The parameter x (the distance from the surface of the plate at which Ψ has fallen to $\Psi/2.718$) has a different physical meaning from the r which is used for the spherical distance from the center of the ion in the Debye-Huckel theory. The parameter "a" that represents the distance of closest approach of the ions has no exact counterpart in double layer theory because the distance behind the surface of the plate does not appear. The radius of curvature, $1/r$ has vanished as $\frac{1}{\infty}$. The quantities "a" and "r" should not be used interchangeably but should be sharply defined and distinguished for each model by assigning different notations to avoid a confusion of concepts.

PHOSPHATE SLIMES

When the problem set by the AEC was first approached we felt confidently that the extensive calculations of Verwey and Overbeek involving application of the double layer theory would solve the problem (15). This pious hope soon proved to be entirely wrong and misleading in its predictions.

Since our preliminary, orientation experiments, in 1951, have necessitated the development of an entirely different set

of concepts and interpretations differing radically from those
of the prevailing popular double layer theory, they will be
described in some detail to document our revolutionary asser-
tions. They are fundamental to colloid science when considering polyelectrolytes.

Firstly, our new treatment demands a critical re-exami-
nation of the terms coagulation and flocculation in the light of
the mechanisms involved and the operations which define these
terms (17). Secondly, the settling of the flocs resulting from
polyelectrolyte addition has to be recognized as subsidence,
sedimentation of small aggregates resulting from the coagulation
of primary particles. Only when this is done, can the following
references published under the title "Flocculation, Subsidence,
and Filtration" be read with profit and comprehended (18, 19, 20,
21, 22, 23, 24, 25).

The original data have appeared in unclassified progress
reports for Columbia University's A E C Contract (30-1)-1189.
They can be obtained from the AEC:

a. N.Y.O. (3286), June 30, 1952. This summarizes work
done to this date on composition of the dispersions, the distinction between coagulation and flocculation, and the simple relationship between them for well flocculated slimes using "floc gel".

b. N.Y.O. (3287), July 30, 1953). This gives the theoretical
equation for subsidence of well flocculated slimes and microscopic observations on the flocculated dispersions of haphazardly
orientated particles produced by polyelectrolytes like Monsanto
Lustrex (Lytron) X-886. They are to be compared with coagula-
tions produced by simple salts. Orienting electrophoretic
studies are reported also.

c. N.Y.O. (3288), July 30, 1953. A theoretical equation
is given for subsidence of flocculated material. Response of
slimes toward flocculating agents is documented in relation to
chemical composition of the slime solid. Potential determining
ions are determined by conductometric titrations.

d. N.Y.O. (3289), August 31, 1964 . Extension is made
of the relation between rate of subsidence and rate of filtration.

e. N.Y.O. (7403), October 30, 1956. (Technical Information
Service, Oak Ridge, Tenn.) Preparation and evaluation of
superior flocculating agents are presented for phosphate slimes -
Columbia University's Super Separan PAM-K2 and salt effects.

Experimental

When $CaCl_2$ or $Ca(OH)_2$ is added to a dispersion of clay-type minerals of particle numbers approximating $10^{10}/cm^3$, the particles coagulate and sediment rapidly under gravity as independent particles obeying roughly some form of Stokes law. The rate of sedimentation is inversely proportional to the square of the radius of a spherical particle. Unfortunately, the coagulated particles formed a compact coagulum which did not filter at all well. Since rapid filtration was an essential factor in the projected U_2O_3 processes, filtration aids other than salts were sought.

Van Iterson discovered that the fine dispersions resulting from the washing of coal could be flocculated by adding boiled starch pastes (26). Schulten and Co. of Holland market a starch product called "flocgel" which has proven to be a causticised starch partially cross-linked with small additions of boron oxide (B_2O_3). Small amounts (70 mg/l) of "flocgel" produced dramatic results on the phosphate rock slimes. However, the mode of action proved to be entirely different from the coagulation produced by simple salt additions which are comprehensible on the basis of the Derjaguin-Landau and Verwey-Overbeek theories.

When dilute (1%) "flocgel" is added drop-wise to a slime with slow stirring to achieve adequate mixing, no immediate effects were observed. In a few minutes, however, a "curdling" of the dispersion is noticed that leads to the formation of flocs which suddenly commence to settle leaving a clear supernatant liquid. In contrast to salt coagulation, a sharp line of demarcation between flocs and supernatant liquid can be followed accurately. The descent of this line represents a compaction of flocs rather than the independent sedimentation of small aggregates. The phenomenon has been called "hindered settling" in the older practical literature, but it is better designated as subsidence to differentiate it from sedimentation. Strangely enough, there does not appear to be any reference to the concept of subsidence in any of the American texts on colloids. Engineers, who must face realities as they find them, have treated the subject since 1940 in papers by Ward and Kammermeyer (27), Steinour (28), and Kynch (29).

Empirically, the sharp line of demarcation has been found to obey a linear law $t/(h - h_o) = \alpha + \beta t$, where h_o is the initial height of the subsidence level, h = height of subsidence level after time t, and α and β are constants of the system.

Smellie and LaMer justified their empirical equation on theoretical grounds (20). It should represent the limiting law of subsidence just as Stokes law represents the limiting law of sedimentation.

When the flocculated material was transferred to filter paper, it filtered rapidly, sometimes as much as 200-fold faster than the untreated slime. The reason, of course, is that the flocs consist of large loosely packed gossamer type structures which produce a filter cake with large pores. Floc-culated material exhibits a larger final volume than does un-treated material or material coagulated by salts.

In searching for an explanation of flocculation, it was reasoned that the Dutch raise potato starch only and no corn (Zea Maize) starch. In 1916, Thomas indicated to the writer that Samec had found that potato starches contain 0.13% phos-phorous as monophosphoryl esters as terminal groups on the glucose chains (30). Corn starch contains no phosphate and tapioca starch only in a small amount.

This finding plus the later finding that the components of the starch molecule could be separated by differential electro-phoresis formed the basis of a series of PhD dissertations in the 1930's under the direction of Professors T.C. Taylor, Mary Caldwell, and Charles O. Beckman (30). The beta amylose fraction of potato starch, which carries the phosphate radical, migrates to the positive pole and hence is negatively charged. Potato starch can accordingly be considered as a phosphoric acid whose hydrogens have been substituted by long dextrose chains; hence, it is a negatively charged polyelectrolyte.

It was postulated that the hydroxyl radicals of the glucose group of the starch are adsorbed on the negatively charged clay particles most probably by hydrogen bonding with hydroxyl groups on the flat clay surfaces. Calcium ions, which were present in the natural waters, combined chemically with these phosphate groups, thus crosslinking the two particles. By successive adsorptions and crosslinking in different directions a "fluffy" three dimensional floc is formed which readily filters. By 1952 further confirmatory evidence was available for the "bridging" concept of flocculation (19, 20).

The extent of flocculation as judged by visual inspection, turbidity, rate of subsidence, and rate of re-filtration through the cake, showed that potato starch (autoclaved for 15 min at 120°C to break up the granules) was most effective, whereas corn starch was completely ineffective as judged by filtration rates.

Tapioca starch was only slightly effective in accord with its phosphate content.

Experiments were then performed using 20 different cations on dispersions in distilled water. Only those cations which formed insoluble compounds with phosphate (Ca, Mg, Ag, etc.) produced good flocculation. Cations (Na, K, NH_4) which did not form insoluble phosphates were ineffective.

A final proof that it was the phosphate groups of potato starch that were the agents in crosslinking was obtained when corn starch was phosphorylated or carboxyl groups introduced by cauticizing with alkali. After such chemical modifications, corn starch became a very effective flocculating agent. Cauticised corn starch has been used for many years as a cheap flocculant since it can withstand further decomposition by alkali at high temperatures, in the Bayer process for the flocculation of causticized bauxite (Al_2O_3). The reasons for the success of the Bayer theory were never recognized until this bridging theory was presented by the writer to the industry in 1954.

In 1952 our attention was directed to the marketing by Monsanto Co. of the soil conditioner "krilium" which is a co-polymer of vinyl acetate partially hydrolysed and maleic anhydride. It also proved to be a negatively charged polyelectrolyte but nevertheless was an effective flocculant for the negatively charged clays at low dosages. Flocculants having superior properties to Separan 2610 were then prepared in this laboratory from polyacrylamide (PAM) by partial hydrolysis and controlled crosslinking with alkaline formaldehyde.

There are three methods for following the extent of flocculation produced by a given amount of flocculant: (a) turbidity of the supernatant liquid above the subsidence line; (b) rate of subsidence, i.e., the rate of fall of the line of demarcation; and (c) re-filtration of the flocculated dispersion under a constant pressure head. Each has its advantages and disadvantages. The onset of flocculation can be detected most simply by the rate of decrease in turbidity at some point near the top of the sedimenting column. This type of observation has been used much because it can be made simply and precisely with photocells. However, the results are not readily amenable to interpretation because of the complex character of light scattering intensity, and the large size and heterodispersity of the flocs. The rate of subsidence has practical application and is reasonably accurate, but it has the disadvantage that one does not know the changing density of the floc with time necessary to interpret the measurements.

Filtration and particularly re-filtration of the filtrate through formed filter cake has been found to be an accurate measure of the state of flocculation if the critical conditions of slow dropwise addition of dilute solutions of the polymer to avoid local supersaturation, and of gentle agitation in respect to type, intensity, and duration to avoid disrupting the flocs are strictly adhered to. Under such controlled conditions the rate of filtration is surprisingly reproducible to $+$ 2%. The re-filtration curves using polyelectrolytes all follow the same pattern as the concentration of the polyelectrolyte (mg/l) is increased; namely, an initially increasing rate of filtration to a characteristic maximum value, followed by a decrease in rate to a value often below that of the untreated slurry. At high concentrations the flocs are re-dispersed or deflocculated yielding a turbid liquid whose fine particles clog the filter.

It suffices at this point to emphasize that the interaction of each particular flocculant with each particular substrate is a highly specific one and that only rough rules of effectiveness can be formulated until more is known quantitatively about the specific adsorptions in each case.

Specificity of action is a strong indication that specific chemical interactions are involved and dominate the process. Any theory which employs only unspecific interactions as does the electrostatic double layer theory is bound to fail. It soon became evident that the extent of adsorption of such groups as carboxyl, hydroxyl, and phosphoryl upon each type of sub-strate would furnish the quantitative key to the mechanism. Electrostatic interactions are correction terms of subordinate value.

The rate of refiltration which increases rapidly as a high power of the concentration of polyelectrolyte (mg/l) passes through a sharp maximum (minimum in time curve). It decreases rapidly for large dosages and finally becomes slower than for the untreated dispersion. In other words, overdosage "peptises" the flocs creating fine particles which produce turbidity and clog the filters. They also change the size of the macroflocs thus effecting the re-filtration rate. Each substrate and flocculant pair exhibit a reproducible maximum in rate (or a minimum in time curve) which is characteristic primarily of the chemical properties of the pair. This maximum value (P_M) has a quantitative interpretation. For this reason turbidity measurements were abandoned in 1952 whereas the simple subsidence measurements were used as a preliminary orienting guide in favor of the more accurate filtration studies.

As Table I shows a number of substrates were studied that used a number of different types of flocculants on each. A flocculant like Separan 2610 which produces a very good result with one of the various substrates will also frequently produce a good result with another similar substrate. This rule, however, is far from being general.

The most general rule that can be derived from the data is that the interaction of each polymer is specific for each substrate. This observation alone indicates that electrostatic interaction must be playing a subordinate role to chemical interaction, which is dependent upon the specific chemical group on the surface of the particle and on the polymer. It also means adsorption is playing the dominant role.

TABLE I

Substrates

All negatively charged except under specifically recognized conditions of pH or of the addition of charge determining ions.

A. Phosphate rocks:
    1. Florida, primarily clays
    2. Colorado plateau, carbonaceous
    3. Canadian plateau, primarily siliceous

B. Pure Compounds:
    1. $Ca_3 (PO_4)_2$
    2. $CaSO_4$
    3. $Al_2 O_3$
    4. Silica - both crystalline and amorphous

Flocculants

A. Coagulating electrolytes: $CaCl_2$, $Ca(OH)_2$, NaCl

B. Natural Polyelectrolytes:
    1. Potato, Tapioca, and Corn Starch

C. Synthetic Polyelectrolytes:
    1. Phosphorylated and Carboxylated Corn Starch
    2. Various dextrans, polymethyl celluloses
    3. Lytrons 886, 887, 888 (co-polymers of vinyl acetate (hydrolysed and maleic anhydrides)
    4. Polyacrylamide (PAM) Series
        a. various degrees of hydrolysis
        b. Separan 2610 (partially hydrolysed PAM and crosslinked)
        c. polyethoxy series
        d. polyethyleneimine series (49)

In 1960, our attention was turned from the uraniferous ores and $Ca_3(PO_4)_2$ to the problem of water purification. Silica was selected as the best prototype normally present in water for study. Somewhat to our surprise, of the long list of good flocculants for the phosphate rocks and the clays, only a few of the flocculants previously studied were found effective with silica.

The pure silicas are noted for being poorer substrates for adsorption than the clays. The polyacrylamides are well adsorbed on the clays and $Ca_3(PO_4)_2$. Hence polymers with less adsorption capacity are not sufficiently adsorbed to promote adequate bridging so that the minimum in the re-filtration time curve is less pronounced. See the treatment of this problem in terms of Langmuir's b value in a series of papers by Kane, et al, (43).

In conducting our synthesis of superseparans in the period 1954-6, we had occasion to test the effect partially hydrolysing polyacrylamide (PAM). PAM is a neutral polymer. Hydrolysis of the amide group makes it progressively more negative or anionic. Our earlier experiments had shown that the minimum in the time of re-filtration which parallels the rate of subsidence after flocculation, becomes an accurate measure of the state or extent of flocculation.

The optimum amounts (P_M) of PAM needed to produce the maximum rate of filtration were unchanged on hydrolysis of polyacrylamide, but the increased extent of flocculation, as measured by the filtration improvement (deeper minimum in the time curve or increased rate of filtration) becomes strikingly evident as we pass from 1% to 10% and finally to 30%. At the same time the polyelectrolyte assumes a greater negative charge.

It was on the basis of such earlier experiments that the categorical statement was made at the Purdue Conference on Clays in 1960 (25) that:

> Our most successful flocculation
> experiments have been achieved with
> negatively charged polyelectrolytes
> acting upon negatively charged particles.

It is accordingly, surprising to read in Van Olphen's recent authoritative monograph on clays the following statement (32):

> In the presence of very small amounts of
> polyelectrolyte, however, the hydrophobic
> sol becomes more sensitive towards
> flocculation by salt, although the poly-

> electrolyte alone does not flocculate the
> hydrophobic sol, if they carry the same
> charge. This effect is called sensitization.
> When the polyelectrolyte and the hydrophobic
> sol particles carry opposite charges, the
> hydrophobic sol is flocculated by extremely
> small amount of the polyelectrolytes, as
> may be expected from the high valence of
> the latter.   (Emphasis added by author.)

The significance of our experiment which has been repeated
hundred of times - was that it demonstrated conclusively that
increasing the negative charge on the flocculant instead of
decreasing the rate of flocculation as predicted on the basis of
primitive electrostatic pictures and reasoning, actually produced progressively increasing flocculation of the negatively
charged clay particles. These findings since have been confirmed
by Russian investigators and by Rehbun and Wachs (31).

It means that, although the repulsive electrostatic barrier
is increased by hydrolysis of PAM, this barrier can be sur-
mounted, just as in the case of the kinetics of simple ionic
reactions between ions of opposite sign, to permit the chemical
forces to take over in the critical complex. It also means that
the magnitude of the electrostatic barrier is of minor importance
when compared to the greatly increased extent of adsorption of
the flocculant on the particle due to the increasing number of
sites on the flocculant arising from the increased number of
OH groups produced by hydrolysis.

A number of prominent polymer and colloid chemists,
who have held the view that the flocculant and particle must be
of opposite electric sign to be effective, suggested that the
introduction of positive charges in the polyelectrolyte would
improve the flocculation. This idea was tested by using a
modified starch designated as 613-45 which had been made
cationic by introduction of pyridinium groups. The results
have been published in several places (18, 24). The cationic
starch 613-45 was somewhat less effective than the negatively
charged Goodman's Long Island potato starch. The introduction
of positively charged radicals should continuously improve
flocculation but the concurrent effect on adsorption cannot be
ignored.

THE ACTION OF ALUM IN WATER PURIFICATION

The view which had dominated for many years the interpretation of the action of alum $(Al_2(SO_4)_3 \cdot 18H_2O)$ was that the

naked Al^{+3} ion because of its high positive charge opposite to that of the clay or silica particles in the water coagulated them by a purely electrostatic action. In modern language, the Al^{+3} reduced the repulsive ψ potential between the particles. The addition of soda ash produced a gelatinous floc of $Al\,(OH)_3$ which entrapped the fine particles and removed them. Although there still remains some basis for these two ideas, they have undergone considerable revision in the past few years.

In the early 1920's Theriault and Clark found that the best and most rapid precipitation of $Al\,(OH)_3$ occurred in the neighbor-hood of pH 5.5 to 5.6 (33). Miller confirmed these findings but encountered an anomalous behavior when $Al_2(SO_4)_3$ was used instead of the chloride (34). In this region the floc of $Al(OH)_3$? settled most rapidly and in the greatest abundance. This finding had a profound effect upon the chemistry of water purification and marks the beginning of the epoch of control of pH. Miller continued these studies but found the most complete precipitation from an alum solution occurred between pH 6.7 and 7.0. Hatfield found the optimum pH range to be 6.1 to 6.3 but noted that the value for maximum floc formations depended upon the anion present in the initial solution, such as SO_4, Cl, C_2O_4, etc. (35). For example, in the presence of oxalate ion, the pH value was 8.5 to 9.5 whereas in the presence of chromate ion a broad range of coagulation from pH 5 to 10 was found.

Brønsted and Volqvartz suggested that Al^{+3} did not exist as such but was hydrated, presumably, with six water molecules in a Werner complex (36). By adding alkali, protons could be removed successively to yield hydroxy ion structures with decreasing charges:

$$\left[Al(H_2O)_6\right]^{+3} + \bar{OH} \longrightarrow \left[Al(H_2O)_5OH\right]^{+2} + H_2O, \text{ etc.}$$

At a pH value of approximately 8.0, neutral $Al(H_2O)_3(OH)_3$ was found. In a more alkaline medium, the well known aluminates, $Al(OH)_6^{-3}$, constituted the end product of this stepwise neutrali-zation. This process is now well established and accepted except that more complex molecules are recognized (41).

A.W. Thomas and his students, in a series of studies that
extended through the 1930's showed that these anions penetrated
many of the Werner complexes; such as Th, U, Ti, and Zn
through substitution for the complexed H_2O molecule (37).
Janek and Jirgensons had observed similar substitutions for
the Co and Cr complexes twenty years earlier (38).

Thomas also showed that these Al complexes "oxalated"
or "olated". In modern terms this means that the OH group
from one molecule interacted with the OH of an another molecule
forming a long, often linear, complex. Unfortunately, inorganic
complexes were not as fashionable in the 1930's as they are
today and Thomas's work passed quite unnoticed for a long
time, even after he had published his prophetic paper bearing
on water purification with Marion (37). The rates at which
these anions penetrated the complex and leave the complex is
specific for the intensity of the co-ordinating binding capacity
for each anion. Hence, an "aged" alum solution behaves
differently from a freshly prepared solution.

Pokras has given a particularly illuminating review of
Thomas's work and its impact on our ideas of colloid chemistry (39
Packham has made further studies of the hydrolysis of $Al_2(SO_4)_3$
in conformity with these ideas for their bearing upon water
purification (40). Stumm and Morgan have recently published
a most important paper in which these ideas are extended to
the ferrihydroxy complexes with the aid of more precise data
which they have obtained or assembled (41). They have made
out a strong case for the need and use of a "more comprehensive
chemical theory" where polynuclear complexes play the predominant role.

We should add that there is evidence from our studies
from 1956 on and particularly our most recent investigations
in which silica is the substrate (43), that the inorganic poly-
molecular complexes exert their influence on bridging mechanisms
in a manner similar to that of the organic polyelectrolytes like
polyacrylamide.

In any case we obtain a somewhat similar filtration curve
exhibiting a minimum time rate, when $Al(ClO_4)_3$ is used as
when the anionic polyelectrolyte is used. If the action of
$Al(ClO_4)_3$ was solely that of electrostatic interaction we should
not expect a minimum in the curves.

LaMer and Healy have discussed these problems, on the
basis of the extent of adsorption, in terms of the Langmuir θ,
which has proven to be of great value in the Smellie-LaMer-Healy

theory of filtration as a quantitative means of estimating the
extent of adsorption (42). The need for distinguishing between
Coagulation and Flocculation is developed in this paper and
again by LaMer (17) who contends that:

> If colloid chemistry is to maintain its
> position as a science, we can no longer
> treat coagulation and flocculation indiscrimi-
> nately as synonymous or interchangeable
> terms. Instead, they should be distinguished
> in terms of the active agent and its
> molecular characteristics, microscopic
> examination, final sediment volume, and
> particularly dependence of rate of
> filtration upon concentration of additive.
> The use of mathematics in treating poorly
> defined concepts only compounds confusion
> with more confusion to the detriment of
> colloid chemistry as a science.

LITERATURE CITED

1. Debye, P.W.J., Trans Am Electrochem Soc, 82, 265 (1942).

2. LaMer, V.K. and T. Mason, J Am Chem Soc, 49, 419 (1927).

3. LaMer, V.K., Trans Am Electrochem Soc, 67, 507 (1927).

4. LaMer, V.K., et al, J Phys Chem, 35, 2245 (1931).

5. Cowperthwaite, I. and V.K. LaMer, J Am Chem Soc, 53,
   4333 (1931).

6. Parks, G.S. and V.K. LaMer, J Am Chem Soc, 53, 2040
   (1931).

7. Gronwall, T.H., et al, Z Physik, 29, 358 (1928).

8. Bjerrum, N., Det Kg Danski Vidensk Math-fysisk Medd,
   VII, #9 (1926).

9. Stern, O., Z Elektrochem, 30, 508 (1924).

10. Derjaguin, B. V., Coagulation and Flocculation, Discussions Faraday Soc, #18, 85, 181, 211 (1954); Also p 193 (J. N. Phillips) and p 187 (S. Levine).

11. Gouy, G., J Phys, 9, 457 (1910).

12. Chapman, D. L., Phil Mag, 25, 475 (1913).

13. von Helmholtz, H., Ann Physik (Wiedemann), 7, 337 (1879).

14. Derjaguin, B. V. and L. Landau, Acta Physiochimica, 14, 633 (1941).

15. Verwey, E. J. W. and J. Th. G. Overbeek, Theory of the Stability of Lyophobic Colloids, Elseiver, New York, N. Y., (1948).

16. Sawyer, W. M. and S. J. Rehfeld, J Phys Chem, 67, 1973 (1963).

17. LaMer, V. K., J Colloid Sci, 19, 291 (1964).

18. LaMer, V. K. and R. H. Smellie, J Colloid Sci, 11, 704 (1956).

19. Smellie, R. H. and V. K. LaMer, J Colloid Sci, 11, 710 (1956).

20. Smellie, R. H. and V. K. LaMer, J Colloid Sci, 11, 720 (1956).

21. LaMer, V. K., et al, J Colloid Sci, 12, 230 (1957).

22. LaMer, V. K., et al, J Colloid Sci, 12, 566 (1957).

23. Smellie, R. H. and V. K. LaMer, J Colloid Sci, 13, 589 (1958).

24. LaMer, V. K. and R. H. Smellie, Proc Intern Conf Peaceful Uses of Atomic Energy, Second Geneva Conf, 3, 178 (1958).

25. LaMer, V. K. and R. H. Smellie, Proc Nat Conf on Clays, Clay Minerals, Pergamon Press, New York, N. Y., 9, 295 (1961).

26. Van Iterson, F. K., Proc Acad Sci, Amsterdam, 41, 81 (1938).

27. Ward, H. and K. Kammermeyer, Ind Eng Chem, 32,
    622 (1940).

28. Steinour, H.H., Ind Eng Chem, 36, 618, 840, 901 (1944).

29. Kynch, G.H., Trans Faraday Soc, 48, 166 (1952).

30. Thomas, A.W., Colloid Chemistry, McGraw Hill Co. Inc.,
    pp 366-370, New York, N.Y., (1934).

31. Rehbun, A. and B. Wachs, 20th Intern Congress IUPAC,
    Moscow, (July 1965).

32. van Olphen, H., An Introduction to Clay Colloid Chemistry,
    John Wiley and Sons Inc., New York, N.Y., p 169 (1963).

33. Theriault, C.J. and W.M. Clark, Public Health Rept,
    38, 181 (1923).

34. Miller, L.B., Public Health Rept, 38, 1995 (1923).

35. Hatfield, W.D., J Am Water Works Assoc, 11, 554 (1924).

36. Brønsted, J.N. and K. Volquartz, Z Physik Chem, 134,
    97 (1928).

37. Marion, S.P. and A.W. Thomas, J Colloid Sci, 1, 221 (1946).

38. Janek, A. and B. Jirgensons, Kolloid-Z, 41, 40 (1927).

39. Pokras, L., J Chem Educ, 33, 152 (1956).

40 Packham, R.F., British Water Res Assoc, Tech Pub No. 12
    (1959); No. 14 (1960); No. 15 (1960); No. 20 (1961).

41. Stumm, W. and J.J. Morgan, J Am Water Works Assoc,
    54, 971 (1962).

42. LaMer, V.K. and T.W. Healy, J Phys Chem, 67, 2417 (1963).

43. Kane, J.K. and V.K. Lamer, H. Linford, A series of
    papers dealing with the flocculation of silica dispersions,
    J Phys Chem, (1963) (1964).

44. Zaiser, A. and V.K. LaMer, J Colloid Sci, $\underline{3}$, 571 (1948).

45. LaMer, V.K., J Franklin Inst, $\underline{225}$, 709 (1938).

46. Amic, B. and V.K. LaMer, J Am Chem Soc, $\underline{61}$, (1939).

47. Turgeon, C. and V.K. LaMer, J Am Chem Soc, $\underline{74}$, 5988 (1952).

48. LaMer, V.K. and T.W. Healy, J Phys Chem, $\underline{66}$, 1835 (1962).

49. Dixon, J.D. (In Press, 1965).

DISCUSSION
CHAIRMAN COHEN: I think there is enough stimulation there for a few questions if we forego dinner. Is that all right? I'll take the first question.

MR. A.J. RUBIN (University of North Carolina): Professor LaMer, would you care to comment on the mechanism of attachment of the Al polymers to a hydrophilic colloid?

DR. LAMER: Yes, in an elementary way. I don't want to give the impression that there is nothing to plus or minus charge interactions; it is a correction to the bridging mechanism.

The presence of positive and negative charges will change the number of collisions to some extent, but that is secondary to firm chemical binding by adsorption. When you have a polyelectrolyte like the linear $Al(OH)_3$ polymers, as studied by A.W. Thomas, flocculating a hydrophilic colloid, the action is almost entirely a bridging mechanism. But the Al complexes do have positive and/or negative charges. The charge on colloids, such as gelatin depends on the pH and isoelectric of the colloid and polyelectrolyte. But it is important to recognize that electrostatic interaction is due to long-range forces, varying as $1/r^2$. At close distances, the chemical interactions which chemists recognize for the actions of carbonate, ferric ions, sulfate ions, etc., involve an inverse 7th or 8th power law and are highly specific for each ion. These highly specific reactions at close distances are superimposed upon the electrostatic interactions that Debye and others have been presenting for many years. I think that is the main answer.

MR. RUBIN: Would that account for the fact that you can use negative polymers to flocculate negative particles?

DR. LAMER: Yes, precisely. Let me explain. We always have thermal agitation acting on the reactant species. Consider a negatively charged particle and a negatively charged polyelectrolyte. On the average electrostatic interaction will reduce the number of collisions and keep them apart, but they do have enough kinetic energy so that occasionally they come close enough to be in the sphere of influence of chemical forces. This is obvious, otherwise there could be no chemical reactions between ions of the same sign. Actually, we have many chemical reactions between ions of the same sign which I studied 30 years ago. The one over r-6th or 8th power law, whatever it is, then, takes over and the particles react chemically or adsorb. The Brønsted primary and secondary salt effects which govern the electrostatic interaction exist in all these cases, but it is a correction factor and not the primary driving force for chemical interaction. Failure to recognize this point has confused the interpretation of colloid interactions for the last thirty years up to the present time.

MR. RUBIN: Thank you. I was looking at the entropy effect.

DR. LAMER: I'll answer that. If you will read the review article of Healy and myself in the Australian Journal, we went into some detail on that question. In my papers on ionic kinetics of the 1930's, we reacted bromphenol blue, a sufonated dye, with two negative charges with 0.1 M NaOH. The blue color fades as a pseudo 1st order reaction. The reaction involves the negatively charged OH ion which unites with the phenolic sulfate or bromphenol blue ion, which in spite of its double negative charge forms a carbonyl which is colorless. Amic and I studied this reaction with precision with a simple colorimeter.

We also studied the temperature coefficients of the reaction and thus separated the so-called free energy of activation into its component energy and entropies of activation.

And then I did something further. Instead of maintaining the alcohol-water composition of the medium constant, I varied the alcohol content with the temperature so that I maintained the same dielectric constant but at different temperatures. When we measure the temperature coefficients in these isodielectric mixtures you get rid of all the electrostatic action, because the factor $1 + \partial D/\partial T$ becomes zero at constant D.

The entropy factor for the electrostatic interaction vanishes.
As I said, in a crude way, we wipe the charges off by studying
the reaction in an isodielectric mixture. What remains is the
actual chemical energy of activation for bromphenol blue with
a zero charge and OH ion with zero charge. The basic chemical
activation energy is about 12, 000 calories. The presence of
electric charges raises this energy of activation by 4, 000
calories to about 16, 000 calories. Thus, we see that the electrostatic contribution of 4, 000 calories is only one-third of the
chemical contribution. Does that help you?

DR. W. P. SHYLUK (Hercules Powder Co.): Floc size
is basic to your refiltration theory. Have you ever measured
floc size by some independent method?

DR. LAMER: Not yet. We should.

DR. SHYLUK: I have.

DR. LAMER: Good.

DR. SHYLUK: I used a Coulter Counter to measure floc
size.

DR. LAMER: I've used this counter. It is very accurate
if you use it properly.

DR. SHYLUK: I have found that there was an increase
in refiltration rate when there was a definite decrease in floc
size.

DR. LAMER: Well now, that stumps me a little. It
doesn't quite fit in with our simple picture without further considerations, such as reshuffling of the network and change in
the pore size between flocs.

DR. SHYLUK: It doesn't fit. I have been forced to think
about a different model for your refiltration theory based on
network formation.

DR. LAMER: I wouldn't quarrel with that.

DR. SHYLUK: What happened was that as the floc size
went down, the packing volume stayed the same, so there was
network formation, and so my concern is about your model.

DR. LAMER: I'd like to think about that and not give you
a hasty answer to an important question. I'd like to see your
data and discuss it with you. You know, I'm now retired and
I don't even have my Coulter Counter, so I can't perform the
experiments.

Did the Coulter Counter tear up the flocs as you forced
them through the capillary? These flocs are delicate gossamers.
They are very sensitive to the slightest agitation and the refiltration rates are highly dependent upon the history of the mixing and
further agitation processes.

DR. SHYLUK: No, the floc size did not change during the stirring time.

DR. LAMER: Well, that would change the floc size, wouldn't it?

DR. SHYLUK: No. the floc size remained constant. I had quite stable flocs because I used strong flocculant.

DR. LAMER: You have evidently obtained new types of evidence. I wouldn't argue that with you. I hope you will do more work along these lines and then we will have to discuss it. I just don't want to say something that I haven't thought out yet.

DR. SHYLUK: Otherwise, you are to be congratulated on bringing order to quite a mess. Thank you.

DR. J.J. MORGAN(California Institute of Technology): I think there are three possibly useful comments. The first is that the inclusion of the Smoluchowski equation that is incorporated in your theory appears actually to be only for the initial conditions. Wouldn't it be the initial rate of the Smoluchowski equation?

DR. LAMER: Correct.

DR. MORGAN: The second point is that a priori I can't see why the Langmuir isotherm should be expected to fit the model. If you study all of the data obtained on the Langmuir isotherm there appears to be some problems in fitting the data.

DR. LAMER: I agree, but I want to have Healy field that question because he did the adsorption studies.

DR. MORGAN: Let me mention the third point. The third point is that to make this theory applicable for a wider range of particle concentration you've really got to accommodate both the coagulation concept and the flocculation concept. In the experiments we have done in the very low particle concentration range flocculation may not occur initially.

DR. LAMER: I'm going to agree with you, of course. At the beginning two particles come together. I call that primary coagulation. As you proved, tertiary and higher forms of coagulation occur finally leading to a three dimensional network. I suggest calling a three dimension network flocculation. This term is used a great deal but in an uncritical way. There is bound to be a gradation representing the concepts of coagulation and flocculation. I have been trying to show how one can distinguish the extreme forms by operational methods, not by idle talk.

DR. MORGAN: There are very striking salt effects.

DR. LAMER: You are quite right about that. Now, Healy.

DR. HEALY: The sol effects first. The profound sol effects could be related to electrical double layer on either the solid particle or on the polymer. The polymer can coil and uncoil depending on the solution conditions. I essentially agree with you, but I think there may be more in it than we all known about, in the sense that there are both polymer effects and solid effects which are difficult to distinguish.

All careful work on polymer adsorption, whether it be aqueous or non-aqueous, seems to give Langmuir adsorption very closely. Why? Langmuir proposed his equation for the very simple process of evaporation-condensation of-or a simple noble gas molecule on a simple regular array or a checkerboard surface. Now, a polymer is just not that sort of molecule, but on the other hand, a polymer is a lot of little molecules (segments) joined together and if it is adsorbed on a solid it forms loops between adsorped segments. And the way I think of the checkerboard. Langmuir adsorption is that one adsorbed segment doesn't know what other adsorbed segments are doing since it is separated by a flexible loop extending into the solution. There is therefore independent adsorption of one segment after another and there is effectively no lateral interaction between adsorbed segments.

DR. MORGAN: May I just say that that's a very good qualitative argument, but the published quantitative work on polymer adsorption with all the recent modifications don't yet prove it. As a matter of fact, this refinement of the model which you have made, which is very interesting, still isn't checkable by any experiments. These constants aren't arrived at unless you separately calculate them for the individual polymer and prove that they are true by the flocculation, unless you know beta values for the floc itself.

DR. HEALY: You are talking about order of magnitude changes in beta, where beta is the number of adsorbed segments per polymer molecule. That's why in our work we always work with the change in beta with molecular weight and other variables. Then again the Simha-Frisch model will reduce to the Langmuir model under certain conditions. And secondly, when you see the Simha-Frisch model and the Langmuir model plotted on the same coordinate they do not look very different.

DR. MORGAN: That might be a point also to worry about.

DR. HEALY: No, I don't think so. This is a fluctuation type theory and there are so many segments along the molecule that a polymer molecule with its very few segments per molecule adsorbed really acts like a series of small independent molecules.

CHAIRMAN COHEN: I think Dr. Packham has a few choice words.

DR. PACKHAM: I have some reservations concerning the application of the polymer bridging model to the clarification of water with $Al_2(SO_4)_3$. Any mechanism based on polymer bridging must lead to a direct relationship between the concentration of suspended solids and the concentration of flocculant required. In the low suspended solids range encountered in most river waters, we have found that an inverse relationship exists. Since the process has been shown to be most efficient under conditions leading to the precipitation of insoluble hydrolysis species this finding is easily explained if it is assumed that flocculation kinetics is the limiting factor. With a very low suspended solids content a greater amount of precipitation is required to achieve a high enough particle concentration for flocculation to proceed at the rapid rate. Conversely, a smaller amount of precipitation is required if the suspended solids concentration of the water is higher.

Although $Al(OH)_3$ undoubtedly forms interparticle bridges during flocculation it would not seem that this process can be described adequately by the LaMer-Healy mode.

DR. LAMER: I haven't made those calculations.

CHAIRMAN COHEN: I think Dr. Stumm might make a comment.

DR. W. STUMM (Harvard University): I would like to partially disagree with Dr. Packham. The occasional observation of non-stoichiometric effects in water treatment cannot be invoked against the bridging model. Coagulation with hydrolyzed Al has been shown to follow stoichiometric relations for SiO_2, MnO_2, clays, microorganisms, and color.

DR. PACKHAM: This is different.

DR. STUMM: In water treatment, frequently, we do not have the necessary detention time and then kinetic considerations obscure the stoichiometry. With kaolonite, considerable self-flocculation occurs, especially at higher concentrations.

DR. PACKHAM: In rivers of high suspended solids content the kinetics of flocculation do not assume such importance and a different coagulation mechanism prevails. Here I would agree that a stoichiometry can be demonstrated although this in itself is not a proof of the polymer bridging model. In the vast majority of cases, however, this is not so and the literature provides ample evidence that the precipitation of $Al(OH)_3$ is the most important function of the coagulant in the removal of turbidity.

DR. STUMM: You might be quite right to emphasize kinetic considerations in the practice of water treatment but such considerations cannot be used as an argument against the bridging model as a relevant model to explain coagulation with hydrolyzed Al.

In addition, I want to emphasize that there are some practical data which show an increase in coagulant dose with increasing concentration of certain clays. For example, Dr. Ludwig's data show such a relationship for montmorillonite and, within a certain concentration range, for kaolinite.

DR. PACKHAM: Dr. Ludwig's data shows for the majority of clays the inverse relationship between clay concentration and coagulant dose that I have described. In the special case of montmorillonite, however, a stoichiometry is shown. This is in line with our observation of the anomalous behavior of dilute montmorillonite dispersions which we have ascribed to the exceptional degree of subdivision of this clay. Dilute dispersions of this clay behave like more concentrated dispersions of other clays due to the much greater number of particles per unit volume.

DR. STUMM: I think this is a kinetic effect. I would like to ask another question.

DR. LAMER: I do want to emphasize what both you gentlemen are saying. The "W" in my equation which comes into the 4th power, that's the number of particles per cc, is going to reflect the distance between the particles. That's very important.

Now, I want to make an observation which I haven't proven but may help some of the practical water chemists. I have a feeling that when you are working with the big particles that are negatively charged you can coagulate these--flocculate these big particles with the negatively charged polyelectrolyte. But when you want to clean up the very fine particles with a negative charge, which are far apart and moving very rapidly, I think you may need cationic polymers. A little cationic polymer at the finish seems to get rid of the turbidity. I don't believe that the industrial men are going to argue that point with me. Some are pushing it vigorously today, I also have evidence that it is true.

Now, your question.

DR. STUMM: I wonder whether the deviations in the relationship between polyelectrolyte dose and concentration of suspended solids that you have observed at low concentrations of suspended solids, cannot be explained kinetically. If we think as a first approximation, in terms of a Fick-diffusion model, the rate of transport of a high-molecular weight polyelectrolyte (or its segments) to a solid interface, must become very slow, at the very low polyelectrolyte concentrations, especially if the molecular weight exceeds a few million.

DR. LAMER: I think that's a good interpretation. You must remember that the coiled polymer will stretch out or coil up more or less, depending on minute salt concentration changes. We just don't have a long bridge string; we have coils that stretch out. It's not an easy problem; it's a very complicated effect.

DR. HEALY: If molecular weight goes above three million, it drops off too rapidly to be just steric hindrance, and that's why Professor LaMer says that there probably is a diffusion controlled adsorption step which is becoming rate controlling.

CHAIRMAN COHEN: I think this ought to end the session. I want to thank all of you for being patient and sitting through all of this.

A. P. Black
University of Florida

ELECTROKINETIC CHARACTERISTICS OF HYDROUS OXIDES OF ALUMINUM AND IRON

At the first Rudolfs Research Conference titled "Principles of Colloidal Behavior and Their Application to Water Sanitation" held in June 1960, it was my privilege to present a paper entitled "Some Applications of the Principles of Colloidal Behavior to Water Treatment" (1). That paper included a rather thorough review of the chronological development of coagulation theory from 1923 to 1960. Since it has been published in full in the Proceedings of that conference, it will not be repeated in this paper. More recently Packham has published a very complete review of the literature on coagulation theory (2). This paper will deal mainly with the studies of four research groups since 1960.

In a series of three papers, the Florida group re-introduced an old and well known technique of the colloid chemist, microelectrophoresis, to the water chemist (3, 4, 5). At the first Rudolfs Conference a preliminary discussion was presented of three papers employing microelectrophoretic techniques in the study of coagulation phenomena in turbidity removal, color removal, and lime-soda softening (6, 7, 8).

Packham, in addition to his very exhaustive literature survey, published a series of five papers in which microelectro-

phoretic techniques were employed (9-13). Professor Matijevic
followed an earlier (1953) paper (14) with three additional papers
of direct and important interest to the water chemist (15, 16, 17).
Stumm and Lee (18) and Stumm and Morgan (19) contributed two
papers which, while not dealing directly with electrokinetic
properties of hydrous oxides, contained material so directly
related to these properties that they should be considered in
this framework.

HYDROLYTIC REACTIONS OF FERRIC AND ALUMINUM IONS

Any discussion of the electrokinetic behavior of hydrous
oxides of aluminum and iron should concern itself with the
chemical composition of these materials. Miller indicated that
the precipitate resulting from the addition of alkali to a solution
of $Al_2(SO_4)_3$ was not pure $Al(OH)_3$ (20). It contained a quantity
of SO_4^{-2} ion that could not be removed by long, continued
washing and that was constant over a wide pH range. More
recently, several investigators, notably, Matijevic (14-17),
Stumm and Lee (18), Stumm and Morgan (19), Brosset (21, 22),
and the Scandinavian school (23, 24) have suggested formulae
for the numerous molecular and ionic species which they believe
to be present in such systems. Several of the papers presented
equilibrium constants for the reactions by which they are formed.
Stumm and Morgan have referenced this literature (19).

Table I shows the composition of several of the ionic and
molecular species which have been suggested for both iron and
aluminum hydrous oxides and equilibrium constants for the
reactions from which they may be formed. These are of
importance because electrokinetic characteristics of the flocs
formed by the interaction of the polymeric species with turbidity
or organic color would be determined by their composition,
valence type, and molecular weight. Furthermore, if it develops
that a specific species formed at a particular pH value is more
effective than the others in destabilization and floc formation,
its formation in actual water plant practice could easily be
accomplished with the sophisticated equipment now available.
Figures 1 and 2 show solubility curves for Al and Fe hydroxides
which have been constructed using these data.

DEFINITION OF TERMS

It is important that a distinction be made between the terms
flocculation and coagulation. They have long been used interchangeably, but as our understanding of the basic mechanisms

TABLE I   HYDROLYSIS EQUILIBRIA OF IRON
           AND ALUMINUM

No.	Reaction	Log of Equilibrium Constants (25°C).
1	$Al^{+3} + H_2O = [Al(OH)]^{+2} + H^+$	-5.03
2	$2Al^{+3} + 2H_2O = [Al_2(OH)_2]^{+4} + 2H^+$	-6.27
3	$Al^{+3} + 3H_2O = Al(OH)_{3(c)} + 3H^+$	-9.1
4	$Al(OH)_{3(c)} + H_2O = [Al(\bar{O}H)_4]^- + H^+$	-12.74
5	$6Al^{+3} + 15 H_2O = [Al_6(OH)_{15}]^{+3} + 15 H^+$	-47
6	$8Al^{+3} + 20 H_2O = [Al_8(OH)_{20}]^{+4} + 20 H^+$	~
7	$Fe(OH)_{3(c)} = Fe^{+3} + 3OH^-$	~ -36
8	$Fe(OH)_{3(c)} = [Fe(OH)_2]^+ + OH^-$	-14.77
9	$Fe(OH)_{3(c)} = [Fe(OH)]^{+2} + 2OH^-$	-24.17
10	$Fe(OH)_{3(c)} = [Fe(OH)_3]_{(aq)}$	-6.54
11	$Fe(OH)_{3(c)} + OH^- = [Fe(\bar{O}H)_4]^-$	~ -5
12	$Al(OH)_{3(c)} = Al^{+3} + 3 \bar{O}H$	-32.3

involved in the destabilization of colloids has progressed, it has
become increasingly clear that different forces are involved.
LaMer has perhaps best defined the two terms (25):

> We propose that coagulation be used for
> the general kinetic process obeying the
> simple Smoluchowski equation independent
> of θ, whereby colloidal particles are
> united (L. coagulare - to be driven
> together) as typified by the effects of
> electrolytes upon gold sols. Coagulation
> is brought about primarily by a reduction
> of the repulsive potential of the electrical
> double layer in accordance with the ideas
> advanced by Derjaguin, Landau, Verwey,
> and Overbeek.
> We propose that the term flocculation
> should be restricted more in accordance
> with original usage corresponding to the
> Latin meaning of 'floc' (L. flocculus-
> a small tuft of wool or a loosely fibrous
> structure).
> Flocculation is usually brought about
> by the action of high molecular weight
> materials (potato starch and polyelectro-
> lytes in general) acting as linear polymers
> of the dispersion into a random structure
> which is three dimensional, loose, and
> porous.

It is necessary to make this distinction since the electrokinetic properties of the hydrous oxides are most important in
coagulation and are measured before a significant amount of
flocculation has occurred.

POSSIBLE APPROACHES TO THE STUDY OF THE BASIC
MECHANISMS OF COLLOIDAL DESTABILIZATION

There are at least two different approaches to the study
of the basic mechanisms by which colloidal suspensions are
destabilized by the ionic and molecular species resulting from
the hydrolysis of metallic salts. The first approach may be
designated, as Stumm and Morgan have done, as the "chemical
approach" (19). It may involve, among other things, determination of solubility constants, stability constants, other equilibrium constants, heats of reaction, chemical composition by

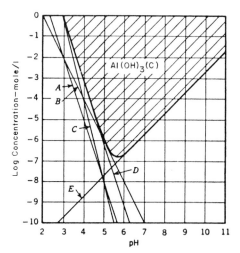

FIGURE 1   SOLUBILITY CURVE FOR ALUMINUM
HYDROXIDE. The key is: A, $\left[Al_6(OH)_{15}^{+3}\right]$; B, $Al(OH)^{+2}$;
C, $\left[Al_2(OH)_2^{+4}\right]$; D, Al^{+3}; E, $\left[Al(OH)_4^{-}\right]$

a variety of sophisticated techniques, and the effective charge
and valence type. The second approach involves the actual
determination of the electrophoretic mobility of the individual
particles. This technique provides a type of information not
possible to obtain by any other approach and is the subject of
this paper.

Electrophoretic Studies of Turbidity Removal
        In 1928, Mattson published his important electrophoretic
study of coagulation of clay colloids and indicated the applicabilit
of his conclusions to water treatment (26). This work minimized
to some extent, the importance of the Schultze-Hardy Rule in
that the products of hydrolysis of Al and Fe^{+3} salts were demonstrated to be more effective than the trivalent cations in reducing
or neutralizing the zeta potential of colloidal particles. Furthermore, the hydrolysis products of $AlCl_3$ were more effective than
those of $Al_2(SO_4)_3$. The difference was ascribed to the repressiv
effect of the bivalent sulfate ion. Aluminum sulfate was found to
exhibit its greatest effect on the zeta potential of clay particles

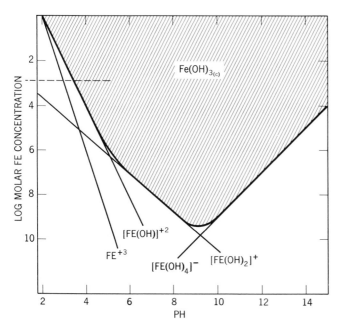

FIGURE 2 SOLUBILITY CURVE FOR FERRIC HYDROXIDE.

at about pH 5.2, which is well within the pH zone of hydrolysis of Al salts delineated by Miller (20). The fundamental and important conclusions and implications of this classical paper remained unnoticed for 30 years. In 1958 Pilipovich, et al, published the first electrophoretic study of water coagulation and confirmed Mattson's basic findings (3).

Black and Hannah studied the coagulation of three clays with $Al_2(SO_4)_3$ (6). The clays were a kaolinite with a base exchange capacity (BEC) of 8.7 meq/100g, a Fuller's earth with a BEC of 26.5 meq/100g, and a montmorillonite with a BEC of 115 meq/100g. These clays were suspended in water containing 50 mg/1 of NaCl or $NaHCO_3$. Figure 3 shows the mobilities of the particles of the three clays before destabiliza- tion. Figure 4 shows the effect of a dosage of 5 mg/1 of $Al_2(SO_4)_3$ on residual turbidity and electrophoretic mobility as functions of pH. This figure shows that a small dosage of $Al_2(SO_4)_3$ is sufficient to reverse the charge of the kaolinite microflocs whereas the floc particles formed with the other two clays of substantially higher BEC were changed only slightly. This

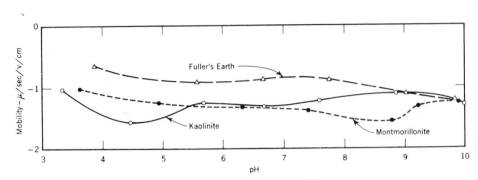

FIGURE 3   MOBILITIES OF CLAYS WITHOUT ALUM.

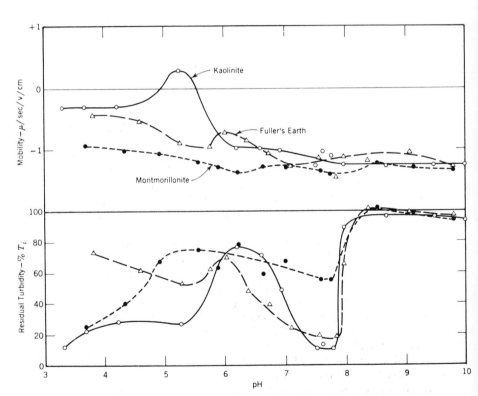

FIGURE 4   COAGULATION OF THREE CLAYS WITH
             A DOSAGE OF 5 mg/l ALUM.

indicated the importance of the BEC of the clay to its destabilization. This is confirmed by the data shown in Figure 5 wherein
a dosage of 15 mg/l of $Al_2(SO_4)_3$ is sufficient to reverse the
charge of flocs formed with both kaolinite and Fuller's earth,
but not with montmorillonite whose BEC is highest of the three.
The curves also indicate the pH zones within which coagulation
and flocculation, as previously defined, occur. All three clays
coagulate, although poorly, within the pH range 3. 5 - 4. 5,
within which particles still have low negative mobilities. The
rather wide pH zone of charge reversal rather exactly defines
a zone of no floc formation. Finally, the curves show that all
three clays flocculate best in the pH range 7. 4 - 8. 2, wherein
the particles have a slight negative charge. Figure 6 shows that
increasing the dosage of $Al_2(SO_4)_3$ to the excessively high
dosage of 100 mg/l will first reverse the charge and subsequently
flocculate all three clays.

Black and Chen investigated the destabilization of natural
clay sediments obtained from three American rivers with
$Al_2(SO_4)_3$ (27). These rivers were the Sacramento, Colorado,
and Apalachicola. The electrophoretic and residual turbidity
data were found to be very similar and all three were found to
behave, in general, in the same manner as the three synthetic
clay suspensions studied by Black and Hannah (6). Figure 7
shows the data for the Apalachicola River suspension for four
$Al_2(SO_4)_3$ dosages.   They show that the lower $Al_2(SO_4)_3$ dosages
did not reverse the particle charge but that charge reversal
took place in approximately the same pH range as was found
for the synthetic suspensions for the highest dosage. The pH
range of optimum flocculation was likewise the same. Black
and Chen concluded that coagulation is strongly controlled by
properties of the coagulant. The characteristics of clay
particles; namely, the base exchange capacity, size, and charge
may influence the coagulant dosage but not the basic mechanisms
of coagulation for a particular coagulant.

Packham summarized the data obtained in four earlier
papers of electrophoretic studies of the coagulation of both
synthetic clay suspensions and water from several English
rivers (13). In evaluating Packham's electrophoretic mobility
and turibity data and comparing it with that of previous studies,
it must be kept in mind that optimum coagulation dosage was
defined as that necessary to reduce the initial turbidity by 50%.
When adjustments are made for this difference, the findings

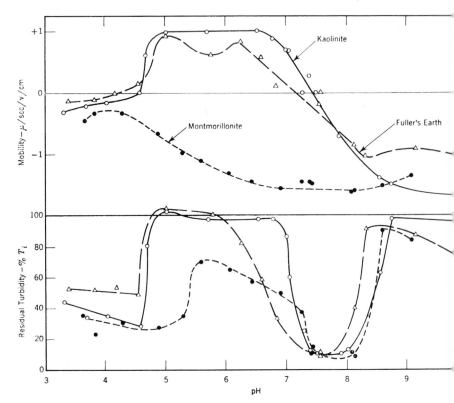

FIGURE 5   COAGULATION OF THREE CLAYS WITH
             A DOSAGE OF 15 mg/l ALUM.

and conclusions are remarkably similar to those of the American
workers.

Black and Walters studied the destabilization of synthetic
suspensions of three clays with $Fe_2(SO_4)_3$ (28). The three
clays, a kaolinite, Fuller's earth, and a montmorillonite, were
the same three employed in earlier studies with alum. In
general, the clay suspensions behaved toward $Fe_2(SO_4)_3$ in a
manner very similar to that exhibited by alum, although substantially lower dosages of $Fe_2(SO_4)_3$ were required for the same
degree of destabilization. Charge reversal took place with all
three clay suspensions when the ratio of coagulant dose to BEC
was more than 3. Higher dosages of $Fe_2(SO_4)_3$ reversed the
charge of the clay suspensions. Optimum flocculation for all

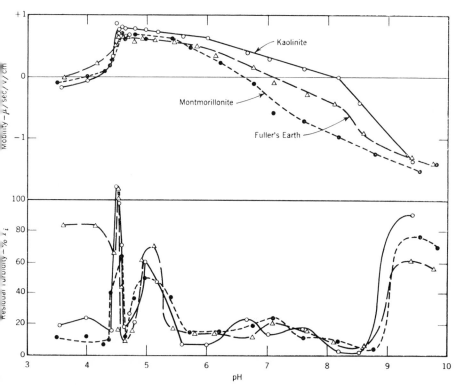

FIGURE 6   COAGULATION OF THREE CLAYS WITH
             A DOSAGE OF 100 mg/l ALUM.

clays occurred at a somewhat lower pH range wherein the floc
particles had a slight negative charge. Figure 8 shows typical
data for the kaolinite suspensions.

Electrophoretic Studies of Color Removal
     It should be kept in mind, in evaluating methods for the
removal of organic color from water, that the exact physical
and chemical nature of this material is unknown. Black and
Christman concluded that the particles that make up the major
portion of the color in water are colloidal and of very fine
particle size, 3.5 - 10 mμ, and that they are negatively
charged (29, 30). They also found definite evidence of aromaticity.
     Hoak employed paper chromotography to identify phenol,
guaiacol, m-cresol, and 3, 5-xylenol in extracts from river

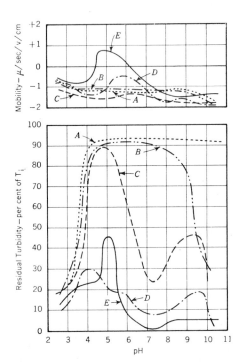

FIGURE 7 EFFECTS OF pH AND ALUM DOSAGE ON
          MOBILITY AND TURBIDITY OF APALACHICO
          RIVER SEDIMENT SUSPENSION.
          The key is A, 0 mg/l alum; B, 5 mg/l;
          C, 10 mg/l; D, 20 mg/l; E, 50 mg/l .

waters and oak leaf fermentations (31). Several other phenolic
compounds were identified tentatively as well as aliphatic fatty
acids. Packham concluded that both aromatic and aliphatic
compounds were present (32). Lamar separated and identified
a number of aliphatic fatty acids (33). Shapiro concluded that
organic color is not colloidal but in true solution and is composed
mainly of low molecular weight polyhydroxy, polycarboxylic
fatty acids (34).

    Black and Willems studied the coagulation of two highly
colored surface waters with both Al and Fe^{+3} sulfates (7).
Figure 9 shows the electrophoretic mobility and residual color
when a highly colored water is coagulated with 60 mg/l of $Al_2(SO$
Figure 10 presents similar data for coagulation of the same water

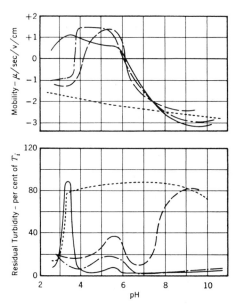

FIGURE 8   COMPARISON OF THE EFFECT OF pH
               AND MOBILITY ON THE COAGULATION
               OF KAOLINITE SUSPENSIONS WITH
               FERRIC SULFATE.
               The dotted curve is: no ferric sulfate added;
               the dashed curve, 3 mg/l; the dot-and-dash
               curve, for 5 mg/l; and the solid curve,
               for 50 mg/l. The coincident isoelectric
               points for the three coagulant doses mark
               the beginning of the pH zone of good ortho-
               kinetic coagulation of the kaolinite suspensions.

with 50 mg/l of $Fe_2(SO_4)_3$. These figures show that, in the case
of both coagulants, charge reversal of the floc particles occurred
and optimum color removal was accomplished at or very near
the same pH value.

Black, et al, developed the first stoichiometric relation
between a measurable raw water property and the conditions
required for treatment of that water with $Fe_2(SO_4)_3$ (35). The
study utilized electrophoretic measurements to establish the
optimum conditions for removal of color from six different
soft and highly colored natural waters. Ferric sulfate dosage

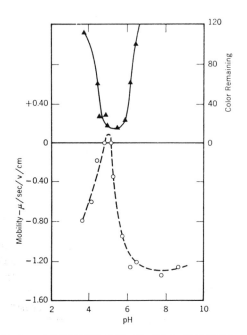

FIGURE 9   EFFECT OF pH AND CONSTANT ALUM
            DOSAGE ON COAGULATION OF WATER B.
            A constant alum dosage of 60 mg/l was
            employed, and the pH was varied with
            HCl and $Ca(OH)_2$. Although the mobility
            curve is shown with a small positive loop,
            actually no definitely positive particles
            were found in any jar.

and the pH of coagulation were shown to be functions of the raw
water color as seen in Figures 11 and 12. The pH for optimum
color removal also was related closely to the pH of zero mobility
of the floc particles. The effect of pH on the mobility curves
is shown in Figure 13 for one of the waters along with the effect
on color removal. Figure 14 shows the relation between the
minimum $Fe_2(SO_4)_3$ dose required and the isoelectric point at
the optimum pH of 3.78 for the same water as above. The
relation between mobility and color removal is shown in Figure 15
for another of the waters studied. It can be seen that the best
color removal occurs at a pH just below the isoelectric point

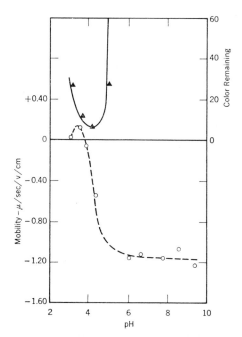

FIGURE 10   EFFECT OF pH AND CONSTANT FERRIC
SULFATE DOSAGE ON COAGULATION OF
WATER B.
A constant $Fe_2(SO_4)_3$ dosage of 50 mg/l
was employed and the pH was adjusted
with HCl and $Ca(OH)_2$.

where the mobility of the floc particles is positive and just above
the pH of the maximum positive charge. It was also shown,
Figure 16, that the optimum pH of coagulation for $Al_2(SO_4)_3$
was well above that of $Fe_2(SO_4)_3$.
    It is of interest to note that many investigators have
observed the so-called "indicator effect" of organic color, i.e.,
the change in color with pH. A nomograph has been prepared
to correct the color measured at any pH to the color value at
pH 8.3, an arbitrary reference pH value (36).

APPLICATIONS OF ELECTROKINETIC DATA TO THE
UNDERSTANDING OF COAGULATION THEORY
    For many years the work of most investigators studying

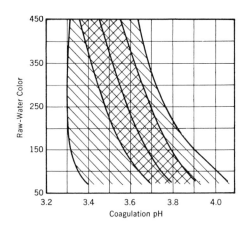

FIGURE 11   RANGE OF OPTIMUM COAGULATION pH
AS A FUNCTION OF RAW-WATER COLOR.
The cross-hatched area is for best color
removal; the diagonally lined area, for
acceptable color removal.

water coagulation followed a uniform pattern. Snythetic waters
were prepared of known type and amount of alkalinity wherein
flocs were formed with pure solutions of Fe^{+3} and Al salts.
The effects of added anions, cations, and variable pH values
on the rates of formation and the physical properties of these
flocs were studied intensively. Some of these investigators
went so far as to assume that flocs so formed might be either
negative, positive, or uncharged. The demonstrated effects
of anions and cations were explained by the Schultze-Hardy
Rule. In 1949, Langelier and Ludwig used a somewhat more
sophisticated approach employing snythetic clay suspensions
and emphasizing for the first time the importance of the BEC
of the clay particles (37). Double layer theory and the zeta
potential were discussed and it was assumed that the most
rapid clarification is obtained when the ultimately formed flocs
attain a zero potential. Langelier and Ludwig clearly distinguished two different types of action which take place when
hydrolyzing coagulants are employed. In their own words:

> ...the most common method of attaining
> flocs of zero or near zero potential is
> the selection of a coagulant chemical
> which, in addition to yielding cations

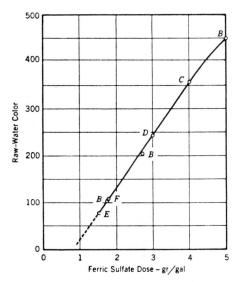

FIGURE 12   MINIMUM FERRIC SULFATE DOSE AS A
FUNCTION OF RAW-WATER COLOR.
The data for the various waters are indicated
by the point associated with the letter designa-
tion of the water.   The data indicate that the
minimum ferric sulfate dose necessary for
good color removal is a simple function of
the raw-water color.

of high positive valence to effect
perikenetic coagulation, will yield
through hydrolysis flocculant precipitates
which serve as a binder material to
accelerate the process of aggregation.

Throughout the entire paper, however, no actual electrokinetic
measurements were reported.
      Now that the determination of the mobilities of colloidal
particles is being rapidly, accurately, reproducibly, and, in
some cases, routinely conducted in water works laboratories
the question can be asked: What have these measurements
added to our understanding of the basic mechanisms of
coagulation?

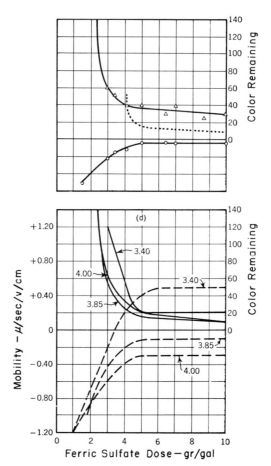

FIGURE 13   EFFECT OF FERRIC SULFATE DOSE ON
             COAGULATION OF WATER A   AT CONSTANT
             pH.

a. In the first place, electrophoretic mobility measurements
have clearly confirmed the early conclusion of Mattson that the
hydrolysis products of Al salts are more effective than the
trivalent ion in neutralizing colloids of opposite charge (26).
Matijevic's work, in particular, has emphasized the importance
of the polymeric hydrous metal oxides in coagulation wherein
the Schultze-Hardy Rule was used to determine the charge on
the hydrolysis species that are most effective in the mutual

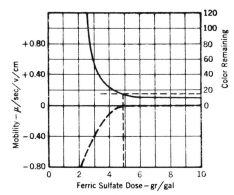

FIGURE 14   EFFECT OF FERRIC SULFATE DOSE ON
COAGULATION OF WATER A AT A
CONSTANT pH 3.78.
The curves are to be read, ● , before
stabilization; □ , stabilized and filtered.
Extrapolation of data and confirmatory
mobility determinations produced zero
mobility at pH 3.78, as predicted. The
best color values obtained ranged from
14 at 5.0 gr/gal to 9 at 10.0 gr/gal.
Minimum ferric sulfate dose to obtain
satisfactory color was 5.0 gr/gal. Iron
was reduced to less than 0.05 mg/l at
5.0 gr/gal ferric sulfate.

coagulation of well characterized colloidal sols (14-17). For
example, in the case of Al salts, the polymeric ion most effective
for charge reversal was calculated to be $[Al_8(OH)_{20}]^{+4}$. Other
high-valence polymeric species have been postulated for Fe^{+3}
and Al salts by Matijevic and others.

b. Electrophoretic techniques make it possible to evaluate
the effect of pH value on both coagulation and flocculation, but
these do not specifically identify the causes for these effects,
either for the relatively low pH values of perikentic coagulation
or for the substantially high pH values of orthokinetic flocculation.
The resulting charge on the floc particle may be due either to
adsorption of the H^+ or OH^- ions, respectively, at a given pH
value. There does not appear, at present, to be any way to
differentiate between these two possible causes.

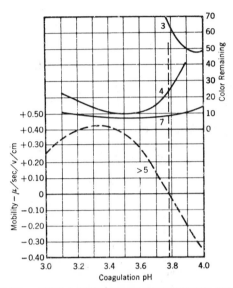

FIGURE 15   RELATIONSHIP BETWEEN ZERO MOBILITY
              AND BEST COLOR REMOVAL FOR WATER C.
              The solid curves are for color; the dashed;
              for mobility. The number associated with
              each curve indicates the ferric sulfate dose
              at which the results were obtained. The
              best color removal at doses equal to or
              greater than the minimum occurs at a pH
              lower than pH_O (indicated by the vertical
              dashed line).

     c. In the coagulation of clay turbidity, these measurements
indicate that charge reversal is to be avoided because it almost
invariably results in redispersion and stabilization of the clay
suspension. Whether the flocs should have zero or slightly
negative mobilities and consequently zeta potential is still
not quite clear, but it does seem definitely established that
the remaining charge on the floc particles, if any, is small
and negative. This is important because it provides an easy
method for preventing overdosing a water and effecting economies
in plant practice.
     d. With respect to color, the few studies which have been
made to date, seem to indicate that optimum color removal is

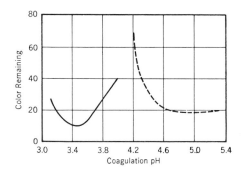

FIGURE 16   COAGULATION OF WATER B WITH
              FERRIC SULFATE AND ALUM.
              The solid curve is for ferric sulfate at
              5 gr/gal; the dashed curve, for alum at a
              10 gr/gal dose. The results show two of
              the principal differences between ferric
              sulfate and alum as coagulants for organic
              color. The ferric sulfate is more effective
              and coagulates at a lower pH.

obtained either at the point of floc neutrality or when the flocs
bear a very slight positive charge.

     e. In coagulating clay suspensions with either Al or Fe^{+3}
sulfate, the coagulant dosage is many times greater than the
BEC of the clay suspension when both are expressed in meq/l.

     f. Microelectrophoresis permits the rapid determination
of both the sign and the relative charge density of organic
polyelectrolytes and provides at least some information with
respect to their molecular weight. Experience to date appears
to indicate that lower molecular weight materials are more
effective as coagulants and higher molecular weight materials
as flocculants or bridging agents.

     g. Microelectrophoresis permits the only sophisticated
approach to the quantitative evaluation of a multi-step process
of coagulation-flocculation where a combination of two or more
materials is employed.

ACKNOWLEDGEMENT
     This investigation was supported in part, by Research
Grant WP-00139 from the Public Health Service, USDHEW,
Washington, D.C. Dr. Black gratefully acknowledges the

assistance of Dr. J.J. Morgan who presented the paper at the conference.

LITERATURE CITED

1. Black, A.P., Proc First Rudolfs Res Conf, p106 (June 1960).

2. Packham, R.F., British Water Res Assoc Tech Pub No. 12 (1959).

3. Pilipovich, J.B., et al, J Am Water Works Assoc, 50, 463, 1467 (1958).

4. Black, A.P., et al, J Am Water Works Assoc, 51, 247 (1959).

5. Black, A.P., J Am Water Works Assoc, 52, 492 (1960).

6. Black, A.P. and S.A. Hannah, J Am Water Works Assoc, 53, 438 (1961).

7. Black, A.P. and D.G. Willems, J Am Water Works Assoc, 53, 589 (1961).

8. Black, A.P. and R.G. Christman, J Am Water Works Assoc, 53, 737 (1961).

9. Packham, R.F., British Water Res Assoc Tech Pub No.14 (1960

10. Packham, R.F., British Water Res Assoc Tech Pub No. 15 (196

11. Packham, R.F., British Water Res Assoc Tech Pub No. 17 (196

12. Packham, R.F., British Water Res Assoc Tech Pub No. 20 (196

13. Packham, R.F., J Colloid Sci, 20, 81 (1965).

14. Matijevic, E., et al, J Phys Chem, 57, 951 (1953).

15. Matijevic, E., et al, J Phys Chem, 65, 826 (1961).

16. Matijevic, E., et al, J Colloid Sci, 19, 333 (1964).

17. Matijevic, E., et al, J Colloid Interface Sci, 21, (1966).

18. Stumm, W. and G. F. Lee, Schweiz Z Hydrol, 22, 295 (1960).

19. Stumm, W. and J. J. Morgan, J Am Water Works Assoc, 54, 971 (1962).

20. Miller, L. B., Public Health Rept, 38, 1995 (1923).

21. Brosset, C., Acta Chem Scand 6, 919 (1952).

22. Brosset, C., et al, Acta Chem Scand 8, 1917 (1954).

23. Sillen, L. G., Quart Rev (London), 13, 146 (1959).

24. Bjerrum J., et al, J Chem Soc (London), (1958).

25. LaMer, V. K., and T. W. Healey, J Phys Chem, 67, 2417 (1963).

26. Mattson, S., J Phys Chem, 32, 1532 (1928).

27. Black, A. P. and C. L. Chen, J Am Water Works Assoc, 57, 354 (1965).

28. Black, A. P. and J. V. Walters, J Am Water Works Assoc, 56, 99 (1964).

29. Black, A. P. and R. F. Christman, J Am Water Works Assoc, 55, 753 (1963).

30. Black, A. P. and R. F. Christman, J Am Water Works Assoc, 55, 897 (1963).

31. Hoak, R. D., Intern J Air Water Pollution, 6, 521 (1962).

32. Packham, R. F., Proc Soc Water Treat Exam, 13, 316 (1964).

33. Lamar, W. L. and D. F. Goerlitz, J Am Water Works Assoc, 55, 797 (1963).

34. Shapiro, J., Limnol and Oceanogr, 2, 161 (1957).

35. Black, A. P., et al, J Am Water Works Assoc, 55, 1347 (1963).

36. Singley, J. E., et al, J Am Water Works Assoc, 58, 455 (1966).

37. Langelier, W. F. and H. F. Ludwig, J Am Water Works Assoc, 41, 163 (1949).

DISCUSSION

CHAIRMAN PACKHAM: Thank you Dr. Morgan. This paper is now open for discussion from the floor.

DR. BIER (University of Arizona): I believe the optimist sees a half-filled glass as full and the pessimist sees that it is half empty. And I saw in many of your curves that a low pH there was poor correlation and at high pH there was good correlation between coagulation and zero charge. Also, in one of the slides, two of the three clays showed very good correlation, the third one precipitated in the same region as the first two, but showed a very high zeta potential or electrophoretic mobility.

DR. W. P. SHYLUK (Hercules Powder Co.): I have been studying the adsorption of polymers and trying to correlate this with electrophoretic measurements very much like Professor LaMer has been doing, and I feel that his surface coverage mechanism offers a good way of interpreting the fact that we we do not always get maximum clarification or coagulation at zero zeta potential. In other words, we are adsorbing on the surface polymer that makes that particular part in the surface stick to uncovered surface of another particle. When we have a high enough degree of such surface coverage we can cross-link all the particles into a coagulated or flocculated mass. I feel that this type of thinking would explain why we see maximum clarification at mobilities other than zero.

DR. MORGAN: Well, I agree with that. No work on poly - mers is shown here, but the work of LaMer and others on polymers and the unpublished work on polymers by Black and his co-workers confirm this observation. Extensive studies involving comparisons of mobility, turbidity removal, and adsorption have been made. Adsorption has been specifically measured by radio tracer techniques. When we consider all the factors together, the polymer adsorption model seems to be correct. Changes of the surface characteristics as a result of adsorption and the bridging mechanism are involved in establishing optimum flocculation. Furthermore, the kinetic conditions might be sufficient to bring about particle collisions to allow bridging.

DR. F. HUTTO (Johns Manville): Your opening remarks today was that there were many colors and many clays that you

were just going to talk about a couple of specific ones, and then
in the latter part of your paper you showed a curve which showed
waters with color being removed and they are all apparently in
one family. Would you care to comment on this?

DR. MORGAN: There are difficulties in the summary
of the paper. The properties of the colored water which were
used in the study are very well catalogued in the earlier papers
of Black. That particular water was from the southeastern part
of the United States. But in the original paper by Black, et al,
(35), the properties in the water are identified as to their source.
This last slide was illustrative of the pattern that repeats for
all the colored waters. I think that of the twelve waters that
were studied eleven behaved essentially the same. There was
one peculiar one which indicates that there are still properties
of the color material that may be specific enough to produce
this kind of behavior.

There were three clays, pure clays. There were three
natural river sediments, and there were about twelve different
colored waters represented in the work which was described
in the manuscript.

CHAIRMAN PACKHAM: I would like to speak on that.
At the Water Research Association we have isolated organic
color from a number of natural waters using the ion exchange
resin technique. This organic material can be divided into
different fractions corresponding to the water soluble fractions
of soil humus; namely, humic acid and fulvic acids. One can
show very clearly that the color of humic acid is approximately
four times more intense in the visible than fulvic acid. All
waters consist of a mixture of these two fractions and the
mixture will vary in different situations and at different times
of the year.

As a very rough approximation, it takes about the same
amount of $Al_2(SO_4)_3$ to remove a given amount of humic acid
or fulvic acid. Therefore, it seems to me rather dangerous
to propose a general relationship between color and the amount
of coagulant that is required because you can have waters of a
particular color that consists of different mixtures of humic
and fulvic acid and which therefore requires very different
doses of coagulant.

I would like to make a second point in relation to the use
of zeta potential measurements as a means of controlling
coagulation. While such measurements can be of great value

in research, I am strongly opposed to the suggestion that as a general principle all practical coagulation problems can be solved by achieving a zeta potential close to zero. There are situations where this condition corresponds to optimum coagulation and there are many where it does not. I would like to provide two examples of experiments made under conditions closely paralleling those encountered in practice where the zero zeta potential criterion fails.

Figure 1 shows the variation of zeta potential with pH for kaolin particles in the presence of varying concentrations of $Al_2(SO_4)_3$. Coagulation under the conditions of the experiment was optimum at a pH of 7.1 with 25 mg/l $Al_2(SO_4)_3$ corresponding to a zeta potential of +10 mv. It is noteworthy that coagulation did not take place at all within a reasonable time under the conditions defined by the isoelectric points at pH values of 3.9, 4.2, 5.3, 7.2, and 7.8.

Figure 2 shows similar data obtained under the same conditions except that 25 mg/l humic acid were present and the coagulant was $AlCl_3$. In this case removal of humic acid was optimum at pH 5.2 and reached a maximum when the concentration of $AlCl_3$ reached 3.9×10^{-4} M corresponding to a zeta potential of approximately +26 mv.

There is nothing basically wrong with the use of zeta potential control in specific instances where it can be shown to be operationally useful, but it would be most unwise at present to assume any general rules concerning the relationship between zeta potential and efficient clarification.

DR. MORGAN: I have one word of rebuttal. It's not a rebuttal against your argument, but merely an attempt to restate once again that the data presented by Black are representative only for his systems. There was never any tendency to overgeneralization, I would say, and certainly Black would be the last one to think that there is a magic formula. So I think we are really quite in agreement on this point.

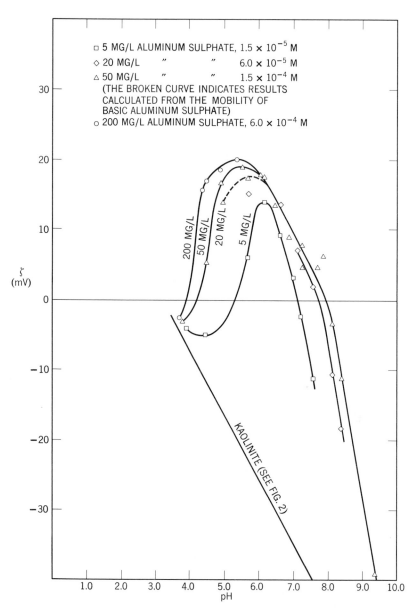

FIGURE 1D ZETA POTENTIAL OF KAOLIN (50 mg/l)
IN $Al_2(SO_4)_3$ SOLUTIONS.

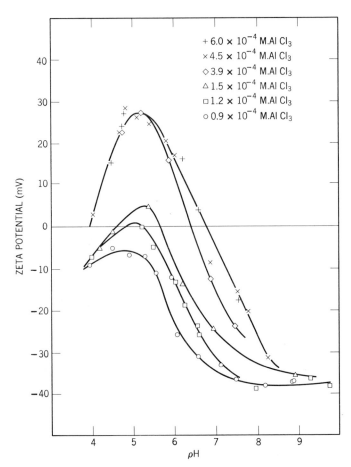

FIGURE 2D ZETA POTENTIAL IN THE PRESENCE OF
25 mg/l HUMIC ACID AND VARIOUS
CONCENTRATIONS OF AlCl$_3$.

J. Fred Hazel
University of Pennsylvania

ELECTROKINETIC CHARACTERISTICS OF SILICIC SURFACES

When a solid is immersed in a liquid, a potential difference between the two phases arises if the ions present have an unequal tendency to distribute themselves between the phases. Silica, whose central atom has a +4 oxidation number, preferentially attracts negative ions while repelling positive ions. An actual separation of charges occurs in a very thin layer in the vicinity of the interface giving rise to a potential at the interface sufficient to bring the system into equilibrium. This excess of negative charges on one side of the boundary layer and of positive charges on the other side constitutes an electrical double layer.

When the boundary layer at a solid-liquid interface is disturbed by the application of an external force, the static equilibrium conditions are destroyed and a series of electrokinetic effects results. There are four primary electrokinetic phenomena corresponding to the application of either mechanical or electrical force and holding either the liquid or solid stationary. In all cases, a relative motion at the solid-liquid interface is brought about.

If a hydrostatic pressure difference exists across a porous diaphragm or capillary, the resulting flow of liquid will give rise to a streaming potential at the ends of the diaphragm or capillary. Conversely, a potential applied to the ends of a porous plug or capillary causes a flow of liquid termed electroosmosis. These effects may be antagonistic. Thus, the potential produced by application of pressure may polarize the positive charges in the diffuse layer nearest the solid tending to cause the liquid to flow in a direction opposite to the pressure gradient (1, 2).

If an electric field is applied to a dispersion of charged solid particles in a liquid, the resulting migration of these particles is called electrophoresis. If solid particles are allowed to fall through a stationary liquid, a sedimentation potential results. This is sometimes called the Dorn effect. These four phenomena are related closely, being different aspects of the same phenomenon. Silicic surfaces have been studied by the first three.

The primary concept of electrokinetics is the zeta potential, ζ , defined as the potential at the surface of shear. The concept of the zeta potential was introduced by Freundlich (3).

STREAMING POTENTIALS

Streaming potentials were discovered by Quincke in 1859 (4). The classical theory for this and all the other primary electrokinetic effects was furnished by Helmholtz (5). The Helmholtz electrokinetic equations, based on the rigid double layer, were modified by Smoluchowski (6). The Helmholtz-Smoluchowski equation for streaming potentials may be written:

$$\zeta = - \frac{4\pi\eta \ kE}{PD} \tag{11-1}$$

where ζ is the electrokinetic potential, $\pi = 3.1416$, η is the viscosity of the solution, k is the specific conductance, E is the streaming potential, P is the hydrostatic pressure difference, and D is the dielectric constant of the liquid. The negative sign is not usually written but it is correct to do so (7).

The electrokinetic equations were derived using Poisson's equation, Poiseuille's equation, and Ohm's law. The derivation assumes that the diameter of the capillary is large in comparison to the thickness of the double layer, that the dielectric constant at the solid-liquid interface is the same as that in the bulk of the liquid, and that streamline flow of liquid through the capillary occurs. The equations do not take into account the diffuse nature of the solid-liquid interface.

The theory of electrokinetic phenomena has been reviewed by Abramson (8), Horowitz (9), Abramson, et al (10), Verwey and Overbeek (11), Gortner (12), Bull (13), and Butler, et al (14). Wood has critically reviewed the streaming potential methods (7).

THE ELECTRICAL DOUBLE LAYER

Helmholtz considered the electrical double layer as two surface charges separated by a constant distance. Gouy (15) introduced the concept of the diffuse double layer to which Chapman (16) applied Poisson's equation to find the equilibrium distance of ions in the double layer. Stern suggested a double layer combining the Gouy-Chapman diffuse layer and the Helmholtz fixed layer (17). The theories of Gouy and Chapman were followed by the concept of the ion atmosphere of Debye and Hückel (18).

SURFACE CONDUCTANCE

Because of the charge on the solid, the liquid near the surfaces in a streaming cell contains more ions of one sign and less of the opposite sign than the liquid farther from the surface. Since the liquid near the solid surface has a composition different from that farther from the solid, its conductivity would differ from that of the bulk of the liquid. The conductance between the ends of a capillary or porous diaphragm in a streaming potential cell is, thus, the sum of the bulk conductance and the surface conductance. Bikerman has reviewed surface conductance and its importance in colloid chemistry (19). In 1928, Briggs showed that k', the specific conductance of the liquid in the capillary or diaphragm of a streaming potential cell, should be substituted for k, the bulk conductance of the liquid, in the Helmholtz-Smoluchowski equation 11-1 (20, 21). The sum of the bulk conductance and the surface conductance in the porous diaphragm or capillary is k'. Since k' = C/R, where C is the cell constant of the streaming cell and R is the resistance across the cell, C/R can be substituted for k' in the Helmholtz-Smoluchowski equation as modified by Briggs (22) giving:

$$\zeta = - \frac{4 \pi \eta \quad EC}{DRP} \tag{11-2}$$

This equation is used almost as standard practice in calculating zeta potentials from streaming potentials (23).

Bikerman has developed electrokinetic equations which include corrections for the surface conductance of capillary

systems (24), the unit of surface conductance, has the dimension ohm^{-1}, whereas specific volume conductivity is measured
in ohm^{-1} cm^{-1}. The correction factor can not be calculated
for real diaphragms with capillaries of various shapes and
dimensions (25).

APPARATUS FOR THE MEASUREMENT OF STREAMING POTENTIALS

The streaming potential apparatus used by Hazel and
Schnable for investigation of silicic surfaces is shown in
Figure 1 (about 1/2 scale) (26). A more detailed drawing of
the streaming potential diaphragm assembly is given in Figure 2
(about 2/3 scale).

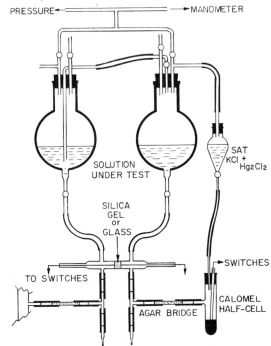

FIGURE 1   STREAMING POTENTIAL APPARATUS.
            (Reprinted through courtesy of J Electro-
            chem Soc).

Regulated pressure was applied to either of the two 2000-ml

liquid storage vessels from a cylinder of compressed water-
pumped nitrogen gas by means of a regulator (Air Reduction Co.,
Style No. 8421). The exact pressure was indicated to the
nearest mm on an open-end U-tube manometer filled with
analytical reagent Hg.

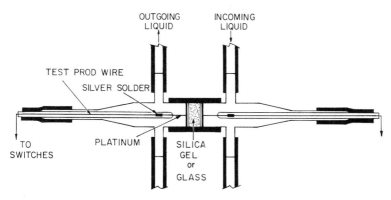

FIGURE 2   STREAMING POTENTIAL DIAPHRAGM
            ASSEMBY. (Reprinted through courtesy
            of J Electrochem Soc).

The streaming cell was connected to the liquid storage
flasks with 1/4" Tygon tubing. The streaming potential diaphragm
assembly and its method of preparation were very similar to
that used by Edelberg and Hazel (27). A detailed description of
the preparation of the diaphragm assembly has been given by
Schnable (28). In the streaming cell the powders under investigation were confined firmly between perforated platinum electrodes
using a section of rubber tubing as a cell compartment. Cell
constants determined before and after streaming of a series of
solutions through a given porous diaphragm agreed with a few
percent, indicating the stability of these porous plugs. The
plugs contained 6 g of powdered material.

ZETA POTENTIAL OF GLASSES
    Zeta potentials of glasses in distilled water and KCl solu-
tions determined with the streaming potential apparatus and
described above are given in Table I (26). Data of several
investigators on various glasses are given in Table II whereas

TABLE I   ZETA POTENTIAL IN DISTILLED
                WATER AND POTASSIUM CHLORIDE
                SOLUTIONS

Substance	Solution	Average Zeta Potential, MV
Corning No.7740 Glass	Distilled Water	-14
	0.01N KCl	-53
Corning No.9010 Glass	Distilled Water	-31
	0.01N KCl	-60
	0.1N KCl	-40
Either Glass	0.6% by volume Kasil No. 1 (a) plus 175-400 mg/1 $Ba(OAc)_2 \cdot 2H_2O$	-14

(a) A commercial product containing
    34% $K_2O \cdot 3.9\ SiO_2$.

Table III gives the zeta potentials of glasses in the presence of
$CaCl_2$ and $BaCl_2$. Figure 3 summarizes the electrokinetic
behavior of Corning No.7740 glass and Corning No. 9010 glass
in the presence of potassium silicate (26).

Molchanov determined the zeta potentials of various glasses
in a number of electrolytes (41). The results confirmed the
theory of the formation of protective layers on silicate glasses.
Because of the protective films, the zeta potentials of various
apparatus glasses should be practically alike. Lengyel and
Vincze investigated the zeta potentials of various glasses and
found they were not affected by the chemical composition of
the glass (42).

The preceding zeta potentials have been presented without
regard to the electrokinetic methods used to determine them.
Bikerman indicates that measurements of two or more effects
at one interface prove that very similar values of the zeta
potential are obtained by using two or more electrokinetic
methods (43). Creeth states that the theoretical background
existing at present for the streaming potential, Dorn, and
electroosmotic effects is generally satisfactory, but wider

TABLE II   ZETA POTENTIAL OF GLASSES

Zeta Potentials, MV

Solution Type of Glass	Water	10^{-5}	10^{-4}	10^{-3}	10^{-2}	Literature Cited
Jena	-	-	-105	-72	-	29
Jena 16III	-	-	-	-121	-82	30
Jena Gerate	-55	-	-	-	-	31
(Unspecified)	-27	-	-	-	-	32
Pyrex	-111	-	-9	-83	-53	33
(Unspecified)	-158	-	-45	-40	-	34(a)
(Unspecified)	-85	-	-79	-49	-	34(b)
Jena 16III	-225	-	-	-	-	35
Jena 16III	-	-204	-166	-	-	36
Jena 16III	-230	-200	-165	-	-	37
Pyrex	-	-151	-122	-69	-	38
Soft	-	-87	-	-57	-	38
(Unspecified)	-	-76	-67	-52	-	39
Jena 16III	-156	-140	-121	-	-	40
Pyrex	-	-	-	-	-56	27

(a) Streaming Potential Method.
(b) Electroosmosis Method.

TABLE III   ZETA POTENTIAL OF GLASSES

Zeta Potentials, MV

Solution Type of Glass	Normality of $CaCl_2$			Normality of $BaCl_2$			
	10^{-6}	10^{-5}	10^{-4}	10^{-4}	5×10^{-4}	10^{-3}	
(Unspecified)	-	-	-	-34	-29	-28	(a)
(Unspecified)	-	-	-	-38	-27	-23	(b)
Jena 16III	-	-217	-86	-	-	-	(c)
Jena 16III	-123	-99	-76	-	-	-	(d)

(a) Streaming Potential Method (Ref. 34).
(b) Electroosmosis Method (Ref. 34).
(c) (Ref. 37).
(d) (Ref. 40).

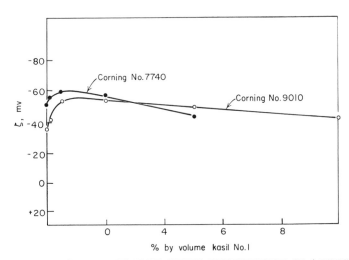

FIGURE 3   RESULTS WITH DIFFERENT GLASSES
                (Reprinted through courtesy of
                J Electrochem Soc).

testing of the present electrophoretic theory is desirable (44).
Overbeek has considered this in a review (45). Conway has
included a number of tables of electrokinetic data obtained
by the streaming potential method in his book of electrochemical
data (46).

In 1945, Jones and Wood stated that it was evident from a
survey of the literature on streaming potential determinations,
especially of glass, that most of the data were unreliable and
it was difficult to determine which, if any, were worthy of confidence (47). They listed as possible sources of variation of
results the type of glass used, previous history and treatment
of the surface, use of inadequately described or unsuitable
measuring instruments, use in calculations of conductance data
taken from the literature without correction for the conductance
of the water used to prepare the solutions, and failure to correct
for surface conductance. For example, it has been shown that
electrokinetic potentials, especially of water and of very dilute
solutions are markedly affected by the CO_2 content (30, 48, 58,
49).

More fundamental than the above experimental difficulties
is a number of theoretical questions concerning the validity of

zeta potentials. Bikerman suggests that the value of the zeta potential may depend on the roughness of the solid surface (43). McBain did not believe in the reality of the electrokinetic potential, which he indicated has never been measured but always calculated (50).

A number of investigators has noticed a variation of zeta potential with time (7, 47, 51, 52, 53, 54). This is in part due to swelling of the solid under test.

Hubbard, et al, have shown that glass does swell measurably in water (55). Mysels and McBain observed that fritted Pyrex glass offered increasing hydrodynamic resistance but unchanged electrical resistance (56). Hubbard and Goldman state the uneven distribution of migratable ions between the inner and outer phases (the glass surface and the ambient solution, respectively) produced osmotic pressure within the surface of the glass, causing swelling and ultimate destruction of the specimen (57).

Schnable observed that the magnitude of the negative zeta potential of Corning No. 9010 Glass in potassium silicate and in potassium silicate-barium acetate mixtures decreased with time (28). An example is given in Figure 4. The change in zeta potential with time can be attributed to changes in the properties of the potassium silicate-barium acetate mixtures with time, to solubility of the solid, swelling of the solid, and base exchange.

ELECTROKINETIC BEHAVIOR OF SILICA GEL AND SILICA SOLS

Glixelli and Wiertelak found that the zeta potential of silicic acid in a given medium depended on the silica concentration and increased with a decrease in silica concentration (58). For inorganic salts they obtained the formula:

$$\zeta = a - k \log c \qquad (11\text{-}3)$$

where ζ is the electrokinetic potential, a and k are constants, and c is the concentration of the electrolyte. The zeta potential was -5.6 mv with distilled water, -2.4 mv with 0.001 N barium nitrate, and -1.0 mv with 0.01N $Ba(NO_3)_2$. Hazel found that silicic acid sols are difficult to recharge with bivalent and trivalent cations (59) but could be recharged with thorium ions (60). An isoelectric concentration of 1.2×10^{-5} M Th^{+4} was found for a silicic acid sol containing 0.59 g of silica

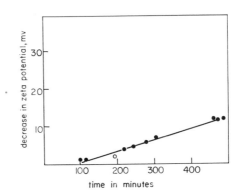

FIGURE 4   RATE OF CHANGE OF ZETA POTENTIAL:
             CORNING NO. 9010 GLASS WITH
             POTASSIUM SILICATE-BARIUM ACETATE
             MIXTURE.

while for a sol containing 0.12 g/l of SiO_2, the concentration
of Th^{+4} ions corresponding to zero mobility was slightly less
than $4 \times 10^{-6}M$. [In the microscopic method for measuring
electrophoretic mobility, one must focus on the stationary
liquid layer (located 0.147% of the diameter of the cell measured
from the top of a cylindrical cell). A study of mobility-depth
curves confirm this and show that the mobility may change
sign (Figure 5) (67). In such cases, there is a large velocity
gradient near the depth at which the stationary liquid layer
exists. This probably serves to magnify mobility measurement
errors due to slight errors in focusing.] It is interesting to
note that White, et al determined the isoelectric concentration
of Th to be of the order of $10^{-6}M$ for a glass surface suggesting
that they, too, were dealing with a silica gel surface at the
glass-water interface (61).

THE ISOELECTRIC POINT OF SILICA SURFACES
     The charge on a silica surface tends to be negative. This
is shown in the following examples:
     a. SiO^- groups (negative) predominate at high pH while
SiOH groups (neutral) are favored at low pH.

$$SiOH \quad \xrightleftharpoons[H^+]{OH^-} \quad SiO^- \qquad\qquad (11-4)$$

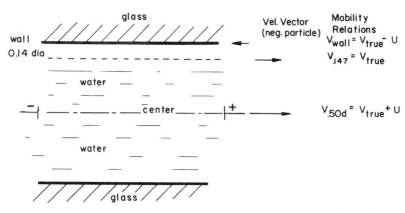

FIGURE 5   MOBILITY-DEPTH RELATIONS, IDEALIZED.
Li = Electroosmotic of water in cell;
V_{wall} = Mobility of particles at wall;
$V_{.147}$ = Mobility of particles at stationary level (After Smoluchowski);
$V_{.50}$ = Mobility of particles at center of cell.

b. The SiOH group is acidic. It is not amphoteric (or basic). Thus:

SiOH	+	OH⁻ =	SiO⁻	+	H_2O
Acid		Base			

$$\text{SiOH} + \text{OH}^- = \text{SiO}^- + \text{H}_2\text{O} \qquad (11\text{-}5)$$

but:

$$\text{SiOH} + \text{H}^+ = \text{No reaction*}$$

Not a base   Acid

*(Si^+ would hydrolyze: $\text{Si}^+ + \text{H}_2\text{O} \rightleftharpoons \text{SiOH} + \text{H}^+$).

c. That the charge on a silica surface has a negative bias can be shown also by the following model in which silicon coordinates with oxygen. Under these conditions silicon is pictured as having an oxidation number of +4.

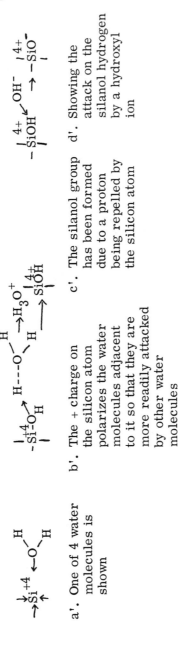

a'. One of 4 water molecules is shown

b'. The + charge on the silicon atom polarizes the water molecules adjacent to it so that they are more readily attacked by other water molecules

c'. The silanol group has been formed due to a proton being repelled by the silicon atom

d'. Showing the attack on the silanol hydrogen by a hydroxyl ion

For a silica surface to have a true isoelectric point (a pH which uniquely determines the condition of zero charge) a positive and a negative species should exist in equilibrium, e.g.:

$$SiOH_2^+ \underset{H^+}{\overset{OH^-}{\rightleftharpoons}} SiO^- \tag{11-6}$$

Although the reality of a species such as the one on the left is improbable, it does appear that negative silica surfaces have been recharged to the positive sign on addition of protons. Moreover, a number of different investigators have found that the change in sign occurs at a pH of approximately 2.

Gordon conducted electroosmosis experiments with silica gel and found that the surface was recharged between pH 3.6 and pH 1.2. These data are given in Table IV (62).

TABLE IV EFFECT OF pH ON SIGN
OF CHARGE OF SILICA GEL

pH	Sign	Rate of Flow of Water, mm/sec	Voltage
6.526	Negative	6.3	116
4.717	Negative	3.1	120
3.567	Negative	2.4	120
1.217	Positive	1.4	119

Schnable made streaming potential measurements with Mallinckrodt No. 2846 silicic acid in HCl (28). His results are given in Figure 6. The isoelectric point occurs at a pH value of 1.9.

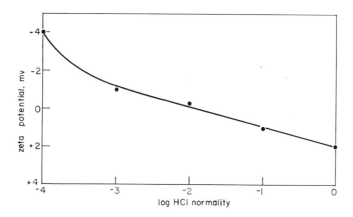

FIGURE 6   ZETA POTENTIAL OF MALLINCKRODT
NO. 2846 SILICIC ACID IN HCl.

Hazel has conducted electrophoretic measurements with dialyzed silicic acid sols in the presence of NaOH and HCl (59). The lowest investigated pH value was approximately 1.5, under which condition the particles had zero mobility in an electric field. Losenbeck employed electrophoresis to find silica to be isoelectric between pH 2 and 3 that depended on the concentration of silica (63).

Iler has concluded that there is considerable confusion concerning the isoelectric point of silica (64). In this regard, it is certainly true in the case of silica, as with other hydrous oxides, that a fixed pH value cannot be assigned to the condition of zero charge. The term "isoelectric point" may be more properly associated with proteins. The electrical neutral condition of silica in relation to pH may be discussed with the aid of Figure 7. The solid curve in this figure represents the zeta potential of a silica surface as influenced by H^+ or $\overline{O}H$ ions. The variation in the isoelectric condition between the two dotted curves is illustrative of the effect of adsorbed cations or anions, and of the concentration of silica. Adsorption sites may be inherently present due to pH conditions or they may be induced by polarization of the surface by the field of the adsorbed ion.

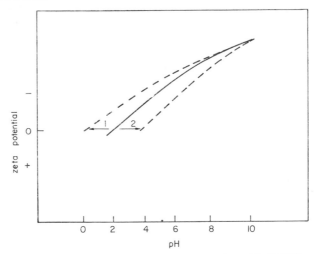

FIGURE 7   FACTORS AFFECTING THE ZETA
                  POTENTIAL OF SILICA.
                  1. Shift caused by presence of anions and
                     increase in concentration of silica.
                  2. Shift caused by presence of cations.

Iler (64) has applied an equation developed by Roller and Evin (65) to silica surfaces. If:
    a = moles/l of ionized surface sites, and
    b = moles/l of nonionized sites

then:
$$a/b = 10^{(-9.8 + pH)} @ 30°C \qquad (11-7)$$

While there are not many data which may be used to calculate the actual maximum number of charged sites per unit area, in such cases as data exist the agreement with the equation is reasonable.

In passing, two implications of the above relation may be pointed out:

pH	Ratio, a/b	Relative Numbers
9.8	1	b = a
1.8	10^{-8}	b = 10^8 a

Thus, it is judged that the H^+ ion in the absence of other cations is incapable of recharging a silica surface.

pH RELATED PHENOMENA

There are pH dependent phenomena to be observed with silicates which lend themselves to interpretation by invoking the idea of the presence or absence of a charge on the surface. These phenomena are:

   a. The formation of silica sols from solutions of alkali silicates.
   b. The irreversible precipitation of silica observed on freezing silica sols.
   c. The formation of silica gels from silica sols (or from solutions of alkali silicates, cf. a).

The above are examples of polymerization.

THE Si-O-Si LINKAGE

The most stable bond between silicon atoms is an oxygen bridge, Si-O-Si. Alkali silicates are characterized by the presence of Si-O-H and Si-O groups although Si-O-Si linkages may be present to an extent in the more silicious silicates. Polymerization or particle growth is associated with the formation of siloxane groups or of hydrogen bonded structures.

The Si-O-Si group (siloxane) may be formed by condensation of silanol groups (Si-O-H). Two models for this process are indicated:

   I. Stoichiometric considerations.

Si-O-H + H-O-Si = Si-O-Si + H-O-H

   A. Two moles of silanol groups form one mole of siloxane groups and one mole of water.

  B. One mole of Si-O bonds and one mole of O-H bonds
     are broken; one mole of O-Si bonds and one mole
     of H-O bonds are formed.
II. Additional considerations.
     The formation of siloxane linkages depends upon
     "fruitful" collisions between Si-O-H groups as
     influenced by the following conditions:
     A. The proportion of Si-O-H groups to Si-$\bar{\text{O}}$ groups.
        The latter decrease with decrease in pH, as
        reflected by the decrease in zeta potential or
        mobility, with decrease in pH.
     B. The amount of silicate in moles/l.
     C. The energy available to break the requisite bonds.
        This may be judged from the expression (65):
        $$E_a = 0.28 \left[D\ (Si\text{-}O) + D\ (O\text{-}H) \right] \qquad (11\text{-}8)$$
        Where:

           E_a = Energy of activation
           D^a = Dissociation energy of bond indicated
     D. An entropy or geometric factor.
        According to modern theory, the reaction:
        $$2Si\text{-}O\text{-}H \longrightarrow Si\text{-}O\text{-}Si + H\text{-}O\text{-}H \qquad (11\text{-}9)$$
        occurs through the formation of an activated complex.
        This complex has its lowest energy when the angles
        and distances between the atoms in the complex
        correspond most closely to the bond angles and
        distances in the molecules comprising the products
        of the reaction.
  In summary, it may be said that neither energy nor entropy
considerations favor polymerization via oxygen bridge formation.

HYDROGEN BONDED STRUCTURES

  The formation of hydrogen bonded structures as a mode of
accounting for the formation of silica sols, gels, and low-
temperature precipitates is suggested by both energy and entropy
factors. As a prerequisite only hydrogen bonds need be broken.
Since these bonds have low energies, E_a, as calculated above,
also has a small value. Furthermore, the entropy factor is
favorable because this type of secondary bond has fewer geometric restrictions than primary bonds. Examples of hydrogen
bonded structures, indicated by three dots (...), are given:

$$
\begin{array}{cc}
\mathrm{Si} & \mathrm{Si} \\
| & | \\
\mathrm{Si\text{-}\bar{O}\cdots H\text{-}O} & \mathrm{Si\text{-}O\cdots H\text{-}O} \\
& \mathrm{H} \\
\text{Structure (a)} & \text{Structure (b)}
\end{array}
$$

pH, ELECTRICAL PROPERTIES, AND POLYMERIZATION

The tendency of silicates to polymerize goes through a
maximum, then a minimum followed by another maximum as
the pH value is decreased from approximately 12 in an alkali
silicate of 3.3 ratio (SiO_2/Na_2O). The first maximum occurs
in the pH range 8 to 6, and the minimum at pH 3. Maximum
polymerization is observed again below about pH 2. It makes
little difference whether the reduction in pH is accomplished by
addition of an acid or by the exchange of Na^+ in the silicate
for H^+ ions in a cation active resin.

An example is given in Figure 8 for the low temperature
irreversible polymerization (flocculation) of silica sols of
varying pH (66). In the scale employed, a value of 4 corresponds to complete flocculation. The sols were prepared with
the aid of an exchange resin. The same figure gives mobility
values of silica sols at the same H^+ ion activities. In the latter
case, pH adjustments were made with NaOH or HCl.

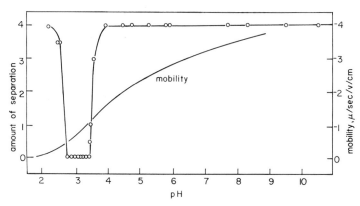

FIGURE 8   DEGREE OF FLOCCULATION OF SILICA
             SOLS BY FREEZING COMPARED TO THEIR
             MOBILITIES.

Figure 9 gives the first maximum (shortest time required
for gelation) and the minimum in silica gel formation under

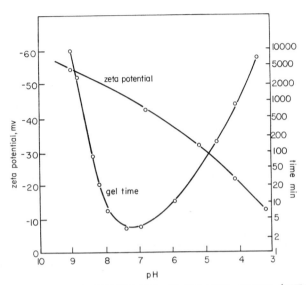

FIGURE 9   EFFECT OF pH ON GEL TIME (MERRILL
                AND SPENCER) AND ON THE ZETA
                POTENTIAL (HAZEL) IN AQUEOUS
                SILICATE SYSTEMS.

conditions of different pH produced by the addition of acid.
Again, the mobilities of silica sols of the same pH are given
for comparison. While the following discussion is directed
to polymerization produced by freezing, Hazel has suggested
that similar factors may apply to silica sol and silica gel
formation (66).

The electric charge is a major factor in determing the
stability of silicate polymers. In highly alkaline solution where
the charge is great, polymerization is reversible. As an
example, a solid gel may be formed by warming a mixture of
equal volumes of 27% potassium (3.34) silicate and 4 M $NaNO_3$
(26). Complete liquefaction occurs when the system is cooled.
Similarly, a solid phase is formed when the unmodified silicate
is frozen, but this disappears on warming.

Consider a ·silicate solution containing
3.3 moles of silica to one mole of sodium
oxide. In terms of molecules this composition lies between that represented by
NaH_3SiO_4 and H_4SiO_4.

$$NaH_3SiO_4 \; + \; H_2O \; \rightleftarrows \; NaOH \; + \; H_4SiO_4$$

$$H_3SiO_4^- \; + \; H_2O \; \rightleftarrows \; OH^- \; + \; H_4SiO_4$$

A   C

It is probable that the structures A and C
more nearly represent the nature of the
solutions than do simple molecules. During
freezing the concentration of the dispersed
silica is effectively increased. This process
may involve the formation of oxygen bridges
and hydrogen bridges. Particles formed by
the growth of A are charged, while those from
C are neutral. Flocculation results when
the particles formed by freezing are not
dispersed on melting.
Hydroxyl ions dissolve or disperse the flocs
by breaking oxygen bridges between the silicon
atoms or by increasing the charge on the
structures. This reaction depends not only
on the hydroxyl-ion concentration but also
on the charge on the particles. The latter
tends to inhibit the dispersing action because
of electric repulsion between the hydroxyl
ions and the charge on the particles. Thus,
a concentration of these ions which will
break the bond in C will not attack A because
of the charge on the structure near the point
of attack. This is illustrated in the following:

$$Si \; :\overset{-}{\underset{..}{O}}: \; Si \; + \; :\overset{-}{\underset{..}{O}}: \; H = \text{no reaction}$$

$$\cdot Si \; :\underset{..}{O}: \; Si \cdot + \; :\overset{A}{\underset{..}{O}}: \; H = \cdot Si \; :\underset{..}{O}: \; H + \; :\overset{-}{\underset{..}{O}}: \; Si \cdot$$

Both the charge on the particles (as reflected
in the mobility) and the hydroxyl-ion
concentration decrease with pH (Figure 9).
At very high alkalinites, such as those
which prevail in unmodified silicate solutions,
pH 12, the flocs are dispersed because of
their large charge. As the hydroxyl-ion
concentration is reduced, the charge on
the particles decreases. In effect this
amounts to a shifting of the charge to a
greater distance from the point of attack,
as indicated below in a comparison of
structures B and A, causing it to be more
soluble in hydroxyl ions.

$$\cdot Si \cdot \text{-----} \cdot Si \cdot \text{-----} \cdot Si \cdot \text{-----} \cdot Si \; :\underset{..}{O}: \; Si \cdot$$
$$\qquad\qquad\qquad\qquad A$$
$$\cdot Si \cdot \text{-----} \cdot Si \cdot \text{-----} \cdot Si \cdot \text{-----} \cdot Si \; :\underset{..}{O}: \; Si \cdot$$
$$\qquad\qquad\qquad\qquad B$$
$$\cdot Si \cdot \text{-----} \cdot Si \cdot \text{-----} \cdot Si \cdot \text{-----} \cdot Si \; :\underset{..}{O}: \; Si \cdot$$
$$\qquad\qquad\qquad\qquad C$$

In the work under discussion it was found
that flocculation on melting remained
complete at pH values above about 3.5.
At this pH, for the systems containing 2.5
percent silica frozen for 15 min at $-10^{\circ}C$,
the bonds holding the structures together
were so weak that even the low concentration
of hydroxyl ions present in the system was
enough to disperse the structures. The
balance between these forces was so nearly
complete when this range was entered that the
precipitate dissolved slowly rather than
disappearing at once on melting. With
further decrease in pH there was no flocculation until a pH of about 2.6 was reached.
Under these conditions the hydroxyl-ion concentration had been diminished to such an
extent that it no longer was able to dissolve
the structure even though the charge had
been reduced further. Accordingly, flocculation
again became considerable.

Condensation occurs in modified silicates
at room temperature but much more slowly
than when the systems are frozen. Moreover,
the same rules which apply to condensation
by freezing hold at the higher temperature.
Thus, there is a connection between the
stabilities of the structures which are
formed and the pH of the system. Separation
of the structures by gel formation or by
flocculation was at a minimum in both cases
at about a pH of 3. When a fresh sol with a
pH of 3 was frozen, the structure which
formed dissolved completely on thawing. On
the other hand, freezing of a sol of the same
pH which had aged for several days and as a
result undergone considerable condensation,
caused complete flocculation.
The stabilities of the structures increase
with concentration of silica, a result
which follows from greater opportunities
for bonding. The stabilities of the
structures increase sharply above a pH of 5.
Flocculation has been produced in systems
containing only a few parts per million of
silica when the freezing was conducted in
the pH range of 5.7 to 7.1 (66).

Iler, noting the sharp increase in mobility above pH 4, has
taken the view that negative charges due to Si-Ō groups are not
important below this pH (64). It was suggested that gel formation
above the minimum (pH 3) is catalyzed by OH^- ions. It has been
shown that traces of fluoride ion, or HF, catalyzed polymerization below the minimum. It has been postulated that $Si(OH)_4$
polymerized only when an OH^- or F^- ion is present to form a
reactive intermediate in which the coordination number of
silicon is 6.

LITERATURE CITED
1. Bender, M., J Colloid Sci, 9, 400 (1954).

2. Michaeles, A.S. and S.C. Lin, Silicate Science, 1, Wilhelm
    Eitel, Ed, Academic Press, Inc., New York, N.Y.,
    p339 (1964).

3. Freundlich, H., Colloid and Capillary Chemistry, Translation,
    Third German Edition by H.S. Hatfield, E.P. Dutton and Co.,
    New York, N.Y., p242 (1926).

4. Quincke, G., Pogg Ann, 107, 1 (1859).

5. Helmholtz, H., Wied Ann, 7, 337 (1879).

6. Smoluchowski, M., Krak Anz, 1903, 182.

7. Wood, L.A., J Am Chem Soc, 68, 432 (1946).

8. Abramson, H.A., Electrokinetic Phenomena, Chemical
   Catalog Co., New York, N.Y.,(1934).

9. Horowitz, C., J Chem Educ, 16, 519 (1939).

10. Abramson, H.A., et al, Electrophoresis of Proteins,
    Reinhold Publishing Co., New York, N.Y.,(1942).

11. Verwey, E.J.W. and J. Th.G Overbeek, Theory of the
    Stability of Lyophobic Colloids, Elsevier Publishing Co.,
    Amsterdam, Holland,(1948).

12. Gortner, R.A., Outlines of Biochemistry, 3rd Ed.,
    edited by R.A. Gortner, John Wiley and Sons,
    New York, N.Y.,(1949).

13. Bull, H.B., Physical Biochemistry, 2nd Ed., John Wiley
    and Sons, New York, N.Y.,(1951).

14. Butler, J.A.V., Electrical Phenomena at Interfaces,
    Methuen and Co., London, England,(1951).

15. Gouy, G., J Phys (4), 9, 357 (1910).

16. Chapman, D.L., Phil Mag, 25, 475 (1913).

17. Stern, O., Z Elektrochem, 30, 508 (1924).

18. Debye, P. and E. Hückel, Physik , 24, 185 (1923).

19. Bikerman, J.J., Kolloid-Z, 72, 100 (1935).

20. Briggs, D.R., J Phys Chem, 32, 641 (1928).

21. Briggs, D.R., Colloid Symp Monograph, 6, 41 (1928).

22. Buchanan, A.S. and E. Heymann, Proc Roy Soc (London), A195, 150 (1948).

23. Creeth, J.M., Electrokinetic Phenomena at Interfaces, Methuen and Co., London, England, p 79 (1951).

24. Bikerman, J.J., Trans Faraday Soc, 36, 154 (1940).

25. Overbeek, J.Th.G. and P.W.O. Wijga, Rec Trav Chim, 65, 556 (1946).

26. Hazel, J.F. and G.L. Schnable, J Electrochem Soc, 100, 65 (1953).

27. Edelberg, R. and J.F. Hazel, J Electrochem Soc, 96, 13 (1949).

28. Schnable, G.L., Streaming Potential Studies of Phosphors, Glasses, and Gels, Ph D Thesis, Un. Penna., Philadelphia, Penna., (1953).

29. Kruyt, H.R. and P.C. Willigen, Kollid-Z, 45, 307 (1928).

30. Lachs, H. and J. Biczyk, Z Physik Chem, 148, Abt. A, 441 (1930).

31. Fairbrother, F. and M. Balkin, J Chem Soc, (London), p 389 (1931).

32. Gostkowski, K., Acta Phys Polon, 3, 343 (1934).

33. Monaghan, B. and H.L. White, J Phys Chem, 39, 935 (1935).

34. DuBois, R. and A.H. Roberts, J Phys Chem, 40, 543 (1936).

35. Rutgers, A.J., et al, Proc Acad Sci Amsterdam, 41, 763 (1938).

36. Verlende, E., Proc Acad Sci Amsterdam, 42, 764 (1939).

37. Rutgers, A.J., Trans Faraday Soc, 36, 69 (1940).

38. Eversole, W.G. and W.W. Boardman, J Phys Chem, 46, 914 (1942).

39. Eversole, W.G. and C.R. Estee, J Chem Phys, 11, 63 (1943).

40. Rutgers, A.J. and M. de Smet, Trans Faraday Soc, 43, 102 (1947).

41. Molchanov, V.S., J Phys Chem (USSR), 13, 1124 (1939).

42. Lengyel, B. and J. Vince, Magyar Kem Folyoirat, 47, 20 (1941).

43. Bikerman, J.J., Surface Chemistry, Academic Press,Inc., New York, N.Y., p 386 (1948).

44. Creeth, J.M., Electrokinetic Phenomena at Interfaces, Methuen and Co., London, England, p386 (1951).

45. Overbeek, J.T.G., Advances in Colloid Science, III, H. Mark and E.J.W. Verwey, Interscience Publishers, New York, N.Y.,(1950).

46. Conway, B.E., Electrochemical Data, Elsevier Co., Amsterdam, Holland,(1952).

47. Jones, G. and L.A. Wood, J Chem Phys, 13, 106 (1945).

48. Lachs, H. and J. Biczyk, Roczniki Chem, 11, 362 (1931).

49. Miyazaki, S. and N. Ando, J Chem Soc Japan, Pure Chem Sect, 165, 144 (1944).

50. McBain, J.W., Colloid Science, D.C. Heath and Co., Boston, Mass., p195 (1950).

51. Wood, L.A. and L.B. Robinson, J Am Chem Soc, 69, 1862 (1947).

52. Lachs, H. and Kronman, Bull Intern Acad Polonaise, 1925A, 289.

53. Fairbrother, F. and H. Varlay, J Chem Soc London, p1584 (1927).

54. White, H.L., et al, J Phys Chem, 36, 120 (1932).

55. Hubbard, D., et al, J Res Nat Bur Std, 22, 339 (1939).

56. Mysels, K.J. and J.W. McBain, J Colloid Sci, 3, 45 (1948).

57. Hubbard, D. and R.G. Goldman, J Res Nat Bur Std, 48, 428 (1952).

58. Glixelli, S. and J. Wiertelak, Kolloid-Z, 43, 85 (1927); Ibid, 45, 197 (1928).

59. Hazel, J.F., J Phys Chem, 42, 409 (1938).

60. Hazel, J.F., J Phys Chem, 44, 422 (1940).

61. White, H.L., et al, J Phys Chem, 39 (1935).

62. Gordon, N.E., Colloid Symp Monograph, 2, 114 (1925).

63. Losenbeck, O., Kolloidchem Beithefte, 16, 27 (1922).

64. Iler,R.K., The Colloid Chemistry of Silica and Silicates, Cornell University Press, Ithaca, N.Y., p107 (1955).

65. Hirschfelder, J., J Chem Phys, 9, 645 (1941).

66. Hazel, J.F., J Phys and Colloid Chem, 51, 415 (1947).

67. Willey, A.R. and J.F. Hazel, J Phys Chem, 41, 699 (1937).

DISCUSSION
CHAIRMAN PACKHAM: Thank you, Dr. Hazel. There is time for a question.
DR. LAMER: I was going to direct this question to Dr. Wayman yesterday, but it fits in better today. We have measured, i.e., Miss Kane has measured a number of silica preparations electrophoretically. I won't claim great precision, but we find different silicas to behave quite differently in flocculation values and electrophoretic mobility. The different crystalline silicas are also different. Does this mean that our silicas are not pure? Can you help us interpret these findings?

DR. HAZEL: I'll tell you, Victor, I think that they should
be dialyzed. The thought did occur to me here--- I haven't
worked with water, but in working with iron oxide and silicates
we have to dialyze things because if we just have everything there
that might be there, you can tell nothing. How would it be if you
dialyze water? I don't know. Maybe you'd have nothing left, do
you see? But couldn't you some way get to these colloids and
have just the colloids. Of course, there has to be some electrolyte
but couldn't you minimize this by dialysis or by some other
purification method? It is necessary, also, to focus on the
stationary level in a microelectrophoresis cell if one expects to
get the true mobility.

DR. R. DEAN (R.A. Taft Sanitary Engineering Center):
This last talk points out the real reason why we should use the
term zeta potential rather than mobility. I will have to admit
that I have preferred mobility for perhaps the reason that my
Greek was never good. I can't write zeta; it always comes out
wrong. However, if you are going to compare the electrokinetic
properties in streaming potential, which is fundamental to filtration, with what you can measure in an electrophoresis cell, we've
got to convert all of the numbers for the same basis. You've
got to use zeta potential, as Helmholtz pointed out many years ago.
It's worth while going back to his derivation to see how simple
this all comes out. Sure, there are corrections for certain ionic
strengths. You can't just multiply by 13, but by expressing the
zeta potential you can always pull all of these phenomena together.

DR. LAMER: I want to answer that quickly, if I may. We
now have some well known expressions from Onsager who has
given the interconnections for steady states. You can show by
his symmetry relation that the streaming potential is just the
inverse of electrophoresis. I'm positive that with the Onsager
expressions you can directly calculate electrophoresis from
streaming potential measurements and vice versa without involving a calculation of zeta potential.

DR. DEAN: That's what Helmholtz did.

DR. LAMER: Yes, but it is not necessary to do this today.
I can translate from German to Japanese to English, but I can
also translate German to English and do not have to get involved
in the Japanese language.

CHAIRMAN PACKHAM: We'll have time for one or two
more questions.

MR. G. CRITS (Crane Company): Have you considered
that there are bisilicates present? From our ion exchange work

in water treatment, we have indications that bisilicate monovalent ions are present in water. Silica forms silicic acid or bisilicates analogous to CO_2 forming H_2CO_3 and HCO_3, and this exists at a concentration of a 100 mg/1 or lower. Above this concentration or at higher pH values (above pH 8.5), divalent silicate ions are prevalent. At high concentration and at low pH values (below pH 4.0), silicic acid and the bridging of silica into the amorphous forms takes place.

DR. HAZEL: Well, always there are OH groups. Never are all four of these negatively charged. Possibly in orthosilicate there one might have four charges, otherwise there are hydrogens attached here and also mostly there are other silicons. I mean, very seldom even in the alkali silicates does one have just one silicon in the formula. There are several of them. Kasil No. 1, by light scattering, has a molecular weight of 2,000 and the formula doesn't indicate this at all. However, some of the lower ratio silicates, e.g., $K_2O \cdot SiO_2$, instead of $K_2O \cdot 3.9 SiO_2$, then these do conform a little better to the formula.

MR. CRITS: We are talking about dilute solutions, and I'm wondering if some of these people who take a gel or glass have considered that an equilibrium exists. With silica or glass in water, bisilicates are forming at a concentration of about 100 mg/1 (as bisilicates or sodium silicate) analogous to HCO_3^- and CO_3^{-2}.

DR. HAZEL: Well, I don't think you could have a monomer with a hydrogen on it. Automatically it will polymerize unless you have in an unpopulated relative system just a few molecules.

MR. CRITS: Under a hundred parts per million?

DR. HAZEL: Well, maybe at a pH of 3 because there polymerization is at a minimum. In the paper I have discussed minima and maxima that relate to polymerization. Iler has a lot of this in his book on silicates (64).

CHAIRMAN PACKHAM: I think I'll have to intervene there and close discussion on this paper.

Egon Matijevic

Clarkson College of Technology
Institute of Colloid and Surface Science

CHARGE REVERSAL OF LYOPHOBIC COLLOIDS

It is well known that lyophobic colloids owe their stability
to the electric charges of their particles. Jordis was apparently
the first one to clearly point out that the presence of a small
amount of an electrolyte is necessary in a colloidal dispersion
in order to obtain a stable sol (1). As a rule, best stabilization
results if the electrolyte contains one of the constituent ions
of the colloid. The electric charge then is due to the adsorption
of these surplus constituent ions on the sol particles. Adsorbed
cations will render a sol positively charged and anions make it
negatively charged. Early in this century, Lottermoser demonstrated that, in the presence of excess of $AgNO_3$, AgI may be
obtained in form of positively charged sols, while in excess
of KI the sols are negatively charged (2, 3). Hydrous ferric
sols are positive in excess of ferric salts, but negative above
a certain pH value. The stability of a sol is not necessarily
produced only by the adsorption of constituent ions. Other
ionic species may often act as stabilizing (or potential determining) ions. For example, the negative charge of synthetic
rubber latex particles is due to fatty acid or similar ions, which
act as stabilizing species.

The purpose of this work is to show procedures by which charge of a stable lyophobic colloid can be reversed. The understanding of the reversal of charge processes is important for a number of reasons. Sometimes it is desirable to reverse the charge of a natural or synthetic colloidal system in order to promote a reaction or produce substantially more stable sols. It will be shown, however, that all additives which cause charge reversal at a given concentration also coagulate the same sols at concentrations lower and higher than those required for the reversal of charge. As a consequence, many coagulating agents will stabilize a colloidal system rather than destroy it by coagulation if added in certain concentrations and over a specific pH range.

The phenomenon of charge reversal is cited frequently (in particular in the older literature) as the "irregular series", because of the property of some compounds to coagulate a lyophobic colloid, if added in low concentrations, stabilize it at intermediate concentrations, and coagulate it again at still higher concentrations.

It appears that the first experimental observation of reversal of charge by a coagulating agent was reported by Hardy (4). Strongly positively charged particles of a ferric hydroxide sol were found to change the direction of movement in the electric field upon addition of 2.5×10^{-4}M citric acid. Much later it was confirmed that citric acid is capable of reversing the charge of silver halide sols (5, 6). More elaborate studies of charge reversal of various sols and of bacteria, particularly by Al and Fe^{+3} salts, were reported shortly after Hardy's work had appeared (7, 8).

Since that time a large number of data on reversal of charge has been reported for many colloidal systems and a variety of additives. The old literature was reviewed in Freundlich's book (9). Other comprehensive articles on this subject were written by Wo. Ostwals in 1936 (10), and by Kruyt and Troelstra in 1943 (11).

In view of the great number of variety of ions which may reverse the charge of lyophobic colloids, if added in appropriate amounts and sometimes over a given pH range, an attempt will be made to classify these into three categories:

A. Constituent ions
B. Ions which obey the Schulze-Hardy rule
C. Ions which disobey the Schulze-Hardy rule

Separation of the agents capable of reversing of charge
into categories B and C is somewhat arbitrary, but it does
provide a classification which includes large groups of similar
compounds in the same category. Thus, most of the simpler
complex inorganic ions; such as, hydrolyzed metal ions,
heteropoly ions, hexols, etc as well as simpler chelates and
quite simple organic ions belong into category B. Larger
organic ions; such as, dyes, alkaloids, surfactants, and all
polyelectrolytes are included in category C.

In order for reversal of charge to occur, the counterions
must adsorb on colloidal particles. As mentioned earlier,
all ions capable of reversing the charge also will coagulate
the same sols if added in somewhat lower concentrations.

The adsorbability of counterions as a function of their
concentrations will then determine their classification in the
above proposed categories. If the adsorption is negligible
over the concentration range of coagulation, the Schulze-Hardy
rule is valid and the counterions coagulate essentially in
accordance with their charges. At higher concentrations these
ions adsorb sufficiently to reverse the charge. All such ions
are classified in category B.

If counterions, however, are being adsorbed strongly in
very low concentration, the coagulation process will be
effected and the critical coagulation concentration becomes
independent of charge, i.e., the Schulze-Hardy rule does not
apply. For example, the critical coagulation concentration
of univalent long-chain surface active ions is several orders
of magnitude lower than that of simple ions of the same charge.
The same ions will reverse the charge when a sufficient amount
is adsorbed. Such ions are classified then in category C.

The adsorbability of counterions depends on steric factors,
such as their size and shape, and on the specific chemical
interactions between the stabilizing and the counterions. It
appears that steric factors play the predominant role in charge
reversal with ions in category C while ionic interactions are
prevalent in category B. Just what the steric and chemical
properties of the counterions must be in order to make the
critical coagulation concentration independent of the ionic charge
has not been elucidated yet. For this reason, the herein
proposed classification of ions into categories B and C is based
actually upon apparently different mechanisms of adsorption as
manifested by the coagulation effect (validity or invalidity of
the Schulze-Hardy rule).

It should be clearly understood that it is not proposed to
apply the Schulze-Hardy rule to processes concerning reversal
of charge. As will be shown later, there is no evidence for any
correlation between the charge of the counterion and the reversal
of charge of the colloid.

In this article, special attention will be paid to certain
phenomena of reversal of charge as caused by ions of categories
B and C.

EXPERIMENTAL PROCEDURES

If an ion, capable of reversing the charge, is added in
small increments, to a lyophobic colloid, the charge will be
reduced gradually until the particles become electrically
neutral. Upon further addition of the ion the particles become
oppositely charged. The concentration of the additive at which
the particle is rendered neutral is called zero point of charge
(ZPC). If the recharging ions are H^+ or $\overline{OH}$ and the process
is followed by change in pH, the pH at which the particles do
not move in an electric field is usually referred to as the
isoelectric point (IEP). There is no essential difference
between ZPC and IEP.

Many colloidal systems show some striking changes in
properties at ZPC; such as, mobility, turbidity, conductance,
viscosity, surface tension, etc. The measurement of any of
these properties may be used as an indicator for establishment
of the ZPC.

Three techniques are most commonly employed in studies
of the reversal of charge phenomena. These are: (a) potentiometric titrations, (b) electrokinetic measurements, and
(c) turbidity measurements.

Potentiometric Titrations

Potentiometric titrations are used to detect the reversal
of charge especially when this is accomplished by addition of
constituent ions. For example, the concentration changes of
silver or halide ions added to a silver halide sol may be followed
conveniently by means of reversible silver halide electrodes.
Hydrogen ion titrations are used commonly when reversal of
charge is accomplished by addition of acids or bases, for
instance in the case of various inorganic hydrous oxides or
some biological systems such as proteins.

Electrokinetic Measurements

Electrokinetic measurements offer the most direct
evidence for charge reversal. Usually electrophoretic mobility

or streaming potentials are experimentally determined. In the case of electrophoresis, the mobility of colloidal particles in an electric field is measured either by observation in an ultramicroscope or by the moving boundary method. The mobility can be used to calculate the zeta potential (ζ), although the relation is neither simple nor straight forward. Most frequently, ζ-potentials are derived from mobility data using simple formulas developed by Helmholtz (12) and Smoluchowski (13):

$$\frac{U}{X} = \frac{\epsilon \, \zeta}{4 \, \pi \, \eta} \qquad (12\text{-}1)$$

or by Debye and Huckel (14, 15):

$$\frac{U}{X} = \frac{\epsilon \, \zeta}{6 \, \pi \, \eta} \qquad (12\text{-}2)$$

Where U is the electrophoretic mobility, $\underline{X}$ is the field strength, ϵ the dielectric constant, and η the viscosity of the dispersion medium. Henry later explained the difference between the two equations (16). A rather simple physical model, which is seldom realized in experimental systems, was postulated in the derivation of the above formulas. This is the reason why calculations of ζ-potentials from mobilities are frequently meaningless. Overbeek refined the model and derived equations for the calculation of ζ-potentials from measurements of mobilities carried out of presence of various types of electrolytes (17). Although Overbeek's model is still based upon a number of simplifications, it does provide a more quantitative approach. In order to use the correct equations, the knowledge of the composition of the medium with regard to electrolyte content required. Since for natural and wastewaters this composition is not always known and can be subject to appreciable changes, the values of ζ-potentials, especially when calculated from simple equations, are open to serious doubt. The measured mobilities represent direct experimental quantities and should be reported in preference to ζ-potential in particular when the composition of colloidal system is not sufficiently well defined.

The misconception is quite common that the stability of a sol is directly related to mobility or to the ζ-potential. While mobilities will clearly show the change in particle charge as a function of an additive, they are by no means always indicative of sol stability or instability. Figure 1 is an example where mobility and scattering intensity of a AgI sol in presence

of a constant concentration of $Ag(NO_3)_3$ are plotted as functions
of pH (18). The charge of the originally negatively charged sol
can be reversed in presence of $Al(NO_3)_3$ by gradually changing
pH. Squares indicate experiments in which freshly prepared
Al $(NO_3)_3$ solution was used. The mobility changes from -1 to
$+1 \mu/sec/v/cm$ over a pH range of 2 - 4.2 and the sol is coagulated (high scattering intensities). At pH > 4.2 and mobility $>$
$+1 \mu/sec/v/cm$, the sol is strongly stabilized due to the reversal
of charge and remains uncoagulated. If an aged $Al(NO_3)_3$
solution of the same concentration is used, the mobility and
scattering data from the same AgI sol are substantially different
for reasons to be explained below. The stability limit, however,
occurs now at a mobility value $> 2 \mu/sec/v/cm$. An even more
obvious example of poor correlation between mobility and stability
of the same sols was demonstrated recently when $Al_2(SO_4)_3$ was
added to lyophobic colloids (19). It appears then that, while
electrokinetic measurements represent a direct method for
detection of charge reversal, they do not necessarily provide a
criterion for sol stability.

Turbidity
    Turbidity measurements represent the most convenient
experimental procedure for the determination of sol stability.
They can be conducted with any kind of spectrophotometer or
light scattering photometer. Frequently, only the detection of
changes in turbidities or scattering intensities is needed; hence
relative measurements, which are quite simple, will suffice.
The procedure is based upon the fact that, in the particle size
range most commonly found in colloid systems, the turbidity
or the scattering intensity in the majority of cases, increases
rapidly with particle size. Thus, if the addition of an electrolyte
to a lyophobic colloid causes coagulation, the sol may become
much more turbid. If the addition of the electrolyte reverses
the charge and the sol remains stable, little or no change in
turbidity is observed. Some sols will peptize on reversal of
charge and as a consequence turbidity may even decrease.
    Occasionally, turbidity measurements are conducted after
considerable time has elasped since the addition of the electrolyte.
The coagulated sols then have usually settled and the supernatant
solutions show very low turbidities. Stable sols, however,
remain turbid. In the latter case, a sol stabilized by reversal
of charge will have a higher turbidity than a coagulated sol.
It is, therefore, important to keep the time element in mind

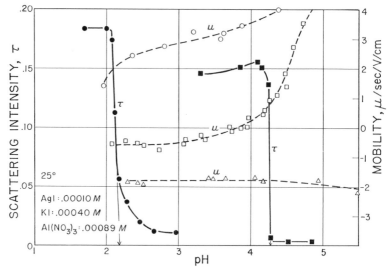

FIGURE 1 SCATTERING INTENSITIES (SOLID LINES) VS.
pH OF A SYSTEM CONTAINING CONSTANT CON-
CENTRATIONS OF A AgI SOL (1×10^{-4}M),
EXCESS KI(4×10^{-4} M), AND Al(NO_3)$_3$ (8.9×10^{-4}M
Squares denote experiment using fresh solution
and circles an aged stock solution (heated for 24
hrs at $90°$C) of Al(NO_3)$_3$. Dashed lines (circles
and squares) denote corresponding mobilities in
the presence of Al(NO_3)$_3$. Triangles give
mobilities of the same sol in absence of Al(NO_3)$_3$.

when either reporting or evaluating turbidity data.

The most convenient procedure for detection of the min-
mum concentration necessary to yield stable sols due to reversal
of charge is to take several samples of the sol and add to each
the electrolyte in increasing concentrations and then to measure
turbidity or scattering intensity of each sample as a function of
time. Turbidities measured at a fixed time plotted against the
concentration of added electrolyte, show characteristic maxima
and minima. An example of such plots is given in Figure 2
which shows the results obtained with a negatively charged
synthetic styrene-butadiene rubber latex hydrosol to which
Al(NO_3)$_3$ was added. The Al(NO_3)$_3$ has no effect at the lowest

concentrations and the turbidity of the sol remains low and constant. At somewhat higher concentrations a maximum appears indicating coagulation, while at still higher concentrations another turbidity minimum range is observed. The latter is caused by stabilization due to reversal of charge. Finally at the highest salt concentrations, the sol of reversed charge is coagulated by NO_3^- ions and the second turbidity maximum is developed. The two turbidity curves represent measurements taken at 10 mins and 60 mins, respectively, after addition of the $Al(NO_3)_3$. The coagulation maximum at high salt concentration disappears at 60 mins because the sol has settled and turbidity readings are, therefore, much lower (hatched area). The minimum concentration of electrolyte which just stabilizes a sol on account of charge reversal is called critical stabilization concentration (csc) and is determined by extrapolation of the stability limit to the turbidity of the blank (arrows). No attempt was made to adjust pH. Triangles give pH values as measured in individual systems of which optical densities are plotted. The mobility data show clearly the effect of charge reversal. The latter measurements were made on a different sample of the rubber latex sol and cannot be directly compared with the turbidity data on the same diagram. This accounts for the ZPC being well in the second stability range.

   As will be discussed later, metal ions reverse the charge only above a certain concentration and pH, which depend on the metal ion in question. In that case, csc may be determined by turbidity measurements of the colloidal system in presence of a fixed concentration of the metal ion made over a range of pH values. Figure 3 is an example of such experiments, where $Al(NO_3)_3$ is added to a negatively charged AgBr sol. Each curve represents a system containing a different amount of $Al(NO_3)_3$. For each concentration of the Al salt there is a characteristic pH value. Below this pH the sol is coagulated and above it the sol is stablized. The transition is extremely abrupt. Thus this method offers a very sensitive tool for the detection of csc as a function of pH. It was confirmed by electrophoresis measurements that this stabilization is definitely due to reversal of charge.

   In addition to methods mentioned above, the stability limit could also be detected by devices which measure change in particle size or number, such as various types of counters. These methods, although useful for certain purpose are time consuming and, unless specific information on the size of

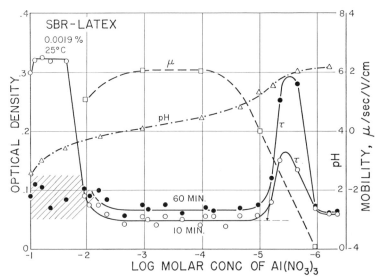

FIGURE 2   OPTICAL DENSITIES OF A STYRENE-BUTADIENE
RUBBER LATEX SOL (0.0019%SBR by weight)
AS A FUNCTION OF ADDED Al(NO$_3$)$_3$ 10 (open
circles) and 60 (dark circles) MINS AFTER MIXING
THE REACTING COMPONENTS (solid lines).
Dashed line (squares) represent mobility data of
another sample of the rubber latex sol.

number of particles is required, they are usually not employed
in reversal of charge determinations.

RESULTS AND DISCUSSION

Reversal of Charge by Constituent Ions
    As was mentioned in the introduction, the charge on colloid
particles is due to the adsorption of potential-determining ions,
the lattice forming or constituent ions being preferentially
adsorbed. A sol stabilized by excess of one of the constituent
ions can be recharge, if sufficient amounts of the oppositely
charged lattice forming ions are added. Only a few examples
will be cited here.
    Hydrous metal oxides represent a large family of colloidal
systems, which can be recharged by constituent ions. Most of
these systems are positively charged at low and negatively

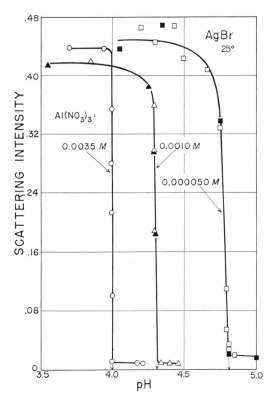

FIGURE 3   SCATTERING INTENSITIES VS. pH OF A AgBr
SOL IN STATU NASCENDI IN THE PRESENCE OF
THREE DIFFERENT CONCENTRATIONS OF
Al(NO$_3$)$_3$; 3.5 x 10^{-3}M (O), 1.0 x 10^{-3}M ($\triangle$)^3;
and 5.0 x 10^{-4}M ($\square$); AgBr, 1 x 10^{-4}M; excess
KBr, 1.9 x 10^{-3}M.

charged at high pH values.   For example, it was established
quite early that positive ferric hydroxide sols can be made
negative by addition of NaOH (11, 29, 30). Simultaneous
measurements of pH, turbidity, and electrophoretic mobility
showed characteristic changes at the isoelectric point (31). It
is obvious that the reversal of charge of such compounds can
be accomplished easily if IEP is known. Very recently, Parks
published a review article on the IEP of a variety of solid oxides,

solid hydroxides, and aqueous hydroxo complex systems which contains a rather complete list of references (32).

Reversal of charge of some other types of colloids will occur also if the values of pH are changed over a range critical for the system in question. For example, it was found that the synthetic lattices can be recharged in that way (33).

It would be beyond the scope of this article to cite all the work on colloid sols, which can be recharged by addition of constituent ions. For instance it was shown recently that some sparingly soluble metallic salts of tetradecylsulfate can be recharged by excess of metal ions forming the corresponding salt, such as thorium and lanthanum (34). Metal phosphates, sulfates, arsenates, uranates, etc can be recharged, although each system will show some different specific effects. None has been studied as intensely as the silver halides, AgI in particular.

Sometimes it is observed that a simple metal ion, although not constituent, will reverse the charge of the sol if it forms a sparingly soluble salt with the oppositely charged constituent ion of the sol. Thus, it was shown that Ag^+ion reverses the charge of a negatively charged HgS sol (35).

Reversal of Charge By Ions Obeying the Schulze-Hardy Rule

Ions capable of reversing the charge, which follow the Schulze-Hardy rule, are either simple inorganic complexes or small organic ions. To this group of ions belongs the citrate ion whose ability to recharge positive sols was mentioned earlier. Also extremely small amounts of heteropoly ions, such as various heteropoly tungstates and molybdates (36, 37, 38), potassium hexacyano ferrate (II) were found to be effective in reversing the charge of various positive sols (11). All of these obey the Schulze-Hardy rule when used as coagulants.

Since most of the natural and many synthetic colloids are charged negatively, cationic species must be employed for charge reversal. Again, various complex ions; such as Co and Cr hexols (11, 37, 39, 40), octammine - -diol-dicobaltic ion (39), and tris-ethylenediamine-platinum (IV) ion (39) have been used successfully for this purpose.

Polyvalent metal ions are most commonly used for reversal of charge and most widely studied in this regard. As mentioned in the introduction, Al and Fe salts were employed first (7, 8). Later Th and some other highly charged ions were studied frequently. Very early, a difference in opinion arose

as to which species actually cause the charge reversal. Thus,
Powis (41), Gorochowski and Protass (26), and Kruyt (in his
earlier work; 39, 42, and 43) believed that the adsorption of
simple highly charged ions on colloid particles or glass was
responsible for the effect. Others proposed that metal hydroxides
must be formed first in order for a salt to produce charge
reversal (7). Kruyt and Troelstra showed very clearly that
certain metal ions which do not reverse the charge in acid
solutions, do so effectively upon addition of a base (11). These
authors made a rather elaborate study describing the reversal
of charge of a AgI sol by Al, Th, Zn, and Be in presence of
various amounts of acids or bases. They concluded from these
experiments that simple metal ions cannot reverse the charge,
instead the presence of insoluble basic compounds (hydroxides)
was considered essential for producing this effect. It should
be pointed out that the amounts of added acids and bases were
reported rather than the resulting pH values of the media and
only schematic diagrams were given which make an analysis
of the data quite difficult.

There is Bosch and Haemers tried to resolve the question as to
whether Th^{+4} or $Th(OH)_4$ is responsible for charge reversal
of a AgI sol. They could not, however, reach a definite
conclusion (44).

There is little doubt that an increase in pH enhances the
reversal of charge by metal ions. Figure 4 gives two examples.
The upper diagram shows the shift of the stability limit due to
reversal of charge (B) of a AgI sol towards higher concentrations
of $Th(NO_3)_4$ as the pH is lowered from 4 to 3. At still lower
pH values (not included in the diagram) the stability range
becomes even narrower until it eventually disappears completely
whereas $TH(NO_3)_4$ coagulates at all concentrations above limit A.

The lower diagram shows the effect of $Al(NO_3)_3$ on the
same sol. At pH 3, $Al(NO_3)_3$ coagulates at all concentrations
above the critical coagulation value (given by the limit A).
At pH 5, however, a very pronounced reversal of charge effect
is observed giving a restabilized sol (low turbidity range between
limits B and C). If aged $Al(NO_3)_3$ salt solutions are used at
pH 3, the curve is similar to that obtained at pH 5 with freshly
prepared solutions. Figure 4 explains why the reversal of charge
effect frequently has been referred to as the "irregular series".

In recent years systematic work has been conducted in our
laboratory. The reversal of charge of various sols by metal
ions was investigated as a function of electrolyte concentration,

pH, sol concentration, age of the electrolyte solution, and temperature (18, 19, 45-50). The results of these experiments led to the conclusion that soluble hydrolyzed metal ions are responsible for the phenomenon of charge reversal. Actually, the same idea was advanced earlier by Mattson based upon electrophoresis experiments with clays and silica in presence of Al and Fe salts (51, 52).

In view of the widespread use of some metal salts in coagulation and various other applications the reversal of charge of Al, Fe(III), Zn, and Th will be discussed below in greater detail.

Aluminum

It was shown repeatedly that Al salts may reverse the charge of colloid particles if conditions; in particular, the salt concentration and pH, are adjusted properly. A variety of colloidal systems have been used in these studies; such as, silver halides (11, 18, 46, 53), clays (15, 54-59), silver (60), platinum (64), gold (60), arsenic trisulfide (61), silica (52, 62), glass (39, 42), mastix (7, 8, 63-65), bacteria (7, 8, 63-65), rubber latex (66-68), oil in water emulsion (41, 69), titan white (70), pulp (71), rosin (72), organic color (73), etc. Most of the reported work consists of one or more cases demonstrating the reversal of charge effect. Little systematic work was available until quite recently.

If the adsorption of hydrolyzed metal ion species onto colloid particles is responsible for charge reversal there must be a close relationship between the hydrolysis equilibria and the reversal or charge. In case of the Al^{+3} ion, it is now almost generally accepted that hydrolyzed species are polymerized (18, 19, 46, 74). Coagulation and reversal of charge experiments indicate the following equilibrium (neglecting water of hydration):

$$8\ Al^{+3} + 20\ H_2O \rightleftarrows Al_8^{+4}(OH)_{20} + 20\ H^+ \qquad (12\text{-}3)$$

Reversal of charge will occur only if a sufficient concentration of hydrolyzed ions is present in solution, which can be achieved either by increasing the concentration of the salt or pH, or both. This is clearly born out by experiments whown in Figure 3. For each concentration of Al salt there is a minimum pH value above which the sol is stabilized. Direct electrophoresis measurements also confirm this as shown in Figure 5 for a rubber latex sol. It is interesting to note that

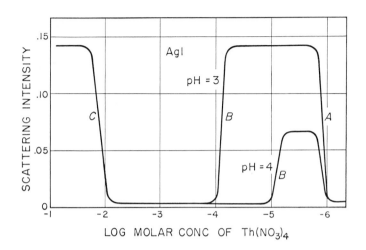

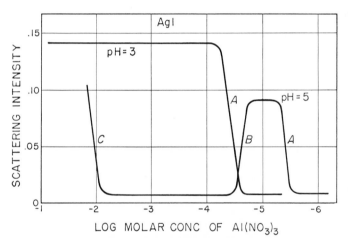

FIGURE 4 SCHEMATIC PRESENTATION OF CHANGES
IN SCATTERING INTENSITIES OF A AgI SOL
AS A FUNCTION OF ADDED $TH(NO_3)_4$ (upper
diagram) AND $Al(NO_3)_3$ (lower diagram).
Various curves represent results obtained at
different pH values. A and C are the coagulation
limits of the original sol and the sol of reversed
charge, respectively, while B is stabilization
limit due to reversal of charge.

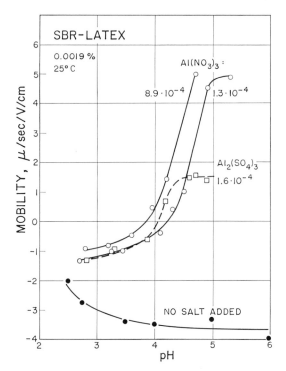

FIGURE 5   MOBILITY VS. pH OF A STYRENE-
BUTADIENE RUBBER LATEX SOL IN PRE-
SENCE OF CONSTANT CONCENTRATIONS
OF $Al(NO_3)_3$ (open circles), $Al_2(SO_4)_3$
(squares) AND WITHOUT ADDED SALT
(blackened circles).   Concentrations: SBR-
latex, 0.0019% by wt; $Al(NO_3)_3$; 8.9×10^{-4} M
$Al_2(SO_4)_3$; 1.6×10^{-4} M

These investigations show clearly that, to reverse the
charge of a sol, there must be a pair of parameters, i.e., Al
salt concentration and pH, which will yield just sufficient
amounts of hydrolyzed species.   Since different sols will require
different amounts of hydrolyzed ions due to specific properties
of the sol, the "pH-salt concentration" conditions at which
stability due to reversal of charge is achieved will vary from
system to system.   Experiments have shown, however, that

these differences are not large.

As an example, Figure 6 gives the boundary between the coagulation and stabilization domains (the latter being caused by charge reversal) for a AgI sol of two different sol concentrations. The dotted line indicates the conditions at which the formation of $Al(OH)_3$ is observed in absence of AgI. These experiments obviously indicate that insoluble hydroxides cannot primarily be responsible for charge reversal.

It was shown that the straight line representing the boundary between the coagulation and the stability range in the plot Al-salt vs. pH can be interpreted in terms of the OH^- : Al^{+3} ratio in the complex hydrolyzed species responsible for the reversal of charge (18). In the case of $Al(NO_3)_3$ the slope of -2.5 was obtained consistently which is in agreement with the ratio 20 OH^- : 8 Al^{-3} corresponding to the species $Al_8(OH)_{20}^{+4}$. When $Al_2(SO_4)_3$ is used instead of the nitrate, the general picture remains essentially the same. The slope of the boundary line, however, has a smaller value which indicates that some of the OH^- groups in the complex ions are substituted by sulfate yielding basic $Al_2(SO_4)_3$ complex ions (19).

It has been known for quite some time that Al salt solutions undergo noticeable changes if kept over long periods of time at room temperature or much more rapidly if heated (18, 19, 53, 75-77). Apparently aging leads to polymerized "oxolated" species which seem to be rather stable and are not easily decomposed by lowering pH (75, 78). It would be then expected that such aged solutions reverse the charge as efficiently or better at pH values lower than those using freshly prepared solutions. This is demonstrated in Figure 1 (circles). The charge of the sol remains reversed even at the lowest pH measured, so that in this case the stability boundary at the low pH values is determined by the coagulation by sols by anions present in the electrolyte solution phase. Dashed line in Figure 6 gives the extended area of stabilization due to reversal of charge as obtained for $Al(NO_3)_3$ solutions aged for 24 hrs at $90^{o}C$ and the same AgI sol. The coagulation measurements were conducted at $25^{o}C$. It appears, therefore, that complex Al-oxolated species formed during the aging process at elevated temperature remain essentially unchanged after subsequent cooling of the solutions.

Figure 6 gives only the boundary between the regions of coagulation and of stabilization due to reversal of charge.

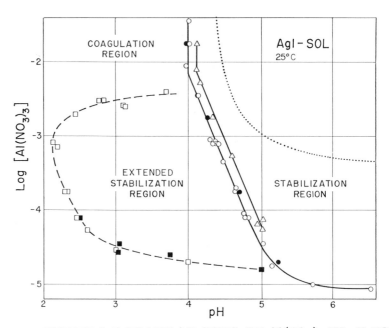

FIGURE 6   LOG MOLAR CONC OF Al(NO$_3$)$_3$ VS. pH FOR
AgI SOLS. Solid lines give the boundary be -
tween the coagulation and the stabilization
domains for two different sol concentrations;
AgI, 1 x 10^{-4}M (circles); 5 x 10^{-4}M (triangles)
Open circles and triangles denote sols in
statu nascendi, blackened circles denote aged
AgI sols. Open squares represent data obtained
from experiments in which $\left[\text{Al(NO}_3)_3\right]$ was
kept constant while pH was varied; blackened
squares are from experiments in which a
constant amount of acid or base was added
while $\left[\text{Al(NO}_3)_3\right]$ varied.

In Figure 7 the entire coagulation region (hatched area) is
reproduced including the boundary between the coagulated and
the uncoagulated sol (lower solid line). Below this line the
negative sol remains uncoagulated due to insufficient concentration of the electrolyte in solution. The upper solid line is
identical with coagulation/stabilization boundary for the same
sol in Figure 6. Thus, Figure 7 presents the complete

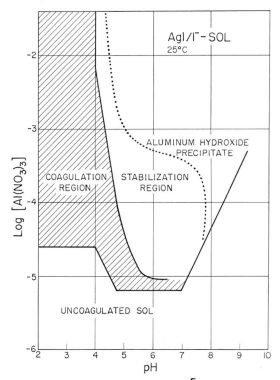

FIGURE 7   THE ENTIRE LOG $\left[Al(NO_3)_3\right]$ -pH DOMAIN
FOR A AgI SOL (1×10^{-4}M AgI, EXCESS KI
4×10^{-4}M) at 25°C. Below the lower solid
line the sol remains uncoagulated. Above
the upper solid line the sol is stabilized due
to reversal of charge. Coagulation region
is indicated by hatching. The dotted line
indicates the formation of $Al(OH)_3$ precipitate in absence of AgI.

"molar concentration $Al(NO_3)_3$-pH" domain for fresh $Al(NO_3)_2$
solutions at 25°C.

It should be pointed out that similar domains were obtained
with $Al(SO_4)_3$ for AgI sols, with $Al(NO_3)_3$ for AgBr sols, and
with both $Al(SO_4)_3$ and $Al(NO_3)_3$ for a synthetic sytrene-butadiene

rubber latex sol. This indicates that the domain of the type presented in Figure 7 is quite characterisitc of the Al^{+3} ion for lyophobic colloids regardless of the chemical composition of sols.

Thorium

Due to the strong hydrolysis of Th^{+4} ion, Th salts reverse the charge at rather low pH values. This is the reason for the view that the high charge of this ion is responsible for the effect. Thorium salts have been used frequently in studies of charge reversal, in particular when attempts were made to explain the mechanism of this phenomenon. As expected, silver halide sols were employed most frequently (11, 26, 40, 44, 45, 47, 79-82), but other systems; such as, glass (39, 83-85), gold (43), oil in water emulsions (41, 69), cellulose fibers (87), lecithin plus diethylphosphoric acid particles (88), sheep leucocytes (89), and arachidic acid sols (90, 91), were shown also to be recharged by addition of thorium salts.

The entire domain "log $[Th(NO_3)_4]$ -pH" is given in Figure The symbols denote experimental variations as described in the legend. Again there is no stabilization below pH 2.7. Above this pH value a stabilization region is found if the concentration of added $Th(NO_3)_4$ is sufficiently high. The dotted line gives the conditions at which the precipitation of $Th(OH)_4$ is observed first (92). Again it is seen that stability due to reversal of charge begins at pH values lower than needed for formation of the insolub hydroxide.

The straight portion of the coagulation/stabilization boundary between pH 2.7 and 3.4 has a slope of precisely -2. This corresponds to the complex species containing 2 OH^- : 1 Th^{+4}. The presence of hydrolyzed thorium species having this composit in particular $Th(OH)_2^{+2}$, was suggested by several independent investigators (92-97). Our earlier coagulation work suggested the species $ThOH^{+3}$ (45). This, however, does not contradict the present results because the coagulation concentrations are lower than csc. Therefore, different species can be predominan over two different concentration ranges. Kraus and Holmberg have shown that the $ThOH^{+3}$ species is expected to be present in thorium salt solutions of very low concentrations (93).

Direct adsorption measurements of thorium on AgI have shown beyond any doubt that the extent of adsorption is related directly to the hydrolysis of thorium ions (47). Figure 9 gives a summary of the adsorption results obtained by radio-tracer

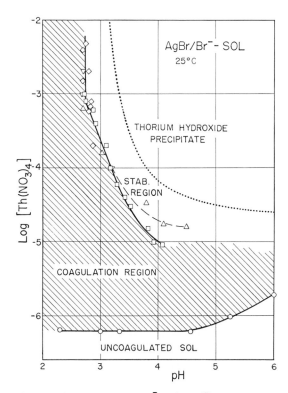

FIGURE 8   THE LOG $[Th(NO_3)_4]$ -pH DOMAIN FOR
A AgBr SOL $(AgBr$ 1.0 x 10^{-4}M, EXCESS
KBr 1.9 x 10^{-3}M , at 25°C.   The boundary
between the coagulation and stabilization
regions was obtained using $Th(NO_3)_4$ in
constant concentration and varying pH
(solid line).   Various symbols denote
experiments using the following concentrations of $Th(NO_3)_4$ stock solution:
2.0 x 10^{-3}M ($\square$), 1.0 x 10^{-2}M ($\diamond$),
and 2.0 x 10^{-2}M ($\triangledown$).   Dashed line and
$\triangle$ represent points obtained by varying
the concentration of $Th(NO_3)_4$ at constant
additions of an acid or base.

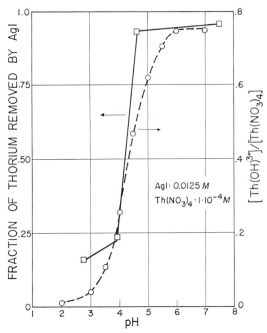

FIGURE 9   FRACTION OF THORIUM REMOVED BY
             A AgI SOL (0.0125 M) FROM A Th(NO₃)₄
             SOLUTION (1 x 10⁻⁴M) AS A FUNCTION
             pH (solid line).

measurements. It also shows the ratio of hydrolyzed to un-
hydrolyzed species $[\text{ThOH}^{+3}]$ / $[\text{Th(NO}_3)_4]$ as a function of
pH, assuming $\underline{K} = 5 \times 10^{-5}$ for the reaction $\text{TH}^{+4} + \text{H}_2\text{O} \rightleftharpoons$
$\text{ThOH}^{+3} + \text{H}^+$ as suggested by Kraus and Holmberg (dashed line)
(93). The similarity of general trends of these two curves is
striking. The data cannot be directly compared to the results
given in Figure 8 because of different experimental conditions,
but they certainly demonstrate the very close correlation between hydrolysis and adsorption of this thorium species.

    Quite recently, Abramson, Jaycock, and Ottewill also
have reported adsorption measurements using thorium and
confirmed the earlier findings of our laboratory (98). These
workers suggest that the absorbed layer of thorium may be

composed of neutral $Th(OH)_4$ together with some hydrolyzed
ions. There is, however, no real evidence for the latter
assumption.

Zinc
    There have been only very few observations made on the
charge reversal by zinc (11, 48). Since zinc is, in general, less
strongly hydrolyzed than some of the other metal ions, it is
expected that it reverses the charge less efficiently, i.e., at
higher pH values than those for the previously described cases.
Experiments confirm this expectation as shown in Figure 10.
Since a sufficient concentration of hydrolyzed zinc ions needed
to reverse the charge becomes available only a rather high pH
values, a very narrow stability region of recharged sols is
observed. This is apparently the reason why so few cases of
charge reversal by zinc have been reported. The effect is
either obscured by the formation of $Zn(OH)_2$, or sufficient
amounts of anions become available to coagulate the weakly
recharged sol.

Iron
    Ferric salts are known to reverse the charge of various
colloid systems; such as, mastix (7, 8, 63, 64), silica (61, 62),
platinum (64), bacteria (7, 8, 63, 64), organic color (73, 99),
and yellow ocher (70). Recently a very comprehensive study
of reversal of charge of AgBr, styrene-butadiene latex, and
polystyrene latex has been conducted in which it was shown
that the effect is strongly dependent on temperature, mode of
preparation, age, dilution effects, and, of course, on the pH
values of ferric salt solutions (50).
    It is well known that the hydrolytic processes of the ferric
ion are manifold and not well understood. This is apparently
the reason why little correlation between the reversal of charge
effects and the composition of ferric salt solutions, as calculated
from the hydrolysis constants available in the literature, was
found. It would lead too far to review in this paper the entire
problem of ferric ions in aqueous solutions with regard to
charge reversal. For those concerned with the use of ferric
salts or their presence in raw or wastewaters, the entire
domain of "log $[Fe(NO_3)_3]$ -pH" is reproduced in Figure 11,
which shows the coagulation range (hatched area) and the
stabilization range due to reversal of charge. The latter is
quite strongly temperature dependent. At temperatures $\geq 13^o C$

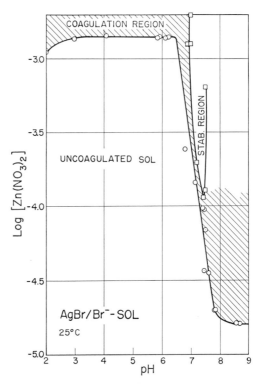

FIGURE 10   THE LOG $\left[Zn(NO_3)_2\right]$ -pH DOMAIN FOR
A AgBr SOL IN STATU NASCENDI (1.0
x 10^{-4} M, EXCESS KBr 1.9 x 10^{-3} M AT
25^{0} C.

an extended stability range is observed which is similar to one
obtained with Al salts. In the latter case, however, Al solutions
had to be heated to 90^{0}C to extend the stabilization range to low
pH values. Similar domains were obtained with styrene-butadiene
latex and polystyrene latex sols.   For a more detailed analysis
of these data, the reader is referred to the paper (50).

In concluding the survey of the reversal of charge by metal
ions, several general remarks are in order. Apparently there
is little doubt that reversal of charge by metal ions, is accomplished by the adsorption of their hydrolyzed species. It is

interesting that most of the compounds active in charge reversal
which have been mentioned in this category contain hydroxyl
groups (all hydrolyzed metal ions, hexols, diol-complexes,
etc). Also, citrate ion reverses the charge while valerate
ion, which has the same chain length, does not (100, 101). It
appears, therefore, that the hydroxyl group is responsible for
the adsorption of these ions on colloid particles leading to
charge reversal. Adsorbed hydrolyzed ions are bonded strongly.
For example, hydrolyzed Al^{+3} ions are nonexchangeable when
adsorbed on an ion exchange resin (102). It is not known what
the mechanism of adsorption is, but since various colloid
systems respond in the same manner, specific chemical interactions are not likely to have a predominant effect. Hydrogen
bonding, however, may play the decisive role.

Sols of reversed charge behave as lyophobic colloids, i.e.,
they can be coagulated by electrolytes and obey the Schulze-
Hardy rule (37, 96). This leads to the conclusion that the adsorbed
species acts as a typical stabilizing ion.

So far it has not been possible to find any correlation between the actual charge of the ionic species and their activity
in charge reversal. The available experimental evidence
indicates that the electrostatic attraction has little effect; thus,
complex ions of higher charge do not necessarily reverse the
charge of the sol particles more easily than the ions of lower
charge. For example, $Th(OH)_2^{+2}$ is more efficient than
$Al_8(OH)_{20}^{+4}$. Although the recent results have contributed
considerably to the better understanding of the reversal of
charge phenomena, more data are needed before the problems
can be elucidated completely.

Reversal of Charge by Ions Which Do Not Obey the Schulze-
Hardy Rule

Some ions of low charge (mainly mono and divalent)
coagulate sols of opposite charge at concentrations several
orders of magnitude lower than expected by the Schulze-Hardy
rule. These are mostly large organic ions and various polyelectrolytes. It is accepted generally that the coagulation in
these cases is due to specific adsorption of the large ions on
colloid particles. The term "adsorption coagulation" was
proposed therefore, to distinguish this process from the usual
electrolytic coagulation (103). Fractional monolayer coverage
of particles by these ions is usually necessary to produce
coagulation (104). If a sufficient amount of these ions is adsorbed

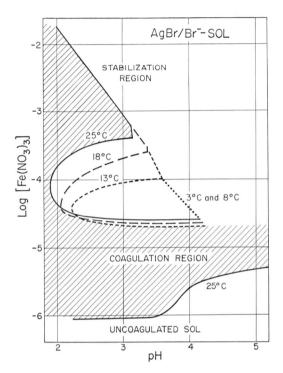

FIGURE 11   THE LOG $\left[Fe(NO_3)_3\right]$-pH DOMAIN FOR
A AgBr SOL (1.0 x 10^{-3} M, EXCESS KBr
1.0 x 10^{-4} M). The lower solid line gives the
critical coagulation concentration as function
of pH at 25°C.   The upper lines give the
boundaries between the coagulation and the
stabilization domains at 3°, 8°, 13°, 18°
and 25°C.

to form multimolecular layers (in particular twofold layers)
the charge of the sol particles is reversed.

    There are many examples showing that the adsorbability
of ions and consequently their ability to reverse the charge is
related to their size.   Thus, a minimum chain length of fatty
acid ions and of other long-chain surface active ions was found
necessary for recharging of inorganic colloid particles.   For
example, octanoate and undecanote were found to be the shortest
ions capable of reversing the charge of a Fe_2O_3 sol and of a

Al_2O_3 sol, respectively (105). Similarly, various amines coagulate lyophobic sols (As_2S_3, ferric hydroxide) but only the long chain amines reverse the charge (101, 106, 107).

It is not absolutely necessary that the ions are long chains in order to reverse the charge. Ions of various steric configurations if sufficiently large and complex will cause this effect. For example, reports on reversal of charge by strychnine (11, 108-110), quinine hydrochloride (86), hydroquine (86), ethylhydrocupreine (86), isoamylhydrocupreine (84, 86), octylhydrocupreine (84, 86) and various dyes, such as, (malachite green (86), chrysoidin (86), neutral red (8), Bismarck brown (8), pinakryptol yellow (130), and phenosafranin (130). Other examples are found in the literature.

In recent years, various surface active agents have been used in coagulation studies. Many of these reverse the charge of a number of colloidal ystems. Since homologous series of surfactants are available in which the length of the chain, the size of the head-group, or other structural properties can be changed systematically, these ions are suitable for the effect of steric properties upon reversal of charge. In general, it has been observed that the longer the chain and the larger the head-group, the smaller is the concentration required to reverse the charge. These concentrations depend also greatly on the colloidal system whose charge is reversed. At present, there are insufficient data available to draw any quantitative conclusions.

Most of the data recorded in the literature are summarized in Tables I and II. Table I contains cationic and Table II anionic surface active agents in order of increasing chain length. The second column give the sols whose charge was reversed, while the third columns contain the concentrations of the surface active agent, expressed in moles/l, which produce the electrophoretic zero point of charge (ZPC). Above this concentration the sol in question has a charge opposite to that in the absence of surfactants.

The tables show that even data obtained in the same laboratory are not always consistent. This may be due to poor reproducibility of the sols, particularly as far as the distribution of particle sizes and charge is concerned. It was shown recently that the mode of sol preparation and the size distribution of particles have a profound effect upon the ZPC of silver halide sols and upon the concentration of the surface active agent required to neturalize the sol (129). Thus, comparison of

TABLE I   REVERSAL OF CHARGE BY CATIONIC SURFACE ACTIVE AGENTS

Surface Active Agent	Colloid System	ZPC moles/l of S.A.A.	Literature Cited
Tri-n-butylammonium chloride	AgI	$3\text{-}4\times10^{-3}$	111
Tetra-n-butylammonium chloride	AgI	$0.6\text{-}1\times10^{-3}$	111
Hexylammonium nitrate	AgI (pI=5)	2.5×10^{-2}	112
Octylammonium nitrate	AgI (pI=5, pI=3)	1×10^{-2}	112
Octylpyridinium bromide	AgI	1.6×10^{-4}	113,114
Decylammonium chloride	AgI	$6\text{-}8\times10^{-3}$	111
	MnO_2, As_2S_3		105,115
Decylammonium nitrate	AgI(pI=5, pI=3)	10^{-3}	112
Decylammonium acetate	Quartz	2×10^{-2}	126,127
Decylpyridinium chloride	AS_2S_3		105,115
1,10-Dipyridinium-decane bromide	AgI	2×10^{-6}	113,114
Dodecylammonium chloride	AgI	1×10^{-4}	113,114
	AgI	$5\text{-}6\times10^{-4}$	107,111
	As_2S_3, MnO_2		105,115
Dodecylammonium bromide	AgI	$5\text{-}6\times10^{-4}$	107
Dodecylammonium iodide	AgI	$5\text{-}6\times10^{-4}$	107
Dodecylammonium acetate	Quartz	3×10^{-3}	126,127
		1×10^{-3}	128
Dodecylammonium nitrate	AgI(pI=5)	6.5×10^{-5}	112
	AgI(pI=3)	1×10^{-4}	112
Dodecyltrimethylammonium chloride	AgI	2.5×10^{-6}	107
	Au, As_2S_3		116
Dodecyltrimethylammonium bromide	AgI	1×10^{-5}	113,114
	AgBr		103
Dodecyldimethyl (methoxybenzyl) ammonium chloride	As_2S_3, Au		116
Dodecylpyridinium chloride	AgCl		103
	AgI		113,114
	MnO_2, As_2S_3		105,115

TABLE I - continued

Dodecylpyridinium chloride	Fe_2O_3	$4x10^{-4}$	125
	Carbon Black	$5.6x10^{-5}$	125
Dodecylpyridinium bromide	AgBr,AgI (in statu nascendi)		103
	AgBr(Monodispersed) 10^{-2}	10^{-3}	129
	AgBr	$6x10^{-5}$	130
	AgI		104
	AgI(pI=4)	$5.4x10^{-6}$	117
	AgI(pI=4)	$4.5x10^{-5}$	118
	AgI	$3.63x10^{-6}$	113,114
	AgI $(3.2x10^{-2}M)$	$2.5-3x10^{-4}$	107
	$Fe(OH)_3$		119
	As_2S_3		132
	Eosin		124
Dodecylpyridinium iodide	AgI (in statu nascendi)		103,120
	AgI(pI=4) $3.6x10^{-6}$		113,114
	AgI(monodispersed)	$2.5x10^{-4}$	
		$5.7x10^{-4}$	129
Dodecylquinolinium chloride	AgI		113,114
Dodecylquinolinium bromide	AgBr		103
	AgI	$7.4x10^{-7}$	113,114
Tetradecylammonium chloride	AgI	$2.5-3x10^{-4}$	107
		$1.5-2x10^{-4}$	111
	MnO_2,As_2S_3		105,115
Tetradecylammonium nitrate	AgI (pI=5)	$6.5x10^{-5}$	112
	AgI (pI=3)	$2x10^{-5}$	112
Tetradecylammonium acetate	Quartz	$3x10^{-4}$	127
		$1x10^{-4}$	126
Tetradecylpyridinium chloride	MnO_2,As_2S_3		105,115
Hexadecylammonium chloride	AgI	$1.5-2x10^{-4}$	107
		$2.5-3x10^{-4}$	111
	MnO_2,As_2S_3		105,115
Hexadecylammonium nitrate	AgI (pI=5)	$4x10^{-5}$	112
Hexadecylammonium acetate	Quartz	$2.5x10^{-5}$	126,127

TABLE I - continued

Hexadecylpyridinium chloride	MnO_2, As_2S_3		105,115
Hexadecylpyridinium bromide	AgI	5.75×10^{-7}	113,114
Octadecylammonium nitrate	AgI (pI=5)	1.7×10^{-5}	112
Octadecylammonium acetate	Quartz	8×10^{-6}	127
Octadecyltrymethylammonium chloride	AgI	$2.5\text{-}3 \times 10^{-4}$	107

TABLE II   REVERSAL OF CHARGE BY ANIONIC SURFACE ACTIVE AGENTS

Surface Active Agent	Colloid System	ZPC moles/l of S.A.A.	Literature Cited
Na-hexanoate	AgI(pAg=4)	10^{-2}	112
Na-octanoate	AgI(pAg=4)	2×10^{-3}	112
K-octanoate	Fe_2O_3		105,115
Na-octylsulfate	$Fe(OH)_3$		119
K-nonaoate	Fe_2O_3		105,115
Na-decanoate	AgI(pAg=4)	10^{-4}	112
K-decanoate	Fe_2O_3		105,115
Na-decylsulfate	AgI(pAg=3)	8×10^{-4}	6,121,122
	Fe_2O_3		105,115
Na-undecanoate	Fe_2O_3, Al_2O_3		105,115
Na-dodecanoate	AgI(pAg=4)	8×10^{-5}	112
K-dodecanoate	Fe_2O_3, Al_2O_3		105,115
Na-dodecylsulfate	AgI(pAg=3)	4×10^{-5}	6,121,122
	Fe_2O_3		105,115,116
	$Fe(OH)_3$		119
	Al_2O_3		105,115
	Malachite Green		124
	Yellow Ocher		70
	Titan White		70
Na-dodecylsulfonate	AgI(pAg=3)	1.5×10^{-4}	6,121,122
Na-dodecylbenzenesulfonate	AgI(pAg=3)	2×10^{-5}	6,121,122
K-tridecanoate	Fe_2O_3, Al_2O_3		105,115
K-tetradecanoate	Fe_2O_3, Al_2O_3		105,115
Na-tetradecylsulfate	AgI(pAg=3)	2×10^{-5}	6,121,122
Na-hexadecylsulfate	Fe_2O_3, Al_2O_3		105,115
Na-dioctylsulfosuccinate	AgI(pAg=3)	10^{-5}	6,121,122

results from various laboratories is precarious and hardly feasible.

It is clear that additional work is required in order to obtain more quantitative relationships between the various parameters involved; such as, surfactant size, particle size, surface area, charge, etc.

Finally, it may be noted that many polymers can reverse the charge of lyophobic sols but this is beyond the scope of the present article.

ACKNOWLEDGEMENTS

This investigation was supported in part by Research Grant WP-815, Public Health Service, USDHEW, Washington, D.C. The author wishes to acknowledge the assistance of Drs. M.B. Abramson, C.G. Force, G.E. Janauer, K.G. Mathai, and K.F. Schulz as well as of Messrs, J.P. Couch, P. Dillon, and L.J. Stryker who conducted the experiments presented in this article.

LITERATURE CITED

1.   Jordis, E., Sitzsber Physik Med Sozietaet Erlangen, 36, 47 (1904).

2.   Lottermoser, A., J Prakt Chem, [2,] 72, 39 (1905).

3.   Lottermoser, A., J Prakt Chem, [2,] 73, 374 (1906).

4.   Hardy, W.B., Proc Roy Soc (London), 66, 110 (1899/1900).

5.   Tezak, B., et al, J Phys Chem, 57, 301 (1953).

6.   Ottewill, R.H. and A. Watanabe, Kolloid-Z, 170, 38 (1960).

7.   Bechhold, H., Z Physik Chem, 48, 385 (1904).

8.   Neisser, M. and U. Friedemann, Muench Med Wochschr, 51, 465 (1904).

9.   Freundlich, H., Colloid and Capillary Chemistry, E.P. Dutton and Co., New York, N.Y.

10. Ostwald, Wo., Kolloid-Z, 75, 297 (1936).

11. Kruyt, H. R. and S. A. Toelstra, Kolloid-Beihefte, 54, 262 (1943).

12. Helmholtz, H. von, Ann Physik, 7, 337 (1879).

13. Smoluchowski, M. von, Z Physik Chem, 92, 129 (1918).

14. Debye, P. and E. Hückel, Physik Z, 25, 49 (1924).

15. Hückel, E., Physik Z, 25, 204 (1924).

16. Henry, D. C., Proc Roy Soc (London), 133, 106 (1931).

17. Overbeek, J. Th. G., Kolloid-Beihefte, 54, 287 (1943).

18. Matijevic, E., et al, J Colloid Sci, 19, 333 (1964).

19. Matijevic, E. and L. J. Stryker, J Colloid Sci, 21 (1966).

20. Lottermoser, A., Z Physik Chem, 70, 239 (1910).

21. Mirnik, M. and B. Tezak, Trans Faraday Soc, 50, 64 (1954).

22. DeBruyn, P. L., Rec Trav Chim, 65, 529 (1946).

23. Kruyt, H. R. and P. L. DeBruyn, Z Physik Chem, 186, 282 (1940).

24. Kruyt, H. R. and J. Th. G. Overbeek, Trans Faraday Soc, 36, 110 (1940).

25. Kolthoff, M. I. and J. J. Lingane, J Am Chem Soc, 58, 1528 (1936).

26. Gorochowsky, N. G. and J. R. Protass, Z Physik Chem, A174, 122 (1935).

27. Lange, E. and P. W. Crane, Z Physik Chem, A141, 225 (1929).

28. Mirnik, M., et al, J Phys Chem, 60, 1473 (1956).

30. Kruyt, H. R. and J. Van der Spek, Kolloid-Z, 25, 1 (1919).

31. Tezak, B. and R. Wolf, Arhiv Kem, 25, 39 (1953).

32. Parks, G. A., Chem Revs, 65, 177 (1965).

33. Panich, R. M. and S. S. Voyutsky, Colloid J (USSR)
    (English Transl) 19, 119 (1957).

34. Horne, R. W., et al, Proc 3rd Intern Congress Surface
    Activity Cologne, 1, 203 (1960).

35. Freundlich, H. and H. Schucht, Z Physik Chem, 85, 641 (1913).

36. Matijevic, E. and M. Kerker, J Phys Chem, 62, 1271 (1958).

37. Matijevic, E., et al, J Phys Chem, 63, 1552 (1959).

38. Matijevic, E., et al, J Phys Chem, 67, 1995 (1963).

39. Kruyt, H. R. and P. C. Van der Willigen, Kolloid-Z,
    45, 307 (1928).

40. Gillis, J. and J. Eeckhout, Natuurw Tijdschr (Ghent),
    19, 49 (1937).

41. Powis, F., Z Physik Chem, 89, 91 (1915).

42. Kruyt, H. R., Kolloid-Z, 22, 81 (1918).

43. Kruyt, H. R. and H. G. Van Arkel-Adriani, Rec Trav Chim,
    39, 609 (1920).

44. Bosch, F. and H. Haemers, Natuurw Tijdschr (Ghent),
    18, 90 (1936).

45. Matijevic, E., et al, J Phys Chem, 64, 1157 (1960).

46. Matijevic, E., et al, J Phys Chem, 65, 826 (1961).

47. Matijevic, E., et al, J Phys Chem, 65, 1724 (1961).

48. Matijevic, E., et al, J Phys Chem, 66, 111 (1962).

49. Matijevic, E., et al, J Phys Chem, 66, 1799 (1962).

50. Matijevic, E. and G. E. Janauer, J Colloid Sci, 20, (Feb, 1965).

51. Mattson, S., J Phys Chem, 32, 1928 (1928); Ibid, 37, 223, (1933).

52. Mattson, S., Kolloid-Beihefte, 14, 227 (1922).

53. Matijevic, E. and B. Tezak, J Phys Chem, 57, 951 (1953).

54. Joly, J., 8th Congres Geol Intern Paris 1900, 2, 710 (1901).

55. Langelier, W.F. and H. F. Ludwig, J Am Water Works Assoc, 41, 163 (1949).

56. Pilipowich, J.B., et al, J Am Water Works Assoc, 50, 1467 (1958).

57. Black, A.P. and S.A. Hannah, J Am Water Works Assoc, 53, 438 (1961).

58. Chamot, W. and B. Stewart, Am Chem Soc, Div Water Waste Preprints, pp 45-9 (March-April 1963).

59. Packham, F.R., J Colloid Sci, 20, 81 (1965).

60. Burton, E.F., Phil Mag, (6), 12, 472 (1906).

61. Kruyt, H.R. and A.E. Van Arkel, Rec Trav Chim, 39, 615 (1920).

62. Mattson, S., Soil Science, 30, 459 (1930).

63. Buxton, B.H. and P. Shaffer, Z Physik Chem, 57, 47 (1907).

64. Buxton, B.H. and O. Teague, Z Physik Chem, 57, 76 (1907).

65. Teague, O. and B.H. Buxton, Z Physik Chem, 57, 76 (1907).

66. Voyutski, S.S. and R. M. Panich, Colloid J (USSR) (English Transl) 19, 273 (1957)

67. Matijevic, E., et al, Abstracts, 147th Natl ACS Meeting, Pniladelphia, Pa., (April 1964).

68. Tucker, G. R., U.S. Patent No. 1, 956, 053 (April 24, 1934).

69. Powis F., Z Physik Chem, 89, 186 (1915).

70. Merguro, K., J Chem Soc Japan, Ind Chem Sect, 58, 905 (1955).

71. Block, C.J.J.N., Pulp Paper Mag Can, 57, 28 (1956).

72. Thode, E.F., et al, TAPPI, 36, 310, 315 (1953).

73. Black, A. P. and D. G. Willems, J Am Water Works Assoc, 53, 589 (1961).

74. Biedermann, G., Svensk Kem Tidskr, 76, 362 (1964).

75. Thomas, A.W. and T. H. Whitehead, J Phys Chem, 35, 37 (1931).

76. Thomas, A. W. and A. P. Tai, J Am Chem Soc, 54, 841 (1932).

77. Pokras, L., J Chem Educ, 33, 152 (1956).

78. Bjerrum, N., Z Physik Chem, 59, 336 (1907).

79. Tezak, B., et al, Z Physik Chem, A191, 270 (1942).

80. Matijevic, E. and B. Tezak, Arhiv Kem, 22, 62 (1950).

81. Tezak, B., et al, J Am Chem Soc, 73, 1602, 1605 (1951).

82. Stubican, V. and B. Tezak, Kolloid-Z, 140, 65 (1955).

83. White, H.L., et al, J Phys Chem, 39, 611 (1935).

84. Freundlich, H. and G. Ettisch, Z Physik Chem, 116, 401 (1925).

85. Elissafoff, G. van, Z Physik Chem, $\underline{79}$, 385 (1912).

86. Freundlich, H. and H. Buchler, Kolloid-Z, $\underline{32}$, 305 (1923).

87. Goring, D.A.I., et al, Can J Res. $\underline{B28}$, 339 (1950).

88. Bangham, D.A. and R.M.C. Dawson, Biochem J, $\underline{72}$, 486 (1959).

89. Wilkins, D. J. and R. H. Ottewill, J Theoret Biol, $\underline{2}$, 165 (1962).

90. Ottewill, R. H. and D. J. Wilkins, Proc 3rd Intern Congress Surface Activity, Cologne, $\underline{II}$, 653 (1960).

91. Ottewill, R. H. and D. J. Wilkins, Trans Faraday Soc, $\underline{58}$, 608 (1962).

92. Bilinski, H., et al, Croat Chem Acta, $\underline{35}$, 19 (1963).

93. Kraus, K. A. and R. W. Holmberg, J Phys Chem, $\underline{64}$, 1157 (1960).

94. Lefevbre, J., J Chim Phys, $\underline{55}$, 227 (1958).

95. Souchay, P., Bull Soc Chim (France), $\underline{15}$, 143 (1948).

96. Chauvenet, E. and J. Tonnet, Bull Soc Chim France, (4), $\underline{47}$, 701 (1930).

97. Chauvenet, E. and Mme, Souteyrand-Franck, Bull Soc Chim France, (4), $\underline{47}$, 1128 (1930).

98. Abramson, M.B., et al, J Chem Soc, p 5041 (1964).

99. Black, A.P., et al, J Am Water Works Assoc, $\underline{55}$, 1347 (1963).

100. Herak, J and B. Tezak, Arhiv Kem, $\underline{25}$, 87 (1953).

101. Freundlich, H. and V. Birstein, Kolloid-Beihefte, $\underline{22}$, 95 (1926).

102. Hsu, P.H. and C.I. Rich, Soil Sci Soc Amer Proc, $\underline{23}$, 21 (1960).

103. Matijevic, E. and R. H. Ottewill, J Colloid Sci, 13, 242 (1958).

104. Lottermoser, A. and R. Steudel, Kolloid-Z, 83, 319 (1938); Ibid, 83, 37 (1938).

105. Strange, H. O. and J. F. Hazel, J Phys Chem, 61, 1281 (1957).

106. Freundlich, H. and G. V. Slottman, Z Physik Chem, 129 305 (1927).

107. Tamamushi, B. and K. Tamaki, Kolloid-Z, 163, 122 (1959).

108. Freundlich, H., Z Physik Chem, 73, 385 (1910).

109. Ostwald, Wo., Kolloid-Z, 26, 69 (1920).

110. Herak, J. and B. Tezak, Arhiv Kem, 22, 49 (1950).

111. Tamaki, K., Kolloid-Z, 170, 113 (1960).

112. Pravidic, V. and R. Mirnik, Croat Chem Acta, 32, 1 (1960).

113. Ottewill, R. H. and M. Rastogi, Trans Faraday Soc, 56, 880 (1960).

114. Ottewill, R. H. and M. Rastogi, Trans Faraday Soc, 56, 880 (1960).

115. Hazel, J. F. and H. O. Strange, J Colloid Sci, 12, 529 (1957).

116. Tamamushi, B., Kolloid-Z, 150, 44 (1957).

117. Jaycock, M. J., et al, Proc 3rd Intern Congress Surface Activity, Cologne, II, 285 (1960).

118. Jaycock, M. J. and R. H. Ottewill, Bull Inst Mining Met No. 677, 497 (1963).

119. Meguro, K. and T. Kondo, J Chem Soc Japan, Pure Chem Sect, 76, 642 (1955).

120. Horne, R. W., et al, Kolloid-Z, 161, 50 (1958).

121. Ottewill, R. H. and A. Watanabe, Kolloid-Z, 170, 132 (1960).

122. Ottewill, R. H. and A. Watanabe, Kolloid-Z, 171, 33 (1960).

123. Meguro, K., J Chem Soc Japan, Pure Chem Sect, 77, 77 (1956).

124. Meguro, K., J Chem Soc Japan, Pure Chem Sect, 77, 72 (1956).

125. Kling, W. and H. Lange, Kolloid-Z, 127, 19 (1952).

126. Fuerstenau, D. W., J Phys Chem, 60, 981 (1952).

127. Somasundaran, P., et al, J Phys Chem, 68, 3562 (1964).

128. Onoda, G. Y. and D. W. Fuerstenau, Proc 7th Intern Mineral Processing Congress, New York, N. Y., p 301 (1960).

129. Ottewill R. H. and R. F. Woodbridge, J Colloid Sci. 19, 606 (1964).

130. LuValle, J.H. and J. M. Jackson, J Phys Chem, 61, 1216 (1957).

DISCUSSION

CHAIRMAN PACKHAM: Thank you, Dr. Matijevic. Now there is time for some questions.

DR. DOUGLAS W. FUERSTENAU (University of California): I don't quite agree with the remarks of Dr. LaMer on Dr. Matijevic on what is wrong with the use of the zeta potential. If you use the concept of the zeta potential correctly you can do very important things. One most important property of any colloid I think is its zero point of charge (ZPC). That is the condition where the electrochemical potential or, ψ_0 in these diagrams is zero. You can determine the ZPC by measurements of zeta potential, and this is one of the simplest ways of doing it.

A second thing that you can do is to determine chemical interactions with the surface, and in this case you determine the amount of chemisorbed reagent that must be in solution to cause the zeta potential to become zero and from this you can calculate adsorption potentials. That last slide which published paper in which we calculated adsorption potentials as a function of the chain length of the amine salts. We found something like 0.6 kcal/more of CH_2 groups as determined by the zeta potential measurements.

Something else that you can get from these measurements are the conditions when detergent ions, such as amine ions, begin to associate at the surface. On that last slide you see where they associate forming agglomerates similar to micelles in solution. You also may be able to ascertain where they begin to form dimers or trimers at the surface.

Then, finally, a fourth thing that you can get of the zeta potential measurements is an indication of monolayer coverage which was the bottom break in the curves shown in the last slide.

DR. MATIJEVIC: I agree with whatever you said. All I'm trying to say is, don't use zeta potential without discrimination. We use it ourselves when we know what we have in the solution and when we can make corrections and do proper calculations. Just putting anything into a cell and then reading a number and multiplying by another number and calling this zeta potential is acting without discrimination and justification.

DR. STUMM (Harvard University): Do you have any means to distinguish numeralogically between your group B and C adsorbents? In other words, how do you know -- now, I have hydroxylated species and I can apply the Schulze-Hardy rule and now I have just some ind of low or medium regular wave surfactant and here I cannot apply the Schulze-Hardy rule.

DR. MATIJEVIC: I think this question has been asked and answered empirically rather than theoretically. It turns out that if you take a surface active agent which acts as a mono-valent ion, this will coagulate at 10^{-5} or 10^{-6} moles/l which is about 5 orders of magnitude lower than what similar divalent ion and find about the same coagulation concentration, obviously the Schulze-Hardy rule is not applicable.

On the other hand, with metal ions we have very systematic changes of coagulation concentration with pH which very well correspond to some simple ions of various charges used for calibration. So, I say, there is no theoretical justification for the true being, but a very useful empirical experiance.

I think the way to answer your question theoretically is to do very exact adsorption measurements, which we hope to do soon.

DR. HEALY (University of California): I want to under-line one comment you made. You cannot expect to know too

much about a system unless you know what preparation the
solid was given. If you know enough about the bulk properties
you should theoretically be able to predict the surface properties.
However, you need the bulk properties within the first few
layers under the surface. It is reasonable therefore, for
example, that crystalline quartz has different surface properties
as defined, for example, by the ZPC, than amorphous silica
and if you grind the surface of quartz you can produce amorphous
silica such that a piece of crystalline quartz is surrounded by
amorphous silica. That is why the zero points of charge of
your type A system where the reversal of charge is due to
potential determining ions are very closely related to the
structure. The pH of the ZPC of alumina is very high, silica
is very low, and other oxides fall at intermediate pH values
that can be from the crystal structure.

DR. MATIJEVIC: I couldn't agree more. This is the
same thing as with AgI. The number of imperfections determine
the ZPC or pAg of ZPC.

DR. MORGAN (California Institute of Technology): I'd
like to show one slide which is related to the very last thing
you talked about, and I think it is interesting because it is
some of the first data we have seen on the effect of particle
size.

The last point that you made is that it is important now
to know more about the properties of the dispersed phase.
These data represent the amounts of cationic polymer required
to bring about optimum flocculation of thin dispersed phases,
which, in this particular case, is a latex suspension (Figure 3).
The particle sizes are given along the axis in different weight
concentrations, and this is very clear evidence of stoichimetry
of the kind that has been demonstrated for the earlier mentioned
work with color. I think now if we start to study well-defined
systems of different particle size distributions we can eventually be able to predict a priori the expected amount of flocculant to deflocculate any heterogeneons system, except for the
fact there is still a kinetic problem. These data were obtained
under the conditions where there were no kinetic restraints.
They were allowed to proceed until kinetics were not the
limiting factors in the reaction. There are no electrokinetics
about this. I'm presenting it to emphasize the importance of
the properties of dispersed phase. Figure 3 was taken from
Vilaret, M., Ellect of Particle Size on the Destabilization
of Colloidal Suspensions in Water, Thesis, University of
Florida, Gainesville, Florida, (1965).

DR. MATIJEVIC: That's fine. It's all in agreement. I
should say there is an indication for stoichimetric adsorption
of metal ions on colloidal particles. Some adsorption work in
our laboratory and work by Mirnik and others, indicates pretty
decently, despite rather large experimental errors, that there
is a stoichiometric relationship. We expect to use perfectly
monodispersed systems of known surface areas which we are
able to make now, and hope to get more accurate results.

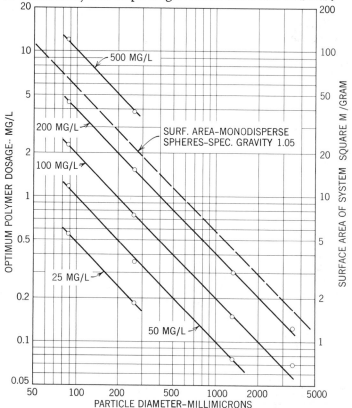

FIGURE 3D EFFECT OF PARTICLE DIAMETER UPON
THE OPTIMUM CATIONIC POLYMER DOSAGE
REQUIRED FOR MAXIMUM DESTABILIZATION
OF MONODISPERSE LATEX SUSPENSIONS OF
GIVEN WEIGHT CONCENTRATIONS-variation
of system area with particle size.

DR. HINRICH L. BOHN (Tennessee Valley Authority): I
believe that you said that the ions adsorbed on the solid phase
are the same species as those in the bulk solution. Isn't it
possible that the adsorbed ions are changed by the electrical
and chemical properties of the colloid surface and, therefore,
are more a function of the surface than of the bulk solution.

DR. MATIJEVIC: This may be the case. However, there
is a correct slope in the "log $[Al^{+3}]_{tot}$ -pH" plot for the
stability/coagulation boundary which gives the ratio of metal
to hydroxyl ions in the Al complex. This is the same as we
believe to be in solution, so we have an indirect evidence for
it. Some people believe that some changes occur upon adsorption of hydrolyzed ions on colloid particles. It was suggested
that thorium adsorbs onto the surface as $ThOH^{+3}$ and then
polymerizes on the surface. Right now there is no way of
clarifying this point. There is some indirect evidence which
indicates that species in solution determine the adsorption
process, although we can't exclude the possibility which you
mentioned. The hydrolyzed species in solution are quite stable,
though. For example, if one takes an aged Al solution, the
hydrolysis cannot be reversed by changing pH. However, there
are some solutions that are less stable. Also, I think there
are different species if the hydrolysis is carried out by changing
pH or by aging.

DR. LAMER: Your work is confined to hydrophobic sols.
My talk of yesterday dealt primarily with hydrophilic sols and
the importance of adsorption in terms of Langmuir's theta.
If I understood correctly what you were trying to show by
classes B and C, obeying and disobeying Schulze-Hardy, whether
the things were or were not adsorbed. If they are not adsorbed,
they don't work, of course. I think you brought this out beautifully.

DR. MATIJEVIC: Dr. LaMer, I was so tempted to make
this classification into constituent ions, coagulants and flocculants.

DR. LAMER: There must be gradations between hydrophobic and hydrophilic sols. Everything isn't white or black.
To simplify matters, I made it all black yesterday; today you
are making it all white.

There is another point that Dr. Morgan makes. Miss Kane's
data which we are going to publish soon shows very clearly that
flocculation values are proportional to the surface area. This
is the factor k W in the equations I showed yesterday. W is
the weight of the solid; k is the fineness of the grinding. The
product k W is the total surface whereas k W O is the fraction

of the surface available for adsorption by the polyelectrolyte.

DR. MATIJEVIC: The best thing, we'll invite Dr. Morgan and Miss Kane to our laboratory and we'll apply all the techniques.

CHAIRMAN PACKHAM: I think on this happy note of agreement we will adjourn.

Frederick R. Duke
Purdue University

FACTORS DETERMINING CHEMICAL OXIDATION AND REDUCTION IN SOLUTION

One of the first things encountered in even elementary chemistry courses is the oxidation-reduction theory. Rarely, however, do such discussion include the mechanistic aspects of oxidation-reduction reactions, which involves how the electron is transferred during the reaction.

Oxidation-reduction reactions in homogeneous aqueous solution appear to proceed through one of two generalized routes: (a) the oxidant and the reductant combine in a generalized acid-base reaction and electron transfer occurs intramolecularly; or (b) the electron moves from reductant to oxidant upon collision by a "tunneling" mechanism. We will consider these two cases in turn.

ACID-BASE REACTIONS

The reaction between substances which are Lewis acids (generally cations) and Lewis bases (generally anions) occurs through the complex formed when the acid-base reaction has been completed. Examples of this type of reaction are presented in Table I.

It has been shown that, when Mn^{+3} reacts with oxalate to produce Mn^{+2} and CO_2, the chief form of Mn^{+3} is the dioxalato complex, $Mn(C_2O_4)_2$ (12). However, the monoxalato complex, $Mn(C_2O_4)^+$, a minor constituent in rapid equilibrium with the dioxalato complex, is responsible for most of the electron transfer. Apparently the free-radical ion $C_2O_4^-$ is formed as a very reactive intermediate. All of the reaction is accomplished by electron transfer within the complex ions.

In the case of the reaction between Fe^{+3} and SO_3^{-2} the intermediate formed is $FeSO_3^+$. Bray studied the reaction formed from FeI_2^+ of $FeI(OH)^+$ (3). If only one iodide was complexed with the iron it would not work very well. The reason for that seems to be that I_2^-, the free radical ion, is very much more stable than the atom and FeI^{+2} would give $I \cdot$, which is not a very stable species. Also IOH^- can be formed, and indeed in all of these cases some unstable intermediate may be formed.

An interesting case is one in which the pairs are reversed. That is, where the reducing agent is the acidic substance, and the oxidizing agent the basic substance. Trivalent titanium reacts with perchlorate ion, the former being oxidized and the latter reduced (4). Perchlorate is a notoriously poor complexer, but it does form complexes sufficiently well with trivalent titanium so that this reducing agent will react in dilute solution albeit slowly.

Another interesting case is the reaction between tetravalent cerium and chloride ion where the complex with one chloride or with two chlorides reacts extremely slowly, so slowly, in fact, that no electron transfer can be observed. However, as soon as three chloride ions enter the tetravalent cerium complexes, a fairly rapid electron transfer is observed.

These reactions between anions and cations are fairly obvious examples of Lewis acid-base reactions. Oxidation-reduction pairs also include, however, anion-anion and cation-cation systems, which at first inspection are not quite as obvious examples.

In the case of many anion-anion systems, when reaction occurs there is not complete saturation of the number of electrons capable of being held in the valence portion of the central atom. Table II gives several examples of this type of reaction.

TABLE I   REACTIONS INVOLVING CATIONS
AND ANIONS

Oxidant	Reductant	Intermediate	Literature Cited
Mn^{+3}	$C_2O_4^-$	$MnC_2O_4^+$, $Mn(C_2O_4)_2^-$	(1),(2)
Fe^{+3}	I^-	FeI_2^+, $FeIOH^+$	(3)
ClO_4^-	Ti^{+3}	$Mn(C_2O_4)_3^{-3}$, $Ti\ ClO_4^{+2}$	(4)
Ce^{+4}	$CH_3CHOHCH-OHCH_3$ (G)	CeG^{+4}, CeG_2^{+4}	(5)
Cu^{+2}	CN^-	$Cu(CN)_4^{-2}$	(6)

TABLE II   REACTIONS INVOLVING TWO ANIONS

Oxidant	Reductant	Intermediate	Literature Cited
NO_2^-	HSO_3^-	$HON{\begin{smallmatrix}\\\end{smallmatrix}}SO_3^{-2}$ SO_3 $(HO)_2NSO_3^-$	(7)
BrO_3^-	$H\bar{S}O_3$	$O_2Br{-}O{-}SO_3$	(8)
MnO_4^-	MnO_4^{-2}	$MnO_4{-}M{-}MnO_4^-$ where M^+ is alkali metal ion	(9)

In the case of the reaction between nitrite ion and sulfite ion, the nitrite ion acts as a base, displacing oxide ion from the sulphur. Trinitrilosulfonic acid is formed which then hydrolyzed to sulfate and ammonia, and thus nitrite is reduced to ammonia and sulfite is oxidized to sulfate (7).

When bromate containing O^{18} is allowed to react with SO_3^{-2}, SO_4^{-2} containing one O^{18} is produced (8). The activated complex, in all probability, is O_2BrOSO_3, the sulfite acting as an acid and the bromate as a base.

In the case of the reaction between periodate and glycol, a famous reaction used very much by organic chemists in the old days to prove structures, there is a very definite addition of the glycol to the periodate ion. Periodate normally exists as a dihydrate with the two waters quite intimately bound to the iodine and it is possible to make Ag_5IO_6, replacing all of the hydrogen in the water that is attached. The glycol displaces the two water molecules, but it does not form an ester because the hydrogens do not leave; they stay with the coordinated oxygens on the glycol.

An internal electron transfer occurs, and the bond between the two carbons disappears and two hydrogen ions and two molecules of formaldehyde are produced along with iodate.

There are other types of anion-anion reactions. For example, bromate does not oxidize certain substances, such as bromide, in an alkaline solution. To make the reaction proceed, hydrogen ions must be added. The hydrogen ions remove an oxide ion from the BrO_3^-, resulting in BrO_2^+ or a hydrated form thereof. This is a cation, and very much unsaturated with respect to the electrons. It combines with whatever anion it is oxidizing, followed by an internal electron shift.

When two cations react, a base such as chloride ion which has more than one electron pair for complex formation is involved. For example, in the electron exchange between Fe^{+3} and Sn^{+2}; Eu^{+3}, Eu^{+2}; Ce^{+4}, Ce^{+3}; Co^{+3}, Co^{+2}; and many other pairs of ions; chloride, bromide, cyanide, hydroxyl, and other ions with two electron pairs available are good catalysts (10, 11, 12, 13). Examples of this type of system are found in Table III.

TABLE III   REACTIONS INVOLVING CATIONS
AND CATIONS

Oxidant	Reductant	Intermediate	Literature Cited
Fe^{+3}	Sn^{+2}	$Fe\_Cl\_SnCl_3{}^{+}$	(10)
Eu^{+3}	Eu^{+2}	$Eu\_Cl\_Eu^{+4}$	(11)
Ce^{+4}	Ce^{+3}	Ce_X_Ce; X is F^-, Cl^-, OH^-	(12)
Co^{+3}	Cr^{+2}	Co_X_Cr; X is OH^-, $SO_4{}^-$, Cl^-, Br^-, CN	(14,15)
Fe^{+3}	Fe^{+2}	Fe_X_Fe; X is OH^-,Cl^-	(16)

$$HOOC\langle\underline{\quad}\rangle COOH$$

The fact that both cations are attached to one anion at the same time has been proven in the case of the reaction between Co^{+3} and Cr^{+2} (14, 15). Co^{+3} in the form of the pentamine chloride complex, $Co(NH_3)_5Cl^{+2}$, does not equilibrate rapidly with other ligands in solution. Thus, the cobalt pentamine chloride complex may be dissolved without loss of the chloride from the cobalt. Also, Cr^{+3} has similar properties of exchanging its ligands very slowly. If a radiochloride ion is attached to the cobalt, and ordinary chloride is present in solution, all of the radiochloride at the end of the reaction with Co^{+2} is attached to Cr^{+3}. This could occur without exchange only if the Co^{+2} and Cr^{+3} both were attached to chloride at the same time. Similarly, when Sn^{+2} reacts with Fe^{+3} the reaction is fourth order in respect to chloride ion (10). Even when ferricinium ion is reduced with Sn^{+2}, the order in respect to chloride ion is four (18). Since ferricinium ion is likely to coordinate no more than one chloride ion, the likelihood is that $SnCl_4^-$ reacts with Fe^{+3} or more properly stated, the activated complex is $FeClSnCl_3$. The three extra chloride ions stabilize the Sn^{+3} intermediate oxidation state.

REACTIONS NOT INVOLVING ACID-BASE MECHANISMS

When large ions, not easily or strongly hydrated are structurally such that in the reduced state, the electron involved is not localized, collision involving the ion can occur without water molecules intervening between ions in the collision; further, if the electron is not localized, it can generally get very close to the periphery of the ion. Then, tunneling of the electron through the barrier from reductant to oxidant may occur (19). Examples of such ions are Fe^{+2} coordinated with 1-10 phenanthroline and phenanthroline derivatives, leuco bases of dye molecules, porphyrins, and the like. Any large unhydrated ion with a delocalized electron may be expected to react in this way with no direct bond formed between oxidant and reductant.

HETEROGENEOUS SYSTEMS

In heterogeneous cases, two types of phenomena may be involved: (a) the surface may be a good adsorber for oxygen, converting molecular oxygen to atomic oxygen; or (b) the surface may be capable of reversible oxidation and reduction. Thus, a platinum surface will catalyze the oxidation of Fe^{+2}, Ti^{+3}, and similar ions by oxygen. Here, the platinum adsorbs the oxygen and very likely the ion to be oxidized and reaction ensues.

The situation is somewhat different when MnO_2, Fe_2O_3, V_2O_5, molybdenum blue, and similar surfaces are involved. All of the metal ions in these oxides have lower states of oxidation, so that the oxides give up oxygen forming ions of the metal in the solid having lower oxidation states. It is probable that a precipitate of hydrous ferric oxide catalyzes the oxidation of Fe^{+2} in solution by this type of mechanism.

Another example is the non-stoichmetric oxide manganese dioxide, actually $MnO_{1.6}$ to $MnO_{1.9}$, which also catalyzes the oxidation of manganese ions of lower valence. In such oxides, the crystal structure does not change in the process of going between these two oxide concentrations or quantities in the oxide, but a trivalent manganese is substituted for tetravalent manganese in the crystal structure, resulting in oxygen vacancies.

Thus, if molecular oxygen is placed in the vicinity of this kind of oxide under the proper conditions, that the higher the pressure of the oxygen, the greater the activity of the oxygen, and the greater this oxygen/manganese ratio is likely to be.

If this oxide is placed in the presence of a reducing agent,
the ratio will be lowered. Actually, it is a device for breaking
the very energetic oxygen to oxygen bond in molecular oxygen.
This is the major difficulty with oxidations with oxygen, and
if a device is available to break this bond, such as these
non-stoichiometric oxides, molecular oxygen can be an
excellent oxidant.

ENZYME OXIDATIONS

Another category of oxidation in natural waters involves
biological oxidation. Enzymes are involved here and many
different types of enzymes involved in oxidation are known.
One example is glucose oxidase, a flavin enzyme which
oxidizes glucose to gluconolactone, in turn being reoxidized
by oxygen (20). This is similar to the quinone-hydroquinone
system, where the oxidized forms pick up a couple of hydrogen
atoms which constitues the reduction. The oxygen takes the
hydrogen atom away from the reduced flavin, oxidizing it and
being itself reduced to hydrogen peroxide. In general, the
enzymes form complexes with the substance being oxidized,
followed by the oxidation reaction, although in some cases
the complex formation may be the slow step in the reaction.

ELECTROLYTIC OXIDATIONS

There is one other type that should be mentioned, and
that is electrolytic oxidation. There seems to be some interest
in the electrolytic oxidation of impurities in waters. This can
be accomplished by two means. In one of them, a voltage high
enough to produce oxygen is employed, which then oxidizes
the material. In the other, adsorption of the organic compound
directly on something like a platinum electrode occurs, and
the electrons can be removed from it because the bonds are
broken when the organic substance is adosrbed.

I understand that if the moon, for example, were made of
platinum, that we would all be driving electric cars as soon
as they got to the moon and started to mine it, but now we
cannot use hydrocarbon fuel cells because there just is not
s ufficient platinum in the world. Nevertheless, the noble
metals have this wonderful facility for breaking bonds and
making new ones in which the electrons become available to
the conductor.

LITERATURE CITED

1. Duke, F.R., J Am Chem Soc, 69, 2885 (1947).

2. Taube, H., J Am Chem Soc, 70, 1216 (1948).

3. Hershey, A.V. and W.C. Bray, J Am Chem Soc, 58, 1760 (1936).

4. Duke, F.R. and P. Quinny, J Am Chem Soc, 75, 3800 (1954).

5. Duke, F.R. and R.F. Bremer, J Am Chem Soc, 73, 5169 (1951).

6. Duke, F.R. and W.G. Courtney, J Phys Chem, 56, 19 (1952).

7. Rutenberg, A.C. et al, J Am Chem Soc, 73, 4487 (1951).

8. Halperin, J. and H. Taube, J Am Chem Soc, 74, 375, 382 (1952).

9. Gjertsen, L. and A.C. Wahl, J Am Chem Soc, 81, 1572 (1959).

10. Duke, F.R. and R.C. Pinkerton, J Am Chem Soc, 73, 3045 (1951).

11. Maier, D.J. and C.S. Garner, J Phys Chem, 56,896 (1952).

12. Hornig, H.C. and W.F. Libby, J Phys Chem, 56, 986 (1952).

13. Flagg, J.G., J Am Chem Soc, 63, 557 (1941).

14. Taube, H. and H. Myers, J Am Chem Soc, 76, 2103 (1954).

15. Taube, H., et al, J Am Chem Soc, 75, 4118 (1953).

16. Silverman, J. and R.W. Dodson, J Phys Chem, 56, 845 (1952).

17. Duke, F.R. and E.D. Wolf, Iowa State College J Sci, 34, 157 (1959).

18. Duke, F.R. and N.C. Peterson, J Phys Chem, 67, 531 (1963).

19. Marcus, R.A., J Chem Phys, 26, 867, 872 (1957).

20. Gibson, Q.H., et al, J Biol Chem, 259, 3927 (1964).

DISCUSSION

CHAIRMAN GREENBERG: (California State Dept. of Public Health): Well I'm not sure that the kinds of questions that we have for Dr. Duke will be questions that are accompanied on the part of the questioner by "I just happened to have a few slides in my pocket." But I'm sure that nonetheless there must be people among you who do have questions.

DR. DEAN (R.A. Taft Sanitary Eng Center): One of our people has been working with the oxidation of organic compounds in very dilute solutions using both the hydrogen peroxide-iron and ozone and he has considerable evidence of a OH-free radical as the principal oxidant. I don't know how that fits into your scheme.

DR. DUKE: It is well established that you do get this hydroxyl radical from the reaction of Fe^{+2} with hydrogen peroxide. Now, the hydroxyl radical is a pretty fair acid, if I may say so, and it is more likely to react with what we would call basic substances than acidic. On the other hand, we really don't know what the dissociation constant of the hydroxyl radical is. The tendency to lose a hydrogen ion undoubtedly is greater than than of water, and when you get the O^- you probably have a fairly basic substance that can plug into acidic substances. On the other hand, free radicals are so reactive that the electrons make very vast excursions to more than an atomic dimension away from the nucleus of the oxygen and be able to get into other reducing agents and other -- well, I'm talking about the electron deficiency feeling its way out so that it can turn back into a hydroxyl ion. It probably reacts by what we would call the thin insulation method except you don't need such thin insulation in this case.

DR. STUMM (Harvard University): Just a short question in connection with these non-stoichiometric manganese oxides. You spoke about the possibility of having a Mn III ion included in these oxides, and I wonder to what extent is it possible to distinguish between a mixture of Mn II and Mn IV and specifically Mn III.

DR. DUKE: I don't think you can tell the difference. The electrons are on the move in these things. Generally speaking, these are semi-conductors or conductors.

DR. MORGAN: (California Institute of Technology): Mr. Greenberg, it's a relief to know that I don't happen to have a slide in my pocket. I do want to ask a question about a kind of substance which is used very frequently in water treatment which is pyrophosphate or a simple analog of pyrophosphate. We have observed that the presence of pyrophosphate in sufficiently large amounts can inhibit reaction between, for example, manganous ion and oxygen. I wonder if you could comment upon it.

DR. DUKE: This is quite a simple thing to explain because if you go with my prior acid-base reaction before the electrons can transfer, when the site is already occupied by pyrophosphate it cannot be occupied by oxygen.

CHAIRMAN GREENBERG: I think we have time time for another question, if there is one more. If not, thank you very much, Dr. Duke.

M. C. Rand
Stephen B. Gale
Syracuse University

KINETICS OF THE OXIDATION
OF SULFITES
BY DISSOLVED OXYGEN

The reaction of sulfites with molecular oxygen has been known for many years, and has attracted widespread attention among chemists since 1880. Presumably this interest was stimulated initially by the use of sodium sulfite in photography which was, at that time, a new and fascinating art. It was observed that the solutions deteriorated when exposed to the air. It was demonstrated also very early that, under most conditions, the principal product was Na_2SO_4 and that atmospheric oxygen was involved in the reaction (1).

Somewhat earlier, it had been established that the so-called "auto-oxidation" of many other compounds was actually a reaction with oxygen of the air (2). Almost simultaneously with the demonstration that the oxidation of sodium sulfite solutions also belonged to this class, it was observed that mixtures of compounds susceptible to "auto-oxidation" often gave results quite different from those found when one compound alone was studied. In particular certain compounds which reacted very slowly with oxygen in pure solutions were oxidized much more rapidly when sulfite was present. It was immediately suggested that the oxygen was in some way "activated" by the sulfite (3). Also, the reaction rate of the sulfite itself was found to be markedly influenced by various materials. Thus, both Bigelow (1) and

Young (4) observed powerful retardation in the presence of
certain oxidizable organic compounds, such as benzyl alcohol
and benzaldehyde and a less marked effect in the presence of
KCN, NH_4Cl, and sodium acetate. Titoff observed marked
acceleration in the presence of certain metallic ions, particularly
Cu (5). Berg reported inhibition by HI (6). In an effort to deduce
the mechanism of catalysis by copper ion, Baubigny suggested
a role for Cu which today would be called that of an electron
carrier (7). Although it now appears that this conjecture may
have been correct, it was abandoned because experimental
evidence was not obtained for the existence of the postulated
intermediates. Mathews and Dewey reported quantitative data
upon the effect of ultraviolet light in the presence and absence
of oxygen, but did not calculate quantum yields from their
results (8). Saillard reported the effect of sulfite upon additional
"auto-oxidations" (9). Mathews and Weeks studied the effects
of accelerators and inhibitors in the presence of ultraviolet
light (10). Millbauer and Pazourek studied concentrated solutions
of sodium sulfite and found very little reaction with atmospheric
oxygen (11). They reported that the principal product under those
conditions was dithionate. Moureu and Dufraisse studied the
action of free sulfur, sulfites, and other sulfur compounds upon
the oxidation of other reductants (12). Mason and Mathews (13)
refined earlier observations reported by Mathews and Dewey (8)
upon the effect of ultraviolet light. Moureau, et al reported
the catalytic action of various nitrogen compounds upon the
auto-oxidation of various compounds, including sulfites (14).

Several of the authors cited in the previous paragraph
attempted to explain their results in terms of various hypothetical
reaction mechanisms. The mechanisms proposed often conflicted
in detail, many were rather vague, and all were basically
speculative in nature, but most of them agreed in suggesting that
postulation of some sort of an activated intermediate molecule,
ion, or radical was necessary to explain the observed results.
Beginning in the early 1920's the theoretical treatment of
catalytic oxidation began to assume more definite and coherent
form. Mittra and Dhar suggested that the mechanism involved
in these reactions might be similar to that involved in the oxidations catalyzed by enzymes in biological systems and was,
therefore, of very wide significance (15). Subsequently, Dhar
suggested a well-developed theory involving the activation of
molecules (16). About the same time, Moureu and Dufraisse,
in a series of articles, proposed a rather similar interpretation

based upon their studies of a wide variety of auto-oxidations
(17, 18, 19, 20). Backstrom in 1927 proposed the chain-reaction
mechanism which is now most generally accepted as the true
explanation (21). There is still doubt as to the intermediates
in this reaction. Hence, the detailed mechanism is unknown.
Haber and co-workers treated Backstrom's theory as a particular case of their general theory of homogeneous catalysis
in aqueous solutions which involves alternate oxidation and
reduction of the catalyst and a series of one-electron oxidations
of the substrate (22, 23). On this basis, Bailey and ffrench (24),
Hagg (25), and Kenner (26) attempted to define the intermediates
involved and the specific site of action of negative catalysts.

Following the proposal and general acceptance of well-
defined theories which seemed to account for the observed
phenomena, other publications usually interpreted their results
on this basis. These included the studies of Reinders and Vles
of the oxidation of various inorganic salts (27), those of Alyea
and Backstrom of the inhibiting action of various alcohols (28),
the studies of Chakravarti and Dhar on oxidation of inorganic
salts (29), those of Briner, et al, in which ozone was involved
as an oxidant and activator (30), and a theoretical treatment
by Jeu and Alyea of the inhibitory action of various organic
compounds (31). In 1934, Hoather and Goodeve published a
series of articles dealing with the catalysis by manganese in
various forms and gave evidence supporting the view, which had
been suggested earlier by others, that activated ions or radicals
rather than molecules, were involved in the mechanism (32, 33,
34, 35). This opinion received further support from Bassett and
Henry (36). Also in 1943, Backstrom published a somewhat
revised and more detailed version of his chain-reaction theory
which took into account the more recent data (37).

Backstrom's theory was widely accepted, and subsequent
to its publication, interest in the oxidation of sulfites appears
to have declined, since publications on the subject appeared
much less frequently. Briner and Biedermann reported further
studies of the system activated by ozone (38) whereas Bassett
and Parker, several years later, reviewed the entire subject
and summarized the theoretical interpretations (39). In 1949,
a series of three articles appeared from the University of
Padua (40, 41, 42), presenting further studies of the reaction.
The workers used a rather elegant polarographic technique for
following the course of the reaction, which apparently was

capable of producing rather precise and reproducible results.
But again, their principal interest was in the subject of catalysis, and they worked only at a single high pH value, 10.38, at
which no perceptible reaction was reported in the absence of
positive catalysts.

When it is considered that the period of more or less
intensive study continued for some thirty years, it is surprising
that very little reliable quantitative data appeared concerning
the basic reaction of sulfite with dissolved oxygen. This was
due largely to the fact that the principal objective of the investigators was not to study the reaction itself, but rather to study
catalysis. As a result, the experiments usually were designed
to give relative reaction rates, and the uncatalyzed reaction
was used only as a control. In most cases, one or more of the
relevant conditions are not defined exactly enough to permit
kinetic calculations, since the only precaution regarded as
necessary to the purpose of the research was to assure that
conditions in the various reactions were the same except for
the presence of the catalyst. Moreover, those who did attempt
to study the uncatalyzed reaction quantitatively found it very
difficult to obtain reproducible results, due to the many complicating factors involved. Some of the difficulties are
summarized by Reinders and Vles (27):

> ....neither Titoff (5) nor we could
> obtain a correct monomolecular reaction
> constant.... This can be caused by....
> change of pH and .... poisoning of the
> catalyst, as small amounts of negatively
> acting substances can always enter the
> solution during the reaction......

In 1941, Fuller and Crist reported their studies of the
absolute rate of the uncatalyzed reaction (43). They concluded
that it was first order with respect to the concentration of
sulfite. They took no account, however, of variations of pH
during the reaction, nor of the resulting changes of the ionic
composition of the reaction mixture, even though such changes
were indicated clearly by the dissociation constants for sulfurous
acid which had been reported by Jellinek (44) and latter corrected
by Kolthoff (45). A still more recent study by Winkelman (46)
using a technique similar to that of the Italian workers (40, 41,
42), suffers from the same deficiency.

In 1951, Abel proposed a revised mechanism, involving
various oxygen ions and radicals (47, 48), and cited the data

of Fuller and Crist (43) in support of his conclusions. In the
first of these articles, 135 references are listed to articles
which either deal directly with the reaction in question, or
contain passing references to it in connection with another
subject. Abel also remarked upon the surprising paucity of
reliable data on the fundamental reaction, in view of the large
number of publications.

EXPERIMENTAL APPARATUS

The technique employed in our studies was basically
similar to that developed by Semerano, et al (40). A glass
electrode and a reference electrode, however, were immersed
permanently in the sample during the course of the reaction
to permit continuous monitoring and recording of the pH of the
solution. This was necessary in order to permit subsequent
calculation of the concentrations of the various ionic species.
A schematic representation of the reaction vessel assembly,
including the combination glass electrode and reference electrode
the dropping mercury electrode, and the glass stirring rod,
is presented in Figure 1. The stirrer is used only for the initial
mixing of the reactants and remains off during the course of
the reaction. The capillary extends into the cell to approximately one cm above the pool, and the diameter of the capillary
opening is such that the drop time is between 2 and 5 sec. A
cork is fitted into the top of the cell and provided with holes
for the capillary, pH electrode, and stirrer. The mercury flow
is regulated by positioning the reservoir level.

DETERMINATION OF DISSOLVED OXYGEN

It has been established experimentally that dissolved
oxygen may be determined polarographically in the presence
of sulfite without interference. This conclusion is based upon
two types of experiments. In the first type, a sample of 0.1 M
KCl containing dissolved oxygen was placed in the polarographic
cell. The dissolved oxygen wave was recorded as the applied
potential was varied from 0 to -2 v. Dissolved oxygen was
removed from the sample by a stream of pure nitrogen, and
the residual current was recorded over the same voltage range.
A new sample of the KCl solution was placed then in the cell,
and sodium sulfite solution was added in quantity sufficient to
react with all the dissolved oxygen present and leave an excess
of residual sulfite in the sample. After allowing time for complete removal of dissolved oxygen, currents were recorded
again at applied potentials from 0 to -2 v. The resulting curve

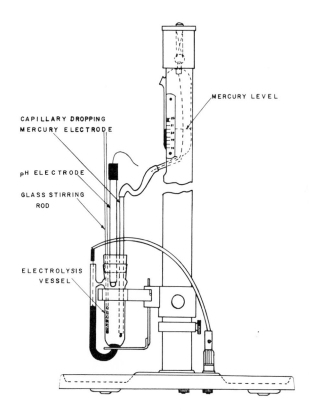

CAPILLARY DROPPING
MERCURY ELECTRODE

MERCURY LEVEL

pH ELECTRODE

GLASS STIRRING
ROD

ELECTROLYSIS
VESSEL

FIGURE 1 DROPPING MERCURY ELECTRODE
ASSEMBLY.

coincided with the curve of residual current obtained after
deoxygenating the first sample with nitrogen, thus demonstrating the absence of a sulfite wave over the voltage range and
under the conditions employed. An example of the results of
this type of experiment is presented graphically in Figure 2

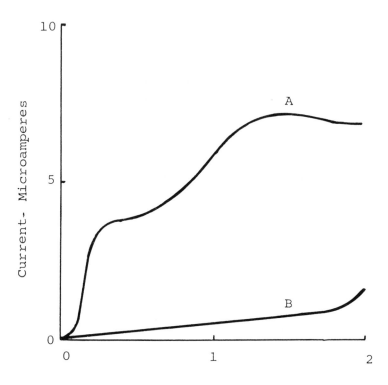

FIGURE 2   TYPICAL DISSOLVED OXYGEN POLAROGRAM.
SUPPORTING ELECTROLYTE, KCl OR
Na_2SO_4.   CURVE A: DISSOLVED OXYGEN
PRESENT, APPROXIMATELY 7 mg/l.
CURVE B: DISSOLVED OXYGEN ABSENT,
SULFITE PRESENT OR ABSENT.

The reduction of oxygen to H_2O_2 is indicated by the first wave:

$$O_2 + 2\,H^+ + 2\,\bar{e}\;-\quad\quad H_2O_2 \text{ (acid solution)} \quad\quad (14\text{-}1)$$

or:

$$O_2 + 2\,H_2O + 2\,\bar{e}\;-\!\!-\;\blacktriangleright H_2O_2 + 2\,OH^- \text{ (alkaline } (14\text{-}2)\text{ solution)}$$

The second wave corresponds to the reduction of oxygen to water:

$$O_2 + 4 H^+ + 4 \bar{e} \qquad 2 H_2O \text{ (acid solution)} \qquad (14\text{-}3)$$

or:

$$O_2 + 2 H^+ + 4 \bar{e} \qquad \text{--}2 OH^- \text{ (alkaline solution)} \quad (14\text{-}4)$$

The same type of experiment has been performed using Na_2SO_4 instead of KCl as the supporting electrolyte with the same results.

The above type of experiment established that the presence of sulfite in solution produces no polarographic wave under the employed experimental conditions. Hence, no interference arises from the polarographic reduction of sulfite nor from the occurrence of overlapping waves. Proof that a given concentration of dissolved oxygen produces the same polarographic diffusion current in the presence of sulfite as in its absence is more difficult to obtain for two reasons. First, under many conditions, sulfite and dissolved oxygen begin to react as soon as they are in contact. Second, the presence of sulfite completely invalidates the Winkler method of measuring dissolved oxygen so that no standard is available for comparison with the oxygen concentrations indicated polarographically (49). Consequently, it is necessary to establish this point by indirect evidence. Experimentally, the problem has been approached by mixing sulfite solutions with solutions of known dissolved oxygen concentration in the polarographic cell and following the diffusion current of dissolved oxygen at a fixed electrode potential. The resulting curves of oxygen concentration vs. time (Figure 3) must be extrapolated to zero time since the turbulence resulting from introduction and mixing of the sample materials produces increased current during the first several seconds. The relation between the current values thus obtained and the known oxygen concentrations agrees with the relation in the absence of sulfite, as shown in Figure 4. Although this evidence is somewhat indirect, it corroborates the indications of earlier work which suggested that the polarographic determination of dissolved oxygen is applicable in the presence of waste sulfite liquor from the manufacture of paper pulp and hence presumably in the presence of sulfites. Its applicability was proposed by Rand and Heukelekian (50), and subsequently confirmed by Busch and Sawyer (51), and Levine and Williams (52).

The technique employed for standardizing the sulfite

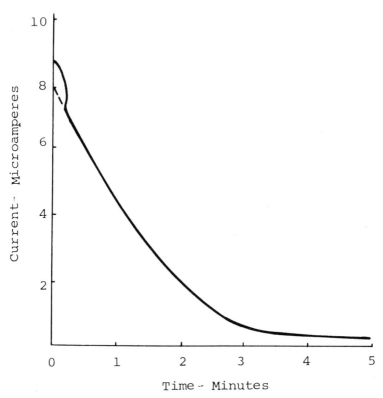

FIGURE 3   TYPICAL REACTION CURVE OF SULFITE
            AND DISSOLVED OXYGEN. OXYGEN
            CONCENTRATIONS RECORDED POLARO-
            GRAPHICALLY. NO SUPPORTING
            ELECTROLYTE: APPLIED POTENTIAL,
            1. 80 v. INITIAL DISSOLVED OXYGEN
            CONCENTRATION, 8 mg/l (1. 0 meq/l).
            INITIAL SULFITE CONCENTRATION,
            APPROXIMATELY 4 meq/l.

solutions is: 20. 0-ml of standard 0. 05 N $K_2Cr_2O_7$ are placed
in an Erlenmeyer flask, approximately 15-ml of concentrated
H_2SO_4 are added, and followed by 10. 0-ml of sulfite solution.
After diluting to approximately 250-ml, the excess dichromate
is titrated with $Fe(NH_4)_2 (SO_4)_2$. The endpoint is indicated by

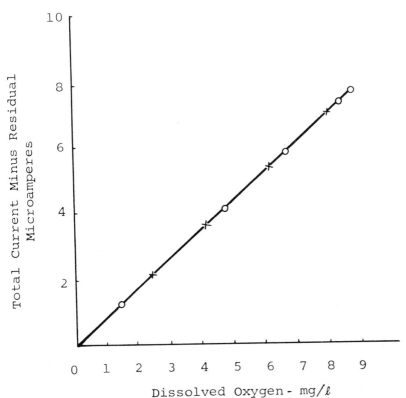

FIGURE 4   DIFFUSION CURRENT AS A FUNCTION
OF DISSOLVED OXYGEN CONCENTRATION.
SUPPORTING ELECTROLYTE KCl OR
Na_2SO_4; APPLIED POTENTIAL, 1.80 v.

o Points obtained by deaeration with nitrogen.
x Points obtained by extrapolation of sulfite
deoxygenation curves.

Ferroin (orthophenanthroline-ferrous sulfate complex).

To prepare for the polarographic measurement of dissolved
oxygen concentrations, it is necessary to establish the relation
between the concentration and the diffusion current under the
conditions to be used in the determinations.   Although theoretical
derivation of the relation is possible, it is usually simpler as

well as more accurate to determine the relation experimentally
because of the approximations involved in the derivation. The
experimental procedure is: from a large stock of distilled water,
50-ml are transferred by pipette to the polarographic cell with
as little aeration as possible; 0.5-ml of 0.1 N Na_2SO_4 is added
as a supporting electrolyte; a potential of -1.8 v is applied to
the cell, and the resulting current is recorded. Deaeration of
the sample by a stream of pure nitrogen is started. Meanwhile,
distilled water from the large stock is transferred by siphoning
to a standard BOD bottle, and its dissolved oxygen determined
by the Winkler method (49). After the sample in the polarographic
cell has deaerated for at least five mins, the nitrogen tube is
raised above the liquid level and the residual current is observed,
with the same potential applied as in the initial current observation. The dissolved oxygen content of the stock then is increased
by aeration or decreased by diffused nitrogen, and the procedure
is repeated. When a sufficient number of points has been observed,
a graph is prepared showing the relation between dissolved oxygen,
as indicated by the Winkler method, and the difference between
initial current and residual current in the polarographic test.
The concentration of inorganic salts in the solutions used in this
work produce fairly high conductivities, resulting generally in a
linear relation between dissolved oxygen and current change
(Figure 4).

    In preparation of the standard curve, the amount of Na_2SO_4
added as a supporting electrolyte is approximately equivalent
to the lowest concentration of sodium sulfite to be used in the
subsequent experiments. At this concentration, a maximum is
evident on the first plateau of the polarogram of dissolved oxygen
whereas the shape of the second plateau is perfectly normal.
Since the diffusion current of oxygen is always well defined on
the second plateau, a single reading is taken with the applied
potential set at -1.8 v and the entire polarogram is not recorded.

    Figure 3 presents an example of the change of current
with time which results when sulfite is introduced into a sample
of distilled water containing dissolved oxygen in the polarographic
cell. The decrease in current is proportional to the decrease
is dissolved oxygen concentration which, in turn, is proportional
to the decrease in total sulfite. The partition of the total sulfite
between sulfite ion and bisulfite ion is a function of the known
pH of the system, and the dissociation constant (45). Thus, the
reaction rate and the concentrations of dissolved oxygen, sulfite
ion, bisulfite ion, and hydrogen ion are known for each point

on the reaction curve. The relation between the rate and each
of the concentrations then may be examined. In order to reduce
the number of variables in this system, the type of experiment
used in establishing the suitability of the polarographic method
in the presence of sulfite has been repeated using phosphate
buffer as the supporting electrolyte in order to control the $[H^+]$.
It was found that under these conditions, however, that decomposition of the solvent began below the potential applied for the
determination of dissolved oxygen. Since the base line became
quite steep at the point to be used, any variations of applied
potential due, for example, to fluctuations of line voltage or
drift of the potential control circuit, produced serious errors
in the dissolved oxygen determination. There was also a problem in proving that any buffer added to the system had no effect
upon the reaction rate. In the end, it was considered preferable
to treat the $[H^+]$ as one of the variables rather than trying to
hold it fixed during the course of the reaction.

EXPERIMENTAL PROCEDURE

The laboratory procedure for collection of the kinetic
data was:

a. The sodium sulfite solution was standardized as
   described in a previous section.

b. The distilled water was stored in pyrex containers
   at $20\,^{\circ}C$ (the temperature at which all experiments
   were performed), and the pH was adjusted for each
   run by the addition to a portion of distilled water of
   the required amount of H_2SO_4 or NaOH.

c. The initial dissolved oxygen concentration of the
   distilled water was measured by means of the polarograph and standard curve (Figure 4) or the Winkler
   Method (49).

d. The reaction vessel was filled with a known volume of
   distilled water, and the cork covering the reaction
   vessel was positioned so that no air remained between
   the water and the cork, and the water level reached
   just to a small (1 mm) notch cut in one edge of the cork.
   The stirrer was then turned on. The sulfite solution
   was added through the notch in the cork by means of
   an accurately calibrated syringe. A small volume of
   water was displaced, therefore, through the notch,
   leaving a known volume within the cell, and sealing
   the notch against the entry of any significant amount

of oxygen from the atmosphere. The stirrer was run for nine sec after the addition of the sulfite, then stopped. The diffusion current was recorded automatically by a recording polarograph attached to the dropping mercury electrode and the pool, and the pH value was indicated continuously by a meter attached to the glass and reference electrodes, and recorded manually from time to time during the run.

e. At the end of the experiment, the reaction mixture was deaerated with a stream of pure nitrogen (if any residual dissolved oxygen remained), and the residual current was read. Then, by the use of the standard curve, the value of the dissolved oxygen concentration was obtained for each point of interest on the current record. Time intervals were determined from the known chart speed of the recorder.

Typical data are presented in Tables I and II. For each point in each run, the total sulfite concentration was calculated by subtracting the dissolved oxygen concentration at each point from the initial dissolved oxygen concentration (both expressed in moles/l), then subtracting this difference from the initial total sulfite concentration. Then, by means of the known pH of the system and the dissociation constant, the partition between sulfite ion and bisulfite ion was calculated for each point.

To determine the reaction rate at each point, the total sulfite concentration was plotted against time. Tangents to the line were constructed at each point. Short equal segments of the line were marked off each side of the point. The enclosed portion of the curve, since it was short, was considered to represent a negligible change of curvature. Construction of a perpendicular line through the point and another line perpendicular to the first then gives the tangent. Figure 5 illustrates this procedure for a few points in Run 9.

After the rates were determined, they were plotted against concentrations of sulfite and bisulfite ion. No relation between bisulfite ion concentration and rate was evident. The rectilinear plot of rate vs. sulfite ion concentration showed a definite, but non-linear relation between the two variables. The curvature suggested a possible relation of the rate to some power ($\neq$ 1) of the sulfite ion concentration. This possibility was explored by plotting the equation:

$$\log (\text{rate}) = x \log \left[SO_3^{-2} \right] + \log f \qquad (14\text{-}5)$$

TABLE I   TABULATION OF TIME, pH (H$^+$), AND
DISSOLVED OXYGEN CONCENTRATION
(DO) FOR RUNS 12, 13, 14A, and 14B

Initial Total Sulfite Conc = 89.94 x 10^{-5} mole/l
Initial Dissolved Oxygen Conc = 7.70 mg/l

Run	Point	Time min	pH	(H+) mole/l	DO (a) mg/l
12	1	0.05	7.70	19.95 x 10^{-8}	5.30
12	2	0.10	7.70	19.95 x 10^{-8}	4.75
12	3	0.20	7.70	19.95 x 10^{-8}	4.25
12	4	0.30	7.68	20.89 x 10^{-8}	3.75
12	5	0.40	7.65	22.39 x 10^{-8}	3.25
12	6	0.60	7.65	22.39 x 10^{-8}	2.53
12	7	0.80	7.60	25.12 x 10^{-8}	1.95
12	8	1.00	7.60	25.12 x 10^{-8}	1.35
12	9	1.20	7.55	28.18 x 10^{-8}	0.80
12	10	1.50	7.50	31.62 x 10^{-8}	0.30
12	11	1.80	7.45	35.48 x 10^{-8}	0.00
13	1	0.10	6.80	15.85 x 10^{-8}	4.75
13	2	0.20	6.75	17.78 x 10^{-8}	3.70
13	3	0.30	6.70	19.95 x 10^{-8}	2.90
13	4	0.40	6.65	22.39 x 10^{-8}	2.27
13	5	0.50	6.60	25.12 x 10^{-8}	1.80
13	6	0.60	6.55	28.18 x 10^{-8}	1.40
13	7	0.70	6.50	31.62 x 10^{-8}	1.13
13	8	1.00	6.43	37.15 x 10^{-8}	0.83
13	9	1.60	6.20	63.10 x 10^{-8}	0.65
13	10	2.80	6.10	79.43 x 10^{-8}	0.60
14A	1	0.10	7.20	6.310 x 10^{-8}	4.70
14A	2	0.20	7.15	7.079 x 10^{-8}	3.60
14A	3	0.30	7.13	7.413 x 10^{-8}	2.87
14A	4	0.40	7.10	7.943 x 10^{-8}	2.28
14A	5	0.50	7.05	8.913 x 10^{-8}	1.75
14A	6	0.60	7.00	10.00 x 10^{-8}	1.35
14A	7	0.70	7.00	10.00 x 10^{-8}	0.90
14A	8	0.80	6.95	11.22 x 10^{-8}	0.60
14A	9	1.00	6.88	13.18 x 10^{-8}	0.40
14A	10	1.20	6.80	15.85 x 10^{-8}	0.30

Table I - cont'd

Run	Point	Time min	pH	(H^+) mole/l	DO mg/l
14B	1	0.07	7.30	5.012×10^{-8}	5.07
14B	2	0.12	7.25	5.623×10^{-8}	4.37
14B	3	0.20	7.22	6.026×10^{-8}	3.26
14B	4	0.30	7.20	6.310×10^{-8}	2.48
14B	5	0.40	7.15	7.079×10^{-8}	1.90
14B	6	0.50	7.10	7.943×10^{-8}	1.38
14B	7	0.60	7.07	8.511×10^{-8}	0.90
14B	8	0.70	7.02	9.550×10^{-8}	0.55
14B	9	1.00	6.90	12.590×10^{-8}	0.25

(a)   DO (mole/l as O) = DO (mg/l) $\cdot$ 6.25 $\cdot$ 10^{-5}

TABLE II   RAW DATA FROM TYPICAL EXPERIMENTS

Initial Conc of Sulfite Plus Bisulfite Ions
Run 9: 2.02×10^{-3} M
Run 17: 0.8994×10^{-3} M
Run 22: 1.6854×10^{-3} M
Run 23: 1.6854×10^{-3} M
Initial Dissolved Oxygen Conc
Run 9: 7.7 mg/l
Run 17: 7.7 mg/l
Run 22: 7.54 mg/l
Run 23: 7.54 mg/l

Run	Point	Time min	pH	(H^+) mole/l	DO mg/l
9	1	0.10	5.70	1.995×10^{-8}	7.13
9	2	0.20	5.65	2.239×10^{-8}	6.05
9	3	0.40	5.55	2.819×10^{-8}	5.35
9	4	0.60	5.45	2.548×10^{-8}	4.75
9	5	1.00	5.27	5.371×10^{-8}	4.12
9	6	1.50	5.00	10.000×10^{-8}	3.65
9	7	2.00	4.60	25.120×10^{-8}	3.40
9	8	3.00	4.20	60.310×10^{-8}	3.20
9	9	4.00	4.10	79.430×10^{-8}	3.14
9	10	9.00	4.00	100.000×10^{-8}	3.10

Table II - cont'd

Run	Point	Time min	pH	(H^+) mole/l	DO mg/l
17	1	0.10	5.90	1.259×10^{-8}	7.00
17	2	0.30	5.85	1.413×10^{-8}	6.27
17	3	0.70	5.75	1.778×10^{-8}	5.85
17	4	1.30	5.60	2.512×10^{-8}	5.57
17	5	2.20	5.40	3.98×10^{-8}	5.25
17	6	4.10	4.80	15.85×10^{-8}	4.95
17	7	6.30	4.45	35.48×10^{-8}	4.80
17	8	9.30	4.35	44.67×10^{-8}	4.75
22	1	0.12	6.45	3.548×10^{-7}	6.30
22	2	0.30	6.40	3.981×10^{-7}	5.93
22	3	0.60	6.35	4.467×10^{-7}	5.52
22	4	1.00	6.30	5.012×10^{-7}	5.00
22	5	1.50	6.25	5.623×10^{-7}	4.50
22	6	2.00	6.17	6.761×10^{-7}	4.07
22	7	2.50	6.10	7.943×10^{-7}	3.67
22	8	3.00	6.05	8.913×10^{-7}	3.40
22	9	4.00	5.95	11.22×10^{-7}	2.95
22	10	6.00	5.70	19.95×10^{-7}	2.42
22	11	9.00	5.35	44.67×10^{-7}	1.72
22	12	13.00	5.00	100.00×10^{-7}	1.54
22	13	20.00	4.70	199.50×10^{-7}	1.40
23	1	0.10	6.35	4.467×10^{-7}	5.70
23	2	0.40	6.25	5.623×10^{-7}	5.07
23	3	0.70	6.20	6.310×10^{-7}	4.64
23	4	1.10	6.15	7.079×10^{-7}	4.14
23	5	1.70	6.05	8.913×10^{-7}	3.52
23	6	2.20	5.95	11.220×10^{-7}	3.08
23	7	2.90	5.80	15.85×10^{-7}	2.53
23	8	4.00	5.45	35.48×10^{-7}	2.03
23	9	5.00	5.10	79.43×10^{-7}	1.72
23	10	6.00	4.90	125.90×10^{-7}	1.60

The log plot, which appears in Figures 6 and 7, shows that the
rate is proportional to some power (x) of the sulfite ion concentration and some other factor f. The value of x is given by
the slope of the plots whereas log f is given by the intercepts.
From numerous experiments, including those represented in
Figure 6, the best value of x in the pH range from 6.5 to 7.7,
was found to be 2.33 ± 0.01.

TABLE III   TABULATION OF TSO_3 (SO_3^{-2}), (HSO_3^-),
RATE, AND f_A FOR RUNS 12, 13, 14A, and 14B

Run	Point	$TSO_3 \times 10^5$ mole/l	$(SO_3^{-2}) \times 10^5$ mole/l	$(HSO_3^-) \times 10^5$ mole/l	Rate mole/l/min	$f_A \times 10^{-8}$ min^{-1}	
12	2	71.50	54.32	17.18	39.35	1,594	
12	3	68.38	51.95	16.43	31.80	1,429	
12	4	65.25	49.02	16.23	30.00	1,544	
12	5	62.13	45.86	16.27	27.80	1,671	
12	6	57.63	42.54	15.09	21.50	1,539	
12	7	54.0	38.63	15.37	17.64	1,582	
12	8	50.25	35.95	14.30	17.50	1,855	
12	9	46.81	32.36	14.45	14.50	1,964	
12	10	43.69	29.10	14.59	7.85	1,362	(a
13	2	64.94	17.01	47.93	63.00	38,180	
13	3	59.94	14.40	45.54	44.50	39,750	
13	4	56.00	12.31	43.69	32.50	41,840	
13	5	53.06	10.65	42.41	29.14	52,570	
13	6	50.56	9.25	41.31	22.22	55,670	
13	7	48.88	8.13	40.75	9.70	32,830	
13	8	47.00	6.82	40.18	3.57	18,200	(a
13	9	45.88	4.17	41.17	1.62	26,580	(a
14A	2	64.31	30.31	34.00	50.00	7,886	
14A	3	59.75	27.47	32.28	39.80	7,895	
14A	4	56.06	24.82	31.24	34.40	8,643	
14A	5	52.75	21.86	30.89	29.50	9,964	
14A	6	50.25	19.44	30.81	27.00	11,985	
14A	7	47.44	18.35	29.09	26.50	13,460	
14A	8	45.56	16.40	29.16	12.40	8,182	(a
14A	9	44.31	14.34	29.97	5.00	4,510	(a
14B	2	69.13	36.55	32.58	97.50	9,942	
14B	3	62.19	31.81	30.38	62.50	8,881	
14B	4	57.31	28.655	28.655	42.00	7,550	
14B	5	53.69	25.30	28.39	34.00	8,170	
14B	6	50.44	22.33	28.11	30.30	9,739	
14B	7	47.44	20.22	27.22	26.50	10,735	
14B	8	45.25	18.00	27.25	17.00	9,030	(a

(a)   These points are not shown in Figure 8.   Dissolved oxygen concentration less than 0.8 mg/l.

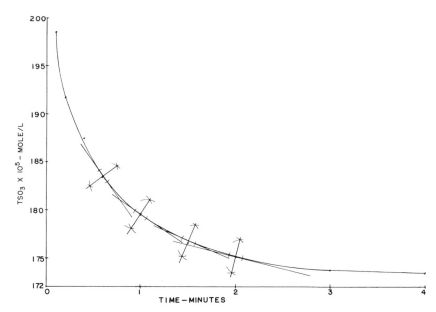

FIGURE 5   GRAPHICAL DETERMINATION OF REACTION
              RATES (RUN 9).

It was then possible to calculate f for each point in each
run, in order to examine its relation to any of the known
variables.   Representative values appear in Table III.
     Figure 8 is a log plot of the values of f against the $\left[H^+\right]$.
From plots of this kind, it was concluded that the best value
of f is $1.48 \times 10^{21} \times \left[H^+\right]^{1.58}$.
     Thus, the overall rate equation, for the pH range from
6.5 to 7.7, at 20°C is:

$$\text{rate} = 1.48 \times 10^{21} \left[H^+\right]^{1.58} \left[SO_3^{-2}\right]^{2.33} \qquad (14\text{-}6)$$

This equation applied at concentrations of dissolved oxygen
above 0.8 mg/l.   Lower concentrations of dissolved oxygen
appear to have some influence upon the reaction rate, but our
data are not yet extensive enough in this range to permit
conclusions.
     At pH values between 4.2 and 6.4, a different equation
applies.   From plots like those presented in Figure 7, it was
found that the best value of x, the power of the sulfite ion concentration related to the rate, was 1.06.   In other words, in

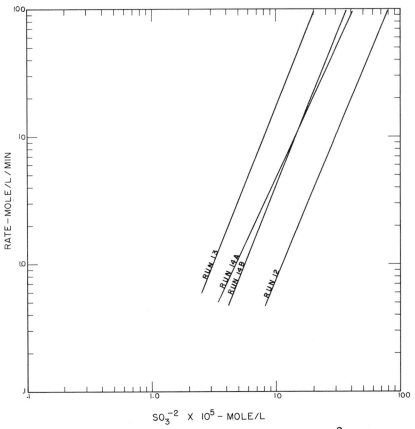

FIGURE 6   RELATIONSHIP OF RATE TO SO_3^{-2}
CONCENTRATION.

pH Range 6.5 to 7.7

this range, the reaction becomes first order with respect to
the concentration of sulfite ion as reported, for example by
Fuller and Crist (43). There is, however, a second factor
involved which has not yet been shown to bear a regular relation
to any of the known and controlled conditions in our experiments.

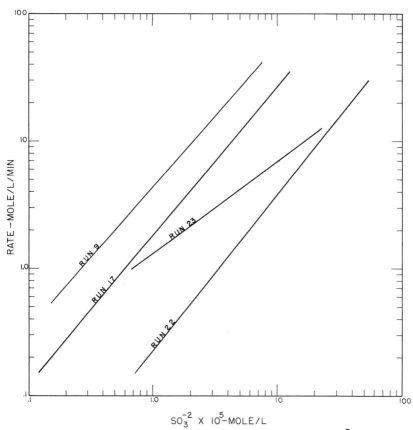

FIGURE 7   RELATIONSHIP OF RATE TO SO_3^{-2}
CONCENTRATION,

pH Range 4.2 to 6.4

In particular, it does not seem to be dependent upon the square
root of $[H^+]$, as suggested by Fuller and Crist (43) and by
Abel (47, 48). These results thus confirm the conclusion of
Fuller and Crist that the rate is independent of the concentration
of bisulfite ion, and that between pH 2.9 and 3.2 the rate decreases
in a complicated manner.

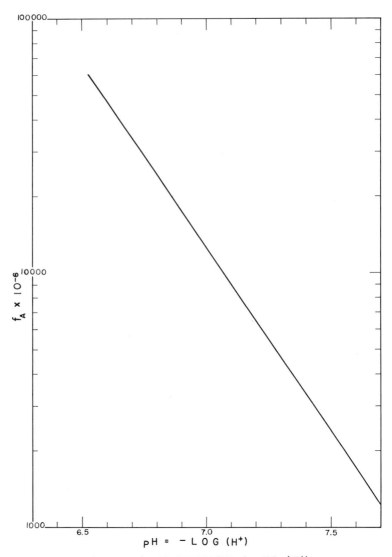

FIGURE 8   RELATIONSHIP OF f_A TO (H^+).

    The work reported herein does not clarify nor further
confuse the question of the reaction mechanism.   The fractional
powers of the concentrations which appear in the equation above
pH 6.5 indicate a complex order.   Many theories have been

advanced for reactions of this kind in general and for this one
in particular. One of the most common views is that such a
reaction involves a chain in which free radicals or other activated
states occur which do not appear in the final products in appreciable proportions. Such a mechanism may well be involved here.
but the experimental support for the theory is not yet entirely
adequate.

SUMMARY

The results of this work define the rate of the reaction of
sulfite with dissolved oxygen as a function of sulfite ion concen-
ration and $[H^+]$ over the pH range between 6.5 and 7.7, dissolved oxygen concentrations greater than 0.8 mg/l, and at a
temperature of 20°C. Under these conditions the rate is:

$$dC/dt = 1.48 \times 10^{21} \left[SO_3^{-2} \right]^{2.33} \left[H^+ \right]^{1.58}$$

When the dissolved oxygen concentration is less than
approximately 0.8 mg/l, it becomes rate controlling. No
extensive data, however, are available in this range to formulate
a rate equation at this time.

It has been shown also that the rate is dependent upon the
first power of the sulfite ion concentration, and some undefined
variable, f, over the pH range from 4.2 to 6.4, with dissolved
oxygen concentrations greater than 0.8 mg/l and the temperature
20°C.

The rate was independent of bisulfite ion concentration for
all cases, and was not related to the square root of the $[H^+]$ as
suggested by some previous authors.

The rate is complex and, at this time, no single rate
equation describes the whole range of the pertinent variables.

ACKNOWLEDGEMENT

This work was supported by the USDHEW, Public Health
Service, Washington, D.C., through Research Grant WP-74.

LITERATURE CITED

1. Bigelow, S.L., Z Physik Chem, 26, 493 (1897).

2. Meyer, L., Ber Deut Chem Ges, 20, 3058 (1887).

3. Jorissen, W.P., Z Physik Chem, 23, 667 (1897).

4. Young, S.W., J Am Chem Soc, 23, 297 (1902).

5. Titoff, A., Z Physik Chem, 45, 641 (1903).

6. Berg, A., Compt Rend, 138, 907 (1904).

7. Baubigny, H., Compt Rend, 154, 434 (1912).

8. Mathews, J.H and L.H. Dewey, J Phys Chem, 17, 211 (1913).

9. Saillard, E., Compt Rend, 160, 318 (1915).

10. Mathews, J.H. and M.E. Weeks, J Am Chem Soc, 39, 635 (1917).

11. Milbauer, J. and J. Pazourek, Bull Soc Chim France, (4), 31, 676 (1922).

12. Moureu, C. and C. Durfraisse, Compt Rend, 178, 1861 (1924).

13. Mason, R.B. and J. H. Mathews, J Phys Chem, 30, 414 (1926

14. Moureu, C., et al, Compt Rend, 183, 408 (1926).

15. Mittra, N.N. and N.R. Dhar, Z Anorg Allgem Chem, 122, 145 (1922).

16. Dhar, N.R., J Phys Chem, 28, 948 (1924).

17. Moureu, C., et al, Compt Rend, 179, 237 (1924).

18. Moureu, C. and C. Dufraisse, Chem Rev, 3, 113 (1926).

19. Moureu, C. and C. Dufraisse, Compt Rend, 185, 1545 (1927).

20. Moureu, C. and C. Dufraisse, Compt Rend, 186, 196 (1928).

21. Backstrom, H.L.J., J Am Chem Soc, 49, 1460 (1927).

22. Haber, F. and R. Willstatter, Ber Deut Chem Ges, 64, 2844 (1931).

23. Haber, F. and O.H. Wansbrough-Jones, Z Physik Chem, Abteil B, 18, 103 (1932).

24. Bailey, K.C. and V.H. ffrench, J Chem Soc (London) 1931, 420 (1931).

25. Hagg, G., Z Physik Chem, Abteil B, 18, 199 (1932).

26. Kenner, J., Ber Deut Chem Ges, 65, 705 (1932).

27. Reinders, W. and S.I. Vles, Rec Trav Chem, 44, 249 (1925).

28. Alyea, H.N. and H.L.J. Backstrom, J Am Chem Soc, 51, 90 (1929).

29. Chakravarti, S.N. and N.R. Dhar, J Phys Chem, 34, 2749 (1930).

30. Briner, E., Helv Chim Acta, 14, 804 (1931).

31. Jeu, K.K. and H.N. Alyea, J Am Chem Soc, 55, 575 (1933).

32. Hoather, R.C. and C.F. Goodeve, Trans Faraday Soc, 30, 627 (1934).

33. Hoather, R.C. and C.F. Goodeve, Trans Faraday Soc, 30, 630 (1934).

34. Hoather, R.C. and C.F. Goodeve, Trans Faraday Soc, 30, 1149 (1934).

35. Haother, R.C. and C.F. Goodeve, Trans Faraday Soc, 30, 1156 (1934).

36. Bassett, H. and A.J. Henry, J Chem Soc (London), p 914 (1935).

37. Backstrom, H.L.J., Z Physik Chem, Abteil B, 25, 122 (1934).

38. Briner, E. and H. Biedermann, Helv Chim Acta, 16, 548 (1934).

39. Bassett, H. and W.G. Parker, J Chem Soc, (London), p 1540 (1951).

40. Semerano, G., et al, Gazz Chim Ital, 79, 395 (1949).

41. Riccoboni, L., et al, Gazz Chim Ital, 79, 419 (1949).

42. Foffani, A., et al, Gazz Chim Ital, 79, 485 (1949)

43. Fuller, E. C. and R. H. Crist, J Am Chem Soc, 63, 1644 (1941).

44. Jellinek, K., Z Physik Chem, 76, 257 (1911).

45. Kolthoff, J. M., Z Anorgan Chem, 109, 69 (1920).

46. Winkelman, D., Z Elektrochem, 59, 891 (1955).

47. Abel, E., Monatsh Chem, 82, 39 (1951).

48. Abel, E., Monatsh Chem, 89, 547 (1951).

49. Standard Methods for the Examination of Water and Waste Water, 11th Ed, American Public Health Assoc, New York, N. Y., (1960).

50. Rand, M. C. and H. Heukelekian, Sew Ind Wastes, 23, 1141 (1951).

51. Busch, A. W. and C. N. Sawyer, Anal Chem, 24, 1887 (1952).

52. Levine, H. S. and O. J. Williams, Anal Chem, 26, 1297 (1954).

E. Edgerley, Jr.
R. T. Skrinde
D. W. Ryckman
Washington University

THE APPLICATION
OF OXIDIZING CHEMICALS
TO ORGANIC COMPOUNDS

The presence of organic contaminants in natural waters has been receiving increased attention over the past several years. Technology for removal of organic matter from water has not kept pace with the problems that have resulted from: (a) increased quantities used; (b) large numbers of new products and formulations placed on the market; and (c) many new sources for entry of organics into the environment. Many organic materials are reaching water courses and water supplies, resulting in an impairment of water quality (1) and influencing the effectiveness of existing treatment methods (2).

Water supplied, following conventional treatment practices often prompts consumer complaints, even though the product may have a clear, sparkling appearance. Objectionable characteristics causing such complaints range from taste and odors, and/or color in the water, to a tendency for the water to foam. Not only are organic contaminants ineffectively removed by conventional treatment practices, there are significant indications that under certain conditions, increases are experienced in the dissolved organic content of water as a result of certain conventional treatment practices (3).

405

The organic chemical compounds utilized in industry and agriculture today are numerous and complex. The physiological effects of most of these compounds, following long-term human consumption, have not been determined as yet. Effective removal of these contaminating components through application of oxidizing chemicals could result in the more effective utilization of our water resources. Chemicals are now being utilized increasingly in present day water treatment practice to oxidize trace organic components in order to eliminate their detrimental effects. While many of these chemicals were employed initially for disinfection, their further uses as oxidants for removal of organics and of inorganics, such as iron and manganese, have developed rapidly.

The increasing importance of controlling tastes and odors in public water supplies is reflected in the larger number of water treatment facilities practicing some form of taste and odor control. This number has more than doubled in the last 15 years, and today includes more than 300 plants. A number of processes has been employed to remove taste and odor from domestic water supplies. In chronological order, these include several variations of chlorine-ammonia treatment, super-chlorination, break-point and free residual chlorination, chlorine-chlorine dioxide treatment, and, currently, application of various other forms of chemical oxidants. The fundamental objective of water treatment always has been to provide a safe and palatable water supply. Control of tastes and odors with chemical oxidants is feasible and appropriate.

Application of chemical oxidants has indicated significant reductions in levels of biochemcial oxygen demand (BOD) and chemical oxygen demand (COD), which are present in water supplies as the result of organic pollution. The removal or neutralization of organic materials contributing to these indices of the pollutional load, through the utilization of selected chemical oxidants again indicates that chemical oxidation procedures are appropriate to water treatment practices.

Pollution caused by the large scale use of chemical toxicants or organic pesticides and herbicides has been publicized widely in recent reports and newspaper articles. Upsets in biological populations in our water bodies including fish kills or the disappearance of certain species of game fish from some of our lakes and streams due to the reduction of required levels of dissolved oxygen, have become common-place news items.

The problem, as related to toxic effects exerted on biological life, is described by new terminology, such as "micro-pollutants" or "micro-contaminants". These are pollutants, including organic as well as other trace materials, found in water supplies in almost negligible concentrations, which affect the biological populations of those waters. Some of these materials are resistent to, or even totally unaffected by today's conventional water and waste treatment practices. Since this concept almost always involves organic chemicals which are biologically resistant in low concentrations, these micro-pollutants must be dealt with effectively if this nation is to make the best use of its own natural resources. Again, chemical oxidation is considered effective and economically reasonable for many applications in light of exploratory laboratory and field studies which have been completed recently.

Organic fouling of ion exchange resins is a problem in practically every application in water treatment where surface waters are involved (4). Numerous attempts have been made to prevent the fouling by use of pre-treatment methods, different types of resins, and varying flow patterns. Most research efforts have been directed toward the type of compound causing the fouling and the ultimate disposition of the material once it is retained by the resin. More recently, results of screening tests appear to indicate that pre-treatment involving the chemical oxidation of certain of these organic contaminants will reduce, if not eliminate, the problem of organic fouling of ion exchange resins.

OXIDIZING CHEMICALS

Among the chemicals, certain basic ones have demonstrated their utility in reducing the concentration of organic contaminants; such as ozone, chlorine dioxide, chlorine, the peroxides, potassium permanganate, and sodium permanganate.

Ozone has been found to be specifically useful for the oxidization of alkyl benzene sulfonate, a principal component of synthetic surfactants. It has been shown that ozone functions also to reduce the foaming characteristics of waters contaminated with this compound (5). Other workers have found ozone effective in the removal of selected pesticides and phenolic compounds from aqueous solutions. This compound, which exhibits strong oxidizing properties, has not been evaluated fully because of factors associated with cost and availability, but its usefulness certainly warrants further study and investigation.

Chlorine is one of the better known oxidants of commercial importance, and ranks next to fluorine among the members of the halogen family in oxidation power. Chlorine has long been used for control of tastes and odors and microorganisms, including algae where copper sulfate utilization was not feasible. The many applications will cause chlorine to continue to be a chemical of great interest in the chemical oxidation of organics in water.

Chlorine dioxide is a very powerful and effective oxidizing agent which is readily available and is quite useful in water treatment processes. It has been found to be quite satisfactory in controlling taste and odor problems, and in oxidizing certain organics. On a weight basis, it has considerably greater oxidizing power than chlorine (2.5 times), and the compound can be easily handled. As it has not been widely studied, but its oxidizing power certainly justifies further study and evaluation for this purpose.

The characteristics of the peroxides, hydrogen and sodium are in general, quite similar. Both have been studied for use in water treatment. Under normal conditions, they are oxidants which produce nacent oxygen. When used in combination with other strong oxidants such as the permanganates, they act as reducing agents, and because of this, are not widely used in water treatment practice. While pesticides are not oxidized easily by peroxides, certain organic compounds, such as the alkyl benzene sulfonates, may be oxidized effectively by the peroxides under controlled conditions.

The permanaganates have been found generally to be effective as chemicals for the removal of tastes and odors, especially those which have their origin with the algae (6). Iron and manganese have been removed effectively from waters with permanganate. These oxidants are used to also remove and destroy certain organic materials; such as, phenols, cyanides, and related compounds contained in industrial waste waters which may be discharged into surface waters.

ENVIRONMENTAL FACTORS AFFECTING CHEMICAL OXIDATION

The use of chemical oxidants for dealing with trace organic pollutants found in surface waters is dependent upon several environmental factors. Reactions of the commonly used oxidants outlined previously are dependent upon such specific variables as temperature, pH, concentration of the oxidant, concentration and nature of the organics, and contact time. It has been observed also that the oxidant reaction rate is almost related directly to the concentration of the oxidant remaining as unreacted compound, thus closely approximating a first-order reaction.

In general, it appears that the best chemical oxidation results are obtained under alkaline, rather than acid conditions, and that, generally, inorganic contaminants in natural river water do not significantly affect the oxidation efficiency of the chemical oxidants previously described (7). In water treatment practice, the number of different organic constituents present may be large, and the reactants are mixed in what are extremely dilute solutions. This, plus relatively cool reaction temperatures, mean that the efficiencies, and perhaps even the nature of the oxidation reactions themselves, are modified greatly over that observed with high concentrations of oxidants and optimum reaction temperatures.

ORIGIN OF ORGANIC MATTER IN WATER

Types and Sources

Most of the specific information concerning characteristics of organic contaminants present in water have been obtained from carbon adsorption studies. In general, it may be stated, however, that these surface water contaminants range from specific industrial waste compounds to a broad classification of compounds entering through natural drainage. Significant quantities of organic pollutants have been shown to occur in all major rivers in the United States.

The relation of organic materials to certain environmental conditions; such as, the mineral and particulate content of surface waters, stream flow characteristics, and biological populations has been documented well. A literature review reveals that most studies on organic pollutants in water supplies have dealt with specific compounds; such as, synthetic detergents, phenolic compounds, cyanides, and pesticides. Also gaining considerable attention have been the nitrogen and phosphorous compounds because of their nutrient values in biological systems. No broad study of the entire spectrum of compounds has been attempted because it has been estimated that perhaps more than 3000 organics may be involved.

The sources of organic materials in surface waters vary greatly, when classified on the basis of artificial vs. natural origin. Microorganisms have proven to be the cause of certain odors which emanate from compounds resulting from the activity of micro-biotic cycles in nature. Decaying vegetation, in general, has been defined as a source of organic materials of

all types, but the specific nature of the compounds resulting
from decay has not been determined. Artificial industrial
chemical wastes are probably the major cause of organic
contamination of our surface waters. The potential for domestic
wastes, specifically sewage, to act as a contaminant by releasing
organic components to surface waters is well understood from
the standpoint of its ability to cause odors and to deplete the
dissolved oxygen in flowing streams. Figure 1 depicts the three
major sources of organic pollution to surface waters.

Quantitative Measurement in the Environment
        Considerable research has been accomplished to qualita-
tively and quantiatively measure the extent and nature of the
organic pollution of our streams. One of the principal methods
for capturing organic materials from polluted waters for measurement and identification is the carbon filter technique (8). This
technique involves the use of columnar carbon filters of a standard
design, through which 5000 gallon increments of contaminated
water are passed at flow rates between 0.25 and 0.50 gpm.
After contact with the water, the carbon is removed from the
filter apparatus and dried in a clean atmosphere. This dried
carbon is extracted then with chloroform or some other suitable
solvent, which is evaporated to leave a fraction containing a
variety of organic substances. Characterization of these
materials is accomplished in a variety of ways; solubility
separation, organoleptic studies, infrared analyses, and paper,
thin-layer, or gas-liquid chromatography.
        A wide variety of organic base, amphoteric, neutral, and
acid compounds has been resolved utilizing the carbon adsorption method whose efficiency is considered good. Consistently,
it has been shown that when two such filters are used in series,
approximately 90% of the organic materials applied to the
system is removed. The data developed from many studies
indicate that the materials recovered by use of the carbon filter
technique are representative of the typical organic components
of contaminated waters, provided the adsorptive capacity of
the activated carbon utilized is not exceeded (9). Extensive
examples of the measurement and identification of organics
contained in river waters, are the Missouri River Studies (10, 11).
        The Missouri River, for a distance of 840 miles above its
confluence with the Mississippi River at St. Louis, was selected
as the source for collection of samples since this water has been
shown to receive a wide variety of industrial, domestic, and

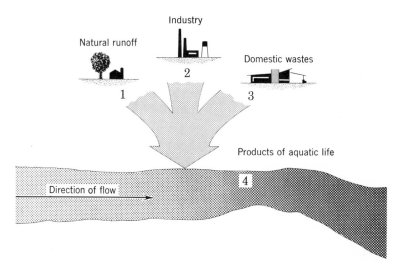

FIGURE 1   SOURCES OF ORGANIC COMPOUNDS.

natural organic chemical pollutants. One phase of these studies involved pre-treatment of the river water with sedimentation and diatomite filtration to remove turbidity without materially changing the other characteristics. The water then was passed through carbon filters in series following pH adjustments. Subsequently, the organic contaminants were extracted with chloroform and alcohol solvents that was followed by characterization studies, including the determination of COD, functional group analysis by solubility, partition and column chromatography, infrared and ultraviolet spectrographic analyses, and organoleptic measurements. In addition, physiochemical removal of the soluble organic materials with selected reactants was evaluated employing re-synthesized organic fortified water containing natural inorganic impurities. Removals of reactants were evaluated with the methods outlined above. In general, it has been shown that in Missouri River waters a definite interrelation exists between the various environmental factors previously discussed and the occurrence and removal of soluble organic pollutants.

Much effort has been made to overcome the taste and odor problems in the Missouri River Valley since the Missouri River is utilized for both wastewater discharge and potable water supplies. This work has been undertaken largely by the operators

of water treatment plants on the Missouri River and by Washington
University, where evaluation of the collected organic extracts
and the chemical oxidation of taste and odor compounds have been
subjects of research since 1956. The extent of the organic pollution problem can be seen in Figure 2 which presents average
concentrations of carbon chloroform extract organics in the
river as it flows from Yankton, South Dakota to St. Louis,
Missouri.

The major chemical oxidants of interest in these studies
are: chlorine, potassium permanganate, chlorine dioxide, and
ozone. These chemicals are, for all practical purposes, the
only chemical oxidants used for potable water treatment today.
The others previously mentioned are still being evaluated, and
have not found application as yet because of such factors as
prohibitive costs, toxic end-products, and restricted specific
reactions.

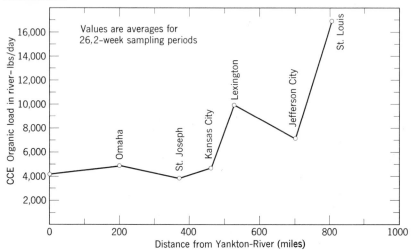

FIGURE 2   AVERAGE ORGANIC CONTENT OF
             MISSOURI RIVER WATER AS MEASURED
             BY CARBON CHLOROFORM EXTRACT.

EVALUATION OF CHEMICAL OXIDATION TECHNIQUES

Following the recovery and characterization of organic
contaminants from surface waters, the methods and techniques
relative to their chemical oxidation must be studied. This
phase of water quality control involves three broad areas of

interest; instrumentation for detection and measurement, studies
of oxidation phenomena using gross organic extract of complex
waste systems, and studies of oxidation phenomena utilizing
pure organic compounds singly and in various combinations.
A discussion of each of these areas is essential to an understanding of the problems related to chemical oxidation of organics.

Instrumentation for Detection and Measurement
     The term "instrumentation" as employed in this sense,
refers essentially to the instruments and techniques inherent
to the measurement of the following specific parameters which
are necessary and useful in evaluating the chemical oxidation
procedure:
     a. Threshold odor
     b. Taste by fish flesh tainting
     c. Physiological response by fish bioassay
     d. Chemical oxygen demand
     e. Biochemical oxygen demand
     f. Carbon by Van-Slyke wet combustion
     g. Carbon by total carbon infrared analyzer
     h. Spectrophotometry - ultraviolet and infrared
     i. Chromatography - gas, paper, column, thin layer
As a fundamental parameter, threshold odor numbers are useful
as a measurement for the presence of odorous materials in
water as a result of foreign substances, which are usually
organic. The threshold odor test is, at best, a gross measurement of the total concentration of such materials present prior
to treatment, and subsequently of their total concentration
following treatment. In this manner, the extent of removal of
such components by chemical oxidation may be determined
empirically by changes apparent in threshold odor values. The
test is specific to the sense of smell, and naturally is subject
to human reaction. Nevertheless, it has proven to be a most
valuable tool that gives information not obtainable by any other
technique.
     A taste sensation is objectively sweet, sour, bitter, or
salty, depending upon the nature of the substance perceived. It
is entirely possible to detect any tainting of fish flesh caused
by organic contaminants in stream waters. This technique also
has application as a measure or method of detection for the
levels of concentration of materials which can cause such tainting. It can be described as a gross survey method of the total
contaminant present like the odor test.

The use of bioassay data, developed as the result of physiological responses by fish to various organic contaminants in water, is well founded (12). In this type of test, the median tolerance limit (TL_m) for the various organic components is established, utilizing the procedures in Standard Methods (13). The precision of toxicity bioassay tests depends upon many factors that includes the uniformity of the test animal, the number of animals used, the number of concentrations within the test range, and the method for determination of the TL_m number. The median tolerance limit (TL_m), is defined for the prescribed measure of acute toxicity:

> The concentration of the tested material in a suitable diluent at which just 50% of the test animals are able to survive for a specified period of exposure (13).

The bioassay tests have good application, in general, to the evaluation of toxicity concentrations of various specific organic components in water. Due to possible variance in factors involved in the tests, however, the reported precision is about 10% under uniform conditions.

The COD determination is used widely for measurement of concentrations of organic materials in water. It involves the strong oxidizing environment of $K_2Cr_2O_7$ and H_2SO_4 in the catalytic presence of Ag_2SO_4, and a refluxing environment. Excess $K_2Cr_2O_7$ is determined by titration with $Fe(NH_4)_2(SO_4)_2$, using Ferroin indicator. The COD is calculated then from the amount of $K_2Cr_2O_7$ consumed. While the COD determination does not yield theoretical values for all substances of interest which are contained in water, it does represent a reliable parameter for studies on simplified systems containing specific organic substances. According to Standard Methods, the accuracy of the COD test, for most organic compounds, is on the order of 95 to 100% of the theoretical (13). Using Ag_2SO_4 catalyst, short straight chain alcohols and acids are oxidized to the extent of 85 to 95% or better.

The BOD test has been employed in the field of water pollution for a number of years. It essentially represents the amount of free oxygen consumed during the aerobic biochemical stabilization of organic constituents found in streams. A somewhat variable and empirical method is described in Standard Methods, which establishes the BOD in terms of the 5-day BOD and presents an acceptable dilution technique for its measurement under controlled laboratory conditions (13). Several modifications

have been proposed but the test, as currently employed, is the
best standard method for determination of the BOD. It is a
useful parameter for the determination of the strength of contaminating bio-degradable organics in water supplies. It would
be well to indicate here that the COD determination can be
correlated well with the BOD test for specific waste streams
and solutions of pure organic materials. The ratio of BOD to
COD does vary, however, from one waste to another or from
one pure compound to another.

The Van-Slyke wet combustion determination depends on
the combustion of organic material in the presence of strongly
oxidizing environments and upon the manometric measurement
of the CO_2 produced. Three types of analyses can be used:
the sub-microanalysis applicable with approximately 0.3 to 0.7
mg of carbon present; the micro-analysis for quantities of 2
to 3.5 mg of carbon; and macroanalysis when 8 to 15 mg of carbon
are present. In the presence of heated H_2SO_4 and H_3PO_4, and
K_2CrO_4 and KIO_3, the organic material is converted to CO_2
and other gases under a vacuum of 600 mm Hg. The CO_2 is
transferred then to an extraction chamber where it is absorbed
in an alkaline hydrazine solution. The combustion tube is dis-
connected, and the other gases evolved are ejected from the
chamber. Carbon dioxide is released then by the addition of a
lactic acid solution into the chamber. The CO_2 is absorbed
then in alkali, and the gaseous space differentials are measured
after which the carbon content of a sample is calculated. The
Van-Slyke method is a precise measurement of carbon, requiring a variety of steps and manipulations. An experienced
analyst usually can complete a determination in about a half
hour, obtaining accurate, reproducible results. The use of
the Van-Slyke determination in the field of water treatment,
however, is not widespread. Importance of the use of the
determination as a parameter lies in the fact that it permits
an actual determination of the carbon content of the samples
and makes possible studies on the rates of the various chemical
reactions. Rates of reaction are an essentially important
factor in evaluating chemical oxidation of organics contained
in water. Accuracy has been determined as close as 5% in some
cases (14). The determination consistently gives theoretical
yields of CO_2 with all types of organic compounds, with a mean
error on the order of approximately one part in 200. A large
number of compounds has been evaluated with excellent results.

The infrared carbonaceous analyzer is an instrument capable of the rapid determination of small amounts of organic matter in water and wastewaters (15). The method involves the rapid combustion of a small sample (20-μl) in a stream of oxygen within a temperature controlled tube. The sample is vaporized instantly and the organic components are oxidized to CO_2 and water. The gas stream is passed through an infrared analyzer sensitized to CO_2. The output of the infrared analyzer is recorded on a strip chart. These data can be evaluated against a calibration curve based on standard solutions of known carbon content (10). The results obtained from this method indicate that it is applicable for most water soluble organic compounds. Non-volatile organic substances, and those, such as CO_2 or light hydrocarbons, can be differentiated by determination of carbon both before and after stripping the sample solution with an inert gas. For effective waste stream control, a method is required that provides continuous sampling and rapid analysis. The carbon analyzer enables the detection of pollutants within 15 min and allows the immediate application of necessary corrective measures. The continuous analyzer has been used in industry as a stream monitor for water pollution control (15). The method is highly reliable, provides reproducible results, and obtains results rapidly as compared to the COD and BOD measurements.

The principle embodied in ultraviolet spectroscopy is the absorbance of ultraviolet light by the molecules of organic compounds containing a resonant structure. Such functional groups as the carboxyl, carbonyl, as well as certain aromatic structures of organic compounds and others are reported to cause absorbances in the ultraviolet light region. Some inorganic materials also absorb in this region, but they are not numerous. The utilization of ultraviolet spectroscopy for the measurement of concentrations of mixed organic materials recovered from natural water has been reported rather widely in the literature (16). The method can be highly useful for measuring organic materials in water. Ultraviolet spectrographs can be prepared on extracts of the organic chemical pollutants contained in water from double-beam recording spectrophotometers. Solutions having a total COD on the order of 50 mg can be effectively analyzed by this method, and the possibility of wide application in the field of water quality control is envisioned.

The use of infrared spectrophotometry for the characterizatic

of organic materials extracted from water by the carbon filter
technique has been reported (11). This method of characterization,
utilizing a double-beam infrared recording spectrophotometer,
enables the preparation of spectrographs of various extracts of
organic chemical pollutants. Utilizing this method of analysis,
the various fractions of organic chemical components of surface
waters may be separated into certain broad chemical groups
on the basis of evaluation following evaporation of chloroform
solutions on a NaCl cell. Chloroform suspensions of alcohol
extracts can be similarly evaporated on a salt cell. Since
absorption of organic compounds occurs in the infrared regions
of the electromagnetic spectrum to yield bands which are characteristic of linkages or bonds in the organic molecule, infrared
spectra can be applied to qualitative and quantitative analyses
of organic compounds (17). This instrumentation technique is
very applicable in the field of water quality control wherever
the chemical oxidation of chloroform extractables can be analyzed
in liquid cells. Applications involving the use of KBr pellets
enable scanning of the entire infrared region with continuous
recording of the absorption bands. These infrared spectra then
may be interpreted by review of published IR plots. Further
development of this method of analysis is required in the field
of water pollution control, but is predicted that its use will
become widespread.

Gas chromatography is a method of analysis which employs
a stationary phase composed of either a liquid or solid and a
gaseous mobile phase to separate the organic components of a
sample. The separation of the mixture is dependent upon a
number of conditions including vaporization of the sample,
adsorption properties of the sample on the solid phase of the
column, the sample to solvent interaction in the liquid phase,
and the molecular weight of the substance. Separation of the
sample usually is followed by the detection of the particular
organic substance by any one of a number of methods. Two
detectors which show great promise in the definition of organic
contaminants are the electron affinity detector and a microcoulo-
metric detector. Gas-liquid chromatographic techniques have
been employed rather extensively in pesticide work with water
pollution studies. Their sensitivity is very great for extremely
small quantities of certain organic materials in aqueous solutions.
Gas-liquid chromatography could be utilized effectively in chemical
oxidation studies as a screening measurement for removals of
specific organic pesticides and/or herbicides as an initial

evaluation measurement. The extreme sensitivity of the method
would tend to encourage its development for other applications
in the field of water treatment.

Paper chromatography has been used in water quality
evaluations primarily in the role of determining concentrations
of pesticides in food residues. The exact procedures have been
described in detail (18). Specific applications for the use of paper
chromatography must be developed before the method will have
a wide application in the field of organic contaminant resolution.
There is every reason to believe, however, that the method would
lend itself well to evaluation programs in chemical oxidation
techniques as a qualitative tool, although its lack of sensitivity
makes it doubtful that precise quantitation of separated materials
could be accomplished. Paper chromatography is fast and simple
to perform, and equipment costs are modest.

Column chromatography has been used rather extensively
for years for specific applications in aldehyde and ketone chemistry
This method is an effective tool for the separation, collection, and
conversion of certain types of organic compounds for further
qualitative refinement by other methods of measurement. As an
unique independent tool in detection and measurement, it is lacking
in some respects but its primary contribution is that of a supporti
role in rounding out other detection and measurement instrumenta

In recent years, thin-layer chromatography, which utilized
a glass plate coated with a silica-gel or other thin layer materials
as the stationary phase, to which a solvent system is applied as
a mobile phase, has proven to be an effective quantitative tool
for the resolution of organic compounds from an aqueous mixture
of groups of compounds. This method requires a great deal of
training and is only as precise as the skill of the technician
employing it. Its greatest use in this field at present, would be
in a supportive role similar to that previously described for
column and paper chromatography. Specific solvent systems,
developers, and stationary phases yet have to be defined clearly
for organic contaminant quantitation in water supplies. Until
further developmental research is accomplished, thin-layer
chromatography will find only limited application in this work.

METHODS OF APPROACH TO STUDIES OF CHEMICAL
OXIDATION OF ORGANIC CONTAMINANTS

Many studies and surveys conducted by the USPHS indicate
conclusively that increasing quantities of organic wastes are
being discharged into the water courses of the nation, to the

extent that virtually every source of water supply eventually could become polluted to some degree. For this reason, as well as others, the detection and characterization of such wastes is a matter of concern to all water pollution control agencies (19). Equally important is the evaluation of water treatment practices, and specifically, evaulation of oxidation phenomena involved in the removal of organic pollutants.

Two major alternatives exist for evaluation of oxidation phenomena affecting contaminating components in water supplies. They are a study of oxidation utilizing the gross organic extract or complex waste systems, or study of oxidation utilizing pure organic compounds in reconstituted water systems. Organic contaminants are certain to be one of the most important aspects of water quality criteria in relation to the Water Quality Act of 1965. The development of specific techniques and methodology is essential to fundamental efforts to establish reasonable base lines for quality criteria and evaluation parameters for oxidative procedures for their removal.

A series of specific examples of the efficiencies and capabilities of chemical oxidation of organic contaminants has been developed at Washington University over a period of several years. A limited number of such examples, representing each major area of interest, is presented to illustrate present developments in these areas.

Chlorine and chlorine dioxide have been used as chemical oxidants in the various research projects. The results of a specific test in which organic materials extracted from Missouri River water were oxidized under controlled conditions are shown in Figure 3 (20). Threshold Odor Number was used as the evaluation parameter with reaction time and temperature as variables. It is readily apparent that significant reductions of organic materials, as evidenced by lower TON values, occurred when reaction temperatures were maintained near 30°C. The reaction time while important, was not the significant controlling factor. Concentration of a specific reactant and temperature appear to be controlling factors in the oxidation of these gross organic extracts. There is a consistent indication that the organic extracts were resistant to complete effective oxidation with chlorine or chlorine dioxide, especially at lower temperatures. It is evident also that the type of chlorine compound determines the concentration of reactant required to accomplish satisfactory oxidation. The creation of complexed intermediates at lower temperatures is probably the responsible factor in the higher TON values which

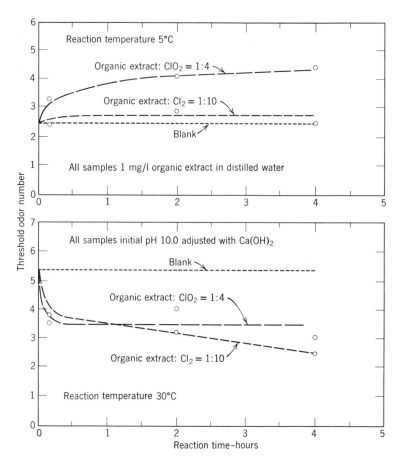

FIGURE 3   EFFECT OF REACTION TEMPERATURE
ON OXIDATION OF CARBON CHLOROFORM
EXTRACT FROM MISSOURI RIVER WATER
BY CHLORINE AND CHLORINE DIOXIDE.

resulted from the low temperature oxidation data.

A complex phenolic industrial waste was oxidized with
ozone to determine fundamental reaction phenomena associated
with such an oxidation procedure (21). Some significant aspects
of the data developed in this work, involving a gross organic
extract, are presented in Figure 4. These data show that
reaction curves for oxidation of the phenolic content varied
greatly as reaction pH of the gross organic waste varied, and

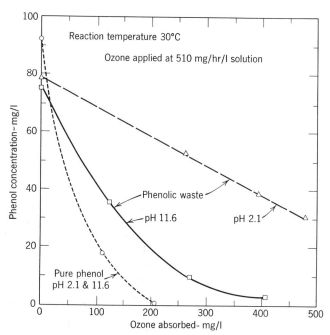

FIGURE 4   EFFECT OF REACTION pH AND TYPE OF
MATERIAL ON OXIDATION OF ORGANICS
BY OZONE.

As the complexity of the waste solution varied. It can be seen
clearly that oxidation in the complex phenolic organic industrial
waste was accomplished far more effectively at a pH value of
11.6 than at a pH value of 2.1. The significance of these data
lies in acceptance of the fact that the ozone requirement, representing cost of treatment necessary to accomplish a desired
degree of phenol oxidation, is based on the amount of ozone
applied, and not on the amount of ozone absorbed. It is realized
also in reviewing these data, that when pure phenol solutions are
oxidized with ozone, the requirement is the same at both pH
values. Ozone absorbance, however, was considerably greater
for the complex waste solutions in each instance to accomplish
similar oxidation efficiency. This is significant in that it clearly
indicates a requirement for additional oxidative power in dealing
with complex gross organic systems as opposed to dealing with

simple or single component systems.

The chemical oxidation of a pure organic compound can be studied for the purpose of developing data from which extra-polations might be made for the formulation of concepts and criterion for the chemical oxidation of more complex systems of organics, provided definite boundary conditions are specified. An example of such a study is presented in the data shown in Figure 5. In this research study, the chemical oxidation of alkyl benzene sulfonate (ABS), a relatively non-biodegradable water pollutant, was investigated using ozone (22). The data demonstrate the effects obtained at variable reaction pH levels. Using ABS reduction as a basis upon which to base oxidation efficiency, it is shown in Figure 5, that the oxidation of ABS was accomplished more efficiently with a shorter reaction period at a pH value of 10 than at pH values of 4 and 7, respectively. At the elevated pH, complete oxidation of the ABS was accom-plished in approximately 3 min, whereas at lower pH values of 4 and 7, the complete oxidation of the ABS was not accomplished after 10 min of reaction time. It is noted also that reaction time is an important factor since the greatest ABS oxidation was accomplished during the first 5 min of ozonation, and that reactio: periods in excess of 5 min netted no significant further reductions in ABS concentration at pH values of 4 and 7. These findings are rather significant in view of the fact that, in general, most other chemical oxidants function best in acid pH ranges, whereas these data indicate rather conclusively that ozone more effectively oxidized ABS in the alkaline range. These factors all confirm the previously advanced concepts that in almost every instance, both avenues of approach to the study of the chemical oxidation phenom must be explored to obtain realistic parameters upon which to evaluate the techniques.

The effects of the ozone oxidation of human urine, a complex organic biological waste, and the resulting reductions in some principal parameters, were observed in a recent study (23). Figure 6 illustrates the relation between the reduction in the concentration of organic matter as reflected by the reduction in evaluation parameters, and the requirement in reactant. These data point to several previously advanced concepts relative to chemical oxidation techniques. Chief among these are the requirements for evaluation of a variety of parameters since no single parameter wo uld provide conclusive evidence of effective oxidation. The parameters of interest in this particular study were: COD, organic carbon, BOD, and NH_3-N. The variables

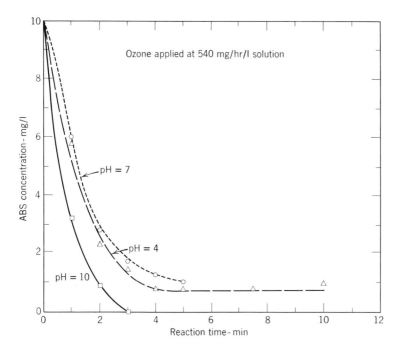

FIGURE 5   EFFECT OF pH ON OXIDATION OF
            ALKYL BENZENE SULFONATE BY
            OZONE.

were parameter concentration, reaction time, and requirement
in reactant material. The clear indication that a variety of
evaluation parameters must be considered is immediately
apparent. It can be seen also in reviewing these data that the
reaction rate is variable. The initial oxidation efficiency becomes
apparent with increasing time and concentration of absorbed
reactant. While significant reductions in the various parameters
did occur, such reductions were not of the order of magnitude
that would result in an acceptable degree of organic contaminant
oxidation and removal. These data further suggest the incomplete
oxidation of initial components which resulted in the development
of complex odorous intermediates. Further research and study
would be essential to the characterization and resolution of such
intermediates. These data do indicate, however, that chemical
oxidation of such a mixture is feasible, but additional study of the

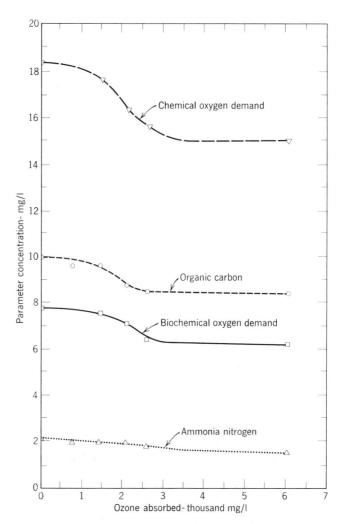

FIGURE 6   EFFECT OF OXIDATION OF HUMAN
            URINE BY OZONE.

phenomena is mandatory to a full realization of the potential
for this method of dealing with certain complex organic systems
contained in water supplies.

    Increased interest in pesticide contamination of water
supplies has prompted many studies relative to their qualitative

and quantitative estimation as well as further evaluations of
techniques for their removal. Chemical oxidation, employing
a variety of reactants, has been explored rather extensively.
One such study involved two specific organic pesticides, aldrin
and lindane (23). In this study, $KMnO_4$ and ozone were employed
as chemical oxidants because of their apparent activity against
certain organic pesticide compounds. The parameter utilized
for measurement of oxidation efficiency was percent removal
of each compound from aqueous solutions, by either chemical
oxidation or simple aeration after various contact times.
Portions of the data from this study are presented in Figures 7
and 8.

In Figure 7, some of the results of pesticide removal,
using ozone as a reactant or simple aeration are presented. The
results show that simple aeration was ineffective in the removal
of lindane, but almost totally removed aldrin from aqueous
solutions. When ozone was employed as a chemical oxidant, it
was fairly efficient in removal of lindane, and almost immediately
removed aldrin from solution. These data further substantiate
the concepts that under given environmental conditions, various
specific organic compounds will react differently to a particular
chemical oxidant. No blanket statement can be made concerning
the oxidation of organic material by a particular chemical. Also,
the physical treatment that is unavoidably employed in the application of chemical oxidants must be taken into consideration in
evaluating overall removal efficiencies.

In another aspect of this same study, $KMnO_4$ was used as
oxidant for these same two pesticides. The variables introduced
in this phase of the study were contact time and chemical reactant
dosages. The results are shown in Figure 8. In this instance,
aldrin was oxidized immediately and completely, at all concentrations of chemical reactant, in less than one min. Only approximately 30% of the lindane was removed, however, regardless of
reactant concentration and period of contact.

Collectively, these data serve to further indicate that the
various interaction effects of environmental conditions, types
and concentrations of reactants, types and concentrations of
organic compounds, and reaction time drastically affect the
efficiency of chemical oxidation techniques.

In each of the examples of chemical oxidation presented
above, regardless of whether complex gross organic material
or pure compounds were evaluated, rather conclusive indications
existed to show that complexing of reactants and organic compounds

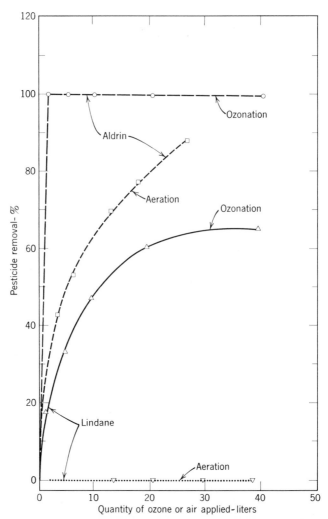

FIGURE 7   REMOVAL OF ALDRIN AND LINDANE
FROM AQUEOUS SOLUTION BY AERATION
AND OZONATION。

operated to create intermediates which, in themselves, remained
as pollutional materials. In most cases, no concrete definition
of these phenomena has been accomplished, nor has the nature

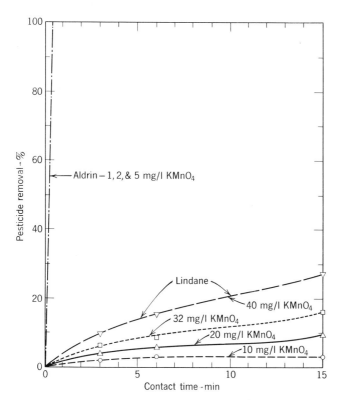

FIGURE 8   EFFECT OF OXIDANT DOSAGE ON
             REMOVAL OF ALDRIN AND LINDANE
             FROM AQUEOUS SOLUTION.

of the resultant products been resolved. A specific chemical
oxidation study was undertaken for the purpose of investigating
the reaction products resulting from the ozone oxidation of
certain aldehydes (24). While the objective of this study was
oriented toward ozone reactivity in polluted atmospheres, it
represents an original source of information on ozone oxidation
of organics in aqueous solutions, and provided a basis for confirmation of the premise that intermediates are created during
chemical oxidation procedures in general.

     In this study, butyraldehyde was ozonated for varying
periods of time, ranging from 20 min to more than 8 hrs. The
selected method of evaluation was paper chromatography, since
it enabled definition of initial and secondary components that

occurred during the process of ozonation. A typical chromato-
gram of the results is shown in Figure 9. These data show
clearly that the absorption of ozone created a series of higher
aldehydes, rather than a single reaction compound. Further
ozonation, however, resulted in the sequential decomposition
of these higher aldehydes to form secondary aldehydes of lower
order. Finally, after extensive ozonation of up to 6 hrs, the
higher compounds are eliminated almost completely.

It seems apparent, from these data, that the higher aldehydes are easily removed by ozonation, whereas the lower aldehydes are not removed similarly at comparable reactant absorbance
or reaction time. These data also suggest that the lower order of
aldehyde is somewhat resistant to further chemical oxidation or
removal from the system. In summary, this study illustrates
that ozone oxidation of certain types of organic compounds results
in the formation of intermediates composed of a rather broad
spectrum of carbon content. The development of this evidence
supports the comments made earlier that the utilization of a
multiplicity of detection tools may well prove to be the requirement for the definition and resolution of the phenomena associated
with chemical oxidation techniques.

Confirmation of the formation of intermediates as the result
of the oxidation of certain organic pesticides with $KMnO_4$ has been
developed in current studies. Preliminary results of these studies
have shown, by solvent-solvent extraction procedures and gas
chromatography, that intermediate compounds which are persistent
and resistant to further oxidation with the employed reactant are
produced as end-products of the chemical oxidation reactions.

SUMMARY
Consistent with the requirements for improved surveillance
methods and more efficient techniques for the detection and
measurement of organic pollutants in water supplies, there exists
an accompanying requirement for a fuller understanding of
removal methods employing various physical and/or chemical
techniques. Among these, chemical oxidation is of prime importan

From information and data derived in the several research
studies summarized, it can be concluded reasonably that several
factors affect the results and removal efficiencies which may be
expected from a variety of chemical reactants, involving a broad
spectrum of organic compounds of either complex or simple nature
Methods of approach to the evaluation of oxidation phenomena have

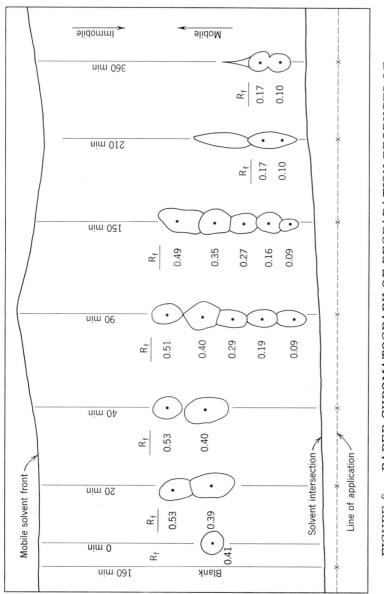

FIGURE 9   PAPER CHROMATOGRAPH OF DEGRADATION PRODUCTS OF
BUTYRALDEHYDE AS A FUNCTION OF TIME UPON OXIDATION
WITH OZONE.

been discussed, as have some typical consequences of oxidation of different organic compounds when a variety of chemical oxidants is employed under different environmental conditions.

Methods of analyses and evaluation of chemical oxidation phenomena have been enumerated and described in the light of their desirable as well as limiting or undesirable characteristics and capabilities.

It has been indicated that there is a continuing need for the development of techniques for evaluation and resolution of the various phenomena associated with chemical oxidation techniques of organic compounds found in water supplies.

The development and availability of new analytical apparatus, and improved techniques associated with standard procedures which have been previously established and widely used in practice collectively provide for more efficient monitoring of such chemical oxidation procedures and techniques that have been established to supplement conventional water treatment practices. New procedure or techniques are currently under development and show promise as being appropriate for future use in the removal or neutralization of organic contaminants in water resources.

On the other hand, further studies are required to more clea define the mechanisms inherent to chemical reactions and the end-products inherent to the utilization of specific chemical oxidants under varied environmental conditions with various types of organic compounds and complex waste systems.

LITERATURE CITED

1. Anon, J Am Water Works Assoc, 53, 1354 (1961).

2. McKee, et al, 100 Problems in Environmental Health, Jones Composition Co., and Kirby Lithograph Co., Washington, D.C., (1961).

3. Skrinde, R.T., et al, Oxidation and Adsorption in Water Treatment Theory and Application, Univ of Michigan, Ann Arbor, Mich., (Feb. 1965).

4. Bacon, H.E. and W.J. Lewis, Combustion, 32, 37 (1960).

5. Buescher, C.A. Jr, M.S. Thesis, Washington University, St. Louis, Missouri, (1961).

6. DuByne, F.T., J Am Water Works Assoc, 55, 710 (1963).

7. Spicher, R.G. and R.T. Skrinde, 83rd Conf Am Water Works Assoc, Kansas City, Missouri, (May 19-24, 1963).

8. Braus, H., Anal Chem, 23, 1160 (1951).

9. Organic Industrial Wastes Characterization, R.A. Taft Sanitary Engineering Center, Cincinnati, Ohio, (May 1959).

10. Ryckman, D.W., et al, Conf Water Pollution Control Fed, Atlantic City, N.J., (October 13, 1965).

11. Ryckman, D.W., et al, J Am Water Works Assoc, 53, 1392 (1961).

12. Burdick, G.E., Trans 2nd Seminar, Biological Problems in Water Pollution, R.A. Taft Sanitary Engineering Center, Cincinnati, Ohio, Technical Report W60-3 (1960).

13. Standard Methods for the Examination of Water and Wastewater, 12th Edition, Am Public Health Assoc, Inc., New York, N.Y., (1965).

14. Van Slyke, D.D. and I. Folch, J Biol Chem, 136, 509 (1940).

15. Kramig, G. and R.B. Schaffer, Ind Water Wastes, 2, 16 (1965).

16. Rice, J.K., et al, 140th National Meeting of Am Chem Soc, Chicago, Illinois, (September 1961).

17. Harley, J.H. and S.E. Wiberley, Instrumental Analysis, John Wiley and Sons, Inc., New York, N.Y., (1963).

18. Mitchell, L.C., J Assoc Agr Chem, N.Y., 40, 999 (1957).

19. Ryckman, D.W., et al, J Am Water Works Assoc, 56, 975 (1964).

20. Grigoropoulos, S.C., PhD Thesis, Washington Univ, St. Louis, Missouri, (June 1961).

21. English, J.N., MS Thesis, Washingting Univ, St. Louis, Missouri, (August 1959).

22. Barttelbort, R.A., MS Thesis, Washington Univ, St. Louis, Missouri, (June 1964).

23. Dougherty, J.H., MS Thesis, Washington Univ, St. Louis, Missouri, (June 1964).

24. Stumph, T.L., MS Thesis, Washington Univ, St. Louis, Missouri, (June 1964).

DISCUSSION

CHAIRMAN GREENBERG: Are there any questions? We have time for about one or two before going on to the next paper.

DR. G. CORSARO (University of Akron): When using permangante, is a residual expected in the effluent water, and if so, what will happen to this small amount of manganese?

MR. EDGERLY: No, there should not be any residuals in the water. You are forced to use sand filtration following permanganate treatment regardless of what you do. If you are going to use permanganate you will have to have some form of filtration. The sand filter generally has sufficient high permanganate demand that there is no chance of permanganate getting out in the treated water.

DR. CORSARO: Has it been substantiated?

MR. EDGERLY: Yes.

QUESTION: Could you describe the method you used to evaluate the tests on the taste and odor of ordinary water samples

MR. EDGERLY: Yes. We have used the same techniques that R.A. Baker developed at the Franklin Institute in Philadelphia Our method of characterizing odor is by an odor panel with temper ture control and serial dilutions with unknowns scattered througho the test group.

T. E. Larson
Illinois State Water Survey
Urbana, Illinois

CHEMICAL OXIDATION AND REDUCTION OXIDATION OF METALS AND IONS IN SOLUTION

Perhaps nothing that is discussed here this afternoon has greater application to millions of home owners, the industries, and the water utilities than oxidation of metals in solution. This is an easy comment to make because iron in water, whether present by nature or as a contribution resulting from corrosion, is a scourge that has not-often-enough been eliminated. The damage to equipment and water handling facilities by loss of metal probably is exceeded only by the loss in carrying capacity from tuberculation and other damages resulting from accumulations of oxidized corrosion products.

It is certain that the vast amount of empirical work on oxidation of metals and ions in solution points directly to the need for a greater detail of basic understanding of the principles. Therefore this discussion will not emphasize what we know but rather what is not known and will raise questions of interest.

This discussion will be limited to oxidation of ferrous metals and ferrous ions, and to begin with a very elementary picture of the problem of corrosion. When dealing with domestic waters, there are two outstanding characteristics that place this problem in a rather isolated category. The first is the range and variety of minerals present, and the second is dissolved oxygen. If it were not for the presence of the latter in all surface waters and in well waters that have been exposed to air, the problem would not be as generally universal as it is. Because the problem is one of oxidation, and oxygen does oxidize, this is a pertinent application to discuss.

The peculiarity of the mineral content is its diverse nature. Domestic waters are not devoid of minerals, nor are these minerals in large concentrations as in brines and sea water. Furthermore, some combinations of these minerals tend to inhibit corrosion while others tend to accelerate it. Making the problem even more difficult is the limit on both type and quantity of inhibitor for corrosion control that can be used in drinking water, and also the limit in cost dictated by the low consumer price of the product.

Two simplified models of the electrochemical activity will be described as a short circuited battery with water as the electrolyte. At the anode, the metal is put into solution as ions, thereby releasing electrons to the metal;at the cathode, electrons are released to the water and the dissolved oxygen to form $O\bar{H}$ ions. For iron, the positively charged Fe^{+2} cations continually are repelled toward the cathode, and at the cathode many of the negatively charged $O\bar{H}$ ions are repelled toward the anode. Simple? Between these two, a multitude of sins occurs.

If the only ions present were those of Na^+ and $\bar{Cl}$, the $\bar{Cl}$ ions would be attracted to the anode and the Na^+ ions to the cathode to form solutions of $FeCl_2$ and $NaOH$, respectively. With dissolved oxygen present, however, the Fe^{+2} ions are oxidized to Fe^{+3} ions which in turn precipitate as $Fe(OH)_3$. Removal of $O\bar{H}$ ions from this portion of the solution results in a local decrease in pH. This further increases the difference in pH between the anode and cathode, and thus increases the current flow and the rate of corrosion.

Now if in this battery, the only ions present were those of Ca^{+2} and HCO_3^-, the acid at the anode would be H_2CO_3. This would result in a high partial pressure of CO_2 with a lesser $[H^+]$. At the cathode, $Ca(OH)_2$ meets with $Ca(HCO_3)_2$ of the main body of the water to form $CaCO_3$, which presumably offers some resistance to current flow.

It will be noted that in either model, the anodic and cathodic surfaces become theoretically devoid of dissolved oxygen. Further participation of dissolved oxygen, therefore, is limited to its rate of diffusion to these surfaces. At the anode,

the area is kept anaerobic because the Fe^{+2} ions consume
dissolved oxygen before it gets to the surface. With only NaOH
present, oxygen can diffuse directly to the cathode's surface,
but, with $CaCO_3$ present there is presumably a barrier to this
diffusion. Of course turbulent flow rates increasingly diminish
the thickness of the laminar layer at the metal surface and
increase the diffusion rates.

Now, from these simplified models, it is apparent that
the mineral composition of the water must play an important
role in the process, even though the fluid composition at both
electrodes is not the same as that of the water itself.

Two types of studies suggest themselves. One would provide systematic anodic and cathodic polarization data for waters
of different ionic compositions at different current densities
and different rates of flow. For this approach, an excellent
reference from workers at the University of Ottawa on the
kinetic theory of inhibition and passivation is recommended (1).
Another type of study would define the migration of ions to and
from the electrodes under different current densities and with
different rates of flow over extended periods of time. For
example, Cl^- ions, with their greater mobility, would tend to
overcome the HCO_3 movement to the anode, yet they cannot
do so completely.

What techniques can be used to determine the relative
concentrations of ions at the electrodes with different water
qualities, and under different current densities? What roles
do small concentrations of organics play at the electrodes?
What actually happens to silica? What role does the Mg^{+2} ion
play in influencing the deposition of $CaCO_3$? Is the deposition
of $CaCO_3$ necessary? What ratios of Ca^{+2} and/or HCO_3
to dissolved oxygen will affect the cathodic and the anodic
polarization? Can solid $CaCO_3$ assume the potential of the
metal cathode to which it adheres? These are some of the
questions that can be raised on principles related to oxidation
of ferrous metals and other metals, from the standpoint of
water quality.

So that the simple battery model does not encompass the
complexity of the problem, the imagination is not stretched
greatly to visualize anodic and cathodic points within an anodic
area, which may be isolated by reacted corrosion products
from the surrounding cathodic area. In such a system, the
internal reaction at the electrodes are governed much more
by the effect of the electrode products than by the mineral

composition of the water itself. For instance, the high CO_2 content may be a controlling factor as an inhibitor.

The handling of water with the variety of available metals often leads to abuses to either the metals or the water or to both. For many years it has been well known that dissimilar metals in contact with each other and exposed to water can lead to galvanic action whereby the more noble metal is protected at the sacrifice of the less noble metal. It seems impossible to get this simple principle across to plumbers, steam fitters, mechanical engineers, and architects. One reason for this may lie in the fact that this galvanic corrosion does not always occur, presumably because the cathode is polarized or protected to the extent that current does not flow. What conditions contribute to such anomalies? Here again, there is room for basic studies on what actually occurs. How can the conditions or degree of hazard or protection in this situation be defined? Next the oxidation of Fe^{+2} ion will be discussed as it concerns the natural waters in east-central Illinois.

Lee and Stumm (2) have shown the rate of oxygenation to follow this relation:

$$\frac{d\,[Fe^{+2}]}{dt} = k\,[Fe^{+2}]^{-}p_{O_2}\,(O\bar{H})^2 \qquad\qquad (16\text{-}1)$$

where k was found to be 1.5 ($\pm$ 0.5) x 10^{13} 1^2 mol^{-2} atm^{-1} min^{-1}. With pH constant at about 7.0, the half life was found to be 11 min for determinations made in 1350 to 1850 mg/l alkalinity. At pH 7.25, the half life was 3 min.

Ghosh, in 1961-62, studied rates of oxidation that occurred with eight municipal water supplies (3). These rates were related statistically to an equation in terms of half life:

$$T\tfrac{1}{2} = 522 - .328\,(O\bar{H})^2\, x\, 10^{14} - 183\, \log\, Alk\, (S.E. = \pm\, 8) \quad (16\text{-}$$

This relation was crude, but does include the effect of alkalinity. Dissolved oxygen ranged from 6.0 to 7.5 mg/l and was not considered sufficiently variable to be included in the calculations.

In 1964-65, Goswami attempted to relate the ORP to the Fe^{+2} - Fe^{+3} equilibrium with no success (4). However, in addition to the collection of data at individual water plants, he also arranged to study the change in ORP and pH with time after aeration of the raw waters in a portable 8-liter container. In the analyses for Fe^{+2}, two determinations were made by the method of Lee and Stumm (5) but one was made after filtering through 0.45 μ filter paper. Typical results for iron are shown in Table I.

TABLE 1   FERROUS IRON - mg/1

Time Min	Hammond		Tolono	
	Total	Filterable	Total	Filterable
0	8.65	6.62	4.58	3.54
5	7.50	5.57	4.58	1.52
10	6.86	4.40		
15			4.05	0.60
20	5.81	3.20		
30			3.38	0.58
35	4.83	2.20		
40			3.54	0.36
50			3.24	0.29
60	3.81	1.07	4.10	0.61

Considerable difference in the two Fe^{+2} iron results are noted. No explanation is available for the increase in total Fe^{+2} iron after 60 min in the Tolono data. Possibly more consistent results might have been obtained if the filter pore size was smaller.

No correlation with ORP could be obtained with the total Fe^{+2} iron, but a reasonable relation was found for the filterable Fe^{+2} iron determinations, as might be expected if colloidal $FeCO_3$ was formed during aeration. This equation was:

$$10\ H_2O + O_2 + 4Fe^{+2} \longrightarrow 8H^+ + 4Fe(OH)_3 \qquad (16\text{-}3)$$

$$Eh = E^O + \frac{0.0592}{4}\ \log\ \frac{(H^+)^8}{(Fe^{+2})^4\ (p_{O_2})} \qquad (16\text{-}4)$$

$$E^O + k = .0592\ (2 \log pH + \log Fe^{+2}) + Eh \qquad (16\text{-}5)$$

where, k is a constant to permit use of Fe^{+2} in mg/1.

In deference to Stumm's excellent explanation of concepts involved in ORP measurement, the dissolved oxygen factor was eliminated from the calculation. This factor is insignificant in any event because 1 mg/1 is equivalent to only 1 mv. The results showed the $E^O + k$ value to be fairly consistent for each

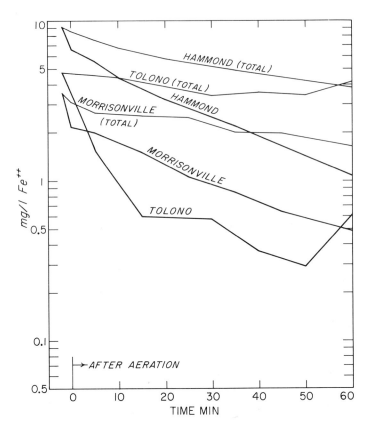

FIGURE 1   TOTAL AND FILTERABLE FERROUS
            IRON FOUND AFTER AERATION, AT
            HAMMOND, TOLONO, AND MORRISONVILLE.

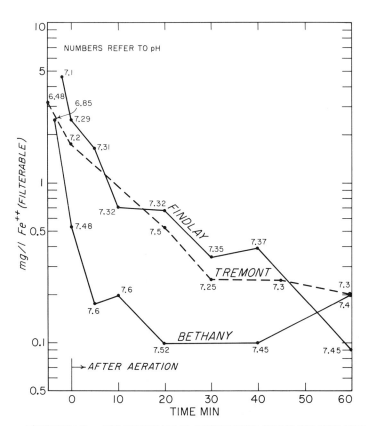

FIGURE 2   FILTERABLE FERROUS IRON IN SOLUTION
AFTER AERATION, AND pH RECORDED
AT TIME OF SAMPLING.

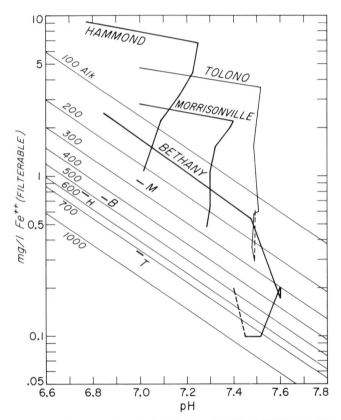

FIGURE 3   RELATION OF pH, ALKALINITY, AND
            SOLUBILITY OF FERROUS IRON TO
            DATA OBTAINED AT FOUR CITIES
            SHOWN IN TABLE II .

water during the period of precipitation, although significant
differences were noted for the different sources of supplies.
The average values of $E^O + k$ and the measured raw water
characteristics for four waters are shown in Table II.

TABLE II

	$E^O + k - v$	Alk mg/l	pH	Eh mv	Temp ^OC
Tolono	$1.304\pm.023$	678	7.0	304	16
Morrisonville	$1.228\pm.008$	254	7.0	384	14.5
Bethany	$1.240\pm.014$	450	6.85	280	14
Hammond	$1.183\pm.010$	510	6.78	220	15

Analytical techniques did not permit the determination
of $FeCO_3$ in the precipitate, but the reduction in filterable Fe^{+2}
iron, coupled with a reasonable relation to the oxidation-reduction
potential, strongly suggests that such precipitation occurred
(Figures 1 and 2).
    If judged on the basis of the total Fe^{+2} iron, oxidation
rates were extremely slow. The decrease in filterable Fe^{+2}
iron, however, was more rapid and also less constant with time.
The path of this precipitation can be followed with relation to
pH, but it serves poorly to define the oxidation rate (Figure 3).
In some instances, the water remains supersaturated with
respect to $FeCO_3$ even after an hour. In others, some oxidation
is evident as the filterable (Fe^{+2}) becomes less than the $FeCO_3$
solubility.
    Several other peculiarities in the data should be considered.
First is the relatively high solubility of iron, for the recorded
pH and total alkalinity in water obtained from the wells. In
several cases the excess was over 90% of the total. One possible
reason for this would be the existence of a $FeHCO_3^+$ species in
the native water. There was no relation, however, between
the excess Fe^{+2} iron and the pH value. Another might be related
to the fact that these waters are notorious for a high methane
gas content. Upon removal from the aquifer and with the pressure
reduced to atmospheric, this gas comes out of solution and the
water is actually milky in appearance. Of course, on release
of methane, a certain amount of CO_2 may be released also
according to the relative partial pressures of the two gases.
The measured pH value, therefore, might be expected to be
higher than that in the aquifer.

At several locations the pH_S for $FeCO_3$ would be more than a full unit below that recorded.

Normally these waters are also at equilibrium with respect to $CaCO_3$. Unfortunately, the Ca^{+2} content was not recorded in these studies so that the pH_S for this equilibrium could be calculated for confirmation. A subsequent examination at one location, however, showed the pH_S value to be exactly equal to the determined pH. Therefore, the excess solubility must be related to the $FeHCO_3^+$ species or to possible complexing by organics in the native water. Chemical oxygen demand data collected at seven of these communities in 1961 by Komolrit (6) showed a reasonable relation for six of these with the excess filterable iron determined by Goswami (4). The ratio of COD to excess Fe^{+2} iron was about 8 to 1.

Even if this relation is accepted as valid, there are still perplexing questions. First, if Fe^{+2} is complexed by organics, is Ca^{+2} also complexed? Probably not, because there is no indication of supersaturation before aeration. After aeration does $CaCO_3$ precipitate concurrently with $FeCO_3$? Probably so, but it is not easily detectable, as the portion precipitated is very small. If excess Fe^{+2} iron is complexed in the water withdrawn from the well, why does it not remain complexed after aeration? Is this pH dependent or does the higher $(CO_3)^{-2}$ provide greater competition for association with the Fe^{+2} ion? If it is the latter, why does not $CaCO_3$ precipitate in preference to $FeCO_3$? Finally, what is the nature of the organic ligand?

Thus it appears that there is a three or four way competition for the Fe^{+2} ion:

$$Fe^{+2} + org. \rightleftarrows Fe^{+2} (org.) \qquad\qquad (16\text{-}6)$$

or:

$$Fe^{+2} + Horg_2 \rightleftarrows Fe (org.) + H^+ \text{ (not likely)} \qquad (16\text{-}7)$$
$$Fe^{+2} + CO_3^{-2} \rightleftarrows FeCO_{3 (c)} \qquad\qquad (16\text{-}8)$$
$$Fe^{+2} + H_2O \rightleftarrows Fe(OH)^+ + H^+ \qquad\qquad (16\text{-}9)$$
$$Fe^{+2} + O_2 + H_2O \rightleftarrows Fe(OH)_{3 (c)} + H^+ \qquad (16\text{-}10)$$

Only one is irreversible, and the hydrolysis by the Fe^{+2} ion results in the release of sufficient H^+ ions to theoretically dissolve an equivalent amount of Fe^{+2} iron from $FeCO_3$.

Now, what significance can be attached to these findings? First, O'Connor reported that iron removal by oxidation in these waters is less significant than by precipitation as $FeCO_3$ (7).

It appears that the major function of aeration is to increase the pH and reduce the solubility with respect to $FeCO_3$. This precipitation rate is slow and is complicated by an accompanying slower rate of oxidation which does not produce a flocculent, easily settleable $Fe(OH)_3$. The experience has been that settling basins serve only as retention basins, and the removal of iron is accomplished largely in the filters.

Significantly, many filters release soluble Fe^{+2} iron to the effluent (8). In such cases little or no dissolved oxygen remains in the effluent, although there may be several mg/l in the water entering the filter. Another important aspect of this water is the presence of 0.5 to as much as 40 mg/l of ammonia in the water. With such concentrations, nitrosomonas can readily convert this cation to the NO_2 anion, and thus reduce the pH within the filter and permit re-solution of the $FeCO_3$. One mg/l NH_4^+ would be equivalent to 3.1 mg/l Fe^{+2}. Also, it may be that methanomonas bacteria contribute to the formation of CO_2 from the residual methane in the water. Chloramines do not appear to be effective on either of these organisms, and in marginal concentrations it does not even get through the filters. Unfortunately, in many cases "breakpoint" chlorination is out of the question.

To come back to oxidation of iron, there is a record at one city where air-lift was used to pump water from the wells. The water was released to a reservoir, and the iron settled so well that filtration was not even practiced. On modernization in the early 1920's, turbine pumps were installed with an aerator at the reservoir. No longer did the iron settle, so it became necessary to install filters. This would suggest the use of pressure aerators, but these are not always successful, probably because the retention time before filtration is not sufficiently long to permit precipitation. Also it does not eliminate bacteriological problems in the filters.

Several other possibilities for iron removal are also apparent. First, the problem of removal by settling prior to filtration might be aided by coagulation with $NaAlO_2$. Marginal treatment with lime to a pH of 7.6 or 7.7 (without aeration) followed by clarification with a $CaCO_3$ slurry and then filtration should be evaluated also. In the absence of dissolved oxygen, the bacteriological problem is eliminated also.

Hale has shown that treatment with lime without aeration can be used to remove iron as $FeCO_3$ by filtration (9).

The major problem with this method for very hard waters would be concurrent precipitation of $CaCO_3$ with cementing of the sand filter. In effect, the addition of an alkali is probably the basis for iron removal with diatomite filters with MgO added to the slurry feed as suggested at one time by Ghosh (3). Of course, iron removal as $FeCO_3$ is incidental in normal lime-soda softening where the $CaCO_3$ slurry also would include $FeCO_3$. These studies at the University of Illinois, therefore, suggest that iron removal by oxidation may not always be the most appropriate method.

ACKNOWLEDGEMENT

All data used for the iron removal portion of this paper were obtained from three MS theses, supported in part by Research Grant No. WP-17, Public Health Service, USDHEW, Washington, D. C.

LITERATURE CITED

1. Gilroy, A. and B. Conway, J Phys Chem, 69, 1259 (1965).

2. Lee, G. F. and W. Stumm, Ind Eng Chem, 53, 143 (1961).

3. Ghosh, M., MS Thesis, Univ of Illinois, Urbana, Illinois, (196?

4. Goswami, S., MS Thesis, Univ of Illinois, Urbana, Illinois, (19

5. Lee, G. F. and W. Stumm, J Amer Water Works Assoc, 52, 1567 (1960).

6. Komolrit, K., MS Thesis, Univ of Illinois, Urbana, Illinois, (1961).

7. O'Connor, J., Symp on Acid Mine Drainage Res, Pittsburgh, Penna., (May 20, 21, 1965).

8. Weart, J. and G. Margrave, J Amer Water Works Assoc, 49, 1223 (1957).

9. Hale, F., J Amer Water Works Assoc, 28, 1577 (1936).

DISCUSSION

CHAIRMAN GREENBERG: Dr. Larson has, in effect, asked a lot of questions and I'm sure that there are some among you who don't want to let him get off without really answering some. I see that Dr. Stumm has a question.

DR. STUMM (Harvard University): I was pleased to see that the data on iron removal, obtained in real systems with natural waters, are in reasonably good agreement with results obtained by Dr. Lee and myself in synthetic systems. I would like to offer possible explanations for the observed difference between total ferrous iron and filtrable ferrous iron: (a) The analytical method for determining ferrous iron in the presence of ferric iron with orthophenanthroline is subject to errors in waters containing organic material. If one boils the acidified sample (for dissolving suspended iron) organic material can reduce ferric iron, (b) Certain organic substances reduce ferric iron with a rate approximately comparable to that of oxygen oxidation of ferrous iron; thus, a near steady state concentration of ferrous iron is maintained. Then, the overall oxidation rate is considerably decreased. I do not believe that there are substances present in ground water that will form stronger complexes with ferrous iron than with ferric iron. All the typical materials in natural waters, such as tannate, phenols, and so on, form much stronger complexes with ferric iron and, if at all, weaker complexes with ferrous iron. However, the situation is in the presence of organic material may build up to some kind of a steady state. You have ferrous iron being oxidized to ferric iron, and the ferric irons now react, are thereby reduced and kinetically what we have is a slow oxidation step which is followed then by a reduction step, or vice versa, and depending on the kinetic mechanism we can get a relatively high steady state concentration of ferrous iron.

DR. LARSON: But we don't know whether we have tannate or what we have in the way of organic matter.

DR. STUMM: With the exception of the orthophenanthroline, dipyridyls, and related substances there are essentially no known reasonably stable complexes with ferrous iron.

DR. LARSON: You are correct, we don't know specifically what is in the water, but something is holding the iron in solution.

DR. J.T. O'CONNOR (University of Illinois): I think I would agree with Dr. Stumm. Lloyd Robinson's work at the University of Illinois indicated that the effect of organics was to peptize rather than to form complexes with iron, and I noted this in the Pittsburgh meeting previously mentioned. Knowing

this, we did not digest the samples. We also knew there was
the possibility of conversion of ferric to ferrous iron under
those circumstances, so we never digested the samples. We
simply buffered to pH 4, added orthophenanthroline and extracted.
For the filtered samples we used two techniques. The filtered
samples were acidified, buffered to pH 4, and orthophenanthroline
added, or we rebuffered directly to pH 7 and added orthophenanthroline immediately. The results weren't entirely comparable
but they were close.

CHAIRMAN GREENBERG: Are there any other questions?

DR. J. J. MORGAN (California Institute of Technology):
I don't think it follows, Dr. Larson, that you have to expect the
same type of behavior with respect to supersaturation of the iron
carbonate as with the calcium carbonate. The driving force is
for precipitation in one case, not in the other.

DR. LARSON: They are both in excess.

DR. MORGAN: They are both in excess, but they are not
in excess to the same degree, because ferrous carbonate is a
thousand times less soluble than calcium carbonate. So the
excess is quite different in these two cases. The other point is
that the observation on possible removal of the iron as ferrous
carbonate is certainly in substantial agreement with the work
by Hale in New York done, I guess, in the early 1940's where
he published a paper called "Iron Removal Without Aeration",
describing processes where he deliberately excluded the iron
as ferrous carbonate. So this looks like a very good possibility
in terms of the experience of Hale.

CHAIRMAN GREENBERG: Are there any other questions
or comments?

DR. A. H. MOLOF (New York University): On the subject
of oxidation-reduction potential you mentioned that you haven't
had much success. I've heard this many times. I've worked
primarily on biological systems which are much more difficult
to reproduce, and I have found great success with it and I
believe that your comment may not represent the actual fair
evaluation of this, I think, very valuable tool.

DR. LARSON: I said the investigator didn't have any
success with it and in using this data I couldn't find anything
that would correlate either until we got down to using the filterable iron rather than trying to take the total ferrous iron. When
we used the filterable ferrous then we obtained a fairly decent
correlation.

DR. MOLOF: You mentioned that you haven't had much

success with oxidation-reduction potential measurements. What did you mean?

DR. LARSON: I think I said the accuracy of the measurements are pretty poor, particularly in field studies that were made.

DR. MOLOF: I'd like to just add the comment that I believe that the use of this instrument has been abused because of lack of careful consideration. I've noticed in other work that people express the same comment, and I have never had the opportunity to defend this instrument which I've used very successfully, and I'd like to take this opportunity to say that with careful consideration and knowledge of the electrode system you can get excellent reproducability and precision with in this instrument.

DR. LARSON: I think you are probably right, depending on where you are using it. If you are dealing with a water system such as ours, this can be pretty delicate. Buffering capacity, particularly the Eh buffering capacity, is pretty poor.

MR. J.D. HEM (U.S. Geological Survey): We have done quite a bit of work with oxidation-reduction potential in the Survey although I have not done any large number of these determinations myself. My colleagues, however, feel that the measurement of redox potential is a very worthwhile tool in evaluating behavior of iron in ground water systems and I would like to talk some more about that tomorrow in my allotted time.

DR. STUMM: In response to the comments made by Dr. Molof and Mr. Hem on the value of redox potential measurements, I would like to issue a reservation which is very similar to the problems discussed earlier concerning zeta potentials. The question is not primarily whether we can measure Eh values in a reasonably reproducible way but whether the measured values are conceptually meaningful. In many systems, where the variables are known and under control, such measurements are amenable to theoretical interpretation (Nernst Equation). In many natural systems, however, we measure mixed potentials, i.e., potentials that are established by oxidants and reductants that do not belong to the same redox couple. The near steady-state potentials obtained in such a case are not equilibrium potentials and cannot be interpreted in the sense of the Nernst Equation. Furthermore, the Nernst Equation, in an operational sense, does not extend to unlimited small concentrations of electroactive species. Many of the redox components of natural waters are not at all electroactive, i.e., these components kinetically are not oxidized or reduced on an inert electrode within the stability limits of water. Such non-electroactive species include for example; sulfides - sulfur - sulfate; NH_4 - N_2 - NO_2^- - NO_3^-; CH_4 - CO_2; and most organic constituents. The $Fe(II)$ - $Fe(III)$ system in natural waters represents an electroactive couple, that establishes a reasonable exchange rate at a bright Pt-electrode. Nevertheless, in the system $Fe(OH)_{3(c)}$ - Fe^{+2} (pH 7), we have found that measured Eh no longer depends on the concentration of ferrous iron if the ferrous iron concentration becomes lower than 10^{-5} M.

MR. TANNER (U.S. Geological Survey): Do you have any indication that there was no suspended iron in the size range smaller than the size of the filter used?

DR. LARSON: The water that came through was perfectly clear, and the total iron determination was equal to the ferrous iron.

Owen P. Bricker
Johns Hopkins University

R. M. Garrels
Northwestern University

MINERALOGIC FACTORS IN NATURAL WATER EQUILIBRIA

Although the composition of surface and sub-surface waters is partly inherited from rain, and is locally influenced strongly by the activities of man, the dominating influence is that of the solid phases with which they come in contact. This paper has been divided into two parts: in the first we attempt to show the influence of the details of carbonate mineralogy on water compositions which we consider an important amplification of classical studies; in the second we have made a first attempt to consider the importance of silicate phases and conclude that several important constituents of natural waters are actually controlled by equilibrium between stable or metastable silicate minerals and the waters that bathe them.

CARBONATE EQUILIBRIA

The $CaCO_3$-H_2O-CO_2 system has received a great deal of attention from geologists, oceanographers, sanitary engineers, chemists, and medical researchers because of its important buffering effect and relation to water hardness. Equations describing $CaCO_3$ solubility equilibria were derived as early as 1890 by van't Hoff. Since then the system has been the object of extensive investigation; a recent systematic treatment summarizing the pertinent data has been given by Weber and Stumm (1).

449

In many cases, workers in the field of carbonate equilibria have dealt primarily with the chemistry of the aqueous phase and the gas-liquid equilibrium, attaching little significance to the solid phases in the system. Let us focus attention on the solid phases in the $CaCO_3$-H_2O-CO_2 system and investigate what effect, if any, the solid phase has on the equilibrium.

Polymorphism

Table I shows that there are three polymorphic forms of $CaCO_3$ and three hydrates. (Two high pressure polymorphs of $CaCO_3$ also have been described by Bridgman, 36). All occur in nature with the exception of the monohydrate. Each of these compounds has a different solubility, making the carbonate equilibrium relations somewhat more complicated than the simple system usually treated. Which of the solid phases should be considered in making equilibrium calculations pertaining to the natural water system? The basic laws of thermodynamics tell us that only one of the $CaCO_3$ compounds can be in equilibrium with nearly pure water at any chosen temperature and pressure. Free energy calculations based on data from Latimer indicate that at $25^{\circ}C$ and one atm total pressure the stable phase is calcite (2). Experimental confirmation is provided by the work of Jamieson who determined the equilibrium P-T curve for the calcite-aragonite inversion (3), by Brooks, et al, who investigated the hydrates of $CaCO_3$ (4), and by Faivre who investigated the precipitation of vaterite and other forms of $CaCO_3$ (5).

At first glance, it would appear that the original simple picture with calcite being the only important phase in natural water systems is justified.

TABLE I   CALCIUM CARBONATE POLYMORPHS
            AND HYDRATES

Calcite	$CaCO_3$
Aragonite	$CaCO_3$
Vaterite	$CaCO_3$
Synthetic	$CaCO_3 \cdot H_2O$
Trihydrocalcite	$CaCO_3 \cdot 3H_2O$
Ikaite	$CaCO_3 \cdot 6H_2O$

A cursory glance at recent carbonate sediments, which are composed to a large extent of aragonite, is enough to dispell that illusion. Aragonite is being deposited in vast amounts

under conditions of temperature and pressure in which calcite
is the thermodynamically stable phase (6). Free energy data
indicate a difference of only about 230 cal between the stabilities
of calcite and aragonite under earth-surface conditions (22).
The precipitation and metastable existence of aragonite under
these circumstances is not too surprising.

Kinetics of Crystallization

A number of natural waters, fresh and saline, are supersaturated with respect to both calcite and aragonite. Barnes
found springs in Inyo County, California that were supersaturated by over 300% with respect to calcite (7). Back investigated groundwaters in central Florida and found that, over
extensive areas, the waters were supersaturated with respect
to calcite, in some cases by over 250% (8).

A device for determing the degree of saturation has been
devised by Weyl, who found that the surface water samples he
examined from the Atlantic Ocean were supersaturated with
respect to calcite (9). Siever, et al, found that the surface
waters of the Atlantic Ocean and the Gulf of California were
uniformly supersaturated with respect to calcite, but inter-
stitial waters squeezed from cores of the bottom sediment
were undersaturated or saturated (10). Schmalz and Chave
observed that the sea waters off Bermuda are supersaturated
with respect to calcite (11). They believe the supersaturation
is due to metastable equilibrium of sea water with magnesian
calcites and fine-grained carbonates with large surface energies.
The solid phase that precipitates first under these conditions
will be governed by kinetic and biologic factors.

Role of Organisms

Organisms that secrete shells and other hard parts composed of $CaCO_3$ are abundant in the oceans and in may fresh
waters. Lowenstam observed a correlation between temperature and the $CaCO_3$ polymorph produced by marine organisms (12).
Aragonite appears to be the dominant form of $CaCO_3$ secreted
by marine organisms, particularly in warm waters. In cases
where aragonite is already present in an environment from
breakup of shell material, it will be available to nucleate inorganic aragonite if concentration factors become favorable
for precipitation. Under these conditions calcite is unlikely
to precipitate even though it is the stable phase.

Organisms apparently can produce local (often, of course, internal) conditions favorable to the precipitation of $CaCO_3$ compounds even where the bulk environment is undersaturated with respect to these materials. Upon death, in many cases, the hard parts produced by organisms are attacked and the more delicate forms completely dissolved before burial, attesting to the undersaturation of the bulk environment. Organisms also can precipitate calcite at 25°C or lower, containing an amount of Mg that would be thermodynamically stable only above 800°C. The highly magnesian calcites precipitated by many organisms are clearly metastable with respect to the bulk environment in which they formed. More will be said about this in a following section.

Stabilization by Trace Elements

The observation that aragonite invariably has a higher Sr content than calcite has led to the speculation that trace amounts of Sr might determine whether calcite or aragonite will precipitate (13). The structure of aragonite can accommodate the relatively large Sr^{+2} ion but the calcite structure cannot. It has been suggested also that trace amounts of Sr might have a stabilizing effect on aragonite (14), but the degree to which aragonite is stabilized by trace amounts of Sr has not been well demonstrated. MacDonald found, on the basis of thermodynamic calculations, that a content of at least 30% of components other than $CaCO_3$ would be required to make aragonite stable with respect to calcite at 25°C (15). It has been observed, however, that aragonite from the Bahama Banks containing a trace of Sr does not invert to calcite when dried and stored in the laboratory, whereas chemically pure aragonite of the same particle size will partially invert to calcite in less than a year under the same conditions (6). Holland, et al, found that it was impossible to precipitate only calcite from solutions of $CaCl_2$ containing $SrCl_2$ at 25°C (16). Some aragonite always was precipitated as well. Only by resorting to high pressures of CO_2 and temperatures above 25°C was it possible to eliminate aragonite from the precipitate.

The stabilizing effect of trace elements on a compound is a factor that must be considered, particularly when dealing with naturally occurring compounds which are seldom pure. The effect of other components in the solution from which the compound precipitates is another factor that may influence the polymorphic form of the precipitating compound.

Metastable Equilibrium
        In order to predict the equilibrium composition of the
aqueous phase in a system containing $CaCO_3$ or to determine
whether a natural water is in equilibrium with the solid carbonate phase, not only the composition, but the structure of
the solid phase must be known as well. It should be apparent
that one cannot make the assumption that the solid phase in the
system will necessarily be the thermodynamically stable phase
for the prevailing conditions. In cases such as the calcite-
aragonite system the metastable precipitation of aragonite and
the sluggish kinetics of its inversion to calcite at low temperature permits the metastable existence of aragonite for geologically important periods of time. In this type of system equilibrium between natural waters and a metastable phase may be
established. Figure 1 compares the stability fields of calcite
and aragonite at $25^{\circ}C$, one atm total pressure, and a total
dissolved carbonate activity of 10^{-3}. In the pH range of natural
waters aragonite will support nearly two times more calcium
in solution than will calcite.

Solid Solution
        This picture is further complicated by Mg, a common con-
stituent of natural waters. Magnesium can substitute for Ca
in the calcite structure, but the size difference between Mg^{+2}
and Ca^{+2} ions precludes a complete solid-solution series at
earth-surface temperatures. Subsolidus investigations by
Graf and Goldsmith show that at $500^{\circ}C$ the extent of solid solution of $MgCO_3$ is about 5 mole % and at $900^{\circ}C$ about 27 mole %
(17). Reactions in this system are too slow at lower temperatures
to permit attainment of equilibrium in the laboratory, but extrapolation of the curve at $25^{\circ}C$ suggests that very little Mg should
be present in calcite at low temperatures.
        Perusal of analyses of natural calcites known to have formed
at low temperatures shows $MgCO_3$ contents as high as 18 mole %.
Chave found that many marine organisms secrete hard parts of
magnesian calcite, the Mg content being a function of the particular
organism (19). The alga lithophyllum secretes calcite containing
about 20 mole % $MgCO_3$. Calcite containing that amount of Mg
is metastable below a temperature of about $850^{\circ}C$. Alderman
and Skinner found magnesian calcites precipitating in the Coorong
and in other saline lakes in Australia (20). Graf and Goldsmith
precipitated highly magnesian calcites from aqueous solution
at room temperature (21).
        Magnesian calcites are metastable under earth-surface

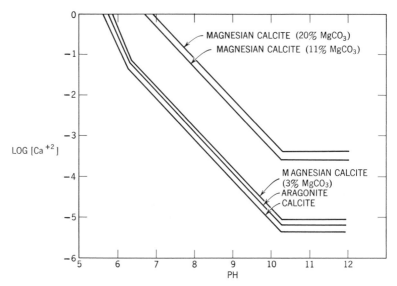

FIGURE 1   SOLUBILITY OF CALCITE, ARAGONITE,
            AND THREE MAGNESIAN CALCITES AS A
            FUNCTION OF pH AT 25°C, ONE ATM
            TOTAL PRESSURE, AND A TOTAL DISSOLVED
            CARBONATE ACTIVITY OF 10^{-3}.

conditions and lose Mg over geologically short time spans. Calcites from Mesozoic and older rocks are very low in Mg except
in unusual circumstances (23). The solubility of magnesian calcites is larger than that of pure calcite (Figure 1) and varies as
a function of Mg content (24). Rapid loss of Mg from these calcites
in some cases without disrupting delicate fossil structures, sugges
incongruent solution. As the magnesian calcite is dissolved, a
purer calcite is reprecipitated, the Mg being lost to the solution.
Groundwaters from magnesian carbonate bedrock will have a Mg/
Ca ratio higher than that of the rock because of selective loss of
Mg^{+2} and may contain Ca concentrations greater than predicted
from the solubility of pure calcite.

    In addition to magnesian calcite solid solutions, two mixed
carbonates of Ca and Mg; dolomite, $CaMg(CO_3)_2$, and huntite,
$CaMg_3(CO_3)_4$, occur in nature. Dolomite is a common constituent of carbonate rocks and occurs in beds hundreds of feet thick
and of large areal extent. Huntite is metastable with respect

to dolomite under earth-surface conditions, and of little importance with respect to the total volume of carbonate sediments.

Huntite precipitates directly from Mg rich groundwaters
and may be important in determining water equilibria in certain
local environments (24, 26). The precipitation of dolomite,
however, is somewhat puzzling. Dolomite constitutes a large
percent of the total volume of carbonate rocks and yet only in
a few cases has the primary precipitation of this compound
been observed. Alderman and Skinner found dolomite precipitating in some saline lakes in Australia (20). The temperature
of these lakes has an annual variation between $5^{\circ}C$ and $27^{\circ}C$
whereas salinity and pH vary through a wide range. Maximum
precipitation occurs in conjunction with maximum photosynthetic
activity during daylight hours, when the pH value may rise as
high as 9.3. The precipitate consists of magnesian calcite and
dolomite in roughly equal proportions, and amounts to as much
as .05 g/100-ml of water. Graf, et al, have described a thin
layer of dolomite occurring about a foot below the surface of
the Lake Bonneville sediments in Utah which may have been
deposited under conditions similar to those presently observed
in the Australian lakes (27). Recent investigations by Deffeyes,
et al, suggest that dolomite may be formed by the reaction of
Mg-rich waters with carbonate sediments (28). On the island
of Bonaire, Netherlands Antilles, waters with a molar Mg/Ca
ratio of 30:1 commonly have been observed in saline lakes and
in pits dug in the carbonate sediment. The high Mg/Ca ratio
arises from evaporation of sea water in basins with limited
access to the open ocean, resulting in precipitation of gypsum.
The Mg-rich waters leave the basins by flowing downward
through the underlying carbonate sediments because of their
high density. By this mechanism about 1/2 cubic kilometer of
carbonate sediments has been dolomitized in less than 10^6
years on Bonaire.

Although precipitation of dolomite from most natural waters
would appear to be unimportant as a controlling factor in carbonate equilibria, the extensive areas underlain by dolomite bedrock
suggests that the solubility characteristics are not. Water in
equilibrium with dolomitic rocks may have a composition quite
different from that of waters in equilibrium with calcite or aragonite. Barnes and Back have investigated dolomite solubility
in groundwater from carbonate bedrock (29). Many of these
waters are supersaturated with respect to calcite but give
a solubility product corresponding to dolomite. The kinetics

of calcite precipitation apparently are slow enough under these conditions to allow supersaturation of Ca^{+2} ion with respect to calcite and equilibrium with dolomite. Other waters investigated by Barnes and Back are undersaturated or saturated with respect to calcite and apparently in equilibrium with dolomite. Hsu found that most waters he examined from aquifers in Florida were in equilibrium with both dolomite and calcite and had a molar Ca^{+2}/Mg^{+2} ratio of 1 (30). Figure 2 shows the variation of Ca activity in equilibrium with dolomite as a function of pH for certain fixed values of Mg activity and a total dissolved carbonate activity of 10^{-3}. The equilibrium curve for calcite is included for comparison. For groundwaters with pH below 7 and $\left[Mg^{+2}\right] \leq 10^{-2}$, dolomite will be more soluble than calcite.

Both calcite and dolomite can accommodate reasonably large amounts of cations other than Ca and Mg in their structures. Iron and manganese are commonly found in calcite and dolomite; more rarely, Zn, Pb, Co, Ni, Cd, Ba, and Sr. Little is known about the extent of solid solution of the latter elements in calcite and dolomite or their effect on the stability of these compounds.

Structural Disorder and Compositional Variation

Many of the primary dolomites are non-stoichiometric to some degree and show varying amounts of disorder in their structure. The term "protodolomite" has been applied to these compounds to distinguish them from stoichiometric, order dolomite (21). The stability of protodolomites would be predicted to vary with degree of non-stoichiometry and degree of disorder, their stability being less the greater the deviation from ideal dolomite. Water in equilibrium with protodolomite thus would vary in dissolved constituents depending upon the composition and degree of order of the solid phase. Detailed information on the variation of stability of protodolomite is not available. Preliminary studies, however, suggest it is small (22).

Figure 3, after Langmuir (22), shows some stability relations in the system $MgO-CaO-H_2O-CO_2$ at $25^\circ C$ and one atm total pressure. The dashed lines represent the change in stability fields resulting from the use of $K_{dol} = 10^{-15}$. The composition of surface sea water is indicated on the diagram. Dolomite is stable in surface sea water although poorly crystalline disordered dolomite, or protodolomite, with a solubility product as large as 10^{-15} is not.

Natural waters may be depleted by Ca both by chemical precipitation of Ca compounds and by utilization of Ca by organism

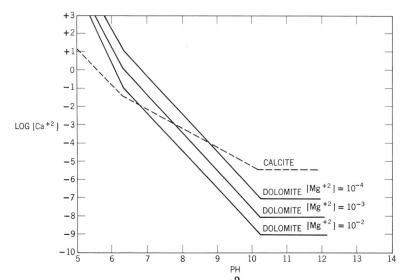

FIGURE 2   ACTIVITY OF Ca^{+2} ION IN EQUILIBRIUM
              WITH DOLOMITE AS A FUNCTION OF pH
              FOR FIXED VALUES OF MAGNESIUM ION
              ACTIVITY AT 25°C, ONE ATM TOTAL
              PRESSURE, AND A TOTAL DISSOLVED
              CARBONATE ACTIVITY OF 10^{-3}. SOLUBILITY
              CURVE OF CALCITE INCLUDED FOR
              COMPARISON.

Under certain circumstances this may cause a high Mg/Ca ratio.
In such cases, with evaporation, Mg concentration can increase
to a level at which $MgCO_3$ compounds begin to precipitate. As
in the CaCO system, there are a number of $MgCO_3$ compounds
(Table II). The stability of each of these compounds is different
and will provide a water of unique composition under equilibrium
conditions. Again, only one phase (or under certain circumstances
two phases) in this system is thermodynamically stable at any
chosen temperature and pressure. Kinetic factors, however,
make possible the metastable precipitation and persistence of
these compounds for relatively long periods of time.

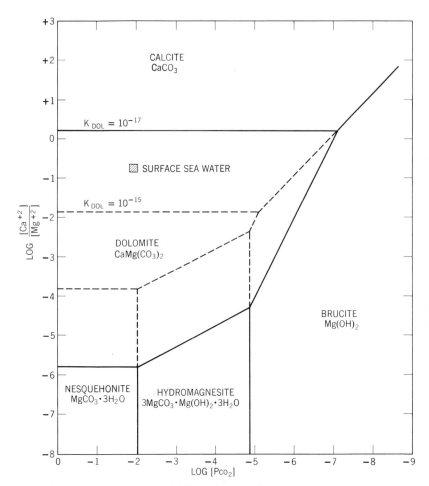

FIGURE 3   STABILITY RELATIONS IN THE SYSTEM
              MgO-CaO-H$_2$O-CO$_2$ AT 25°C AND ONE ATM
              TOTAL PRESSURE. Dashed lines represent
              change in stability fields resulting from a
              hundredfold increase in the solubility of
              dolomite. (After Langmuir, 22).

Summary
In summary, the composition of surface and near-surface waters is strongly influenced by the carbonate phases present, and especially by the presence of magnesian calcite and dolomite. Furthermore, the processes of solution and precipitation are not symmetric; magnesian calcites exposed to rain water yield solutions with a Mg/Ca ratio equal to that of the solid; the same solution will only precipitate nearly pure calcite, so that Mg becomes enriched relative to Ca. Interpretation of chemical equilibria in natural water systems containing Ca and Mg carbonate compounds can be meaningful only if the detailed chemical and structural variability of the solid phases are considered.

TABLE II   MAGNESIUM CARBONATE COMPOUNDS

Magnesite	$MgCO_3$
Nesquehonite	$MgCO_3 \cdot 3H_2O$
Lansfordite	$MgCO_3 \cdot 5H_2O$
Hydromagnesite	$3MgCO_3 \cdot Mg(OH)_2 \cdot 3H_2O$
Artinite	$MgCO_3 \cdot Mg(OH)_2 \cdot 3H_2O$

SILICATE SYSTEMS

In the preceding section, attention was called to the importance of detailed mineralogy of the carbonate minerals in controlling water compositions. The high rate of reaction of water with carbonate minerals generally is accepted, and it does not seem unreasonable to make calculations based on equilibrium of natural waters with stable or metastable carbonate phases. But the carbonates can be important controls only of Ca, Mg, HCO_3^-, and H^+ ions. What of the Na, K, and silica that are also among the major species in natural waters?

The most obvious source of these constituents is the great variety of silicate minerals that make up 70% or more of the rocks in contact with underground waters and streams. In general, except for their ion exchange properties, these minerals have been ignored or regarded as unimportant in controlling water compositions. Here the bold assumption will be made that silicate minerals, considered as bulk phases, are rapidly reactive and that many water constituents are controlled by equilibrium with one or more silicate phases. Eventually we will retreat somewhat from this extreme view, but think we can document the usefulness of this assumption.

Dissolved Silica and Quartz

The major clue to reactivity of silicate minerals is the concentration of silica in natural waters. The solubility of quartz is about 8 mg/l, and that amorphous silica is about 115 mg/l. The world average for streams (sampled chiefly at the mouths of master streams) is about 13 mg/l, and a plot of the distribution of silica values in streams and in subsurface waters from sandstones and shales shows an abrupt minimum at about 1-2 mg/l and a fairly sharply defined maximum at about 60 mg/l. Furthermore, as shown by Feth, et al, (31) and by Davis (32), silica rises abruptly when rainwater or snow melt comes in contact with silicate rocks, and may be unique in showing little variation of concentration with stream discharge. The picture that emerges is that neither quartz nor amorphous silica exert a control on the silica content of streams or shallow groundwaters, and that the silica is derived from the weathering of silicates. This conclusion has been documented for spring waters from the Sierra Nevada by Feth, et al, who showed that the water compositions are exactly those predicted from altera- tion of the rocks by soil waters high in CO_2 (31). Calculations based on their data show, in fact, that almost all the dissolved silica must come from silicate minerals, chiefly feldspars. Thus, less than a few percent can be attributed to direct solution of quartz despite the fact that quartz is an abundant constituent of the rocks. More studies like that on the Sierras are needed before this conclusion on the natural chemical inertness of quartz at room temperature can be put to general use, but it is in accord with experimental work in quartz solubility and growth.

Weathering of Silicates

The probable derivation of dissolved silica from silicates indicates structural breakdown of silicate minerals, with con- comitant release of cations. The Al in most silicate phases, however, is not at all mobile, so that reactions with surface waters must produce solid products higher in Al than the origi- nal silicates. Aluminum is characteristically so low in natural waters (0.1 mg/l) that it is convenient to assume that Al is con- served among the solid phases during reactions. With this stipulation it is possible to make stability diagrams for many of the common silicates on which the phases are described in terms of dissolved constituents of the coexisting solution. No attempt will be made here to utilize such diagrams extensively but one example will show how plotting of natural water compositions on these diagrams almost forces one to conclusions regarding the chemical genesis of the water.

Figure 4, after Hess, (37), is a stability diagram showing relations among some silicate minerals and the aluminum oxide hydrate gibbsite, as best they can be calculated from existing free energy data and inferred from natural occurrences.

Details of the construction of silicate diagrams are given by Garrels and Christ (33). Figure 5 is a plot of the analyses of waters from various rock types showing the ratio of Na^+, H^+, and SiO_2 of a given water are plotted on the silicate diagram, and the resulting point falls into a field containing the point. On the other hand, it definitely is not in equilibrium with the other phases depicted. Figure 6 was obtained by super-imposing Figure 5 on Figure 4. Two obvious relations and their possible explanation are:

a. There is a silica cut-off at about 2 mg/l. This may, of course, be related to the minimum reported analytically, but reasonably can be attributed to a silica control by the two-phase equilibrium gibbsite-kaolinite. Waters draining the Jamaican bauxitic soils, that are dominantly gibbsite-kaolinite mixtures, range from 3 to 6 mg/l SiO_2 close to the theoretical 1 to 2 mg/l calculated from free energy values for equilibrium between the crystalline phases (35).

b. Most of the analyses fall within the field of stability of kaolinite, and seem to be limited more or less by the phase boundaries of kaolinite with the other phases depicted. The sharply defined silica cut-off in the right, at about 60 mg/l SiO_2, may well be the boundary between kaolinite and montmorillonite if other constituents of the waters are taken into consideration.

It seems to us that the picture that emerges is reasonably clear cut. When "aggressive" waters, high in CO_2 and low in dissolved solids, encounter silicates high in cations and silica such as feldspars, they leach silica and cations and leave an aluminosilicate residue with an increased Al-Si ratio (i.e., kaolinite). Initial water attack yields a gibbsite residue but reaction is so rapid that it is only under exceptional conditions that the silica in solution can be kept low enough to prevent the gibbsite from being converted to kaolinite, or to prevent kaolinite from forming in addition to the initial small amount of gibbsite. As the waters continue to attack feldspar, the pH rises, cations and silica increase in concentration, and kaolinite forms until the cations and silica content rise high enough so that montmorillonite begins to form. At that stage, kaolinite apparently tends

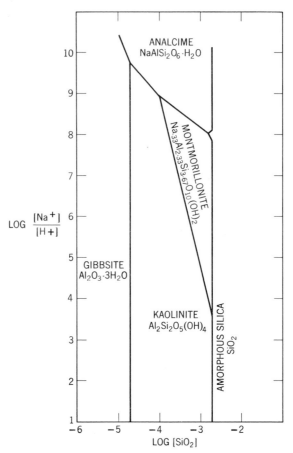

FIGURE 4   STABILITY RELATIONS AMONG SOME SILICAT
             MINERALS AND GIBBSITE AT 25°C AND ONE
             ATM TOTAL PRESSURE. (After Hess, 37).

to be converted to montmorillonite, accounting for the limitation
of silica content to abut 60 mg/l at the two phase boundary kaolinit
montmorillonite.

The chemical reactions involved in weathering are typified
by the alteration of Na feldspar to kaolinite:

$$2\ NaAlSi_3O_8 + 2CO_2 + 3\,H_2O = Al_2Si_2O_5(OH)_4 + 2HCO_3^- +$$
$$2Na^+ + 4SiO_2 \qquad (17\text{-}1)$$

Na-feldspar   Kaolinite

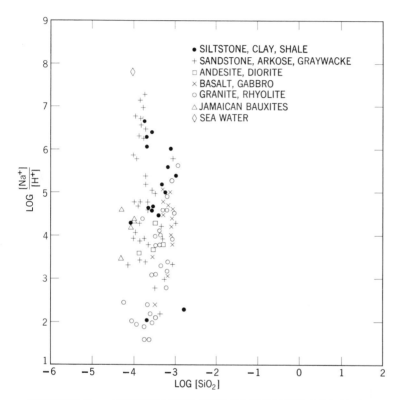

FIGURE 5   SODIUM ION: HYDROGEN ION RATIO OF
WATERS FROM VARIOUS ROCK TYPES
PLOTTED AS A FUNCTION OF SiO_2
CONCENTRATION.

The picture drawn here is that at any stage of the reaction
the solution is in equilibrium with kaolinite, but not with Na-
feldspar.   Note that for a given initial dissolved CO_2, it is
possible to calculate pH, Na^+, SiO_2, HCO_3^-, and the amount of
kaolinite formed as a function of the amount of CO_2 consumed.
In a system isolated from the atmosphere, CO_2 would obviously
drop as the reaction proceeds.   The parallelism with carbonate
equilibria is apparent.   Most silicate phase changes can be
written similarly if, as postulated, reactions of this type occur
rapidly in natural waters, they must be considered in any analysis
of pH-controlling factors.

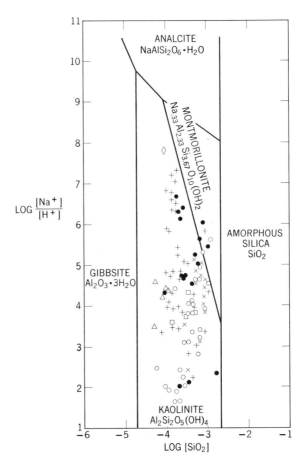

FIGURE 6   SILICATE STABILITY DIAGRAM WITH WATER
             ANALYSES SUPERIMPOSED.

In Figure 7, an idealized diagram of a part of the Na_2O-Al_2O
SiO_2-H_2O system, the shaded area shows predicted changes in
water composition of an initially pure water charged with CO_2, on
the assumption that it reacts with Na-Ca feldspar (oligoclase) to
produce the appropriate stable phases instantaneously. Such a
water should form gibbsite until it reaches the gibbsite-kaolinite
phase boundary, then convert the gibbsite to kaolinite, and continue to react, producing kaolinite, until the two-phase boundary
kaolinite-montmorillonite is reached, after which it should follow
the boundary. The points represent water compositions from the

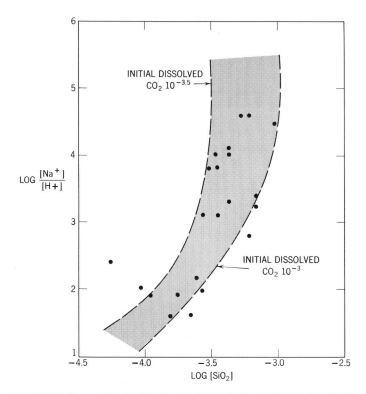

FIGURE 7   COMPOSITION OF EPHEMERAL SPRINGS
FROM THE SIERRA NEVADA IN RELATION
TO COMPOSITION CHANGES CALCULATED
FROM ASSUMPTION OF ATTACK ON Na-Ca
FELDSPAR OF SOLUTION ORIGINALLY
CONTAINING $10^{-3.0}$ AND $10^{-3.5}$ MOLES
DISSOLVED CO_2.

ephemeral springs of the Sierra Nevada, where the chief mineral
being attacked is a high Na-feldspar. The correlation of calculation and prediction is interesting if not convincing.

Conclusions
      The preceding brief discussion is probably all that is worth

presenting at this stage concerning the role of silicate minerals
in controlling natural water compositions. But it is perhaps
enough to permit some tentative conclusions:

a. Silica in natural waters is commonly a major dissolved
constituent and is derived from silicate minerals.

b. The silica in low temperature natural waters is seldom
controlled by the pure silica phases, such as quartz and amorphous silica.

c. The reactions of waters with silicates, in terms of release
of constituents to solution and the production of new solid phases,
is so rapid that the waters remain in near-equilibrium with one
or more phases at all times.

d. Because of silicate control, silica concentrations and
ratios of cations to H^+ have certain genetic patterns. The simple
of these can be traced under well controlled conditions. Extension
of investigations of this kind should eventually permit better prediction of water compositions.

e. The chief buffer system in many natural waters is CO_2
system, but silicate equilibria as well as carbonate equilibria
must be considered. It is not inconceivable that the deviation of
partial pressures of CO_2 from that of the atmosphere in many
stream waters are controlled by silicate equilibria.

SUMMARY

The important but often neglected role of the solid phase in
natural water systems has been stressed. In the first part of
the paper, some aspects of the chemical and structural variation
of $CaCO_3$ and $MgCO_3$ minerals and the influence of these factors
on water composition have been discussed. In the second part
of the paper, an attempt was made to show that silicate equilibria
may exert the dominant control over a number of major constituents in natural waters, and must make an important contribution
to hydrogen ion buffering.

ACKNOWLEDGEMENT

This work was supported by research grant from the National
Science Foundation (GP4140), the Petroleum Research Fund of the
American Chemical Society and the Public Health Service, USDHF
Washington, D.C., Research Grant No. TIES20.

LITERATURE CITED
1. Weber, W.J.Jr. and W. Stumm, J Am Water Works Assoc,
        55, 1553 (1963).

2. Latimer, W.M., Oxidation Potentials, 2nd Ed., Prentice-Hall, New York, N.Y., (1952).

3. Jamieson, J.C., J Chem Phys, 21, 1385 (1953).

4. Brooks, R., et al, Proc Royal Soc (London) Philos Trans, 243A, 145 (1950).

5. Faivre, R., Comp Rend, 222, 227 (1946).

6. Cloud, P.E., U S Geol Surv Prof Paper No. 350 (1962).

7. Barnes, I., Geochim Cosmochim Acta, 29, 85 (1965).

8. Back, W., Intern Assoc Sci Hydrol, VIII Annee, No. 3, 43 (1963).

9. Weyl, P.K., J Geol, 69, 32 (1961).

10. Siever, R., et al, J Geol, 73, 39 (1965).

11. Schmalz, R.F. and K.E. Chave, Science, 139, 1206 (1963).

12. Lowenstam, H.A., J Geol., 62, 284 (1954).

13. Daniels, F., Geochim Cosmochim Acta, 22, 65 (1961).

14. Siegel, F.R., Bull Geol Soc Am, 69, 1643 (1958).

15. MacDonald, G.J.F., Am Mineralogist, 41, 744 (1956).

16. Holland, H.D., et al, The Coprecipitation of Metallic Ions With Calcium Carbonate, Annual Report, Contract A.P. (30-1) 2266, Princeton, N.J., (1960).

17. Graf, D.L. and J.R. Goldsmith, Geochim Cosmochim Acta, 1, 109 (1955).

18. Chave, K.E., J Geol, 62, 266 (1954).

19. Chave, K.E., J Geol, 62, 587 (1954).

20. Alderman, A.R. and H.C.W. Skinner, Am Jour Sci, 255, 561 (1957).

21. Graf, D. L. and J. R. Goldsmith, J Geol, 64, 173 (1956).

22. Langmuir, D., Stability of Carbonates in the System:
    $CaO-MgO-CO_2-H_2O$, PhD Thesis, Harvard University,
    Cambridge, Mass., (1964).

23. Goldsmith, J. R., et al, Geochim Cosmochim Acta, 7, 212
    (1955).

24. Chave, K. E., et al, Science, 137, 33 (1962).

25. Faust, G. T., Am Mineralogist, 38, 4 (1953).

26. Skinner, B. J., Amer Mineralogist, 43, 159 (1958).

27. Graf, D. L., et al, Geol Soc Amer Bull, 70, 1610 (1959).

28. Deffeyes, K. S., et al, Science, 143, 687 (1964).

29. Barnes, I. and W. Back, U S Geol Survey Prof Paper
    No. 475-D, 179 (1964).

30. Hsu, K. J., J Hydrol, 1, 288 (1963).

31. Feth, J. H., et al, U S Geol Survey Water Supply Paper
    No. 1535 (1964).

32. Davis, S. N., Am J Sci, 262, 870 (1964).

33. Garrels, R. M. and C. L. Christ, Solutions, Minerals, and
    Equilibria, Harper and Row, New York, N. Y., (1965).

34. White, D. E., et al, U S Geol Survey Prof Paper No. 440-F
    (1963).

35. Hill, V. G. and A. C. Ellington, Econ Geol, 56, 533 (1961).

36. Bridgman, S., Am J Sci, 237, 7 (1938).

37. Hess, A., Personal Communication.

DISCUSSION
    DR. ZENCHELSKY (Rutgers University): Are there any
questions?

DR. J. J. MORGAN (California Institute of Technology): I wouldn't like to let such a marvelous paper go without discussion. I would like to ask you to speculate, in terms of these conclusions about silicates in sea water, about the pH control mechanism in sea water, which apparently is not explainable in terms of carbonate equilibrium?

DR. BRICKER: Whether or not it is explainable in terms of carbonate equilibrium is a matter of considerable debate. If you consider the total volume of carbonate sediments in the sea as opposed to the total volume of silicates and of silicates that are capable of undergoing reactions such as I had on the board a little while ago, you must arrive at the conclusion that silicate minerals play an important, if not dominant role in controlling pH in sea water.

DR. H. L. BOHN (Tennessee Valley Authority): Your conclusion that aragonite is more stable than calcite is based on a small difference between two large free energies of formation. Isn't this difference the same order of magnitude as the experimental error of the free energies?

Your free energies of montmorillonite, while the best presently obtainable, are probably not very satisfactory. I wonder if you would care to comment.

DR. BRICKER: With regard to the free energy difference between calcite and aragonite, I think the value has been pretty definitely established. Langmuir completed a thesis at Harvard last year in which he investigated the thermodynamic properties of calcite and aragonite, and I think his free energy data is pretty good (22).

With regard to montmorillonite, I will agree that the free energy value is not as good as we would like to have. The value we used to draw the diagrams is for an ideal sodium montmorillonite. Of course, if you had a calcium or aluminum montmorillonite, the free energy would be somewhat different. We are working on this problem now, trying to get some idea of how large the differences are. We feel condident, however, that the phase relations shown in Figure 6 are essentially correct and that refinements in the free energy value of montmorillonite will not alter the diagram significantly.

Gerald Corsaro
Steven Sutherland
University of Akron

THE FORMATION
AND BEHAVIOR OF
HYDROXYAPATITE

Bone and tooth structure, the formation of "stones" in humans, and the deposition of phosphate-bearing scale on boiler and heat exchanger surfaces appear to have a common origin; the formation of hydroxyapatite (HAP) for which the formula $Ca_{10}(PO_4)_6(OH)_2$ generally is accepted. This report is a review of a paper already published (1). The main considerations are a demonstration that HAP can form either by reaction of a solid phase $CaHPO_4$ with different solution environments or by direct precipitation from solution from various ionic concentrations of HPO_4^{-2} and Ca^{+2} over a wide range of initial pH conditions. Further, this report shows that HAP may be reactive at its surface with hydroxide and other ionic species.

CHARACTERISTICS OF HAP

A natural or synthetic sample of HAP prepared by slow hydrolysis of $CaHPO_4$ in water at high temperature and pressure may be identified by its Ca/P ratio, X-ray diffraction (single crystal and powder), crystal habit (dipyramidal hexagonal), refractive index, etc. (2). It should be noted, however, that samples prepared by precipitation from different solution environments give the same powder X-ray diffraction patterns

but may have different Ca/P ratios varying from 1.4 to 1.71 (3).
This result may be ascribed to formation of defect structures
as indicated by varying refractive index values. The precipitation
of a true ortho phosphate, β-$Ca_3(PO_4)_2$ or its formation by the
bomb hydrolysis of $CaHPO_4$ in the presence of metallic impurities has been reported (2). The latter apparently form seeds
of ortho phosphate on which the calcium ortho phosphate grows.
The presence of β-$Ca_3(PO_4)_2$ in human "stones" has been
confirmed, although in minor amounts. An excellent review
of these and other structural characteristics of calcium phosphates has been reported by Mooney and Aia (3).

SOLUBILITY BEHAVIOR OF HAP

The solubility behavior of HAP has been given a good deal
of attention in an endeavor to obtain information about the
nucleation process thru which solid HAP forms. Lavinskas and
Neuman (4), Neuman and Neuman (5), Rootare, et al, (6,7),and
LaMer (8) provide much of the recent information on this subject.
LaMer's comments on the conclusions by Neuman and Neuman
should be noted. These latter investigators have reported an
extensive summary of HAP behavior, attempting to correlate
the observation that HAP's solubility depends on the weight of
HAP used in a given volume of water with their proposed
solubility theories. Rootare, et al, apparently have resolved
the problem of varying solubility with slurry density. They
postulate that solid HAP placed in water undergoes a surface
hydrolysis reaction:

$$Ca_{10}(PO_4)_6(OH)_2 + 6H_2O \rightarrow 4\left[Ca_2(HPO_4)(OH)_2\right] + 2Ca^{+2}$$
$$+ 2HPO_4^{-2} \qquad\qquad (18\text{-}1)$$

and that the subsequent surface complex provides the ionic
solubility equilibria. In more recent studies, Rootare, et al,
calculate the number of moles of Ca and P expected from a
given weight of HAP based on a knowledge of the specific surface area of their sample and the unit cell lattice dimensions (7).
They demonstrate that, on summing the solution concentrations
found in successive extracts, the concentration which would
accrue from the hydrolysis reaction and eventual equilibrium:

$$Ca_2(HPO_4)(OH)_2 = 2 Ca^{+2} + HPO_4^{-2} + 2OH^- \qquad (18\text{-}2)$$

comes to that expected from a single layer of the HAP solid surface. The solubility product should be governed by reaction 18-2 in environments of varying Ca^{+2} and PO_4^{-3} concentrations.

There is one feature in the solubility studies which must be noted. At pH values higher than 8.0, the solubility of HAP rises sharply. The presence of NaCl causes a decrease in solubility. Both results are unexpected on purely ionic electrostatic and equilibria considerations.

EXPERIMENTS

Experiments were designed to demonstrate that $CaHPO_4$ hydrolysis could proceed under a variety of solution environments and that the rate of hydrolysis is dependent on initial $[OH^-]$ and independent of other ionic species. It was hoped that electron micrographs of solid residues after different reaction times might reveal whether reaction proceeds from homogeneous phase or at the solid $CaHPO_4$ surface. Three series of experiments were conducted. In the first series, one g samples of ground $CaHPO_4$ were loaded in polyethylene bottles and 200-ml solutions of different initial concentrations of OH, CO_3^{-2}, and SO_4^{-2} ions were added. These particular species were chosen since they are common to practical water compositions. The use of Mg was avoided in view of its participation in forming the calcium ortho phosphate. The closed bottles were placed in $100^{\circ}C$ ovens. Different bottles from a given replicate solution composition were taken at 2.5, 5.0, 7.5, 10, and 20 hrs. The solutions were filtered quickly under nitrogen pressure and analyzed. Solid residues were examined by X-ray, thermal analysis, infrared, and electron micrography. A second series of experiments duplicated the first except that the reactions were allowed to occur in stirred flasks. A third series of experiments concerned the precipitation by mixing Ca^{+2} bearing solutions with HPO_4^{-2} solutions each at the same initial pH values obtained by addition of NaOH so that a pH range of 6-11 was covered. The same type of examination as above was conducted on dried residues.

In another series, duplicate sets of 1, 2, 3, and 4 g of HAP in 900-ml of deionized water were prepared. Conductance titrations on one set were made after preparation and again on the remaining set after allowing the suspensions to stand for 7 days. The titrations were followed by measuring resistance changes with a line operated bridge. A dip type cell was fixed in the suspension; readings were recorded after 0.5-ml additions of 0.1 N NaOH and after at least one minute mixing time. A similar series of suspensions was titrated with base but using pH changes recorded by a precision pH meter. While no signficance can be attached to individual resistance or pH readings, the technique is useful in manifesting reaction of the added base with HAP surfaces. The pH titrations show apparent equivalence end points, using the method of finding maxima by Δ pH/ Δ ml vs. ml plots.

Precipitates of calcium phosphate were formed by mixing equivalent concentrations of Ca^{+2} and HPO_4^{-2} in separate initial solutions with each adjusted to the same pH value. A range of pH values from 6-11 was used. Again duplicate runs for each pH value were made. In one set the formed precipitates were allowed to reflux with the equilibrium solutions for 90 hrs before filtration and drying the precipitate, whereas for the other set the precipitates were recovered shortly after their formation. In still another series of experiments, the calcium phosphates were precipitated from 1 M NaCl solutions. Also, a calcium polyphosphate precipitate was prepared by using a sodium polyphosphate (M W = 7000) for the phosphate solution. The latter was recovered shortly after its formation. The precipitated solids were examined by electron micrography, X-ray, and in some cases nujol mull infrared spectrophotometry.

RESULTS

Electron Micrographs

Figures 1a and 1b are photographs at 25,000X of bottle experiment residues formed from $CaHPO_4$ and solutions with 40 mg/1 initial $[O\bar{H}]$ after two different time intervals. Figure 1c shows a residue after complete conversion of $CaHPO_4$ to HAP crystallites. These are typical results obtained with bottle and stirred flask experiments in which the solution composition of $[CO_3^{-2}]$, $[SO_4^{-2}]$, and $[OH]$'s were varied over a wide range. Particular attention is called to the first figure showing unreacted $CaHPO_4$ solid but whose surface appears to be breaking up into HAP crystallites. This suggests that the reaction leading to HAP proceeds at the solid-solution interface rather than by homogeneous precipitation from solution.

Figures 2 and 3 show the difference in crystallites prepared by precipitation reaction with and without refluxing. The formation of imperfect crystallites for the unrefluxed sample is to be noted.

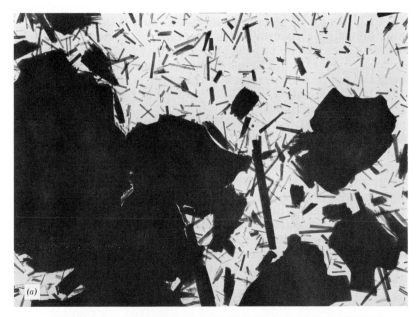

FIGURE 1a   ELECTRON MICROGRAPH OF RESIDUE
             AFTER CaHPO₄ HYDROLYSIS WITH 40 mg/l
             [OH⁻] .   TIME 2. 5 HRS.   NOTE SURFACE
             STRUCTURES.

Figure 4 also shows a photograph of a precipitated
phosphate, in this case precipitated from a 1 M NaCl solution.
Again note the apparent imperfect crystallite formation although
the solid was refluxed for several days. It should be noted
here that X-ray diffraction patterns were essentially the same
for all these solids.

Figure 5 is a photograph of calcium polyphosphate. It is
shown here for purposes of comparison and also to note whether
surface hydrolysis of this solid would reveal HAP crystallites
which could form from the ortho phosphate hydrolysis product
of the polyphosphate.

Differential Thermal Analysis
Figure 6 shows a group of thermal analysis traces for
residues taken from bottle experiments after different time

FIGURE 1b SAME AS FIGURE 1a AFTER 5 HRS.

intervals. The endotherm peak is characteristic of $CaHPO_4$ solid. Its disappearance with time could serve as a measure of reaction rate of $CaHPO_4$ with its solution environment.

The absence of other than $CaHPO_4$ endotherms indicates that no other species than HAP and $CaHPO_4$ solids are present, assuming that such species would reveal endotherms reflecting transition of phases intermediate between $CaHPO_4$ and HAP. The apparent stability of HAP through 1100°C temperature range is to be noted.

Figure 7 shows several X-ray diffraction patterns from bottle experiment residues after completed reaction. The only differences in such patterns noted for all precipitated HAP or bottle residue solids were slight variations in the relative intensities of the pattern. The spacings and angles at which the line intensities are shown agree in both relative magnitude and number with those reported by Rootare, et al, on a well characterized HAP which they used in their solubility studies (6).

It has been observed by a number of workers (3), that a HAP diffraction pattern can be obtained for solids prepared by methods other than those described here, and that the Ca/P

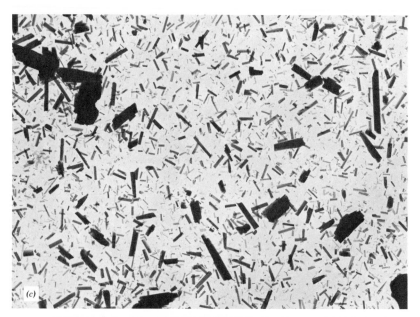

FIGURE 1c   SAME AS FIGURE 1a BUT WITH 100 mg/1
[OH$^-$] AFTER 20 HRS.

molar ratio may vary over a range of values from 1.41 to 1.71
in contrast to 1.67 expected from the stoichiometric formula
given for HAP.   The variation in Ca/P ratios is attended also
by variation in refractive indices.   The postulate of a defect
structure or the probability of isomorphous exchange of lattice
Ca^{+2} ions with others of comparable size has been advanced to
account for these observations.   The problem has by no means
been resolved.

Conductance and pH Titration
        Figure 8 summarized the results of conductance titrations
on HAP suspensions shortly after their preparation. The lower
linear portions suggest reaction of base with acidic sites in the
HAP surface.   Similar plots are obtained, for instance, when
precipitated silicas are titrated with base.   The author believes
that the silanol groups on such silica surfaces are reactive
as acidic sites if pairs of adjacent silanol groups interact through
hydrogen bonding.   This makes one silanol OH group more acidic
than its adjacent neighbor.   Hence, from a knowledge of the BET

FIGURE 2   ELECTRON MICROGRAPH FOR
              PRECIPITATED HAP AND REFLUXING
              90 HRS (50, 000x).

specific surface area of the silicas and the generally accepted
fact that about 8 silanol groups should be present on 1 sq m of
surface, conductance titrations can demonstrate, as herein
described, that one half of the total silanol groups is the
maximum number which respond as acidic sites. The interaction through hydrogen bonding is analogous to the effect of
hydroxide ortho substitution on benzoic acid for which the pK
values decrease by at least one order of magnitude for each
ortho substitution.

     Conductance titration results with HAP suggest that
even the weak HPO_4^{-2} groups formed on the HAP's surface by
hydrolysis may respond to conductance. The apparent end
points as indicated by the break in the linear slopes of the plot
may or may not be significant as it relates to the number of
acid sites on the HAP surfaces. It is true, however, that coin-
cident with the "break" in the plots that the phosphate concentration in solution increases. This suggests a breakdown of the
HAP structure.

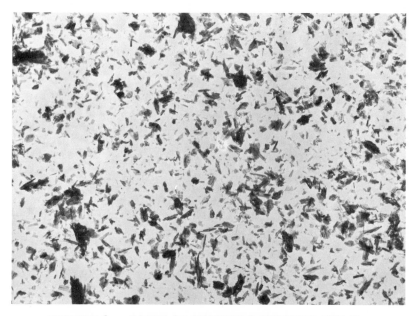

FIGURE 3   SAME AS FIGURE 2 EXCEPT THAT
            PRECIPITATE IS RECOVERED SHORTLY
            AFTER FORMATION (50, 000x).

The same type of plots (Figure 9) with samples that are
allowed first to stand for 7 days shows that much more base
is required to reach the "end points" and that the lower portions
of the plot deviate from linearity. These results reflect the
prior surface hydrolysis of HAP surface groups.

The pH titration results (Figure 10) show that the apparent
equivalence points are proportional to the weight of sample used.
Similar to conductance results, the end points are attained with
higher concentrations of base after the samples are allowed to
stand. As noted before, no significance can be attached to individual pH or conductance readings as they cannot reflect the true
equilibrium ionic concentration in the immediate locale of the
particle surface.

A general conclusion may be reached regarding the results
of titrations; namely, that there is reason to believe that surface acidity exists which increases in magnitude when the suspensions are allowed to stand. Further, that excess base can

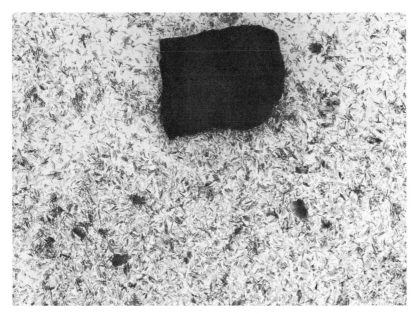

FIGURE 4 ELECTRON MICROGRAPH OF PRECIPITATED
HAP FROM 1 M NaCl SOLUTION (25, 000x).

cause the HAP to "dissolve" insofar as increasing phosphate
concentration is detected in solution when base is added in
excess of the amount indicated by the apparent end points.

Infrared Absorption Spectra
    A rough outline of infrared spectra is reproduced in
Figure 11. This figure shows the spectra obtained from:
(a) the precipitated calcium polyphosphate; (b) the HAP precipitated from 1 M NaCl; and (c) HAP precipitated from solution
by mixing HPO_4^{-2} and Ca^{+2} ions in the manner previously
described.
    Although it is possible to reproduce the lower spectra on
samples prepared by precipitation or by bottle experiments, it
is difficult to assign structural groups to characteristic
frequencies. Those shown on Figure 11 have been observed for
both ortho phosphate salts and some organic phosphates.
    Nevertheless, certain bands can be reproduced. The
contrast between the "NaCl" precipitated sample and the "normal"

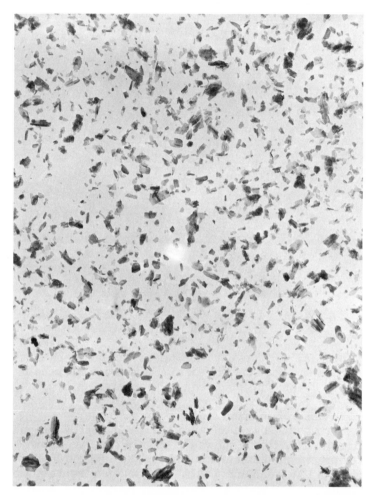

FIGURE 5   ELECTRON MICROGRAPH OF PRECIPITATED
CALCIUM POLYPHOSPHATE (50, 000x).

sample should be noted. This along with the electron micrograph differences for these two precipitated phosphates, does
suggest some influence of Cl^- ions on the formation of HAP.

On shaking HAP samples with NaCl for several days only
a slight decrease in pH of filtered samples was observed. An
attempt to measure the adsorption from dilute solution of Cl^-

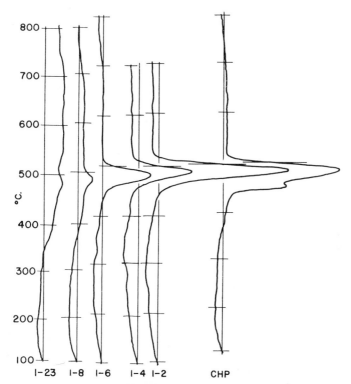

FIGURE 6 DIFFERENTIAL THERMAL ANALYSIS
TRACES FOR BOTTLE RESIDUES FORMED
AFTER DIFFERENT TIME INTERVALS.
THE TRACES SHOW THE VANISHING
$CaHPO_4$ PEAK. NO NEW ENDOTHERMS
ARE DETECTED UP TO 1100°C.

ions by HAP showed that only slight adsorption was detected.
On the other hand, if HAP precipitates are shaken with F⁻
ion solutions, a very large increase in OH⁻ in solution is found
that was in proportion to the amount of HAP used in suspensions
with 1 M fluoride solutions. Although chloroapatites are known
to exist it appears that they do not form by exchange of OH⁻
with Cl⁻ by the simple expedient of mixing HAP and Cl solutions.
These spectra are influenced by Cl⁻ ions and the fact that the
solubility of HAP decreases rather than increases, as may be
expected in the presence of high ionic solution concentrations,

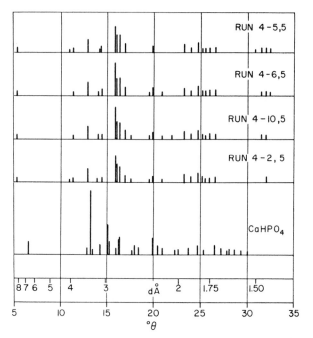

FIGURE 7   X-RAY DIFFRACTION FOR BOTTLE
RESIDUES FOR DIFFERENT BOTTLE
EXPERIMENTS AFTER COMPLETED
REACTION. CaHPO4 IS SHOWN ALSO
FOR COMPARISON. PRECIPITATED
RESIDUES SHOW SAME TYPE OF PATTERN.
SEE (5) FOR COMPARISON WITH HAP
USED BY ROOTARE, ET AL.

suggests a surface reaction between HAP and chloride which
alters the surface complex composition. Fluoride ions
apparently exchange with OH^- ions, although it is noted that
phosphate concentration also increases in such solutions along
with hydroxide.

CONCLUSIONS
All of the experiments described herein show that HAP
crystallites may be formed by either $CaHPO_4$ hydrolysis in
various environments or may be precipitated from solutions of
various initial pH values, $[Ca^{+2}]$, and $[HPO_4^{-2}]$. Although

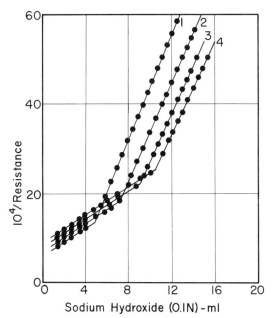

FIGURE 8   CONDUCTANCE TITRATION RESULTS IN
HAP SUSPENSIONS. THE NUMERALS
INDICATE GRAMS HAP IN 900-ml WATER.
THESE RESULTS ARE FOR TITRATIONS
ON FRESHLY PREPARED SUSPENSIONS.

the X-ray diffraction and infrared patterns may be duplicated,
there is no assurance that the Ca/P ratio of all such samples
prepared is the same for reasons already cited.

The experiments appear to support the idea that surface
hydrolysis is a definite factor in establishing equilibria between
solid and solution species. The possibility that nucleation of
HAP proceeds through intermediate species is indicated by the
fact that, in $CaHPO_4$ hydrolysis, crystallites form on the $CaHPO_4$
surface rather than from homogeneous precipitation resulting
from solution of surface groups from $CaHPO_4$. Electron
micrographs of precipitates taken shortly after formation also
suggest this conclusion.

The reactivity of HAP solid with a higher concentration
of OH^- indicates that, in practical systems, the dissolution of
phosphate solid and reprecipitation on heat exchange surfaces
is a possible mechanism in boiler scale formation. In systems

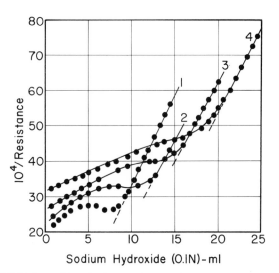

FIGURE 9   SAME AS FIGURE 8. THE SUSPENSIONS
              WERE FIRST ALLOWED TO STAND 7 DAYS
              BEFORE MAKING THE TITRATION.

where the pH value is maintained below 8.0, scale deposition
can be minimized. This is a general field observation. The
influence of NaCl in biological systems may be important. Also
in the latter, the tendency for surface hydrolysis, selective
adsorption through hydrogen bonding, and or the possibility of
deflocculation effects by "natural" constituents should be
investigated. In addition, the possibility of solubilization of
HAP crystallites first formed by nucleation by "natural" constituents in biological systems should be investigated also.
This aspect of the problem concerns $CaCO_3$ precipitates (9).

LITERATURE CITED
1. Corsaro, G., et al, J Am Water Works Assoc, 36, 347 (1964).

2. Perloff, A. and A.S. Posner, Science, 124, 583 (1956).

3. Mooney, R.W. and A.M. Aia, Chem Revs, (Oct. 1961).

4. Levinskas, G.J. and W.F. Neuman, J Phys Chem, 59,
      164 (1955).

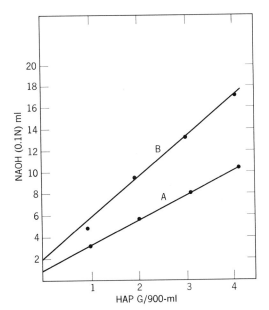

FIGURE 10   PLOT OF APPARENT pH EQUIVALENCE
POINTS WITH DIFFERENT WEIGHTS OF
HAP. LOWER CURVE AFTER PREPARATION.
UPPER AFTER 7 DAYS STANDING,

5. Neuman, W. F. and M. W. Neuman, The Chemical Dynamics
   of Bone Minerals, University of Chicago Press, Chicago
   Illinois, (1958).

6. Rootare, H. M., et al, J Coll Sci, 17, 179 (1962).

7. Deitz, V. R., et al, J Coll Sci, 19, 87 (1964).

8. LaMer, V. K., J Phys Chem, 66, 973 (1962).

9. Corsaro, G., J Am Water Works Assoc, 48, 683 (1956).

DISCUSSION
      DR. S. ZENCHELSKY: Are there any questions of this
paper ?
      DR. V. K. LAMER (Columbia University): I want to
congratulate the speaker on making progress in a subject of
importance in biology and medicine; namely, the fundamental

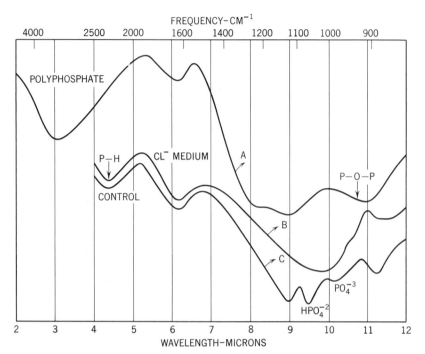

FIGURE 11   A ROUGH OUTLINE OF THE INFRARED
             ABSORPTION ON SAMPLES OF PRECIPITATE
             PHOSPHATES. (a) CALCIUM POLYPHOSPHAT
             (b) SAMPLE OF HAP FORMED IN THE
             PRESENCE OF 1 M NaCl. (c) HAP FORMED
             BY THE METHOD DESCRIBED.

problem of calcification of living tissues and the questions of
why our bones and teeth harden or soften and why some children
have rickets. The chemistry of calcifications has been badly
advised and misinterpreted by some members of the dental
and medical professions. A few words about the history of the
subject are in order.

In early 1920's the pediatricians at Johns Hopkins had
found an empirical rule regarding rickets. If the product of the
calcium (in mg) in the blood multiplied by the total phosphate
(in mg) exceeded a value of about 40, the child would be free of
rickets. If this product was below this value, rickets would
appear.

One of their number, Dr. L. Emmett Holt, Jr., had been

well schooled in chemistry, for a medical pediatrician, and appreciated the limitations which the phase rule placed upon equilibria in the calcium and phosphate systems. He quite properly contended that this empirical product should be replaced by the solubility product if a meaningful elucidation of the processes of calcification were to be found. He enlisted my cooperation in investigating the effects in the blood of pH, the concentrations of Ca and phosphates, and the newly discovered effects of ionic strength on solubility (Brönsted and LaMer, J Am Chem Soc, 1924).

The phase rule chemist, Bassett, had shown in 1908 that one could not investigate the solubities of the various basic phosphates by the usual methods because they hydrolyzed. For that reason, Holt, LaMer, and Choun titrated orthophosphorous acid by progressive additions of $Ca(OH)_2$ and analysed the solid phase in equilibrium after prolonged shaking. On the other hand, Levinakas and Neuman (4) prepared very fine crystals of pure hydroxyapatite and analysed the aqueous solution after shaking these crystals in pure water. They obtained a curious set of values which defied all of the normal laws of solubility. Rootare, et al, (6) and LaMer (8) have given the reason for these paradoxical results.

Hydroxyapatite, as a salt of a weak acid (secondary phosphoric), is subject to hydrolysis in spite of the fact that it is very insoluble. Since the hydrolysis product is also insoluble, the hydrolysis reaction is restricted to the surface layer or layers, and the reaction is controlled by the ionic (not the solubility) product of (Ca^{+2}) (HPO_4^{-2}). This finding explains the curious fact that this ionic product is often constant (a well known empirical finding of Hodge) yet the system is not saturated in respect to solid $CaHPO_4$. If it were, the phase rule would be violated. There is consequently no need for the contention of Neuman and Neuman, that all of our well recognized laws of solubility must be replaced. Hydrolysis must always be considered, not neglected.

Congratulations, Dr. Corsaro.

DR. ZENCHELSKY: Are there any further questions or discussion?

DR. L. SHEDLOVSKY (Colgate-Palmolive Company): Besides hydroxyapatite, various defect apatites of the type described by Posner also can be formed. Furthermore, there are a number of other possible solid phases of calcium phosphates.

The only point I want to make is in connection with the

presence of a surface complex shown on the board, which has
the composition $Ca_2(HPO_4)(OH)_2$. How does one draw conclusions about the composition of the solid phase only from an
examination of the solution and from the solubility product?
It seems desirable to characterize the solid phase in order to
identify it. I realize that it is difficult to separate and examine
some of the solid phases.

DR. CORSARO: In a second paper by Rootare, et al, (7)
they examined the beta surface area, 60 m^2/g and calculated
the number of atoms they would expect in the surface based on
the unit cell structure. They demonstrated that, according to
their solubility studies which consisted of taking successive
extracts and analyzing, they could account for the composition
of the single first layer on the calcium phosphate they had. The
results are convincing to the effect that at least the solubility
accumulations can account for the surface structure which then
is responsible for the equilibrium in the solution. This has
nothing to do with the structure.

DR. SHEDLOVSKY: Couldn't the compositions also be
considered in terms of suitable proportions of various calcium
phosphates?

DR. CORSARO: This compound when prepared is not
stable. You cannot prepare the compound in brackets and have
it as stable species.

DR. SHEDLOVSKY: Can we know whether we have this
particular compound, until we have identified the solid phase?

DR. CORSARO: It has only been identified indirectly
from the solubility conclusions and the calculation of the surface layer that Deitz has made.

DR. SHEDLOVSKY: I would like to ask why you have
carbonate in your solutions?

DR. CORSARO: Very good question. McConnell, from
Ohio State Dental Research, insists there is a carbonate apatite
structure as this probably forms in many cases, I put the
carbonate into my experiments to show or to see whether or
not the crystallites which would form would show something
different in the X-ray diffraction patterns, which they did not.

DR. SHEDLOVSKY: Except that X-ray diffraction does
not distinguish carbonate from other groups.

DR. CORSARO: That is a point I made before. You cannot tell specifically from the X-ray diffraction that you have
a particular structure. You may have a carbonate but, as I
said, the only evidence is the ability to produce X-ray diffraction

patterns without carbonate and with carbonate in the environment,
the same spacing, same intensity, etc. There may be more
valid methods of calculation. Dr. McConnell believes calculat-
tions do support the carbonate apatite.

DR. SHEDLOVSKY: Dr. McConnell says it is almost
impossible to form hydroxyapatite which is completely free
from carbonate.

DR. CORSARO: Of course, we did measure the equilibrium
concentrations but did not think the results were consistent
enough to draw any conclusions. I think the work of Rootare,
et al, (6, 7) probably is the only consistent work done on solubility
equilibrium that is significant to any extent.

I must admit carbonate and, of course, the whole research
is, shall we say, at a point of transition in terms of getting
conclusive answers. None of these researches are conclusive,
by any means.

DR. E. MATIJEVIC (Clarkson College): I would like to
disagree with you a little. I agree with the speaker. It is
possible to obtain the composition of the solid phase from
solubility data if you know the composition of the solution, and
vice versa. So this may not be definite proof, but it is a way
for indirect determination of the solid phase, where direct methods
are inadequate.

DR. BOHN (Tennesse Valley Authority): In partial answer
to Dr. Shedlovsky, TVA has prepared fluorohydroxyapatites that
are carbonate-free. Natural apatites, however, usually contain
2 to 5% carbonates unless they have been exposed to high temperatures whereupon the carbonate content decreases to several
tenths of one percent. X-ray diffraction was used to determine
the structure of the apatites.

DR. LAMER: Dr. Shedlovsky has an important point, but
are we talking about teeth or hydroxyapatite as a compund? I
think you are talking about hydroxyapatites. They have made
pure material, no carbonate in it.

When you have teeth you have carbonate, and we may
have a solid solution.

When we have real thermodynamic stability, according to
Gibbs, everything is dead, the lowest state. A tooth is a living
substance. It changes according to the composition of the saliva
from day to day in hardness and softness, so we cannot apply
the Gibb's equilibrium conditions rigorously to living tissues.
Instead we have to consider living tissue as an open system in
steady or nearly steady states. That is what the biologists are

now doing.

But Dr. Corsaro is trying to interpret the chemistry, where we have a pure compound. I think the carbonate issue is beside the point here. For biology it is important.

DR. A. BAIDINS (E. I. du Pont de Nemours & Company): I would like to make one comment. You have been looking at the X-ray diffraction patterns and making conclusions about the presence of phases, but when you get to the particle of the surface area, having tens of m^2/g, sometimes it doesn't matter what the bulk phase is, but what the surface composition is.

In my work I have found that surface structure plays a frequently dominant role; surface properties may be more important than the composition or the crystalline structure of the bulk material. Infrared spectra of high surface area materials, are frequently different from those of coarsely crystalline materials, which indicates the presence of a surface layer with a different structure or composition than the bulk material.

Perhaps you could use some of the techniques used for studying catalysts, such as the flash desorption method described by Cvetanovie (J Phys Chem, 67, 144,1963). I have had no experience with hydroxyapatites, but from what I know of the chemistry of phosphorous and calcium, just a few carbonate ions which you could not detect in any other way may have quite an important effect on the surface properties of the substance.

DR. CORSARO: I want to mention the residue usually obtained from the experiments is about 12 or 15 m^2 specific surface area.

DR. LAMER: Neuman's were 60 m^2.

DR. CORSARO: Yes, 60.

DR. LAMER: Of crystalline material.

J. Walden
Food Machinery Chemical Corporation
Princeton, New Jersey

H. P. Gregor
Polytechnic Institute of Brooklyn

ION EXCHANGE IN SOLUTION

This paper will describe a new class of ion exchange resins designed for use in non-aqueous systems. This discussion is limited to their use in organic solvents and with some information as to their properties which may be useful in water technology. In particular, these resins may be used for analysis of organic matter in water by column chromatography.

PREVIOUS WORK ON NON-AQUEOUS ION EXCHANGE

Many attempts have been made in the past to extend the use of ion exchange resins to non-aqueous solutions. As an example, conventional sulfonated polystyrene resins have been used in solvents; such as, the lower alcohols, acetone, or dioxane. These uses were practical but rates of absorption sometimes were reduced. In the majority of organic solvents, however, ion exchange with conventional resins is unsuccessful. The principal difficulty with conventional resins is that they do not swell sufficiently in the organic solvent to allow for an appreciable rate of sorption or exchange. There have been many attempts to circumvent the low swelling of ion exchangers in non-polar solvents. First, water wet resins have been used in water immiscible solvents, but this method is restricted to a limited number of solvents and solutes. The second method

491

used the macroporous resins of Kunin (1) and Millar (2). These
resins are highly cross-linked networks prepared from styrene-
divinylbenzene copolymers that contain a large number of sub-
microscopic pores, so as to have a large internal surface.
Macroporous resins are relatively rigid and hence are non-
swelling. Their full capacity to high molecular weight solutes
cannot be realized in non-polar or even in polar solvents because
of the density of most of the gel.

A different approach to the problem of non-aqueous ion
exchange recently was made that represents the most general
solution to the problem of poor swelling in organic solvents
(3, 4, 5, 6). It modifies the resin structure by the introduction
of hydrophobic or oleophilic groups which reduce the polarity
of the resin structure and make for its swelling in solvents that
do not solvate the ordinary ionic functional groups. These
resins are called "oleophilic" ion exchange resins. Several
different oleophilic ion exchange resins have been prepared.
For example, styrene was copolymerized with isobutylene and
then sulfonated; polystyrene was acylated and then sulfonated;
polyvinylimidazole was quaternized with long chain alkyl halides;
and chloromethylated polystyrene was aminated with long chain
teritary amines. In this manner resins were prepared which
had appreciable swelling in a wide range of solvents varying
from hexane or benzene to water. The rates of exchange of
certain of these oleophilic ion exchange resins in non-polar
solvents were shown to be comparable to those of conventional
ion exchange resins in aqueous media.

SWELLING DATA

The poor swelling of conventional resins in organic solvents
as contrasted with the swelling of oleophilic resins which do
swell in such solvents is shown in Tables I and II. Table I
presents swelling data of three polystyrene-based anion exchange
resins having a nominal divinylbenzene content of 8% that were
prepared with dimethyldodecyl, tribenzyl, and trimethyl amine.
The column headed capacity in meq/g is the dry weight capacity.
The dimethyldodecyl and trimethylamine resins were aminated
to 96 and 100%, respectively. The difference between the two
capacities is due to the difference in the molecular weight of
the repeating groups. The other resin was not aminated as
completely. These swelling data show the principal difference
between oleophilic resins and commercial anion exchange resins.
The trimethyl amine resin is typical of the commercial Dowex-1

TABLE 1 OLEOPHILIC ANION EXCHANGE RESINS

RESIN	AMINE	CAPACITY meq/g	HEXANE	% SWELLING ACETONE	WATER
1	$(CH_3)_2C_{12}H_{25}N$	2.1 (96%)	20	35	30
2	$(C_7H_{15})_3N$	1.3 (50%)	13	45	18
3	$(CH_3)_3N$	3.2 (100%)	5	20	138

$$— CH_2 — CH —$$

TABLE II   OLEOPHILIC CATION EXCHANGE RESINS

RESIN L %	S %	CAPACITY meq/g	n-Heptane	% SWELLING Benzene	Water
1 42	78	3.17	<5	19	421
2 88	24	0.83	67	196	29
3 98	84	2.57	6	64	83
4 Dowex 50 -x8		5.0	3	4	50

L = Lauroylation
S = Sulfonation

resin. Note that the trimethylamine resin swells least in hexane and acetone but most in water.

These swelling measurements are made by placing a small quantity of resin in equilibrium with the solvent of choice. This may take from several hours to a few days. The resin then is transferred to a glass tube having a glass filter at the bottom. The tube and resin then are centrifuged for three minutes at a fixed RPM. The difference in resin weight gives the weight percent gain in solvent content by the resin.

Table II presents swelling data of three polystryrene-based cation exchange resins. These were prepared by first acylating, then sulfonating cross-linked polystyrene. The three resins differ from each other in the percent lauroylation and sulfonation. The swelling data are again in g of solvent per g of resin times 100. Resins 1 and 3 swell very little in n-heptane compared to Resin 2, which is explained mainly by the percent sulfonation. A higher percent sulfonation gives a lower swelling in the two organic solvents, although the lauroylation also effects the swelling strongly. It is the balance of these two kinds of groups with their antagonistic swelling that determines the final effect. Thus, cation exchange resins were prepared which swelled to different extents in organic solvents. The swelling was determined by the relative percentages of lauroylation and sulfonation.

ACID-BASE REACTION STUDIES

Acid-base reactions in organic solvents employing the above kinds of resins were studied. The acid was a strong acid cation exchange resin of the oleophilic type. The bases were weak base organic amines.

An association-dissociation reaction can be used to describe the neutralization of a sulfonic acid resin by an organic base in a nonpolar solvent. Such a reaction is:

$$RSO_3H + B = RS\bar{O}_3\overset{+}{H} B \qquad (19\text{-}1)$$

where R represents the oleophilic cation exchange resin and B an organic base. It is assumed that the base and the sulfonic group are not ionized in this solvent. There is an analogy between equation 19-1 and the corresponding reaction in water:

$$H_2O + B = OH^- + HB^+ \qquad (19\text{-}2)$$

The equilibrium constant K of equation 19-1 is a measure of the strength of the base towards the sulfonic group. Since the resin sulfonic group is a much stronger acid than water, the equilibrium position can be expected to be far to the right for bases that are weak in water. K is evaluated by substituting concentrations for activities to obtain:

$$K = \frac{\left[RSO_3^- \overset{+}{H} B \right]}{\left[RSO_3H \right]\left[B \right]} = \frac{\bar{X}}{(1 - \bar{X})\left[B \right]} \tag{19-3}$$

where $\bar{X}$ is the fraction of exchange sites occupied by the base, or:

$$\bar{X} = \frac{\left[RSO_3^- \overset{+}{H} B \right]}{\left[RSO_3^- \overset{+}{H} B \right] + \left[RSO_3 H \right]} \tag{19-4}$$

As a first approximation, the concentration of free base in the resin phase B is taken to be equal to the concentration "C" of the base in the solution outside of the resin. Thus:

$$K = \bar{X}/(1 - \bar{X})C \tag{19-5}$$

If we expose the resin to two bases, B_1 and B_2, simultaneous equilibria will result:

$$RSO_3H + B_1 = RSO_3^- \overset{+}{H} B_1 \; ; K_1 \tag{19-6}$$

$$RSO_3H + B_2 = RSO_3^- \overset{+}{H} B_2 \; ; K_2 \tag{19-7}$$

Using the previous notation, let:

$$\bar{X}_1 = \frac{\left[RSO_3^- \overset{+}{H} B_1 \right]}{\left[RSO_3^- \overset{+}{H} B_1 \right] + \left[RSO_3^- \overset{+}{H} B_2 \right] + \left[RSO_3H \right]} \tag{19-8}$$

and let:

$$C_1 = \left[B_1 \right], \quad C_2 = \left[B_2 \right]$$

then:

$$K_1 = \frac{\bar{X}_1}{(1 - \bar{X}_1 - \bar{X}_2)C_1} \tag{19-9}$$

and:

$$K_2 = \frac{\bar{X}_2}{(1 - \bar{X}_1 - \bar{X}_2)C_2} \tag{19-10}$$

Since the quantity $(1 - \bar{X}_1 - \bar{X}_2)$ is usually too small to determine readily, the ratio of the two equilibrium constants is all that can be obtained experimentally:

$$\frac{K_1}{K_2} = \frac{\bar{X}_1 \, C_2}{\bar{X}_2 \, C_1} \tag{19-11}$$

The expression for the ratio of the two equilibrium constants is identical to that of the rational selectivity coefficient K_2^1. If it is assumed that the strength of the bases toward the resin sulfonic group parallels their strength in water, then the selectivity coefficient of the two bases on the resin can be predicted from the ratio of their dissociation constants in water.

The three resins used in this study were prepared from polystyrene beads crosslinked with 1% divinylbenzene by lauroylation and sulfonation. They have the following symbols and characteristics (3, 5): LSl' -1 (42, 78, 3.17); LSl' -7 (98, 84, 2.57); and LSl' -2 (88, 23, 0.83). The numbers in parentheses represent the percent lauroylations based on styrene, the percent sulfonation based on styrene, and the capacity in meq/dry g, respectively. Analytical grade bases and solvents were used in this work. The semipurified vinca alkaloids were obtained from Eli Lilly and Co.

For example, Figure 1 shows a shaking experiment with two bases. Diphenylamine, an extremely weak base, (pKa = 0.9), was sorbed only partially by the LSI' -1 resin. The course of neutralization of this resin in cyclohexane is shown in Figure 1. There was a total of 7.50 meq of diphenylamine in solution, but only 3.13 meq was bound by the resin which represented 58% of the available capacity. When diethylamine was added to the system, it was removed rapidly from solution while some diphenylamine was released by the resin. At equilibrium, the amount of diphenylamine on the resin was reduced to 50% of the reduced available capacity. When more diethylamine was added, more diphenylamine was released by the resin until, at equilibrium, the diphenylamine occupied 52% of the reduced available capacity. Similar experiments were conducted in acetone and methanol. In these solvents the diphenylamine tended to occupy 35-40% of the cation exchange sites available to it. Thus, the reaction between the sulfonic group of the LSl' -1 resin and diphenylamine is an example of the association-dissociation equilibrium as characterized by equation 19-1.

There were instances when the base removed from solution

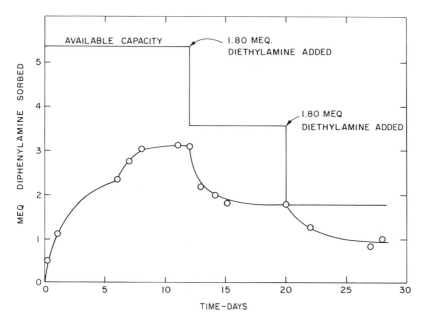

FIGURE 1   NEUTRALIZATION OF AN OLEOPHILIC
              CATION EXCHANGE RESIN (LSl' -1) WITH
              DIPHENYLAMINE AND DIETHYLAMINE
              IN CYCLOHEXANE.

was in excess of the capacity of resin, where capacity is determined by the number of cation exchange sites present. This
non-ion exchange sorption was directly proportional to the solution concentration. Since this non-ion exchange sorption is due
to interactions between the resin matrix and the base, bases
show individual variations. Among the bases of lower molecular
weight, aniline had the strongest tendency for non-ion exchange
sorption. Both resins LSl' -1 and LSl' -7 showed the same affect
toward aniline in water as indicated by the slope of the capacity
(in meq/g) vs. base concentration (in meq/l) curves. The slopes
were the same and were within experimental error, 0. 0145 l/g.
The slope for pyridine and LSl' -7 was 0. 0050 l/g. In subsequent
equilibria work, care was taken to have rather dilute final solutions
in equilibrium with the resin so as to minimize the effect of
non-ionic sorption.

It was observed that under certain conditions one base replaced

another base almost quantitatively. This occurred with low
molecular weight bases whenever the pKa values for the bases
in water differed by 2-3 units or more. The stronger base
replaced the weaker one regardless of solvent. For example,
diethylamine replaced pyridine, aniline, and diphenylamine.
Pyridine and aniline each replaced diphenylamine. Benzylamine
replaced aniline. Benzylamine was partially replaced by
n-butylamine.

Some work was done also with divalent bases. Nicotine
behaved as monobasic in exchange reactions because the pyridine
nitrogen is a much weaker base than the tertiary amine nitrogen.
A different effect was observed with ethylenediamine which acted
as both mono and dibasic. At an equilibrium solution concentratio
of about 0.02 M, 1.65 eq of ethylenediamine were held per resin
eq indicating that 65% of the base is present in its monobasic form
and 35% is in its dibasic form. The dimeric indole alkaloids
leurosine and vincaleukoblastine show similar, divalent behavior.

SEPARATION STUDIES

Several attempts were made to separate aniline from nicotine
by column chromatography (5). The separation shown in Figure 2
was made with the resin ground to 70 mesh. For this separation,
3.21 g of resin LS1 -5 (a total of 2.50 meq) were used in a bed 0.8
in diameter and 28.0 cm high. Heptane (n) was used as the solvent
The column was charged with a mixture of 1.08 meq of aniline and
1.24 meq of nicotine in 25-ml. The bed was eluted with 0.02 N
n-butylamine in n-heptane.

A chromatographic separation of two vinca alkaloids, leurosine and vincaleukoblastine was made on resin LS1' -2. The
results are presented in Figure 3. An approximately equimolar
mixture was separated on one g of resin originally in the hydrogen
form. The feed charge consisted of about 0.525 mM (400 mg)
of the alkaloid mixture dissolved in a 1:1 methanol-dichloroethane
mixture. The methanol was added only to decrease the density of
the solvent to below that of the resin. First, pyridine and then
n-butylamine in 1:1 methanol-dichloroethane was used to elute
the alkaloids from the resin. Pyridine removed only 0.155 mM
of leurosine, remained on the resin. The dilute n-butylamine
solution eluted the remainder of the alkaloid. Apparently the
pyridine was not capable of removing more alkaloid. It left 0.37
mM on 0.78 meq of resin, or one mole of alkaloid per two eq
of resin. Literature values for the first ionization constants
of these alkaloids were reported as Ka = 5.4 - 5.5 (7).

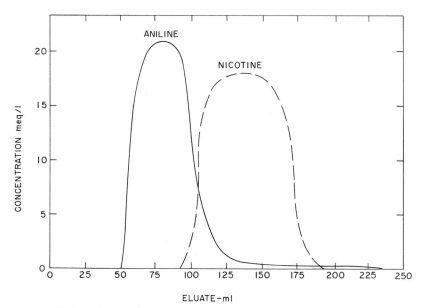

FIGURE 2   COLUMN CHROMATOGRAPHIC
              SEPARATION OF ANILINE FROM
              NICOTINE.

Apparently, there is an increased selectivity for these alkaloids,
which might be due to the divalent nature of the molecule.
      Analyses were performed by infrared spectroscopy and
thin layer chromatography. The middle portions of each eluate
showed that a very high degree of purity was achieved.

CONCLUSIONS
      It has been demonstrated that when an ion-exchanger is
modified to increase its swelling in non-polar solvents, its
behaviour in non-polar and polar solvents becomes similar.
The reacting species in solution needs only to form a salt with
the resin sulfonic acid group. As long as the resin has a swollen

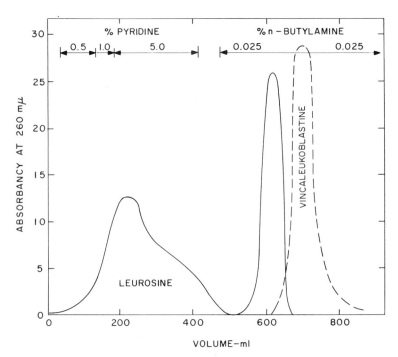

FIGURE 3   COLUMN CHROMATOGRAPHIC
              SEPARATION OF THE ALKALOIDS
              LEUROSINE AND VINCALEUKOBLASTINE.

open structure, the solvent has only minor effects on exchange
rates and selectivities.

The postulated mechanism for the reaction between an
organic base and the sulfonic acid group in non-aqueous media
appears to be an association-dissociation equilibrium. The
equilibrium constant is dependent on the strength of the organic
base, and this mechanism is supported by results obtained for
diphenylamine. When two organic bases were present in the
same system the selectivity coefficient was predicted qualitatively
by the ratio of the base dissociation constants in water. Since
other assumptions were involved, the predicted selectivity
coefficients have limited validity. The predictions, however,
were qualitatively correct of bases of widely varying strengths.

Column chromatography successfully separated nicotine
from aniline, although non-ionic sorption hindered the process.
By not overloading the bed and using a preliminary wash of pure

solvent, a good separation was achieved. A small particle size was required also. Two vinca alkaloids were successfully separated by column chromatography with selective eluants.

The oleophilic resins were capable of rapid removal of basic substances from organic solvents. The column chromatography work was aided by selecting eluting bases of varying pKa values at different concentrations.

These oleophilic resins show many applications of interest to the water technologist, as they act as excellent absorbents for organic matter. For example, a typical oleophilic anion-exchange resin was found to sorb benzene from aqueous solution along with an alkylbenzenesulfonate (8).

ACKNOWLEDGEMENT

This work was supported in part, by a grant from the Public Health Service, USDHEW, Washington, D.C. The alkaloids were obtained and analyzed through the courtesy of Eli Lilly and Co.

LITERATURE CITED

1. Kunin, R., et al, J Am Chem Soc, 84, 305 (1962).

2. Millar, J.R., et al, J Chem Soc, p218 (1963).

3. Gregor, H.P., et al, J Am Chem Soc, 87, 5525 (1965).

4. Tsuk, A.G. and H.P. Gregor, J Am Chem Soc, 87, 5534 (1965).

5. Tsuk, A.G. and H.P. Gregor, J Am Chem Soc, 87, 5538 (1965).

6. Shida, M. and H.P. Gregor, J Polymer Sci, (In Press).

7. Svoboda, H., et al, J Pharm Sci, 51, 706 (1962).

8. Gregor, H.P. and J. Walden, (In Press).

DISCUSSION

DR. ZECHELSKY: Any comments or questions?

DR. MATIJEVIC (Clarkson College): I have a question. You mentioned in Table II that sulfonation determines the swelling, I couldn't see it. I think your figures were at 78% of sulfonation you had 42% of swelling. You increase sulfonation by 6%, the swelling goes down to 80%. You decrease 24%, it goes down again.

I don't see any regularity. I don't know whether I missed some-thing or did I misunderstand?

DR. WALDEN: May we have Table II.

DR. LAMER (Columbia University): What are the percentages based on?

DR. WALDEN: The percentages refer to the available groups which can be substituted. For example, Resin 1 has 42% of its aromatic rings lauroylated and a total of 78% of these rings sul-fonated. Since sulfonation proceeds more easily with rings which are not substituted, we may assume that 58% of the rings have the sulfonic group only and 20% both the sulfonic group and the acyl group. The former group is more polar with 5 times the water sorbing capacity of the latter which can form a cyclic structure.

These are polymeric structures of considerable variability. A degree of 78 or 84% sulfonation at constant percent lauroylation is essentially the same. Resins 1 and 3 have a major difference in lauroylation (42 compared to 98%) and negligible difference in sulfonation (78 to 84%). Only major differences are significant.

It may help to clarify these data if one simplifies the treat-ment of swelling data by setting the extent of swelling V of a given structure as being equal to the volume fraction of a given substituent group ϕ times the cohesive energy density of the solvent δ times the swelling parameter for the group and the solvent Ψ. Then for resins ', ", and "' with solvents a, b.... and substituents 1, 2, 3...., we can write:

$$\Delta V'_a = \phi'_1 \delta_a \Psi_{1a} + \phi'_2 \delta_a \Psi_{2a} + \phi'_3 \delta_a \Psi_{3a} + ...$$

$$\Delta V''_a = \phi''_1 \delta_a \Psi_{1a} + \phi''_2 \delta_a \Psi_{2a} + \phi''_3 \delta_a \Psi_{3a} + ...$$

$$\cdot$$
$$\cdot$$

$$\Delta V'_b = \phi'_1 \delta_b \Psi_{1b} + \phi'_2 \delta_b \Psi_{2b} + \phi'_3 \delta_b \Psi_{3b} + ...$$

Therefore, each substituent group at its volume fraction contributes to the total swelling of the structure. Resin 1 swells most strongly in water because of its low degree of lauroylation, which means that polar sulfonic groups dominate the swelling; its swelling in n-heptane is negligible and in benzene it is low. When the structure is highly sulfonated and also highly lauroy-lated (Resin 3), the swelling in water drops because the sulfonic group is now largely cyclized, and the aliphatic group gives much higher swelling in benzene. An examination of Table II suggests that the simplified picture of the linear swelling relationship is inadequate, and that second order interaction terms are needed for a more exact description of these phenomena. These second-order coefficients may have negative ψ terms.

DR. G. E. JANAUER (State University of New York at Binghamton): I would just be interested in the stability of these resins. Is there anything known to you? Have you done experiments that show they hold up? Can you recycle them, and how many times? How do they compare to commercial resins?

DR. WALDEN: The anion-exchange resins appear to be comparable to Type II resins of which Dowex-2 is an example. These are not as stable as the Type I materials, but quite useful in almost all applications. The sulfonic resins are not as stable as those which do not have lauroylation; they show a decomposition at 100°C in the acid state. The salt forms are more stable.

DR. W. RIEMAN (Rutgers University): You stated a possible use of these resins. How about removal of organic solutes from water? What advantages do the oleophilic have over ordinary resins for that purpose? Ordinary resins also remove organic compounds from water.

DR. WALDEN: These resins are strong adsorbents of organic materials from aqueous media, considerably stronger than the ordinary commercial materials. Also, because they swell in the presence of organic molecules, their capacity is higher.

MR. R. E. FRIEDRICH (Dow Chemical Co.): Would you care to comment on the difference or degrees in swelling, comparing the acid forms and various salt forms?

DR. WALDEN: We have very little information on the points you raise; I will estimate that the differences for different organic salts will be minor.

DR. E. H. CROOK (Rohm & Haas Co.): Have you carried out any contemplated measurements with these resins to support your theories? Perhaps they would be better for organic removal or organic type compound removal as opposed to other resins used primarily in aqueous systems.

DR. WALDEN: No, the main work that we have discussed up to now has been limited largely to studies in non-aqueous media. We are now looking at the use of these resins in treatment of secondary sewage effluents. However, there is a problem here recognized by everyone, and that is regenerating

the resin economically.   Charcoal is quite popular, and so far
charcoal is holding out.

DR. CROOK: Have you compared these with the macroporous
types?

DR. WALDEN: Yes, we have. In non-aqueous media the oleophilic resins are much more rapid and have a higher capacity; a
reference for this is (5). We have very limited data in aqueous
media.

DR. CROOK: I assume these are gel type. Hav e you tried
to make these as macro-porous? I think you might do better yet.

DR. ZENCHELSKY: If there are no further questions, I
want to thank you very much, and we will adjourn.

W. L. Polzer

U. S. Geological Survey
Menlo Park, California

GEOCHEMICAL CONTROL OF SOLUBILITY OF AQUEOUS SILICA

An understanding of the processes involved in the acquisition of chemical substances by natural waters is, in effect, an understanding of some of the rock weathering and soil formation processes found in nature. A knowledge of these processes will contribute also to an understanding of how to pretreat natural waters, if necessary, in order to make their quality suitable for industrial, agricultural, and technological uses as well as for human consumption.

The purpose of this paper is to give a general background on the chemistry of aqueous silica and to discuss some of the geochemical factors which may control silica concentrations in ground water. The chemistry of aqueous silica will be restricted to discussion of hydration, polymerization, and ionization processes in relation to the conditions found in most natural environments. The geochemical controls on aqueous silica in ground water are discussed from two points of view: (a) a general comparison between laboratory experiments and actual data obtained from ground water studies; and (b) an interpretation of the processes responsible for control of silica in ground water from granitic rocks and their weathering products.

CHEMICAL CHARACTERISTICS

Iler discusses in detail the chemistry of aqueous silica with respect to some of its observed behavior (1). The results of his study are summarized below.

Silicon in the solid forms of silica has a coordination number of 4 (4 oxygen anions surrounding the silicon ion). In water below pH 9.0, the solid probably depolymerizes through hydration and dissolution to an aqueous form that also has a coordination number of 4. This form is probably monomeric silicic acid (H_4SiO_4). In an alkaline solution, however, OH^- ions will react with silicic acid molecules to form silicate ions. Neutralization of silicate ions with an acid would involve a decomposition to silicic acid molecules which, in turn, would polymerize into silica.

The primary reactions which involve the different forms of aqueous silica are given below with respect to the pH of the solution.

At pH values 1 - 9 :

$$\frac{1}{x} (SiO_2)_x + 2H_2O = H_4SiO_{4\,(aq)} \tag{20-1}$$

$Keq = [H_4SiO_4]$ where $[H_4SiO_4]$ is a function of the solid silica. According to Morey, et al, (2): Keq (quartz) = $[H_4SiO_4]_{quartz} \approx 1 \times 10^{-4}$ moles/1 (6 mg/1). According to Krauskopf (3): Keq (amorphous) = $[H_4SiO_4]_{amorphous} \approx 2 \times 10^{-3}$ moles/1 (120 mg/1).

At pH 11:

$$H_4SiO_4 + H_2O + OH^- = \{H_2OSi(OH)_5\}^- \tag{20-2}$$

$$Keq = \frac{[\{(H_2O) Si(OH)_5\}^-]}{[H_4SiO_4] [OH^-]} = 1.85 \times 10^4$$

At pH values 11 - 13.8:

$$\{(H_2O)Si(OH)_5\}^- + OH^- = Si(OH)_6^{-2} + H_2O \tag{20-3}$$

$$Keq = \frac{[Si(OH)_6^{-2}]}{[\{(H_2O)Si(OH)_5\}^-] [OH^-]} = 69.2$$

Another reaction may be present also:

$$2 \left\{ (H_2O) \; Si(OH)_5 \right\}^{-} = \left\{ Si_2 \; (OH)_5 \right\}^{-2} + H_2O \qquad (20\text{-}4)$$

$$Keq = \frac{[\left\{ Si_2 \; (OH)_5 \right\}^{-2}]}{[\left\{ (H_2O) \; Si \; (OH)_5 \right\}^{-}]^2} = 2.2 \times 10^3$$

The silicate ions in equations 20-2, 20-3, and 20-4 are indicated with a coordination number of 6 rather than 4 as found in solid forms of silica. Although the existence of 6 coordinated silicate ions has not been demonstrated, it is known that when an H^+ ion penetrates the electron cloud of the O^{-2} ion, the diameter of the O^{-2} ion is reduced by polarization. The resultant OH^- ion resembles the F^- ion in size and $(SiF_6)^{-2}$ is known to exist.

Iler prefers to show the silicate ion with a coordination number of 6 because this allows a mechanism to be postulated for the depolymerization (or polymerization) of silica equation 20-1 (1). This mechanism allows a temporary change in the coordination number from 4 to 6 of a hydrated silica, which is effected through catalysis by a OH ion.

Before depolymerization occurs, however, the silica solid becomes hydrated. A silica particle may be visualized as being constructed of SiO_2 in which every oxygen atom lies between two silicon atoms (a 3-dimensional network of SiO_4 tetrahedra). At the surface of the particle one of the oxygen bonds is broken which forms an incomplete tetrahedron. When the silica surface comes in contact with moisture the tetrahedron will be completed by formation of a OH^- ion.

The chemical reaction for the decomposition of a silicate mineral, as explained by Frederickson, involves the penetration of H^+ ions into a silicate lattice where they replace metal ions so that electrical neutrality is maintained (4). Silica is released also by the process. The released silica could possibly go into solution by the same mechanism as postulated by Iler (1). It should be emphasized, however, that additional knowledge is needed before mechanisms for the solution of silica and silicate minerals are understood fully.

Krauskopf concluded from laboratory experiments and a review of the literature that, in natural waters, silica may be either colloidal or in true solution (3). However, if total silica concentration is less than 100 mg/l, the colloidal particles are

unstable and will disappear spontaneously in short time.   It
was concluded also that the form of silica in most natural
waters (pH< 9) is that of monomeric silicic acid which agrees
with the conclusions of Iler (1).

GEOCHEMICAL CONTROLS

Geochemical controls on the silica concentrations in
ground water have been summarized by Davis (5) and by Feth,
et al, (6). Davis compared results of laboratory experiments
to published ground-water data obtained from a wide range of
conditions.

Laboratory studies of silica solubility suggest that the
mineral composition of material in contact with water should
be the most important control of silica in ground water. For
example, water in equilibrium with quartz will have from 6 to
12 mg/l silica in solution (2, 7). Water in equilibrium with
amorphous silica will have from 100 to 140 mg/l silica (3).
Water in equilibrium with clay minerals, feldspars, micas,
and other siliceous rock-forming minerals is probably intermediate in silica concentration (10). According to Jones and
Handrick, the presence of oxides of iron and aluminum will
decrease the silica in solution (8). It is not known, however,
whether reversible equilibria are attainable for all these
minerals at temperatures and pressures commonly prevailing
in ground water. Incongruent solution may occur with silica
being controlled by whatever form precipitates. Reaction rates
may be slow.

Patterson and Roberson found only 5 mg/l silica in water
from weathered basalt which contained abundant clay minerals
and other products of weathering (11). However, 50 mg/l silica
were found in water from unweathered basalt in the same area.
Davis, from studies of published analyses of ground water,
reported that the largest amounts of silica in ground water are
associated with volcanic rock; intermediate amounts in association with plutonic rocks and sediments containing feldspar and
volcanic rock fragments; small amounts of silica are found in
water from marine sandstones; and the least from water in
carbonate rocks (5).

Feth, et al, studied the relation between the chemical
character of water from granitic terrane in the Sierra Nevada
and the composition of the rocks and their weathering products (6)
The purpose of their study was to determine, if possible, the
processes responsible for the chemical character of the water.

The conclusions presented here were derived from chemical analysis of water from 56 nonthermal perennial springs and 15 ephemeral springs or "seeps". The geologic settings of these springs showed quartz monzonite and granodiorite to be the most abundant rock types with andesine the most abundant feldspar. Hornblende and biotite were the only ferromagnesian minerals present in any abundance. Biotite was most abundant in the quartz monzonite and hornblende in the granodiorite.

An X-ray diffraction study was made of clay-size mineral samples taken in or near the orifices of some of the springs. A variety of clay minerals was found to be present near or in the spring orifices. Poorly crystalline substances were found most abundant. Well crystallized montmorillonite, kaolinite, and micaceous-clay minerals, however, were identified either singly or in combination of two or all three varieties. The identification of these crystalline-clay minerals in the sediment samples indicates that many of the spring waters were in contact with clay minerals as the water passed through the underground system.

The ground water sampled at different locations was derived from snowmelt. Water from a snowbank travels on and in the soil and saprolite for a few tens to a few hundreds of feet before entering and moving through rock crevices in the solid rock of the mountain. Water samples taken before the water entered the rock crevices were classified as representing ephemeral springs and those that were taken of water issuing from rock crevices were classified as from perennial springs. The water of perennial springs spent most of its time in a system closed to the soil and the atmosphere.

The principal control over dissolved mineral content of the water was believed to be the availability of CO_2 except for a few samples where contact time with the rock probably was too short for equilibrium to be established. This inference was based on assumptions that the initial partial pressure of CO_2 was acquired during contact of the water with the atmosphere and more significantly with the soil before entering into the crevices of the rocks. During this time the water, being continuously replenished with air and CO_2 from the soil, would remain aggressive with respect to the minerals throughout the time of contact. Perennial spring water, being in a system closed to the atmosphere and the soil for the bulk of its travel time, could not replenish its supply of air and CO_2.

The amount of mineralization, therefore, would be limited by exhaustion of the supply of reactive gases in the water.

The form of the CO_2 content and the chemical reactivity of the water can be evaluated from:

$$CO_{2(g)} + H_2O = CO_{2(aq)} + H_2O \qquad (20\text{-}5)$$

$$CO_{2(aq)} + H_2O = H_2CO_3 \qquad (20\text{-}6)$$

$$H_2CO_3 = H^+ + HCO_3^- \qquad (20\text{-}7)$$

The $[H^+]$ derived from the reaction of CO_2 in water would then control the ability of the water to obtain mineral constituents from the rock. The H^+ ion, as explained by Frederickson, penetrates the mineral lattice, upsetting the electrical neutrality of the mineral (4). A metal atom is removed so as to maintain electrical neutrality. In the process, silica also would be released and the crystal would be disrupted, thus a new surface area would be exposed.

In the waters studied, virtually the only source of inorganic acid is the reaction of CO_2 with water. This reaction is, therefore, the main source of H^+ ions. The strong dependence of total dissolved-solids content on HCO_3^- content for water from both ephemeral and perennial springs (Figure 1) emphasized the action of CO_2 in the weathering process. The coefficient of correlation is significant at levels of confidence in excess of 0.01 in both cases. This means there is less than 1 chance in 100 that the relations result from chance. The relation of HCO_3^- to total dissolved solids content confidently may be considered to be real.

In order to understand the release of silica to solution, the relation of silica to the rocks and their weathering products in contact with the solution was considered. Also, the relation of silica to other dissolved chemical constituents was taken into account. Knowledge that the most abundant feldspar is andesine and the identification of well crystallized clay minerals at some localities suggests several possible reactions responsible for the chemical character of these waters.

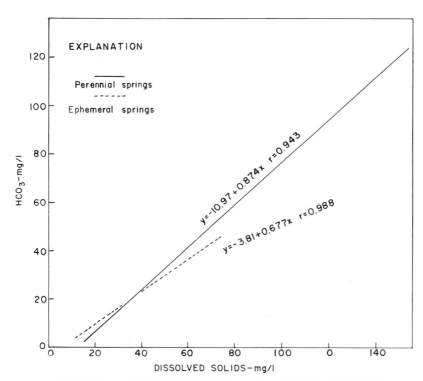

FIGURE 1   GRAPH SHOWING RELATION BETWEEN
DISSOLVED-SOLIDS CONTENTS AND
SELECTED CONSTITUENTS IN WATER
FROM PERENNIAL AND EPHEMERAL SPRINGS
(After Feth, et al, 1964).

The formation of kaolinite and montmorillonite during the
weathering of plagioclase feldspars may be written:

$$3Na_{0.66}Ca_{0.33}Al_{1.33}Si_{2.66}O_8 + 14H_2O + 4CO_2$$
(andesine)

$$=2H_4Al_2Si_2O_9 + 2Na^+ + Ca^{+2} + 4H_4SiO_4 + 4HCO_3^- \quad (20\text{-}8)$$
(kaolinite)

and:

$$\text{\textcircled{}}Na_{0.66}Ca_{0.33}Al_{1.33}Si_{2.66}O_8 + 6CO_2 + 18H_2O$$
(andesine)

$$= 3Na_{0.66}Al_{2.66}Si_{3.33}O_{10}(OH)_2 + 2\ Ca^{+2} + 2\ Na^{+}$$
(montmorillonite) $+6H_4SiO_4 + 6HCO_3^{-}$ (20-9)

A plot of the silica content in solution vs. $H\bar{C}O_3$ is given in Figure 2. The results show that for every mole of $H\bar{C}O_3$ nearly one mole of silica was released in solution until the first limit of about 20 mg/l silica is approached. In some samples, this limit extends up to silica concentrations of about 50 mg/l. In other samples, where the $H\bar{C}O_3$ exceeds 40 mg/l the silica concentration levels off at limits between 20 and 30 mg/l.

Figure 3 indicates that many of the springs have a 2:1 mole ratio of silica to Na^{+}. A group of samples also show a 1:1 mole ratio of silica to Na^{+}. The mole ratios of silica to other cations indicate that the ratio of silica with respect to Ca^{+2} is about 5:1 although there is a considerable scatter of points. The identification of well crystallized clay minerals at some localities and the initial mole ratios of silica to Na^{+} (2:1) and of silica to HCO_3^{-} (1:1) support the hypothesis that kaolinite is formed during the weathering of plagioclase feldspars.

The granitic waters also were studied with respect to stability relations (Figures 4 and 5). The results indicated that the granitic waters were stable with respect to kaolinite in both the Na_2O and K_2O systems. The assumptions are made that all other minerals in contact with these waters do not have their field of stability in the same field as does kaolinite and that the fields of stability of the minerals shown are correct. That the granitic waters are stable with respect to kaolinite implies that they are in equilibrium with kaolinite provided the mineral is in contact with these waters.

These diagrams also suggest that potassium mica and montmorillonite could be unstable. The presence of mica and montmorillonite probably means that these minerals will dissolve until an equilibrium is reached between kaolinite and these clay minerals. Other wise these clay minerals would eventually dissolve completely or be converted into some other product.

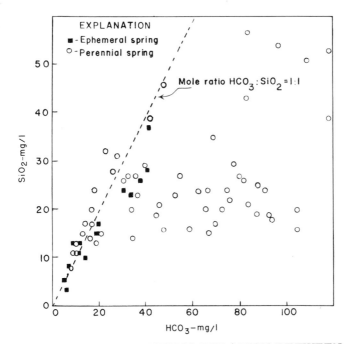

FIGURE 2   PLOT SHOWING RELATION BETWEEN
              BICARBONATE AND SILICA CONTENT
              IN WATER FROM EPHEMERAL AND
              PERENNIAL SPRINGS (After Feth, et al, 6).

Hemley, et al, found that when albite was altered to montmorillonite, the released silica was crystallized into cristobalite (12). With alteration of montmorillonite to kaolinite, however, a crystalline silica phase did not appear. But the stable silica phase is still probably cristobalite. Figure 5 indicates that the silica concentration does not exceed the solubility of cristobalite and that the higher $\log[Na^+]/[H^+]$ ratios are approaching the montmorillonite-kaolinite boundary. This evidence favors the possibility of an approach towards an equilibrium between kaolinite and montmorillonite.

CONCLUSIONS
      The solid forms of silica, when exposed to aqueous media, become hydrated at the surface and then dissolve to form aqueous silica. In natural water with a pH value less than 9, the most probable form of aqueous silica is monomeric silicic acid

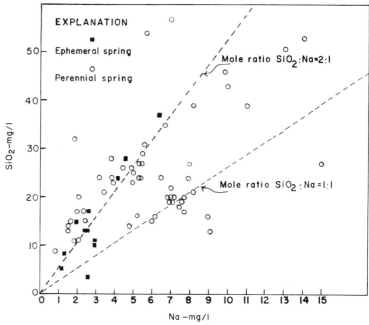

FIGURE 3   PLOT SHOWING RELATION BETWEEN
              SODIUM AND SILICA IN WATER FROM
              EPHEMERAL AND PERENNIAL SPRINGS
              (After Feth, et al, 6).

(H_4SiO_4). Above pH 9, aqueous silica becomes ionized thus
forming silicate ions.

        The most important geochemical controls of aqueous silica
in ground water are the minerals in contact with the silica
solution. Water in equilibrium with amorphous silica contains
between 100 mg/l to 140 mg/l silica, that in equilibrium with
quartz contains about 6 mg/l to 12 mg/l silica, and water in
equilibrium with clay minerals, feldspars, mica, and other
siliceous rock-forming minerals probably contains intermediate
concentrations of silica.

        A study of silica in water from the granitic terrane of
the Sierra Nevada indicates that weathering of rock minerals
in contact with water not only dissolves silica in relatively
large amounts but also produces siliceous weathering products,
such as clay minerals. According to estimated stability relations,

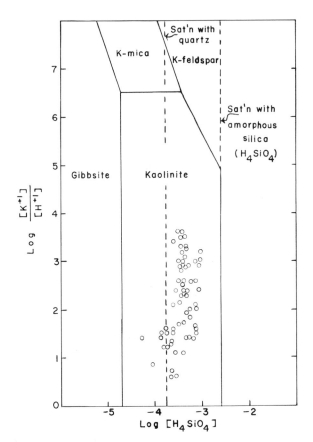

FIGURE 4   STABILITY RELATIONS OF PHASES IN
THE SYSTEMS K$_2$O-Al$_2$O$_3$-SiO$_2$-H$_2$O AT
25°C AND 1 ATM TOTAL PRESSURE AS
FUNCTIONS OF [K$^+$] / [H$^+$] AND
[H$_4$SiO$_4$] . (After Feth, et al, 6).

water from granitic rocks of the Sierra Nevada is stable with
respect to kaolinite. These relations imply that the water may
be in equilibrium with kaolinite. Evidence also suggests that
some of the chemical constituents of water, including silica,
may be controlled in some localities by montmorillonite-kaolinite equilibrium reactions.

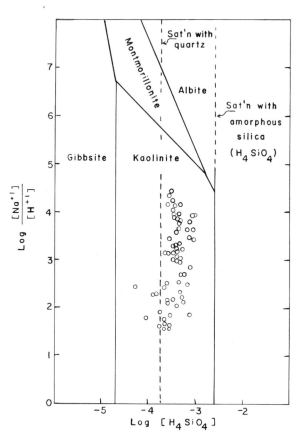

FIGURE 5   STABILITY RELATIONS OF PHASES IN
THE SYSTEM Na_2O-Al_2O_3-SiO_2-H_2O AT
$25^{\circ}C$ AND 1 ATM TOTAL PRESSURE AS
FUNCTIONS OF $[Na^+]$ / $[H^+]$ AND
$[H_4SiO_4]$. (After Feth, et al, 6).

ACKNOWLEDGEMENTS
        The author wishes to acknowledge the helpful suggestions
and criticisms by J. D. Hem during the preparation of the
manuscript. A discussion with J. J. Hemley of his work on
mineral stability relations also has contributed much to the
contents of this manuscript. This publication was authorized
by the Director, U S Geological Survey, Washington, D. C.

LITERATURE CITED
1. Iler, R.K., Colloid Chemistry of Silica and Silicates,
      Cornell University Press, Ithaca, N.Y., (1955).

2. Morey, G.W., et al, Geochim Cosmochim Acta, 26, 1029
      (1963).

3. Krauskopf, K.B., Goechim Cosmochim Acta, 10, 1 (1956).

4. Frederickson, A.F., Geol Soc Am Bull, 62, 221 (1951).

5. Davis, S.N., Am J Sci, 262, 870 (1964).

6. Feth, J.H., et al, U S Geol Survey Water-Supply Paper
      1535-I, (1964).

7. Lier, J.A. van, The Solubility of Quartz, Utrecht Kemink
      en Zoon, (1959).

8. Jones, L.H.P. and K.A. Handrick, Nature, 198, 4883 (1963).

9. Siever, R., J Geol, 70, 127 (1962).

10. Keller, W.D., et al, J Sedimen Petrol, 33, 191 (1963).

11. Patterson, S.H. and C.E. Roberson, U S Geol Survey Prof
       Paper 424-C, p195 (1961).

12. Hemley, J.J., et al, U S Geol Survey Prof Paper 424-D,
       pD338 (1961).

DISCUSSION
   DR. RIEMAN (Rutgers University): Thank you for a brief
and intelligent presentation. This paper is open for discussion.
   DR. BRICKER (Johns Hopkin University): I would just
like to point out that an alternative to the control of the upper
limit of dissolved silica in natural waters by the solubility of
cristobalite is the equilibrium of these waters with montmorillonite. An aluminous montmorillonite (beidellite) would give
the same value, approximately 60 mg/l dissolved silica and
would plot as a straight vertical boundary independent of the
Na^+/H^+ ratio, just as the cristobalite boundary you showed

on your last figure. In view of the common occurrence of
montmorillonite in the weathering profile and the relative
scarcity of cristobalite, I think that control of the upper limit
of dissolved silica in natural waters by equilibrium with montmorillonite would be more likely than control by cristobalite.

DR. LANGMUIR (U S Geological Survey): I am wondering,
it is always nice to find the minerals you think should be present.
Didn't you find kaolinite forming in the texture which you described

MR. POLZER: I'm not sure just what you mean. We
tried to identify some weathered material on granitic rocks.
There was an indication of clay mineral formation, but we had
no real proof. D.A. YOUNG (Union Oil Company): I would be
curious to know whether you or anyone has attempted to carry
out these transformations synthetically, and if so, what was
the result?

MR. POLZER: I would like to mention Hemley's work
at higher temperatures. He is using synthetic materials at
about 200° to 300^OC or lower and is getting good results.

DR. BRICKER: That is what I was going to add. We are
doing some work at 25^OC on the stability of feldspars and clay
minerals in the aqueous environment. Preliminary results show
that the path followed by solution composition in the lateration
of albite, plotted on a $\log[Na^+]/[H^+]$ vs. $\log SiO_2$ diagram,
is just what you would predict for the incongruent dissolution
of albite forming kaolinite and releasing Na^+ and silica to the
solution. As alteration proceeds, the solution becomes enriched
in sodium ion and silica and depleted in hydrogen ion. The
reaction path (see Figure 5, Bricker and Garrels) is from lower
left to upper right across the kaolinite field and presumably will
proceed until the montmorillonite boundary is reached, at which
point the reaction path should follow the two phase boundary
kaolinite-montmorillonite.

Jim Kittrick (Washington State University) also has been
working for a number of years on the stability of clay minerals
and has obtained what appears to be a good free energy value
for kaolinite from both under saturation and over-saturation
at 25^OC. The value, incidentally, agrees very well with the
value determined by Barany and Kelley of the Bureau of Mines
who used a calorimetric method.

The point I would like to stress is that silicate minerals
are quite reactive in the natural water environment and cannot
be considered to be inert materials with respect to their effect

on the composition of natural water.

MR. POLZER: We are working on that, too, and we have concluded that we have reached equilibrium with respect to kaolinite.

DR. DOUGLAS (Rutgers University): Two questions. Did you analyze these waters for Al? You may assume from some of your data you would not expect to find Al; it would be tied up in kaolinite.

MR. POLZER: You may find Al in water, however, the beauty of these diagrams is that aqueous Al need not be represented. In other words, we can write equations without aqueous Al species for each of these equilibrium lines. Aluminum species may be present in the water, but at the pH values observed we do not know the form of these species.

DR. DOUGLAS: I was thinking especially of Al in relation to your model that you put on the blackboard. You assumed it was tied up there.

MR. POLZER: That is right, but you might very well have Al in solution.

DR. DOUGLAS: Second question. In your diagram you showed your log ratio between K and H and the K mica stability to be about 6.5 to 8.0. Do you find these ranges in natural waters, in other words, do you find conditions in which you would expect to find K micas precipitating?

MR. POLZER: I don't know. There may be some, but I do not know of any.

Werner Stumm
Harvard University

METAL IONS IN AQUEOUS SOLUTIONS

In all solution environments bare metal ions are in continuous search of a partner. The environment of interest is water wherein metal cations are hydrated to form aquo complexes. All coordinati reactions which metal cations undergo in aqueous solutions are exchange reactions in which the coordinated water molecules are exchanged for some preferred ligands. The barest of the free meta cations is the free hydrogen ion, the proton. This statement shoulc simply indicate that there is no difference in principle between a free metal ion and a proton.

All chemical reactions have one common denominator; the atoms molecules, or ions involved in the reaction try to improve the stability of the electrons in their outer shell. In a classification of chemical reactions, two broad groups of reactions can be distinguis by which atoms can achieve such stabilization: (a) redox processes which the oxidation state of the participating atoms change; and (b) reactions in which the coordinative relations are changed (1). What is meant by a change in coordinative relations? These are changed if the coordinative partner is changed or if the coordination number of the participating atoms is changed. (The coordination number is indicative of the structure and specifies the number of the nearest neighbors (ligand atoms) of a particular atom). This may be Illustrated:

520

A. If an acid is introduced into water:

$$HClO + H_2O = H_3O^+ + ClO^- \qquad (21\text{-}1)$$

the coordinative partner of the hydrogen ion (which has a coordination number of one) is changed from ClO^- to H_2O.

B. The precipitation that frequently occurs in the reaction of a metal ion with a base:

$$Mg \cdot aq^{+2} + 2OH^- = Mg(OH)_{2(c)} + aq \qquad (21\text{-}2)$$

can be interpreted in terms of a reaction in which the coordinative relations are changed. This is true in the sense that a three-dimensional lattice is formed in which each metal ion is surrounded and coordinatively "saturated" by the appropriate number of bases.

C. Metal ions can also react with bases without formation of precipitates:

$$Cu \cdot aq^{+2} + 4NH_3 = \left[Cu(NH_3)_4\right]^{+2} + aq \qquad (21\text{-}3)$$

In this simple classification of reactions no distinction need be made between acid-base, precipitation, and complex formation reactions. They are all coordinative reactions. It is valuable, at least didactically, to realize that all these reactions are phenomenologically and conceptually similar.

BRÖNSTED ACIDITY AND LEWIS ACIDITY

In Figure 1, alkalimetric titration curves for the reaction of phosphoric acid and $Fe(H_2O)_6^{+3}$, respectively, with a base $(OH^-$ ion) are compared. The first acidity constant of H_3PO_4 is similar in magnitude to that of $Fe(H_2O)_6^{+3}$; thus, equimolar solutions of H_3PO_4 and ferric perchlorate have a similar pH value. Both acids $(Fe \cdot aq^{+3}$ and $H_3PO_4)$ are multiprotic acids, i.e., they can transfer more than one proton.

In Figure 2a the titration of H_3O^+ with ammonia is compared with the titration of $Cu \cdot aq^{+2}$ with ammonia. pH and pCu $(-\log[Cu \cdot aq^{+2}])$ are plotted as a function of the base added. In both cases "neutralization curves" are observed. In the case of the $H_3O^+ - NH_3$ reaction, a pronounced pH jump occurs at the equivalence point. The pCu-jump is less pronounced in the $Cu \cdot aq^{+2} - NH_3$ reaction because NH_3 is

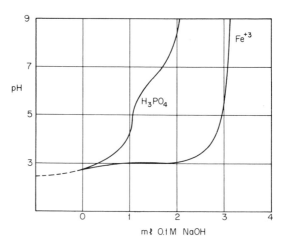

FIGURE 1   ALKALIMETRIC TITRATION OF H_3PO_4
AND Fe . aq^{+3}. Both H_3PO_4 and
Fe . aq^{+3} are multiprotic Brönsted acids.
The first acidity constant of both acids
are of similar magnitude; thus, equimolar
solutions of H_3PO_4 and $Fe(ClO_4)_3$ have a
similar pH value.

bound to the Cu^{+2} ion in a stepwise consecutive way: $CuNH_3^{+2}$
$Cu(NH_3)_2^{+2}$; $Cu(NH_3)_3^{+2}$; $Cu(NH_3)_4^{+2}$; and $Cu(NH_3)_5^{+2}$ (Figure 2d).
If, however, four NH_3 molecules are packaged together into one
single molecule, such as trien (triethylenetetramine, H_2N-CH_2-
$CH_2-NH-CH_2-CH_2-NH-CH_2-CH_2-NH_2$), a 1:1 Cu-trien complex
is formed and a simple titration curve with a very pronounced
pCu jump is observed at the equivalence point (Figure 2b). In
this case the Cu-trien equilibrium (Figure 2e) is as simple as
the H^+ - NH_3 equilibrium (Figure 2c). Such neutralization
reactions are exploited analytically for the determination of
acids or metal ions wherein a sensor is used for H^+ and Me^{+n};
a hydrogen ion electrode (glass electrode) and a metal ion
sensitive electrode (e.g., a copper electrode for Cu^{+2}), or a
pH or pMe indicator, respectively.

    The above examples illustrate the phenomenological simi-
larity between the "neutralization" of H^+ with bases and that
of metal ions with complex formers. The bases, molecules
or ions that can "neutralize" H^+ or metal ions, possess free

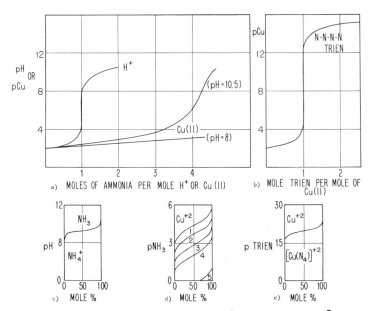

FIGURE 2   TITRATION OF H_3O^+ AND Cu . aq^{+2} WITH
AMMONIA (a) AND WITH TETRA-AMINE (b).
Equilibrium diagrams for the distribution
of NH_3-NH_4^+ (c) of the amino copper (II)
complexes (d) and of Cu^{+2}, Cu-trien (e).
Cu(II) = 10^{-3}M.   The similarity of titrating
H_3O^+ with a base with that of titrating a
metal ion with a base (Lewis acid-base interaction) is obvious.   Both neutralization
reactions are used analytically for the determination of acids and metal ions; a pH or a
pMe indicator or indicator electrodes (glass
electrode for H_3O^+ and copper electrode for
Cu . aq^{+2}) can be used for the endpoint
indication.

pairs of electrons. Acids are proton donors according to Brönsted.
Lewis, on the other hand, has proposed a much more generalized
definition of an acid in the sense that he does not attribute acidity
to a particular element but to a unique electronic arrangement;
the availability of an unfilled orbital for the acceptance of a pair
of electrons (2). Such acidic or acid-analogue properties are
possessed by H^+, metal ions, and other Lewis acids: $SOCl_2$;

$AlCl_3$; SO_2; and BF_3. In aqueous solutions, protons and metal
ions compete with each other for the available bases.

DEFINITIONS

In the following, any combination of cations with molecules
or anions containing free pairs of electrons (bases) is called
coordination, and can be either electrostatic or covalent or a
mixture of both. The metal cation will be called the central atom
and the anions or molecules with which it forms a coordination
compound will be referred to as ligands. If the ligand is composed
of several atoms, the one responsible for the basic or nucleophilic
nature of the ligand is called the ligand atom. If a base contains
more than one ligand atom, and can occupy more than one coordination position in the complex, it is referred to as a multidentate
complex former. Ligands occupying one, two, three, etc. positions
are referred to as unidentate, bidentate, tridentate, etc. Typical
examples are oxalate and ethylenediamine as bidentate ligands,
citrate as a tridentate ligand, and ethylenediaminetetraacetate
(EDTA) as a sexadentate ligand. Complex formation with multidentate ligands is called chelation and the complexes are called
chelates. The most obvious feature of a ring. For example,
in the reaction between glycine and $Cu \cdot aq^{+2}$, a chelate with
two rings, each with five members is formed:

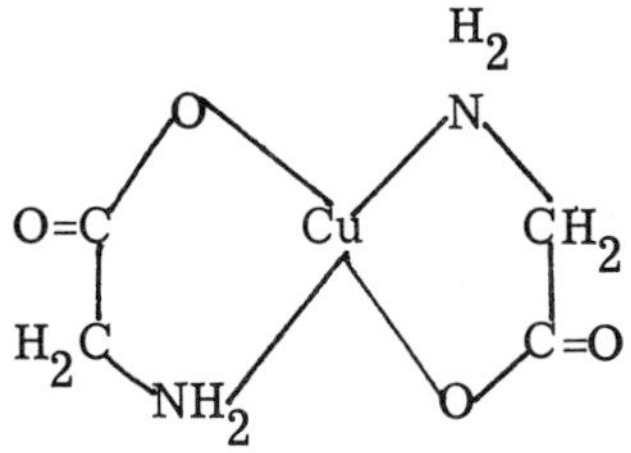

Glycine is bidentate since O- and N- are the two donor atoms.
If there is more than one metal atom (central atom) in a complex,
multi- or polynuclear complexes are formed.

One essential distinction between a proton complex and a
metal complex is that the coordination number of protons is
different from that of metal ions. The coordination number of
a proton is one. (In hydrogen bonding, however, H^+ can exhibit
a coordination number of two). Most metal cations exhibit an
even coordination number of 2, 4, 6, or occasionally, 8. In
complexes of coordination number 2, the ligands and the central
ion are linearly arranged. If the coordination is 4, the ligand

atoms surround the central ion either in a square planar or in
a tetrahedral configuration. If the coordination number is 6,
the ligands occupy the corners of an octahedron in the center
of which stands the central atom.

THE ACIDITY OF AQUEOUS METAL IONS

Hydration
    It has been indicated that metal cations in aqueous solutions
exist as aquo complexes. It is frequently difficult to determine
the number of H_2O molecules of the hydration shell but many
metal ions coordinate 4 or 6 H_2O molecules per ion. Water is
a weak acid. The acidity of H_2O molecules in the hydration
shell of a metal ion is much larger than that of water. This
enhancement of the acidity of the coordinated water may be
visualized in a primitive model as the result of the repulsion
of the protons of H_2O molecules by the positive charge of the
metal ion or as a result of the immobilization of the lone
electron pair of the hydrate - H_2O molecule.
    Hydrated metal ions are Brönsted acids:

$$\left[Al(H_2O)_6\right]^{+3} + H_2O = \left[Al(H_2O)_5OH\right]^{+2} + H_3O^+ \quad (21\text{-}4)$$

Their acidity increases with decrease of the radius and an
increase of charge of the central ion. Figure 3 attempts to
illustrate how the oxidation state of the central atom determines
the predominant species (aquo, hydroxo, hydroxo-oxo, and oxo
complexes) in the pH - range of aqueous solutions. Metal ions
with z = 1 are generally coordinated with H_2O atoms. Most
bivalent metal ions are also coordinated with water up to pH
values of 6 to 12. Most trivalent metal ions are coordinated
already with OH^- ions within the pH range of natural waters.
For z = +4, the aquo ions have become too acidic and are not
in the accessible pH range of aqueous solutions with few
exceptions, such as Th (IV). At these high oxidation states,
O^{-2} already begins to appear as a ligand, for example, C (IV)
has oxo-hydroxo complexes: $H_2CO_3 = CO(OH)_2$; or $HCO_3^- =$
$CO_2(OH)^-$, in the pH range 4.5 to 10. Above pH = O^{-2} becomes
the exclusive ligand (CO_3^{-2}). With even higher oxidation states
of the central atom, hydroxo complexes can only occur at very
low pH values. The scheme in Figure 3 represents an over-
simplification primarily because for every oxidation state, a
distribution of acidity exists according to the ionic radius.

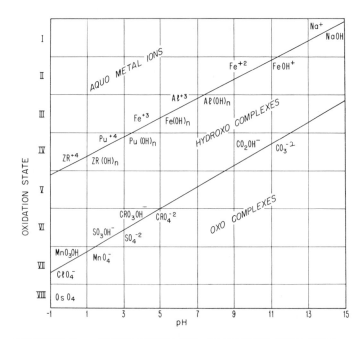

FIGURE 3   PREDOMINANT pH RANGE FOR THE
              OCCURRENCE OF AQUO, HYDROXO,
              HYDROXO-OXO, AND OXO COMPLEXES
              FOR VARIOUS OXIDATION STATES.
              This Scheme attempts to show a useful
              generalization but many elements can not
              be properly placed in this simplified
              diagram because other aspects such as
              radius and factors related to electron
              distribution have to be considered in
              interpreting the acidity of metal ions.
              A similar diagram has been given by
              Jorgensen (8).

Thus, the acidity, as indicated by the pK values in parentheses,
increases in the series of the following aquo ions of $z = +2$:
Ba^{+2} (14. 0); Ca^{+2} (13. 3); Mg^{+2} (12. 2); and Be^{+2} (5. 7).
    The rules are quite useful but the picture is still too simple
and other factors related to the electron distribution are involved.

For example, $Cd \cdot aq^{+2}$ is a stronger acid than $Ca \cdot aq^{+2}$, although these ions have the same charge to radius ratio.

Hydrolysis of Metal Ions

Hydrolysis of acids or bases is a somewhat antiquated term, which according to the Brönsted theory, is no longer necessary in order to describe the proton transfer from an acid to water or the proton transfer from water to a base. Perhaps unfortunately, the term is still used, especially if the acid is an aquo metal ion.

More than 30 years ago, Brönsted postulated that multivalent metal ions participate in a series of consecutive proton transfers:

$$Fe(H_2O)_6^{+3} = \left[Fe(H_2O)_5OH\right]^{+2} + H^+ = \left[Fe(H_2O)_4(OH)_2\right]^+$$
$$+ 2H^+ = \left[Fe(OH)_3(H_2O)_3\right]_{(c)} + 3H^+ = \left[Fe(OH)_4(H_2O)_2\right]^-$$
$$+ 4H^+ \qquad (21\text{-}5)$$

Hydrolysis can go beyond the uncharged species $Fe(OH)_3(H_2O)_{3(c)}$ to form anions, such as the ferrate (III) ion, probably $\left[Fe(OH)_4 \cdot 2H_2O\right]^-$. All hydrated ions can, in principle, donate a larger number of protons than that corresponding to their charge and can form anionic hydroxo-metal complexes. But, because of the limited pH range of aqueous solutions, not all elements can exist as anionic hydroxo or oxo complexes.

Polynuclear Hydroxo Complexes

The scheme of a consecutive stepwise hydroxide binding is too simple. Although the hydrolysis products listed for hydrolysis of $Fe \cdot aq^{+3}$ are all known and identified, the intermediate steps are frequently much more complicated. In a few cases, such as Hg(II) and Tl(III), the main products are monomeric. Polymeric hydrolysis species have been reported for Be(II), Sc(III), Ce(IV), Cr(III), Mo(V), U(VI), Fe(III), Co(III), Ni(II), Rn(IV), Cu(II), Zn(II), Al(III), Ga(III), Sn(II and IV), Pb(II), Bi(III), and others. Thus, the existence of multinuclear hydrolysis products is a rather general phenomenon. The hydrolyzed species, such as $Fe(H_2O)_5OH^{+2}$, can be considered to dimerize by a condensation process:

$$2\left[Fe(H_2O)_5\right]^{+2} = \left[(H_2O)_4 Fe \overset{OH}{\underset{OH}{\diagdown\diagup}} Fe(H_2O)_4\right]^{+4} + 2H_2O \quad (21\text{-}6)$$

The existence of the dimer has been corroborated experimentally by potentiometric, spectrophotometric, and magnetochemical methods. The dimer may undergo additional hydrolytic reactions which could provide additional hydroxo groups which then could form bridges. The prefixes "ol" and "oxo" are used often in referring to the -OH and -O- bridges. A sequence of such hydrolytic and condensation reactions, sometimes called olation and oxolation, leads, under conditions of oversaturation with respect to the (usually very insoluble) metal hydroxide, to the formation of colloidal hydroxo polymers and ultimately to the formation of precipitates. (Olation may be followed by oxolation, a process in which the bridging OH-group is converted to a bridging O-group). In the pH range lower than the zero point of charge of the metal hydroxide precipitate, positively charged metal hydroxo polymers prevail. In solutions more alkaline than the zero point of charge, anionic hydroxo complexes and negatively charged colloids exist. Although multinuclear complexes have been recognized for many years for a few hydrolysis systems, such as $Cr(III)$ and $Be(II)$, and for anions of $Cr(VI)$, $Si(IV)$, $Mo(VI)$, and $V(V)$, the detailed and quantitative studies of Sillen and co-workers have shown that multinuclear hydrolysis products of metallic cations are of almost universal occurrence in the water solvent system (20). Table I gives an illustration for some of the hydrolysis species which have been reported for various metal ions of interest in water. Additional information and corresponding equilibrium constants may be found in "Stability Constants" (17). Table I is not comprehensive and further developments in the near future may lead to corrections. The opinion on the main hydrolysis products of certain metals has oscillated as a function of time (5).

The number of conceivable combinations $Me_q(OH)_p^{+2}$ is very large, but for a number of cation systems, Sillen had developed a "core and links" theory which is able to account for many experimental facts. According to this theory, the predominating complexes have the general formula $M[(OH)_t M]_n$ where t is a constant indicating the number of ligands in a link, and n is an integer indicating the number of links in a "core and links" complex. Good agreement with experimental data is observed by assuming that complexes with all values for $n = 1, 2, 3 \ldots \ldots$ are formed and that the equilibrium constants for their formation vary with n in some regular manner. For example, $Th_2(OH)_6^{+6}$ and $Th_4(OH)_9^{+7}$ correspond to the general formula $Th[(OH)_3 Th]_n^{+4}$

Thus, the hydrolysis of Th^{+4}, UO_2^{+2}, Sc^{+3}, and other metal cations has been described rather quantitatively with the help of this theory.

TABLE I   REPRESENTATIVE EXAMPLES OF HYDROLYSIS
            SPECIES REPORTED IN THE LITERATURE (a)

Be(II)	$Be_3(OH)_3^{+3}$, Be_2OH^{+3}, $Be(OH)_2$
Mg(II)	$MgOH^+$
Sc(III)	$Sc\left[Sc(OH)_2\right]_n^{3+n}$, $n = 1,2,3...$
Y(III)	$Y(OH)^{+2}$, $Y_2(OH)_2^{+4}$, $Y_3(OH)_5^{+4}$
La(III)	$LaOH^{+2}$, $LaOH_2^+$, $La_5(OH)_9^{+6}$ or $La_6(OH)_{10}^{+8}$
Th(IV)	$Th(OH)_3^+$ (?), $Th\left[Th(OH)_4\right]^{+4}$ (?)
Cr(III)	$CrOH^{+2}$, $Cr_2(OH)_2^{+4}$, $Cr_6(OH)_{12}^{+6}$, $Cr(OH)_4^-$
UO_2^{+2}	$(UO_2)_2OH^{+3}$, $(UO_2)_2(OH)_2^{+2}$, $(UO_2)_3(OH)_5^+$, $(UO_2)_3(OH)_4^{+2}$ $(UO_2)_3(OH)_4^{+2}$, $(UO_2)_4(OH)_6^{+2}$, $(UO_2)_4(OH)_7^+$
Mn(II)	$MnOH^+$, $Mn(OH)_3^-$
Fe(II)	$FeOH^+$, $Fe(OH)_3^-$
Fe(III)	$FeOH^{+2}$, $Fe_2(OH)_2^{+4}$, $Fe(OH)_2^+$, $Fe(OH)_4^-$ (additional multinuclear intermediates in the precipitation of $Fe(OH)_{3(c)}$.
Cu(II)	$CuOH^+$, $Cu_2(OH)_2^{+2}$, $Cu(OH)_3^-$, $Cu(OH)_4^{-2}$
Ag(I)	$AgOH$, Ag_2OH^+, $Ag_2(OH)_2$, $Ag(OH)_2^-$
In(II)	$InOH^+$, In_2OH^{+3}, $In(OH)_3^-$
Hg(II)	$HgOH^+$, Hg_2OH^{+3}, $Hg_2(OH)_2^{+2}$
Al(III)	$Al_8(OH)_{20}^{+4}$ or $Al_7(OH)_{17}^{+4}$, $Al_{13}(OH)_{34}^{+5}$, $Al(OH)_4^-$
Pb(II)	$Pb_4(OH)_4^{+4}$, $Pb_6(OH)_8^{+4}$, $Pb_3(OH)_4^{+2}$, $Pb(OH)_3^-$

TABLE I - cont'd

Bi(III) $BiOH^{+2}$, $Bi_6(OH)_{12}^{+6}$, $Bi_9(OH)_{20}^{+7}$, $Bi_9(OH)_{22}^{+}$

Si(IV) $SiO(OH)_3^{-}$, $SiO_2(OH)_2^{-2}$, $Si_4O_6(OH)_6^{-2}$

(a) Not all the hydrolysis species that have been clai
    by various authors have been listed. Stability
    constants for the hydrolysis species given and
    literature references are quoted in reference 17.

For some other cation systems, however, only one or two
predominating multinuclear species have been claimed, such as
Be(II) and Al(III) (Table I).

Quantitative Description of Metal Ion Hydrolysis
    The calculations of hydrolysis equilibrium concentrations
are based on the law of mass action. The equilibrium constants
should be ideally defined in terms of activities. Since infinitely
dilute solutions are never used, it has become convenient to use
concentration equilibrium constants rather than activity constants
A concentration constant depends on the medium which must be
defined. Most hydrolysis equilibrium constants have been determined in the presence of a swamping "inert" electrolyte of constant ionic strength I = 0.1, 1, or 3). The simplest case, the
formation of a mononuclear hydrolysis product, can be formulate
in terms of an acid base equilibrium (for simplicity, the water
bound to the metal ion and to H^+ is omitted):

$$Fe^{+3} + H_2O = FeOH^{+2} + H^+ \tag{21-7}$$

Where the first acidity constant, $^*K_1$, is defined by:

$$\frac{[FeOH^{+2}][H^+]}{[Fe^{+3}]} = {}^*K_1 \tag{21-8}$$

Similarly the second acidity constant, $^*K_2$, can be defined by:

$$FeOH^{+2} + H_2O = Fe(OH)_2^{+} + H^+; \quad {}^*K_2 \tag{21-9}$$

For the two protolysis equilibria 1 and 2, a cumulative or gross
acidity constant $^*\beta_2$ can be defined:

$$\frac{\left[Fe(OH)_2^+\right]\left[H^+\right]^2}{\left[Fe^{+3}\right]} = {}^*\beta_2 = {}^*K_1 \, {}^*K_2 \tag{21-10}$$

Sometimes it is as convenient (and mathematically equivalent) to formulate the hydrolysis equilibria in terms of hydroxo complex formation:

$$Fe^{+3} + OH^- = FeOH^{+2}; \; K_1 = {}^*K_1/K_w \tag{21-8a}$$

$$FeOH^{+2} + OH^- = Fe(OH)_2^+; \; K_2 = {}^*K_2/K_w \tag{21-9a}$$

$$Fe^{+3} + 2OH^- = Fe(OH)_2^+; \; \beta_2 = K_1K_2 = {}^{**}\beta_2/(K_w)^2 \tag{21-10a}$$

where K_w is the ion product of water.

The formation of $Fe_2(OH)_2^{+4}$ can be formulated by:

$$2Fe^{+3} + 2H_2O = Fe_2(OH)_2^{+4} + 2H^+; \; {}^*\beta_{22} \tag{21-11}$$

or:

$$2Fe^{+3} + 2OH^- = Fe_2(OH)_2^{+4}; \quad {}_{22} = {}^*\beta_{22}/(K_w)^2 \tag{21-11a}$$

In the hydrolysis of Fe(III), the complexes listed above ($FeOH^{+2}$, $Fe(OH)_2^+$, and $Fe_2(OH)_2^{+4}$) are the predominant soluble components in the lower pH range of $Fe(ClO_4)_3$ or $Fe(NO_3)_3$ solutions. In such solutions, total Fe(III) is given by:

$$\left[Fe(III)_t\right] = \left[Fe^{+3}\right] + \left[FeOH^{+2}\right] + \left[Fe(OH)_2^+\right] +$$

$$\left[Fe_2(OH)_2^{+4}\right] \tag{21-12}$$

or:

$$\left[Fe(III)_t\right] = \left[Fe^{+3}\right]\left(1 + K_1\left[OH^-\right] + \beta_2\left[OH^-\right]^2 + \right.$$

$$\left. 2\left[Fe^{+3}\right]\left[OH^-\right]^2 \, \beta_{22}\right) \tag{21-12a}$$

Thus, for any pH and any Fe $_t$ the equilibrium concentration for all participating Fe(III) species can be computed from equations 21-8 to 21-12 . The quantitative evaluation of the systematic relations that determine equilibrium concentrations of a solution constitutes a purely mathematical problem that is subject to exact and systematic treatment.

Figures 4b and 4c give distribution diagrams for Fe (III) spec at low pH values. Similar distribution diagrams for Cu^{+2} complexes are given in Figures 2d and 2e. The distances between the curves indicate the percentages of the metal in the form of the various species. It is obvious from Figure 4 that the extent of hydrolysis depends on pH and total Fe (III) concentration. As can be seen from equation 21-12a, and the last term formation of a binuclear complex depends not only on pH but also on $[Fe^{+3}]$ In other words, at a given pH, the concentration of the binuclear complex increases with $[Fe(III)_t]$. For example, at pH= 3 and at concentrations of $[Fe(III)t] < 10^{-4}M$, the percentage contribution of $Fe_2(OH)_2^{+4}$ becomes negligible; while the binuclear compound is the predominant iron (III) species at concentrations of $[Fe(III)_t] > 10^{-2}M$. An important rule is that at any given and constant pH, the fraction of polynuclear complexes decreases upon dilution. At some particular dilution, a "mononuclear wall" is attained (5, 20).

In Figure 4a the average ligand number, $\bar{n}$, i.e., the average number of OH^- ions bound per Fe (III) atom, is presented for a concentration of $[Fe(III)_t] = 10^{-4}M$ as a function of pH (i.e., as a function of log $[OH^-]$). Diagrams of this kind can be obtained directly from potentiometric measurements recorded over a wide range of $[Fe(III)]$ and $[H^+]$. Complex formation can be measur also in principle by direct determination of the complexes or by the direct determination of the free metal ion. Experimental techniques include spectrophotometric, polarographic, potentiometric, and, occasionally, magnetochemical methods. The results of such measurements can be expressed frequently in terms of a distribution coefficient:

$$\alpha Fe = [Fe(III)_t] / [Fe^{+3}] \qquad (21-13)$$

In Figure 4a, $\log \alpha_{Fe}$ is plotted as a function of pH for a $10^{-4}M$ iron (III) solution. It may be noted that:

$$\log \alpha_{Fe} = pFe^{+3} - pFe(III)_t = \Delta pFe \qquad (2-14)$$

The degree of complexation by OH^- (or generally by any ligand) is best judged by ΔpM. The higher ΔpM, the better the cation is complexed.

For an evaluation of equilibrium constants, attempts are made to interpret data of $\bar{n}$ or α (or both) in terms of the most

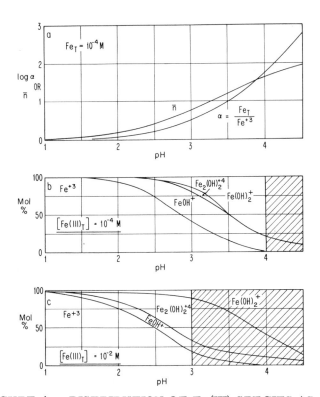

FIGURE 4   DISTRIBUTION OF Fe(III) SPECIES AS A FUNCTION
OF pH. The extent of hydrolysis depends on pH and
the Fe(III)$_t$ concentration. Figure (a) plots the
average ligand number $\bar{n}$ and the distribution coefficient α, respectively, as a function of pH for a 10^{-4}M
Fe(III) solution. $\bar{n}$ is experimentally accessible from
$[H^+]$ measurements in alkalimetric titrations; α can
be determined independently from potentiometric
(ferro-ferri cell) spectrophotometric or magnetochemical measurements. Either one or both parameters can be used to arrive at equilibrium constants.
Using representative equilibrium constants (17) for
the species listed in equation 21-12, distribution diagrams for the various Fe(III) species are depicted
in Figures (b) and (c). In the shaded areas, the
solution becomes oversaturated with respect to
Fe(OH)$_{3(c)}$ (K$_s$=10^{-36}); in this pH range additional
polynuclear hydrolysis species occur as kinetic
intermediates in the usually slow transition to Fe(OH)$_{3(c)}$.

probable hydrolysis species. Si llen and co-workers have develop
mathematical and graphical procedures in order to treat the resul
in terms of all possible interpretations until an acceptable agreement is found between the postulated stability constants and the
experimental results.

Representative examples of distribution diagrams involving
multinuclear hydrolysis species are given for Pb(II) and Bi(III)
in Figures 5 and 6, respectively. Both figures are from the work
of Olin (21).

It is evident from the examples given in Table I that, with
the exception of the earth alkali metals, most multivalent metal
ions form hydroxo complexes in the pH range of natural waters.

Kinetics

The establishment of hydrolysis equilibria is generally very
fast as long as the hydrolysis species are simple. (There are
some exceptions: metal ions like Cr(III), Co(III), Pt(II), Pt(IV),
and ruthenium ions form their complexes very slowly). Equilibria with polynuclear complexes, however, frequently are established very slowly. In solutions that are incipiently oversaturated with respect to the insoluble metal hydroxides, and in the
kinetic transition from free metal ions to precipitates, progressive condensation and hydroxylation can lead to highly multimeric
soluble intermediates until ultimately, insoluble polymeric complexes of indefinite size are formed. These latter ones are
usually referred to as the insoluble metal hydroxides. In Figure
the shaded areas indicate the pH range where the iron (III)
solutions become oversaturated with respect of $Fe(OH)_{3(c)}$. Iron
(III) solutions in this pH range show continuously changing spectra
(UV and visible). Within a few days, the solution becomes turbid
and after a few weeks ferric hydroxide precipitates. The precipi
tation becomes more rapid in solutions of higher OH^- ion concent
tions. Figure 7 gives some representative results on the rate of
polymerization of Fe(III) as measured by the rate of decrease in
$[Fe \cdot aq^{+3}]$.

Metal hydroxylation generally can be accelerated by heating
the solutions. Sometimes the complexes formed in such artifical
"aged" solutions are kinetically stable beyond the regions in whic
they are thermodynamically stable.

Adsorption of Hydroxylated Metal Ions

It has been realized for a long time, but not sufficiently
appreciated by water treatment experts, that coagulation is effect

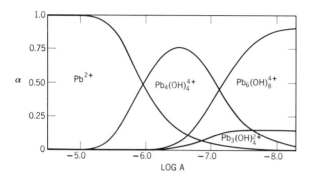

FIGURE 5   DISTRIBUTION OF Pb(II) - HYDROLYSIS
             SPECIES. (After Olin, 21). $\left[Pb(II)_T\right] = .04M$.

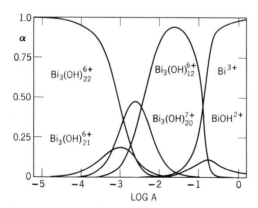

FIGURE 6   DISTRIBUTION OF Bi(III) - HYDROLYSIS
             SPECIES. (After Olin, 21). $\left[Bi(III)_T\right] = .01M$.

usually by metal ion hydrolysis species and not by the free
multivalent metal ions (28). Matijevic and his co-workers have
shown that metal ion hydrolysis species can be detected by coagulation (22). They have proposed methods to determine the charge
of the hydrolzyed species which are based upon determination of
the concentration of the metal salt necessary to coagulate a
lyophobic sol (e.g., silver halogenides). This concentration, the
critical coagulation concentration, depends upon the charge of the
counterion of the coagulating electrolyte.

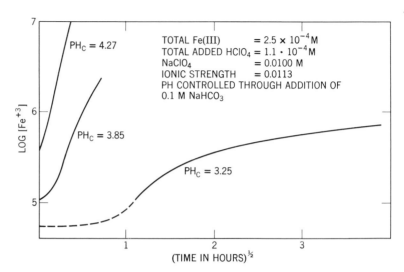

FIGURE 7   RATE OF HYDROLYSIS AND POLYMERIZATIO
OF Fe(III). Measurements in the rate of decrea
of $[Fe \cdot aq^{+3}]$ using a ferro-ferri cell in soluti
of constant and controlled $[H^+]$. (C. Schneider
and W. Stumm, unpublished data).

If the Schulze-Hardy rule can be applied to adsorbable specie
(i.e., if the energy of interaction due to adsorption can be neglec
in comparison to the energy of electrostatic interaction), then
Matijevic's method of determining the charge of hydrolysis specie
should be a valuable supplement to the potentiometric investigatio
at least in those cases where a particular hydrolysis species pre-
dominates. Matijevic, et al, have shown also that metal ion hydr
lysis products are sorbed on colloidal dispersions and are able to
reverse the charge and restabilize lyophobic colloids. Non-hydro
lated metal ions are generally not able to cause charge reversal
and restabilization. The concentration-pH domain of coagulation
and stabilization has been estimated by these investigators for ma
"salts" of polyvalent metal ions, including Fe(III) and Al(III) (22).
Adsorption of hydrolysis products must be assumed to occur on
most interfaces and has been demonstrated on polystyrene (22),
silica (33), clays, (34), and bacteria (34). Figure 8 gives some
representative results on the interaction of hydrolyzed ferric iron
on crystalline silica (33). In this case the coagulation and the
restabilization due to adsorption has been measured by a refiltrat
technique similar to the method used by LaMer and co-workers (?

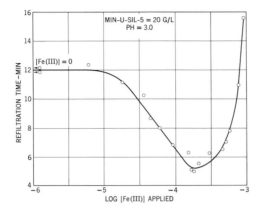

FIGURE 8   COLLOID-CHEMICAL INTERACTION OF
              HYDROLYZED IRON (III) AND CRYSTALLINE
              SILICA. Coagulation and restabilization of
              the silica suspension is measured by the
              refiltration time. The refiltration time is
              directly proportional to the square of the
              effective area in the filter cake. Thus,
              coagulation and restabilization (due to adsorp-
              tion) is reflected in a decrease and increase,
              respectively, in refiltration time. (After O'Melia
              and Stumm, 33).

The refiltration time is, according to the Carman-Kozeny equation, directly proportional to the square of the effective area in
the filter cake. Coagulation of the silica suspension leads to a
decrease in the effective area (at $[Fe(III)] > 10^{-5}M$ in Figure 8).
At higher concentrations ($[Fe(III)] > 10^{-4}M$) restabilization and
decrease in area due to adsorption and charge reversal leads to
a redispersion of the incipiently coagulated silica and to a corresponding increase in the refiltration time.
      Cationic and neutral multinuclear hydroxo species as well
as anionic multinuclear hydroxo or oxo complexes can be formed
in aqueous solutions. Figure 9 shows coagulation and charge
reversal of a positively charged (positive potential) AgBr sol by
polysilicate at pH = 7. Here the extent of coagulation, similar
to the techniques employed by Matijevic, is detected by the
intensity of light scattered by the sol particles. The polysilicate
used for this experiment is thermodynamically unstable and has
been prepared by partially neutralizing and subsequently diluting
a concentrated sodium silicate solution. It is evident from Figure 9

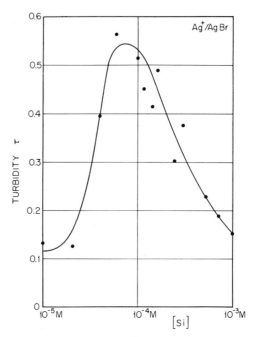

FIGURE 9   COAGULATION AND CHARGE REVERSAL OF
             A POSITIVELY CHARGED COLLOID (AgBr)
             BY POLYSILICATE. Coagulation results in
             increase in turbidity. Restabilization and
             charge reversal due to adsorption is accom-
             panied by a reduction in turbidity. (After
             Stumm and Hüper, 35).

that the polysilicate coagulates and restabilizes the sol at $[Si]>$
10^{-5}M and at $[Si]>10^{-4}$M, respectively. The formulation of the
polysilicate and its coagulative effect and sorbability depend
strongly on the method of its preparation. Results, such as those
depicted in Figure 9, can be used expediently to develop procedures for preparing so-called "activated silica" (35). The
sorption of polysilicates not only plays an important role in
coagulation and in the use of "activated silica" as a coagulant
aid, but also in the use of silicates as a corrosion inhibitor.

    The sorption of hydroxylated metal ions at solid-solution
interfaces is of considerable significance in the limnological
transformations of multivalent metal ions and in the fate of

radionuclides in natural water systems. Sorption of hydrolyzed
species is a significant factor in sand filtration (36). Pronounced
adsorption effects may be observed even under conditions in which
only a small fraction of the metal ion is hydrolyzed. Hydrolyzed
species are frequently significant in electrode processes (corrosion, polarography, and electrode potential measurements).
For example, hydrolyzed La(III) species play an important role
in the polarographic reduction of NO_3^- in the presence of La^{+3}
In the Eh measurement of the Fe(II) $\overset{-}{-}$ Fe(III) system on Pt
electrodes, the electroactive species appears to be a hydroxylated
Fe(III) at pH values above ca. 4.

HYDROUS METAL OXIDES

It has been shown already that the formation of a precipitate
can often be considered the final stage in the formation of polynuclear complexes. Aggregates of ions which form the building
stones in the lattice are produced in the solution. These aggregates combine with other ions to form neutral compounds. On
the basis of magnetochemical evidence, Mulay has proposed a
structure for polymeric hydrous ferric oxide (24).

In concurrence with the scheme depicted in Figure 3, there
is a continuous transition between metallic and metalloid behavior.
This may be evident also by comparing the metal hydroxides in
a section of the Periodic Table (Figure 10). Many multivalent
hydrous oxides are amphoteric owing to the acid-base equilibria
involved in the hydrolysis reactions of aquo-metal ions. Thus,
H^+ and OH^- are primarily the potential determining ions for
hydrous oxide precipitates. Alkalimetric or acidimetric titration
curves for hydrous metal oxides provide a quantitative explanation
for the manner in which the charge of the hydrous oxide depends
on the pH of the medium. The amphoteric behavior of solid metal
hydroxides becomes evident from such titration curves. From an
operational point of view, such hydrous oxides can be compared
with amphoteric polyelectrolytes and can be considered as hydrated
solid electrolytes, frequently possessing a variable space lattice,
in which the proportion of different ions, cations as well as anions,
is variable within the limits of electrical neutrality of the solid
(28, 29). These hydroxides show a strong tendency to interact
specifically with anions as well as with cations, as outlined in
Figure 11. Interactions with anions predominate under conditions
where the metal oxide is positively charged, i.e., at pH values
below the isoelectric point. At pH values higher than the isoelectric point, the relative number of extra coordinated OH^- ions

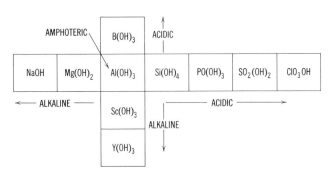

FIGURE 10   ACIDITY AND BASICITY OF SOME METAL
                      HYDROXIDES.

(or of hydroxo groups that have dissociated H^+ ions) will increase
with increased concentration of base. Under such conditions the
solid phase is capable of interacting with cations.

The specific interaction with anions can be explained most
satisfactorily in terms of ligand exchange (competitive complex
formation of the metal ion with OH^- and other bases). The
interaction of the hydrous oxides with cations can be interpreted
also as complex formation. It is, however, more frequently
referred to as cation exchange or exchange adsorption. A
representative example of the pH dependent cation and anion
exchange on hydrous SnO_2, taken from the work of Kraus (37),
is given in Figure 12.

Cation sorption on metal oxides is comparable to cation
exchange on clay materials. The exchange capacities of hydrous
oxides occasionally can exceed those of clays. (For example,
sorption of Mn^{+2} on δ-MnO_2 and active $Fe(OH)_3$ at pH 8 are in
order of 1. 0 and 0. 3 moles of Mn(II) sorbed per mole of MnO_2
and $Fe(OH)_3$, respectively, 38). Thus, ferric oxide and MnO_2
may contribute significantly to the adsorptive powers (ion
exchange capacity) of rivers and lake sediments.

Mixed oxides can be prepared in which a second cation of
different charge than the parent cation is introduced into the
structure, often resulting in remarkable alterations of the
surface chemical behavior of these oxides. The most representative example is the isomorphic replacement of a silicon

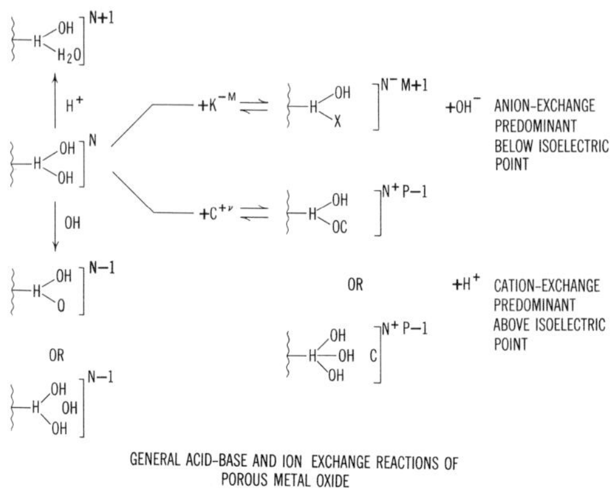

GENERAL ACID-BASE AND ION EXCHANGE REACTIONS OF
POROUS METAL OXIDE

FIGURE 11   SPECIFIC INTERACTIONS OF ANIONS AND
CATIONS WITH MULTIVALENT HYDROUS
METAL OXIDES.   At pH values below the
isoelectric point anion exchange (ligand
exchange due to interaction of anion bases
that compete with OH^- for the coordinative
positions on the metal ion).   At pH values
higher than the isoelectric point, the number
of extra coordinated OH^- ions (or of OH^-
groups that have dissociated H^+ ions) leads
to a cation exchange that increases with
increasing pH of the medium.

tetrahedra network by an Al tetrahedron.   The structure of such
an Al tetrahedron, which shares corners with Si-tetrahedra,
acquires a structure similar to the ClO_4^- with the acid obtained
by replacing the K^+ a mica and similar clays by H^+ becoming
very strong (25).   Similar marked changes in surface chemical
behavior can be achieved by introducing certain anions (phosphate, chromate, silicate, and molybdate) into the solid structure.
For example, hydrous oxo-phosphato zirconium (IV) precipitates
have rather spectacular cation exchange capacities (16).
        The formation constants of hydroxo complexes are remark-
ably large when compared to most other ligands.   This explains
why, with most tri- and tetra-valent metal ions, the hydroxides
or hydrous oxides are the only thermodynamically stable precipitates in the pH range of natural waters.   Insoluble phosphates
are formed with Al(III), Fe(III), and a few quadrivalent metal
ions in solutions of low pH (32).   With many bivalent ions, however,

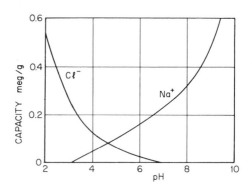

FIGURE 12   pH - DEPENDENT CATION AND ANION
             EXCHANGE ON HYDROUS SnO_2. (After
             Kraus, et al, 37).

CO_3^{-2}, S^{-2}, S_2^{-2}, and PO_4^{-3} may successfully compete with OH^-
to "satisfy" the coordinative requirements of the metal ions. Thus
$FeCO_3$, $MnCO_3$, $CaCO_3$, and $ZnCO_3$ are the predominant solid
phases in carbonate bearing water systems.   The solubility of
Cu^{+2}, Mg^{+2}, and Be^{+2}, however, is predominantly controlled
by the solubility of the respective hydroxides. Hydrolysis species
however, frequently influence the solubility of these precipitates
and have to be considered in making solubility calculations. Most
metal ion precipitates become soluble again at very high pH value
because of the formation of soluble anionic hydroxo complexes.
Occasionally other ligands beside OH^- may participate in the
formation of soluble complexes.   For example, $[Cu(CO_3)_2]^{-2}$
renders Cu(II) soluble in carbonate bearing high pH waters.

METAL IONS AS LEWIS ACIDS

Considerable emphasis has been placed so far on hydroxo
complexes which is amply justified by the ubiquitous presence
of OH^- in water and by the strong affinity of metal ions for OH^-.
Hydrolysis, or complex formation by OH^-, can be explained without any difficulty in terms of Brönsted acid-base behavior. There
is no a priori need to invoke the Lewis concept since hydrolysis
can be interpreted in terms of a proton transfer.

In addition to the OH^- ion, all other proton acceptors (bases)
can serve as electron pair donors and thus coordinate as Lewis
bases with metal ions (and other Lewis acids).   The strength of
a series of bases can be measured by their basicity constants or

by the acidity constants of their conjugate acids (reciprocal of proton stability constants). As a first approximation, the stability of proton complexes may be compared with the stability of metal complexes. In other words, the question is asked whether Lewis basicity has a similar trend as the Brönsted basicity. Although some weak bases such as ClO_4^- and NO_3^- have very little tendency to form metal complexes, no broad generalization is possible. Only if the ligands are similar in structure, the stability of metal complexes increases with the stability of hydrogen complexes. Otherwise there is little correlation between hydrogen and metal complexes. This lack of correlation is partially due to entropy factors that depend on the nature of the ligand atom.

The properties of a complex compound having oxygen as a donor atom differ remarkably from those having nitrogen as a donor atom. In the case of oxygen, the bonds are more ionic whereas if nitrogen is the donor atom, the bonds are more covalent in character. Ahrland, et al, divided metal ions into two categories that depended on whether the metal ions formed their most stable complexes with the first ligand atom of each periodic group (F, O, N), or whether they formed their most stable complexes with a later member of the group (I, S,) (26). Other generalized Lewis acids besides metal ions may be classified in the same way. Such a division into two groups, based on conceptual and operational characteristics, has ultimately led to Pearson's concept of Soft and Hard Acids and Bases (SHAB-Concept, 27. This concept can be used conveniently to explain and qualitatively predict chemical reactions and stabilities of compounds. A classification of hard and soft acids is given in Table II. It is beyond the scope of this discussion to elaborate on various ramifications of the SHAB concept but some useful qualitative trends on the preferences of the two groups of metal cations for different kind of donor atoms are indicated in Table II. For example, metal cations in class A (hard acids) preferentially form complexes with the fluoride ion and ligands having oxygen as a donor atom. Water is more strongly attracted to these metals than ammonia or cyanide. No sulfides (precipitates or complexes) are formed, since OH^- ions are bound before HS^- or S^{-2}. Chloro or iodo complexes are weak and can occur at best in acid solutions. The univalent alkali ions essentially form complexes only with water (some weak complexes of Li^+ and Na^+ with chelating agents such as EDTA and polyphosphates are known). Chelating agents containing solely nitrogen or sulfur as ligand

TABLE II   CLASSIFICATION OF METAL IONS AND
OTHER LEWIS ACIDS INTO HARD AND
SOFT ACIDS (a)

HARD ACIDS (Class A)	SOFT ACIDS (Class B)
Small size, low polarizability, high positive oxidation state.	Large size, high polarizability, low electronegativity.
Most A-metal cations have outer shell of 8 electrons.	Filled outer orbitals (Most B-metal cations have an outer shell of 18 electrons).
H^+, Li^+, Na^+, K^+	Cu^+, Ag^+, Au^+, Hg^+
Be^{+2}, Mg^{+2}, Ca^{+2}, Sr^{+2}	Pd^{+2}, Cd^{+2}, Hg^{+2}, CH_3Hg^+
Al^{+3}, Sc^{+3}, La^{+3}, Cr^{+3} Co^{+3}, Fe^{+3}, As^{+3}	Tl^{+3}, Au^{+3}
Si^{+4}, Ti^{+4}, Zr^{+4}, Th^{+4}, Pu^{+4} UO_2^{+2}, VO^{+2}	
BF_3, BCl_3, $B(OR)_3$ SO_3, RSO_2^+, RPO_2^+ I^{+7}, I^{+5}, Cl^{+7} CO_2, RCO^+, R_3C^+	All metal atoms, bulk metals I_2, Br_2, ICN I^+, Br^+, HO^+

Ligand Atom Preference: $N \gg P$ $O \gg S$ $F \gg Cl$	Borderline Fe^{+2}, Co^{+2}, Ni^{+2}, Cu^{+2} Zn^{+2}, Pb^{+2}, Bi^{+3} $B(CH_3)_3$, SO_2, NO^+	Ligand Atom Preference: $P \gg N$ $S \gg O$ $I \gg Br > Cl > F$

Qualitative Generalization:

Preference by hard acids

$\longleftarrow$

F, O, N = Cl, Br, I, S = C

(a) After Pearson (27).

Preference by soft acids

atoms do not coordinate with hard acids to form complexes of appreciable stability.

On the other hand, metal ions belonging to the category of soft acids (class B) coordinate preferentially with soft bases, i.e., with bases containing I, S, P, and N as donor atoms. Thus, metal ions in this class may bind ammonia stronger than water, CN^- in preference to OH^-, and form more stable I^- or Cl^- complexes than F^- complexes. These metal cations as well as those which have to be grouped in the border line category form insoluble sulfides, and soluble S^{-2} and HS^- complexes. Table II contains other reagents that can form complexes with bases. Many substances possess properties similiar to metal ions and can coordinate with bases.

Complex Formation in Natural Water

Fresh natural waters represent rather dilute solutions. A precise definition of "dilute" is difficult to give. At infinite dilution, the ions do behave as independent species. In real solutions, various forces act between ions with the much disputed question arising; what species are actually present? This question has not been answered unambiguously. It has been suggested that two types of species s hould be considered: (a) the inner sphere complex in which the base (usually an anion) is immediately adjacent to the metal cation; and (b) the outer sphere complex where the cation and anion are separated by one or two water molecules. Beyond the outer sphere range, ionic interactions do not give rise to chemical species, i.e., any interaction is not specific and should be treated by the activity coefficient theory of Debye-Huckel.

In fresh water, the distribution of the various soluble and insoluble forms can be described quite adequately in terms of mass law equilibrium relations especially if the equilibrium constants have been corrected for non-ideal behavior. In order to apply the law of mass action the exact species must be known because the concentration must be introduced into the equilibrium expression.

It has already been shown that OH^- ions form complexes within the pH range of natural waters with many multivalent metal cations. What complex formation is expected from other ions indigenous to natural waters; such as Cl^-, SO_4^{-2}, and HCO_3^- ? At the great dilutions encountered in these waters, very little complexing occurs. There have been some indications that Ca^{+2} can form a rather unstable $CaHCO_3^+$ comples. Similarly, stability constants for $MnHCO_3^+$ and $FeHCO_3^+$ complexes have been reported but the stability constants are very small. In most natural waters, the bicarbonate complexes are too weak to affect materially the solubility relations of the solid carbonates. Similarly, chloro complexes are quite insignificant at the dilutions and within the pH ranges encountered in fresh waters. Even in sea water, the affinity of OH^- to most metal ions is larger than that of Cl^-, thus chloro complexes of iron (III), Al(III), and Mg(II) are not preponderant. A few trace metals; such as Ag^+, Cd^{+2}, and Hg^{+2}, conceivably form chloro complexes in sea water.

Since the oxygen in sulfate is not very basic, only weak metal complexes are formed with sulfate. Those metal ions that have a preference for oxygen donor atoms will bind OH^- before sulfate. Insoluble sulfates are formed by the alkaline earth ions, but generally not at the concentrations encountered in fresh waters. Sulfate complexes of Al (III), Fe (III), and Cu(III) are stable only at low pH. The same is true for phosphate complexes.

This brief, qualitative survey should indicate that most metal cations in solution in fresh water are present as either the free aquo or the hydroxylated species. Coordination chemistry, however, plays an important role in the composition of the solid phases which are in contact with the solution. Natural waters acquire their chemical characteristics through direct solution and chemical reactions with solids and gases with which they have come in contact during the various parts of the hydrological cycle. Sillen (18), Bricker and Garrels (19), and others (31, 32) have emphasized the significance of heterogeneous equilibria with clays and minerals in the interpretation of the composition of fresh waters. Plausibly, such equilibria comprise the principle pH buffer systems of fresh and oceanic waters. A lot has to be learned in the immediate future on coordination reactions in the solid phases, on thermodynamic stabilities of the various clays, and on solid solutions. Natural waters are buffered not only with respect to H^+, but also with respect to other soluble components. Equilibria with OH^-, ion exchange, and other equilibria with solid phases (pure minerals and solid solutions) represent metal ion buffer systems.

UNIDENTATE AND MULTIDENTATE METAL COMPLEXES

One of the reasons why metal ions in solution in natural waters are not complexed appreciably by ligands other than H_2O or OH^- is that most bases indigenous to natural waters are unidentate ligands. As it will be seen, unidentate ligands form less stable complexes than multidentate ligands, especially in dilute solutions. (Carbonate, sulfate, and phosphate, in principle, can serve as bidentate ligands). The solid carbonates of Ca^{+2}, Mn^{+2}, Fe^{+2}, Co^{+2}, and Zn^{+2} have six oxygen atoms around the metal ion; however, soluble carbonate complexes may exist only at high pH for Be(II), the heavier lanthanides, UO_2^+, and possible for Cu(II). Perhaps for steric reasons, these anions usually act as unidentate ligands.

Stepwise Complex Formation

   As with hydroxide, complexes with other ligands are formed in a stepwise manner. In a series; such as, Cu^{+2}, $Cu(NH_3)^{+2}$, $Cu(NH_3)_2^{+2}$, $Cu(NH_3)_4^{+2}$, and $Cu(NH_3)_5^{+2}$, the successive stability constants generally decrease; i.e., the Cu^{+2} ion takes up one NH_3 molecule after the other (there are exceptions to this behavior). As can be seen from Figure 2d, relatively high concentrations of NH_3 are necessary to effectively complex Cu(II) and to form a tetra-amine complex. In natural waters, the concentrations of the ligands and the affinity of the ligands for the metal ion, with the exception of H_2O and OH^-, are usually sufficiently small so that, at best, a one-ligand complex may be formed.

The Chelate Effect

   Complexes with unidentate ligands are usually less stable than those with multidentate ligands. Perhaps more important is the fact that the degree of complexation decreases more strongly with dilution for unidentate complexes than for multidentate complexes (chelates). This is illustrated in Figure 13 where the degree of complexation is compared as a function of concentration for uni, bi, and tetradentate Cu(II) amine complexes. Free $\left[Cu \cdot aq^{+2} \right]$ is plotted as a function of dilution in the left hand graph whereas the quantitative degree of complexation, as measured by ΔpCu, is given in the right hand graph. It is obvious from Figure 13 that the complexing effect of NH_3 on Cu^{+2} becomes negligible at concentrations that might be encountered in natural water systems. Chelates, however, remain remarkably stable even at very dilute concentrations.

   The curves in Figure 13 have been calculated on the basis of stability constants taken from Sillen and Martell (17). These calculations are essentially the same as those outlined for the

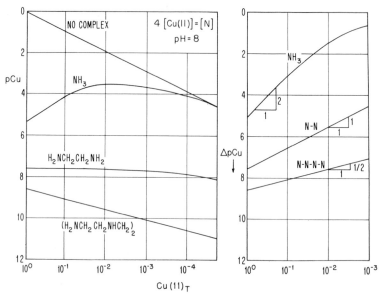

FIGURE 13   THE CHELATE EFFECT; COMPLEX FORMA-
TION OF Cu · aq^{+2} WITH MONODENTATE,
BIDENTATE, AND TETRADENTATE AMINES.
pCu is plotted as a function of concentration
in the left hand diagram; on the right, the
relative degree of complexation as measured
by ΔpCu as a function of concentration is
depicted. The extent of complexing is larger
with chelate complex formers than with unidentate ligands. Unidentate complexes are
dissociated in dilute solutions, while chelates
remain essentially undissociated at great
dilutions.

hydroxo complex formation. Although algebraically simple, they
are tedious and time-consuming. In the case of the Cu-NH_3
system, these species have to be considered: Cu^{+2}; $Cu(NH_3)^{+2}$;
$Cu(NH_3)_2^{+2}$, $Cu(NH_3)_4^{+2}$, $Cu(NH_3)_5^{+2}$; NH_4^+; and NH_3. Thus
for every $[H^+]$, eight equations have to be solved simultaneously in order to compute the relative concentrations of each
species present. Six mass laws (five stability expressions for
the five different amine complexes and the acid base equilibrium

of $NH_4^+ - NH_3$ and two concentration conditions make up the eight equations. As concentration conditions, equations defining $[Cu]_t$ and $[NH_3]_t$ might be formulated:

$$[Cu]_t = [Cu^{+2}] + [Cu(NH_3)^{+2}] + [Cu(NH_3)_2^{+2}] + \ldots \quad (21\text{-}15)$$

$$[NH_3]_t = [NH_4^+] + [NH_3] + [Cu(NH_3)^{+2}] + 2[Cu(NH_3)_2^{+2}] + \ldots \quad (21\text{-}16)$$

Guidelines for coping with these and other more involved types of calculations have been provided by Ringbom (5), Schwarzenbach (4), and others. Computers are, of course, also very useful.

In Figure 13, an equivalent concentration of complex former to that of metal ion was considered. Of course, pM increases with increasing concentration of the complex former over the metal. Figure 14 shows the effect of various ligands on the complex formation with ferric iron. Here the concentration of the complexing agent is kept at a constant value and in excess of $[Fe(III)]_t$. If the ligand is in large excess over the metal, the quantitative degree of complexation, ΔpM, is independent of the total metal ion concentration. In Figure 14, an increase in stability is observed again in going from unidentate (F^-, SO_4^{-2}, HPO_4^{-2}) to bidentate (oxalate), to tridentate (citrate), and to sexadentate (EDTA, DCTA) ligands. Figure 14 also illustrates that in all aqueous solutions, $[H^+]$ and $[OH^-]$ influence markedly the degree of complexation. At low pH, H^+ competes and successfully with the ligand for the coordinative positions on the metal ion. Furthermore, at low and high pH, mixed hydrogen-metal and hydroxide-ligand complexes can be formed. (In the case of EDTA (=L), in addition to FeL^-, the complexes FeHL, $FeOHL^{-2}$, and $Fe(OH)_2L^{-3}$ have to be considered). Because of the competing influence of H^+ or OH^-, the complexing effect cannot be estimated solely from stability constants.

It is also seen from the relations depicted in Figure 14 that relatively high concentrations of complex formers are necessary to keep ferric iron in solution. Thus, the calculations predict that a 10^{-2}M solution of sulfate, fluoride, phosphate, oxalate, or citrate can keep 10^{-3}M ferric iron in solution only up to pH values of 3.3, 4.7, 4.8, 6.9, and 7.6, respectively.

These inferences are quite interesting in connection with the use of ferric iron (similar inferences pertain to Al(III)) as

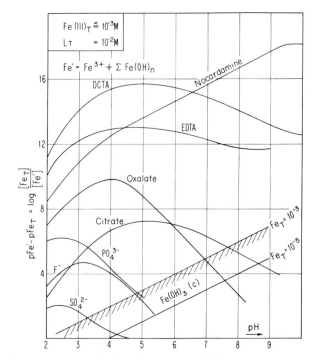

FIGURE 14   COMPLEXING OF IRON (III). The degree
of complexation is expressed in terms of
ΔpFe for various ligands (10^{-2}M). The
competing effect of H^+ at low pH values and
of OH^- at higher pH values explains that
effective complexation is strongly dependent
on pH. Mono, di, and tri-dentate ligands
(10^{-2}M) are not able to keep a 10^{-3}M Fe(III)
in solution at higher pH values. EDTA is
Ethylenediaminetetracetate. DCTA is 1,2-
diaminocyclohexane-tetraacetate. Nocordamine
is a trilydroxamate (a related structure is
shown in Figure 16).

a coagulant. Because of coordinative interaction, such anions
can influence the coagulative behavior of iron (III). Similarly,
the pH of ferric iron precipitation will be strongly affected by
the presence of coordinating anions. For example, Figure 14
illustrates that, in the presence of 10^{-2}M ligand, a 10^{-3}M

solution of ferric iron will form precipitates around pH 4.5 if
the ligand is phosphate (or $H_2PO_4^-$) whereas precipitation will
not occur until pH values around 7.5 if the ligand is citrate.
The precipitates formed in the presence of such ligands are
usually non-stoichiometric mixed precipitates (phosphato-
hydroxo or citrato-hydroxo iron (III) precipitates).

Metal Ion Buffers
      The analogy between metal ions and H^+ ions can be extended
to the concept of buffers. pH-buffers, i.e., solutions that re-
sist a change in $[H^+]$ are made by mixing acids and conjugate
bases in proper proportions:

$$[H^+] = K \; [HA]/[A^-] \tag{21-17}$$

Metal ions can be similarly buffered by adding appropriate ligands
to the metal ion solution:

$$[Me] = K \; [MeL]/[L] \tag{21-18}$$

      It is well known that the living cell controls not only pH but
also pCu, pMn, pMg, etc., and that complex formers are used
as the buffering component. pMe buffers are convenient tools
for investigating phenomena pertaining to metal ions. Very
few people prepare a pH = 6 solution by diluting a concentrated
HCl solution but this mistake is made frequently with metal ion
solutions. If, for example, one wants to study the toxic effect
of Cu^{+2} on algae, it might be more appropriate to prepare a
suitable pCu buffer. If a copper salt solution is simply diluted,
the concentration (or activity) of the free Cu^{+2}, because of
hydrolysis and adsorption and other side reactions, may be
entirely different from that calculated by considering the dilution only.

Iron (III) in Natural Waters
      Iron (III) is very insoluble within the pH range of natural
waters. In the absence of complex formers other than OH^-,
the solubility of ferric iron (i.e., the sum of Fe^{+3}, $FeOH^{+2}$,
$Fe(OH)_2^+$, and $Fe(OH)_4^-$) cannot exceed concentrations of
ca. 10^{-8}M within the pH range 6 - 9. Since this does not appear
to be in accord with the analytical findings for natural waters,
it has been suggested by various authors that the Fe(III) is
frequently present as an organic complex. While this possibility

cannot be excluded in all cases, it is analytically very difficult to distinguish between dissolved and suspended iron. Lengweiler, et al, have shown that with very dilute Fe(III) solutions containing Fe^{59} as a tracer, and brought to a pH between 5 and 10, essentially all the iron hydroxide can be sedimented by ultra centrifugation (93,000 G, 180 min) (39). The size of the $Fe(OH)_3$ particles varies with the pH of the solution. The diameter can be as small as 100 A°.

Many organic substances, especially those of decaying vegetable matter, the so-called humic acids, carry carboxyl and hydroxyl functional groups. These substances can coordinate and form chelates with Fe(III). Such substances undoubtedly can bind ferric iron. Colored water usually contains higher Fe(III) concentrations. But it is not yet certain whether such substances can really keep ferric iron in solution at the pH values of interest. It might be more probable that the coordinative products formed between the color bases, OH⁻, and Fe(III) are insoluble and are present as highly dispersed colloids. In a similar way, small quantities of phosphates or polyphosphates, usually present in concentrations far below those required for the formation of soluble complexes, aid markedly in the formation of stable, negatively charged colloidal dispersions.

One other argument is important in this connection. So far, only the competition between hydrogen ions and a metal cation for the ligands has been considered. In natural water systems, a metal cation is not only exposed to the influence of H^+ but also to the influence of other metals, especially Ca ions. Although Fe^{+3} usually forms stronger complexes than Ca^{+2}, its complex formation is still influenced very strongly, especially since the concentration of Ca^{+2} is much larger than that of Fe(III) and usually larger than the complexing ligand. An example of this is given in Figure 15 where it is seen that in the presence of an excess of Ca^{+2}, not even EDTA, (stability constant with $Fe^{+3} = 10^{25.1}$, with $Ca^{+2} = 10^{10.7}$) at a concentration of 10^{-3} M, can keep 10^{-5} M Fe(III) in solution at pH values above 8. At low pH, Ca^{+2} does not compete with the Fe^{+3} complex formation because of the overwhelming effect of H^+. But at higher pH values, ΔpFe falls drastically.

Polyphosphates

Pyrophosphates and other polyphosphates are used extensively in water treatment. These polyphosphates form rather stable chelate complexes with Ca^{+2} and with Fe^{+2}, but no

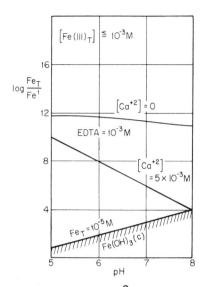

FIGURE 15   EFFECT OF Ca^{+2} ON COMPLEX FORMATION
OF Fe(III) BY EDTA. In most practical systems,
ions other than H^+ and OH^- compete with the
complex formation.

consistent stability constants have been reported. Polyphosphates, however, in the concentrations commonly used in water
treatment (a few mg/l) for the prevention of precipitation of
$CaCO_3$ or Fe(OH)$_3$, do not sequester the Ca and the Fe. For
complexing 1 mg/l of Ca^{+2}, at least 10 mg/l of sodium polyphosphate must be used. Polyphosphates that probably are
adsorbed (surface complex formation) on the $CaCO_3$ crystals
and on the Fe(OH)$_3$, inhibit the growth and further precipitation
of $CaCO_3$ and render the Fe(OH)$_3$ colloidally dispersed.

Ferrichromes
    Figure 14 shows the complexing tendency of Nocardamine
for Fe^{+3}. Nocardamine belongs to a group of compounds generally known as ferrichromes. It is classified also as a side-
rochrome compound by some workers. These ferrichromes
represent a class of naturally occurring heteromeric peptides,
containing a trihydroxamate as an iron (III) binding center.
Figure 16 represents a structure of one of these ferrichromes,
Desferri-ferrichrome. Polyhydroxamic acid forms rather

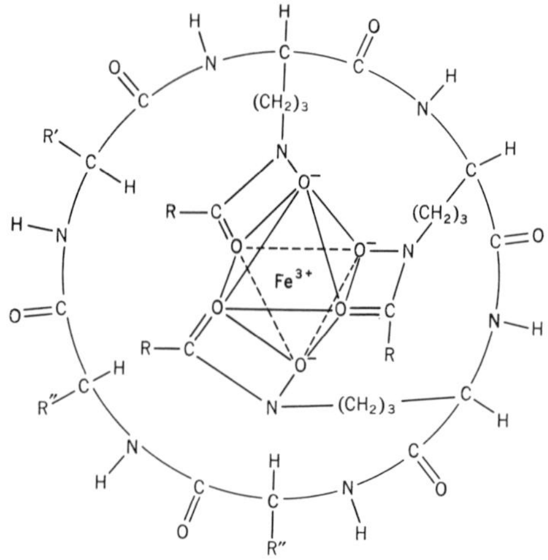

FIGURE 16   STRUCTURE OF A FERRICHROME
(Desferri-ferrichrome), One of the strongest
complex formers presently known for Fe(III).
The iron binding center is a trihydroxamate.
It has been suggested that such naturally
occurring ferrichromes play an important
role in the biosynthetic pathways of iron.
(After Neilands, 40).

specifically, strong complexes with Fe(III) and Mn(III). For
example, formaldoxime can be used analytically for the determination of Fe and Mn. The ferrichromes appear to be the strongest
Fe(III) complex formers presently known. The complexes are
soluble. The strong affinity of Fe^{+3} for the trihydroxamate is
plausible in view of the tendency of Fe^{+3} to coordinate preferentially with basic oxygen donor atoms. The binding center
(Figure 16) consists of an octahedral arrangement of oxygen
ligand atoms which satisfies all the coordinative requirements
of Fe^{+3}. These natural trihydroxamates bind iron so strongly
that iron remains complex bound in solution even at great dilutions and high pH. Furthermore, competition of alkaline earth
ions with iron (III) appears to be rather weak thus making the
ferrichromes relatively specific for ferric iron.

Ferrichromes appear to be widely distributed in microorganisms. Fungi have been used for the routine preparation
of ferrichromes in the laboratory (40). Ferrichrome has been

suggested as a cofactor in microbial iron metabolism. According to Neilands, the ferric ion, once coordinated as soluble trihydroxamate, can be transported to or into the cell and donated to the iron enzymes (40). Neilands has shown also that many microorganisms are capable of augmenting the biosynthesis of metal-free trihydroxamic acids during iron deficiency and infers that this may represent an evolutionary invention whereby the organism protects itself against iron deprivation.

In natural water systems, it is of course not known yet to what extent this special ligand serves the dual function of dissolving iron and specifically donating it to biosynthetic pathways at the point of demand for iron. It certainly makes, however, an elegant model.

FINAL REMARKS

Obviously, the foregoing discussion cannot be comprehensive. The author has attempted to illustrate a few case histories, each of which might have been discussed in much more detail. Emphasis was on qualitative illustration rather than on a quantitative interpretation. For more exacting discussions and for the modern theories, the reader is referred to some of the numerous reviews and monographs (1-17). Complex-formation of metal ions with OH^- particularly has been stressed since many multivalent metal ions undergo hydrolysis in natural waters and since hydroxylated metal ions are used extensively in water treatment.

It would have been desirable to treat some of the biological ramifications in the control of metal concentrations and to speculate how living cells can differentiate, more effectively than chelating agents in solution, between metal cations.

The dominating influence of the solid phases with which natural waters come into contact cannot be underestimated. The composition and structure of the solid phases represent an important branch of coordination chemistry. For some valuable illustrations on mineralogical factors in natural water equilibria, the article by Bricker and Garrels should be consulted (19).

It may not have become sufficiently obvious from this discussion, that the dividing line between inorganic and organic chemistry is no longer as sharp as it used to be. Coordination chemistry has become the common meeting ground not only for inorganic and organic chemists but also for reaction kineticists, surface chemists, geologists, and biologists. The water chemist should join them because the environment in which he is interested and seeks to control, is really a world of coordination compounds.

ACKNOWLEDGEMENTS
In writing this discussion, the author was influenced particularly by the publications of Schwarzenbach (1), Heller (2),
Ringbom (5), and Jorgensen (8). The author's experimental
research on the chemistry of aqueous iron and on coagulation
has been supported by Research grants WP-00013 and WP-00098
from the Public Health Service, USDHEW, Washington, D.C.

LITERATURE CITED
Reviews and Monographs
1. Schwarzenbach, G., Chimia, (Aarau), 3, 1 (1949).

2. Heller, H.J., Some Aspects of Chelation Chemistry, Inter
   Atomic Energy Agency, Vienna, Austria, (1963).

3. Schwarzenbach, G., Advan Inorg Chem Radiochem, 3, (1961).

4. Schwarzenbach, G., Complexometric Titrations, Interscience,
   New York, N.Y., (1959).

5. Ringbom, A., Complexation in Analytical Chemistry, Interscience, New York, N.Y., (1963).

6. Martin, D.F. and B.B. Martin, Coordination Compounds,
   McGraw Hill, New York, N.Y., (1964).

7. Hunt, J.P., Metal Ions in Solution, W.A. Benjamin, Inc.,
   New York, N.Y., (1963).

8. Jørgensen, C.K., Inorganic Complexes, Academic Press, Inc.,
   New York, N.Y., (1963).

9. Graddon, D.P., An Introduction to Coordination Chemistry,
   Pergamon Press, New York, N.Y., (1961).

10. Orgel, L.E., An Introduction to Transition Metal Chemistry:
    Ligand Field Theory, John Wiley & Sons, New York, N.Y.,
    (1960).

11. Rossotti, F.J.C. and H. Rossotti, The Determination of
    Stability Constants, McGraw Hill, New York, N.Y., (1961).

12. Basolo F. and R.G. Pearson, Mechanism of Inorganic Reactions, A Study of Metal Complexes in Solutions, John Wiley & Sons, New York, N.Y., (1958).

13. Chabereck, S. and A.E. Martell, Sequestering Agents, John Wiley & Sons, New York, N.Y., (1959).

14. Jones, M.M., Elementary Coordination Chemistry, Prentice Hall, Englewood, N.J., (1964).

15. Edwards, J.O., Inorganic Reaction Mechanisms, W.A. Benjamin, Inc., New York, N.Y., (1964).

16. Amphlett, C.B., Inorganic Ion Exchangers, Elsevier, New York, N.Y., (1964).

17. Sillen, L.G. and A.E. Martell, Stability Constants of Metal-Ion Complexes, Special Publication No. 17, The Chem Soc, Burlington House, W.I. London, England, (1964).

18. Sillen, L.G., Publ No 67, p 549, Am Assoc Advan Sci, Washington, D.C., (1961).

19. Bricker, O.P. and R.M. Garrels, This volume, Paper No 17.

20. Sillen, L.G., Quart Revs, 13, 146 (1959).

21. Olin, A., Svensk Kem Tidskr, 73, (1961).

22. Matijevic, E., et al, J Phys Chem, 65, 826 (1961).

23. LaMer, V.K. and T.W. Healy, Rev Pure Appl Chem, 13, 112 (1963).

24. Mulay, L.N., Inter Conf Coordination Chem, Wayne State Univ, Detroit, Michigan, (1961).

25. Pauling, L., The Nature of the Chemical Bond, Cornell Univ Press, Ithaca, N.Y., (1963).

26. Ahrland, S., et al, Quart Rev, 12, 265 (1958).

27. Pearson, R.G., J Am Chem Soc, 85, 3533 (1963).

28. Stumm, W. and J.J. Morgan, J Am Water Works Assoc, 54, 971 (1962).

29. Morgan, J.J. and W. Stumm, J Colloid Sci, 19, 347 (1964).

30. Galal-Gorchev, H. and W. Stumm, J Inorg Nucl Chem, 25, 567 (1963).

31. Weber, W.J. Jr. and W. Stumm, J Am Water Works Assoc, 55, 1553 (1963).

32. Stumm, W., USPHS Publ No. 999-AP-15, (1964).

33. O'Melia, O. and W. Stumm, Interaction of Hydrolyzed Iron (III) with SiO_2, Am Chem Soc, Atlantic City, N.J., (Sept.1965).

34. Tenney, M. and W. Stumm, J Water Pollution Control Fed, 10, 1370 (1965).

35. Stumm, W. and H. Hüper, Unpublished Results, Harvard Univ, Cambridge, Mass.

36. O'Melia, C., J Sanit Eng Div Am Soc Civil Eng, (1965).

37. Kraus, K.A., et al, Proc Second Intern Conf Peaceful Uses of Atomic Energy, United Nations, Geneva, Switzerland, 28, 3 (1958).

38. Morgan, J.J. and W. Stumm, Proc Second Intern Conf Water Pollution Control Res, Tokyo, Japan, (1964).

39. Lengweiler, H., et al, Helv Chim Acta, 44, 796 (1961).

40. Neilands, J.B., Essays in Coordination Chemistry, W. Schneider, et al, Eds, p 222, Birkhauser, Basel, Switzerland, (1964).

DISCUSSION

DR. RIEMAN (Rutgers University): We should have an opportunity for a few questions and a little discussion after this very provocative paper. Who wants to begin?

DR. BOHN (Tennessee Valley Authority): Some of the very stable ligands you mentioned in EDTA and the others I don't

recall, are they easily metabolized by natural organisms. Their
lives are not very long.

DR. STUMM: Some are readily biodegraded.

DR. T. W. HEALY (University of California): I would like
to underscore your remarks concerning the relation between
coordination chemistry and surface chemistry. Based on one
of your figures, it would be our prediction that the surface
properties of alumina would be more basic than silica. Titania
would be in between and so on for each of the inorganic oxides.
The graduation from acidic to basic is regular and predictable
and in accord with the graduation in the coordination chemistry
of the cations.

The other thing I would like to recommend, and which you
emphasized, is that one must first establish which ions are
determining the potential around the shell of the cation, and in
the same way what ions are potential determining for each
colloidal solid in the system.

In the same way that pH plays an important role in aqueous
cation reactions so the surface properties of oxides, silicates,
and clay are determined by the pH of the solution.

Having established the role of pH, it becomes a little easier
to establish the role of such ions as sulphate or citrate at a
solid-liquid interface. At pH 6-7 sulphate is specifically adsorbed
on alumina in the same way that cations are adsorbed specifically
on silica or manganese dioxide at the same pH.

DR. MATIJEVIC (Clarkson College): It is seldom that two
scientists agree as well as Dr. Stumm and I do. I have no
comments to make with regard to his lecture, but I would like
to give a warning or point out to some dangers of being in such
good agreement.

It was implied in the lecture that we think we understand
what is happening if we have a little iron in solution and change
pH. Some of you may have gotten the impression that all has
to do is look up the hydrolysis constants and calculate the species.
Since it is now known what effects these species may cause, one
should be able to predict what is going to happen to the colloid
in the dispersion.

The trouble is that whatever we have in the literature on
the hydrolysis constants may be imperfect. As Dr. Stumm
pointed out, agreements using different techniques are excellent
in the case of some ions. However, don't ever try to use the
constants, calculate the species and attempt to predict what is
going to happen.

DR. LAMER: Why?

DR. MATIJEVIC: We don't have a sufficiently sophisticated technique to get to the bottom of the story. I made here a very simple quick calculation. If we have 10^{-5} moles/l of iron in solution which is approximately one ppm or 10^{-6} moles/l which is one part in ten million, this is a rather small quantity. However, only if 1% or even 0.1% of this extremely small quantity is present in the form of a very highly polymerized species, which is quite likely to be the case with iron, as pointed out here, this small amount of the highly charged species will overshadow the effects of all other species in solution. Thus, one may be correct in calculating the composition of the solution using known hydrolysis constants but there may be a very minute quantity of highly powerful species which will either coagulate or stabilize depending on the conditions. We have direct evidence that some highly charged ions, which represent perfectly bonafide species (unlike a mixture of various hydrolysis species), can coagulate at concentrations below 10^{-8} and exactly at 8×10^{-9} moles/l. This represents fewer ions than in pure water, and the effect is identical with what one would get with K at 0.6 moles/l. Thus, while we agree on everything, I wouldn't like to leave you with the impression, neither after my nor Dr. Stumm's lecture, that because we understand a little better what happens in the presence of complex ions, one could just take a slip of paper, a computer, calculate a few things, and have all the answers.

DR. STUMM: I appreciate this comment. I would like to endorse your warning.

DR. LAMER: I would like to say I want to be the third man to agree with Dr. Stumm and Dr. Matijevic.

James J.Morgan
California Institute of Technology

CHEMICAL EQUILIBRIA AND KINETIC PROPERTIES OF MANGANESE IN NATURAL WATERS

The chemical studies reported herein are concerned with certain thermodynamic and kinetic properties of the II and IV oxidation states of manganese in simple aqueous systems at ordinary temperature and pressure. Particular attention is given to solubility equilibria, mainly those involving carbonate and hydroxide, to simple ion-pair formation by carbonate, to the stoichiometry of the reaction between dissolved oxygen and reduced manganese, and to some important features of the kinetics of the oxidation reaction.

GENERAL CHEMICAL PROPERTIES OF MANGANESE

Manganese, atomic number 25, is the fifth member of the first transition series of the elements. It falls between chromium, element 24, and iron, element 26, in subgroup VIIA.

Like the other transition elements, manganese can exist in a number of oxidation states, examples of which range from -III to +VII (1). The aqueous chemistry of manganese involves primarily the II, III, IV, VI, and VII oxidation states. Of these, the II and IV states are, perhaps, of greatest importance in connection with manganese in natural waters. Permanganate [Mn(VII)] is important because of its role as a strong oxidant in analytical chemistry and in water technology. It is thermo-

561

dynamically unstable with respect to reduction by water. Manganate, MnO_4^{-2}, is stable only in very basic solutions.

The chemistry of Mn(III) is not very extensive. The aquo Mn(III) ion is a rather strong oxidant $(E^O_{Mn^{+3}/Mn^{+2}} \cong 1.6v)$ and is reduced easily to Mn(II). In the absence of a reductant, it is still unstable because it is subject to disproportionation as shown by the approximate equilibrium constant:

$$2\ Mn^{+3} + 2H_2O = Mn^{+2} + MnO_2 + 4H^+,\ K \cong 10^9 \qquad (22\text{-}1)$$

Mn(III) can be stabilized by strong complexing agents (e.g., ethylenediamine-tetraacetate, pyrophosphate, oxalate, fluoride, and chloride). Sulfate complexes are formed also but their stabilities have not been studied extensively. They may be subject to slow hydrolysis.

Mn(II) is the most important and generally speaking, the most stable oxidation state of the element. Its stability has been attributed partly to the half-filled d-level $(3d^5)$. In neutral and acid aqueous solutions, the II state exists as the hexaquo ion, $[Mn(H_2O)_6]^{+2}$. Its resistance to oxidation may be compared with that of Cr^{+2} and Fe^{+2} by noting the corresponding potentials:

$$Mn^{+2} = Mn^{+3} + e^-,\quad -1.5\ v \qquad (22\text{-}2)$$

$$Fe^{+2} = Fe^{+3} + e^-,\quad -0.77v \qquad (22\text{-}3)$$

$$Cr^{+2} = Cr^{+3} + e^-,\quad 0.41v \qquad (22\text{-}4)$$

The ionic radius of Mn^{+2} is 0.80 A^O whereas that of Fe^{+2} is 0.76 A^O and of Mg^{+2} is 0.65 A^O. The acidity constant of $[Mn(H_2O_6)]^{+2}$ is $10^{-10.6}$, whereas that for $[Fe(H_2O_6)]^{+2}$ is $10^{-9.5}$ and for $[Mg(H_2O_6)]^{+2}$ is $10^{-11.4}$ (2).

Among the many compounds formed by Mn(II) are the hydroxide (having the same crystal structure as $Mg(OH)_2$), the carbonate, the sulfide, the phosphate, sulfate, and the perchlorate. Mn(II) forms many complexes and chelates (2, 3). The stability constants of these are not large as compared to those for the succeeding transition metals (Fe(II) through Cu(II)).

Aside from MnO_2, the only stable compounds of Mn(IV) are a few complexes. MnO_2 is a moderately strong oxidizing agent $(E^O_{MnO_2/Mn^{+2}} \cong 1.2v)$. It is rather inert to most acids.

Charolot has estimated an $Mn(OH)_4$ solubility product of 10^{-56} (4).
MnO_2 can be fused with other metal oxides to give substances
called manganites, e.g., $MnO_2 \cdot ZnO$ and $CaO \cdot MnO_2$.

OCCURRENCE AND SIGNIFICANCE OF MANGANESE
     Manganese is a relatively abundant element, amounting to
roughly 0.1% of the earth's crust, and ranking about tenth in
the order of abundance of elements. Among the heavy metals,
only Fe is more abundant. The geochemical ratio for Fe and Mn
in the earth's lithosphere is approximately 50:1. Manganese is
widespread throughout the world as an essential constituent of
over 100 well-defined minerals and is a minor constituent of
several hundred more (5). Among the important Mn minerals
are pyrolusite[MnO_2], manganite[$MnO(OH)$], rhodonite [$MnSiO_3$],
braunite [$3Mn_2O_3 \cdot MnSiO_3$], hausmannite [Mn_3O_4], pyrochroite
[$Mn(OH)_2$], rhodochrosite [$MnCO_3$], and alabandite[MnS].
Manganese is found in every kind of plant and animal tissue. It
is an essential element in both plant and animal nutrition (6).
     Manganese is distributed in rivers, lakes, ocean waters,
and subsurface waters. It is found also as an important constituent of certain industrial wastes. Rather little is known about
the state of Mn in most surface waters. The Mn content of sea
water is approximately 0.002 mg/l (7). Manganese is deposited
on the floors of the oceans in the form of the ferromanganese
minerals which are the major components of the so-called Mn
nodules. The Mn oxides in the nodules are reported to consist
of ∂-MnO_2 and manganites wherein the Mn is present in the II
and IV oxidation states (8). The mode of formation of these
nodules appears largely to be a matter for speculation (9,10,11).
     At the Mn levels normally encountered in water supplies,
this element does not appear to be of great significance from
the viewpoint of toxicity. The standard for Mn in drinking water
in the 1962 U S Public Health Service's Drinking Water Standards
is a maximum concentration of 0.05 mg/l (12). The principal
reason for limiting the concentration of Mn is to provide water
quality control that reduces esthetic and economic problems.
Of some economic significance is the loss of carrying capacity
and the occasionally high turbidities released as a result of Mn
oxide formation in water pipelines (13).

THERMODYNAMIC PROPERTIES OF AQUEOUS MANGANESE
     The relations of Mn species with the major components found

in typical natural waters are generally of two kinds; (a) those involving the solubility, hydrolysis, and complexing of Mn(II); and (b) those involving oxidation and reduction equilibria between II, III, and IV oxidation states of Mn and various oxidation states of other elements. An understanding of these relations is relevant to the behavior of Mn in different natural environments and in water treatment technology.

It is appropriate to remark upon the limitation of the thermodynamic approach in answering questions concerning Mn chemistr Thermodynamics indicate whether a certain reaction may proceed and what maximum yield may be obtained but gives no information as to the time required. The latter is a question for chemical kinetics. For a number of reactions, particularly those involving change in oxidation number, the equilibrium state may be approac slowly under given solution conditions of pH, temperature, and concentrations of reactants.

The thermodynamic systems for which calculations are made in this paper are somewhat oversimplified of necessity. Only species could be considered in the models for which free energy data could be found. As emphasized by Sillen, there is considerable uncertainty about the stability of certain states in nature, e.g several of the oxides of Mn, solid solutions, such as certain silica phases and polysulfides (14). Equilibria data are not available for Mn silicate species. The existence of impure solid (metastable) phases such as $Mn_2(OH)_2CO_3$ has not been considered. It is poss ble that a pertinent species may be overlooked. It is, therefore, difficult to make a comprehensive discussion of the physical chemistry of Mn in natural waters.

The solubility of Mn(II) in natural waters is most likely limite by the solubility of the hydroxide, carbonate, and the sulfide, depending upon the composition of the water. Accordingly, only these phases have been considered in describing Mn solubility under reducing conditions. The III and IV oxides or hydroxides of Mn are considered as essentially completely insoluble under natural water conditions.

The Solubility of Manganese (II) Carbonate

In most natural waters the equilibrium concentration of aqueous Mn(II) is controlled by the solubility of $MnCO_{3(c)}$. It is, therefore, important to have a sufficiently accurate knowledge of the solubility product of $MnCO_{3(c)}$, and other pertinent equilibria which, together with the solubility product, determine the total solubility of Mn(II) under given conditions of pH, CO_2

partial pressure, alkalinity, and ionic composition. For example, the total solubility of Mn(II), $[Mn(II)]_t$, can be calculated as a function of the pH in a water of given alkalinity under the assumption that these equilibria are pertinent: solubility of $MnCO_3$; HCO_3^- acidity; hydrolysis of Mn^{+2}; $Mn(OH)_2$ solubility; and the ion product of water. In the case of $MnCO_3$, it is necessary to consider the effect of complexing of Mn^{+2} by carbonate species in order to estimate the correct equilibrium solubility.

$MnCO_3$ Solubility Product

Latimer gives a value of -194.3 kcal for the free energy of formation of precipitated $MnCO_{3(c)}$ (15). This value has been obtained from the measurement of the solubility of $MnCO_{3(c)}$ in water at 25°C by Ageno and Valla (16). A more correct expression for evaluation of the solubility product with the original data of Ageno and Valla can be derived using the values given by Latimer for the first and second acidity constants of H_2CO_3, 4.16 x 10^{-7} and 4.84 x 10^{-11}, respectively. Employing these values of the acidity constants, K_1 and K_2, and a value of 3.388 x 10^{-2} for the Henry's law constant for CO_2, and making corrections for activity coefficients, as described later, the solubility product for precipitated $MnCO_3$ has been re-evaluated from the solubility data of Ageno and Valla. The recalculated results yield a mean ion-activity product (six experiments) of 3.82 x 10^{-11} compared to the value of 8.83 x 10^{-11} given by Latimer (15).

The standard free energy for the reaction:

$$MnCO_{3(c)} = Mn^{+2} + CO_3^{-2} \qquad (22\text{-}5)$$

is related to the equilibrium constant by:

$$\Delta F^o_{298.16} \text{ (kcal)} = 1.3643 \log K \qquad (22\text{-}6)$$

from which it is calculated:

$$\Delta F^o = -1.3643 \times \log 3.82 \times 10^{-11} = 14.2 \text{ kcal}$$

Taking the values for the standard free energies of formation for CO_3^{-2} and Mn^{+2} given by Latimer, -126.22 and -54.5 kcal, respectively, the standard free energy of formation of $MnCO_3$

is calculated:

$$\Delta F^O{}_{MnCO_3}{}^+ = \Delta F^O{}_{Mn}{}^{+2} + \Delta F^O{}_{CO_3} = -\Delta F^O \qquad (22\text{-}7)$$

$$= -54.4 - 126.22 - 14.2 = -194.8 \text{ kcal}$$

This value should replace the -194.3 kcal deduced by Latimer from the reported solubility data of Ageno and Valla.

The stabilities of a number of carbonates have been determined recently by Garrels, et al [17]. The carbonates were dissolved in water under a CO_2 atmosphere of one atm total pressure at $25^O C$. The equilibrium pH values of the solutions were used to obtain the standard free energies of formation of the carbonates. For the standard free energy of formation of synthetic rhodochrosite, a value of -194.7 kcal was obtained. This free energy of formation of the synthetic $MnCO_3$ determined by Garrels, et al, corresponds to a solubility product of 4.68×10^{-11}. No attempts were made to evaluate the effect of soluble complexes of $Mn(II)$ with carbonic species upon the apparent solubility product in these earlier researches.

Bicarbonato or Carbonato Complexes of Mn(II)

A dissociation constant for the $MnHCO_3{}^+$ species has been reported by Nasanen, who conducted potentiometric titrations of alkali carbonate solutions with $MnCl_2$, under hydrogen, and evaluated the dissociation constant from the minimum buffer capacity of the titration curve [18]. These equilibria were considered by Nasanen to be important under conditions of the experiments:

$$Mn^{+2} + 2 \; OH^- = Mn(OH)_2 \; (c) \qquad (22\text{-}8)$$

$$Mn^{+2} + HCO_3{}^- = MnHCO_3{}^+ \qquad (22\text{-}9)$$

It appears, however, that precipitation of manganese carbonate:

$$Mn^{+2} + CO_3{}^{-2} = MnCO_3 \; (c) \qquad (22\text{-}10)$$

might have been expected to occur under the alkaline conditions and high Mn concentrations used. Nasanen found a mean value for the dissociation constant of 3×10^{-4} at $25^O C$ at an ionic strength of 0.29. Hem recently reported a mean value of an association constant for reaction 22-9 of 63 [19]. Hem measured pH, soluble Mn and alkalinity in bicarbonate solutions equilibrated with suspensions of analytical reagent grade $MnCO_3$ which have been previously equilibrated with distilled water under one atm CO_2 at 25°C. The CO_2 had been partially desorbed from portions of the resulting suspension. The measured quantities were used to compute equilibrium concentrations of Mn^{+2}, HCO_3^-, and $MnHCO_3^+$ through successive approximation by application of the appropriate mass law expressions and the electroneutrality condition.

Experimental Studies of Mn(II) - Carbonate Equilibria

The reported data on Mn(II) solubility equilibria in carbonate waters are not extensive and the results of different investigators have not been in very good agreement. Recalculation of the data of Ageno and Valla (16) has indicated that good accord actually exists between their data and those of Garrels, et al (17). It is desirable to confirm the apparent solubility product obtained in these previous studies by specifically considering the effect of carbonato complexes upon the solubility equilibria. The stability constant determinations of Nasanen and Hem for the $MnHCO_3^+$ species differ by considerably more than an order of magnitude when Nasanen's constant, obtained at an ionic strength of 0.29 is corrected to approximately ideal solution conditions. Because of this disagreement, it was considered necessary to establish the magnitude of the complexing of the Mn(II) ion in HCO_3^- solutions.

A constant for the stability of $MnHCO_3^+$ was estimated in homogenous systems under conditions where formation of $MnCO_3$(c) was observed not to occur. In addition, the constant was checked in heterogeneous systems by considering equilibria between $MnCO_3$(c) and aqueous Mn(II). The magnitude of the constant was confirmed further in polarographic experiments on the reduction of Mn(II) in $NaHCO_3$ solutions.

Homogeneous Equilibria Involving Mn(II) and Bicarbonate or Carbonate

Under suitable conditions of pH < 6.5, $[Mn(II)]_t < 5 \times 10^{-3} M$, and $C_t < 10^{-1} M$, the precipitation of $MnCO_3$ is not expected. By equilibration of Mn(II) salt solutions of known alkalinity ($[HCO_3^-] + 2[CO_3^{-2}] + [OH^-] - [H^+] = $ alkalinity) under definite CO_2 partial pressure, it is possible to determine a stability constant for either of the assumed species, $MnHCO_3^+$ or $MnCO_3$(aq).

$MnHCO_3^+$ Formation

Consider the case in which a measured quantity of $Mn(ClO_4)_2$ is dissolved in distilled water and to which a known quantity of NaOH has been added and exposed to a partial pressure of CO_2. The electroneutrality condition is defined by the approximation:

$$[H^+]+[Na^+]+ 2[Mn^{+2}]+[MnHCO_3^+]=[HCO_3^-]+[OH^-]+$$
$$[ClO_4^-] \qquad (22\text{-}11)$$

The total concentration of Mn(II), $[Mn(II)]_t$, is related to the per-chlorate concentration through the equation:

$$[ClO_4^-] = 2 [Mn(II)]_t = 2[Mn^{+2}]+ 2[MnHCO_3^+] \quad (22\text{-}12)$$

combining 22-11 and 22-12, and neglecting $[OH^-]$:

$$[MnHCO_3^+]=[Na^+] + [H^+] - [HCO_3^-] \qquad (22\text{-}13)$$

HCO_3^- can be calculated from the measured pH value by applying equation 22-23 and the "mixed" equilibrium constant:

$$K_1^{\prime\prime} = \frac{(H^+)[HCO_3^-]}{[H_2CO_3]} \qquad (22\text{-}14)$$

where $K_1^{\prime\prime} = K_1/f_{HCO_3^-}$ was estimated by means of the Debye-Hückel expression with the values of the ionic strength calculated by successive approximation. $[Mn^{+2}]$ is obtained by deducting $[MnHCO_3^+]$ from $[Mn(II)]_t$. Then a "mixed" stability constant is computed from:

$$K^{\prime\prime} = \frac{[MnHCO_3^+]}{(Mn^{+2})[HCO_3^-]} \qquad (22\text{-}15)$$

which may be interpreted as a thermodynamic constant by making the assumption that, for the relatively dilute solutions involved in the experiments ($I \cong 0.015$), $f_{HCO_3^-} = f_{MnHCO_3^+}$.

$MnCO_3$(aq) Formation

If it is assumed that a soluble $MnCO_3$ species, designated as $MnCO_3^0$, is the predominant form of complexed manganese and not $MnHCO_3^+$, then the electroneutrality equation is:

$$2 [Mn^{+2}] + [H^+] + [Na^+] = [HCO_3^-] + 2 [CO_3^{-2}] + [OH^-] + [ClO_4^-] \quad (22\text{-}16)$$

The total manganese concentration is related to $[ClO_4^-]$ by:

$$2 [Mn(II)]_t = 2 [Mn^{+2}] + 2 [MnCO_3^0] = [ClO_4^-] \quad (22\text{-}17)$$

Neglecting $[CO_3^{-2}]$ and $[OH^-]$ in 22-16 and substituting 22-17 into 22-16:

$$2 [MnCO_3^0] = [Na^+] + [H^+] - [HCO_3^-] \quad (22\text{-}18)$$

By successive approximations, $MnCO_3^0$, Mn^{+2}, and CO_3^{-2} can be calculated. The "mixed" stability constant is determined from:

$$K'' = \frac{[MnCO_3^0]}{(Mn^{+2})(CO_3^{-2})} \quad (22\text{-}19)$$

It may be assumed that, at low ionic strengths, the activity coefficient for the $MnCO_3^0$ species is close to unity.

Heterogeneous Equilibria Involving Mn(II) and $MnCO_{3(c)}$

A complete description of the equilibrium distribution of species in an aqueous suspension of $MnCO_{3(c)}$ is provided by the set of expressions below. An assumption is involved whereby Mn^{+2} and either $MnHCO_3^+$ or $MnCO_3$(aq) constitute the soluble forms of $\overline{Mn(II)}$.

$$K_w = (H^+)(OH^-) \quad (22\text{-}20)$$

$$K_1 = \frac{(H^+)(HCO_3^-)}{(H_2CO_3)} \quad (22\text{-}21)$$

H_2CO_3 as used here applies to the analytical sum of CO_2 and H_2CO_3.

$$K_2 = \frac{(H^+)(CO_3^{-2})}{(HCO_3^-)} \quad (22\text{-}22)$$

$$K_{CO_2} = \frac{(H_2CO_3)}{P_{CO_2}} \tag{22-23}$$

$$K_{MnCO_{3(c)}} = (Mn^{+2})\,(CO_3^{-2}) \tag{22-24}$$

and:

$$K_{MnHCO_3^+} = \frac{(MnHCO_3^+)}{(Mn^{+2})\,(HCO_3^-)} \tag{22-25}$$

with:

$$2\left[Mn^{+2}\right] + \left[MnHCO_3^+\right] = \left[HCO_3^-\right] + 2\left[CO_3^{-2}\right] + \left[OH^-\right] - \left[H^+\right] \tag{22-26}$$

or:

$$K_{MnCO_{3(aq)}} = \frac{(MnCO_3^0\ )}{(Mn^{+2})\,(CO_3^{-2})} \tag{22-27}$$

with:

$$2\left[Mn^{+2}\right] = \left[HCO_3^-\right] + 2\left[CO_3^{-2}\right] + \left[OH^-\right] - \left[H^+\right] \tag{22-28}$$

For the assumption of no complexing, i.e., for both $(MnHCO_3^+)$ and $(MnCO_3^0)$ equal to zero, $K_{MnCO_{3(c)}}$ is obtained by applying equation 22-21, equation 22-22, and the approximate electro-neutrality condition:

$$2\left[Mn^{+2}\right] = \left[HCO_3^-\right] - \left[H^+\right] \tag{22-29}$$

For the measured pH value under known CO_2 partial pressure. For the assumed existence of $MnHCO_3^+$, $K_{MnCO_{3(c)}}$ may be evaluated by applying equations 22-20, 22-21, 22-22, 22-23, 22-2 22-25, and 22-26 to measured pH values under fixed CO_2 partial pressure and knowing a value for $K_{MnHCO_3^+}$.

ACTIVITY CORRECTIONS

Two methods have been used by others with reasonable success in estimating activity coefficients of ions in dilute and slightly concentrated solutions: (a) the mean activity coefficient method; and (b) Debye-Hückel theory approximation. These have been detailed by Klotz (20), Robinson and Stokes (21), and Latimer (15). A comparison of the results for several ions of interest in natural waters has been presented by Garrels (22).

Individual Ion Activity Coefficients from Mean Coefficients

The mean activity coefficient of $MnCl_2$ in solution, $f_{\pm MnCl_2}$, is related to individual ion coefficients by:

$$f_{\pm MnCl_2} = (f_{Mn^{+2}} \; f^2_{Cl^-})^{\frac{1}{3}} \tag{22-30}$$

Making the arbitrary assumption that $f_{Cl^-} = f_{\pm KCl}$ which is not in disagreement with various lines of evidence (22), it is possible to compute $f_{Mn^{+2}}$:

$$f_{Mn^{+2}} = \frac{f^3_{\pm MnCl_2}}{f^2_{\pm KCl}} \tag{22-31}$$

Table I presents values of mean activity coefficients for KCl and $MnCl_2$ at different ionic strengths as well as the compound activity coefficients for Mn^{+2}.

Individual Ion Activity Coefficients from the Debye-Hückel Expression

In more dilute solutions, individual activity coefficients may be obtained from the modified Debye-Hückel expression:

$$\log f_i = \frac{A z_i^2 \; I^{\frac{1}{2}}}{1 + a_i \; B \; I^{\frac{1}{2}}} \tag{22-32}$$

where f_i is the individual activity coefficient of an ion of charge number z_i, and a_i is an "effective" ion size parameter, and I is the ionic strength. A and B are parameters which depend upon the solvent's dielectric constant, temperature, and pressure. For water at 25^0C, A is 0.5085 and B is 0.3281×10^8 (20). The following values of $a_i \times 10^8$ are taken from Klotz (20):

(a) for HCO_3^-, 4.5; (b) for H^+, 9; (c) for CO_3^{-2}, 4.5; and (d) for Mn^{+2}, 6. Individual activity coefficients for HCO_3^-, CO_3^{-2}, Mn^{+2}, and H^+ at different ionic strengths have been computed using equation 22-32. The relation between activity coefficients and ionic strength is shown in Figure 1 as well as the experimenta derived values for HCO_3^- and CO_3^{-2} of Walker, et al, (23) and the values of $f_{Mn^{+2}}$ computed by the mean activity coefficient method. The activity coefficient-ionic strength relation for carbonic acid has been estimated by Garrels from vapor pressure and absorption data in NaCl solutions (22).

EXPERIMENTAL PROCEDURES

Equilibration of solutions and suspensions was conducted in a cylindrical vessel of approximately 650-ml capacity with a cover made of 1/4" lucite cut to fit the flange of the vessel. The outer 5/8" of the bottom surface of the lucite cover was recessed approximately 1 mm and made as smooth as possible in order to provide good fit. Electrodes, gas delivery tube, thermometer, and solution ground were immersed by fitting them into No. 4 rubber stoppers and placing these in the cover openings.

TABLE 1   ACTIVITY COEFFICIENTS FOR Mn^{+2}
COMPUTED BY MEAN ACTIVITY COEFFICIENT
METHOD
25^oC

I (a)	$f_{\pm MnCl_2}$(b)	$f_{\pm KCl}$(c)	$f^3_{\pm MnCl_2}$	$f^2_{\pm KCl}$	$f_{Mn^{+2}}$
0.3	0.518	0.687	0.1390	0.472	0.294
0.6	0.471	0.637	0.1045	0.406	0.258
0.9	0.452	0.609	0.0922	0.371	0.248
1.2	0.444	0.595	0.0878	0.354	0.255
1.5	0.442	0.585	0.0868	0.342	0.254

(a) Ionic Strength
(b) Robinson and Stokes (21).
(c) Harned and Owen (24).

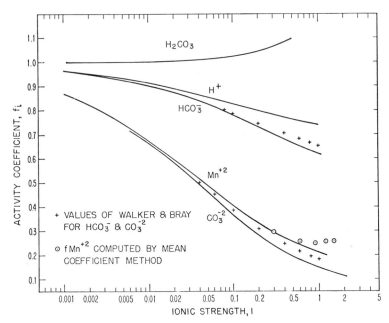

FIGURE 1   INDIVIDUAL ACTIVITY COEFFICIENT
CURVES COMPUTED BY DEBYE-HÜCKEL
APPROXIMATION AT 25°C.

One additional stoppered opening allowed for addition of reagents
and removal of samples. A sketch of the vessel, cover, and
appurtenances is shown in Figure 2. Vessel contents were mixed
by a magnetic stirrer. The reaction vessel was placed in a con-
stant-temperature water bath.

    Measurements of pH were made with a Beckman Model G
pH meter. For measurement of pH (assumed in subsequent calculations to represent hydrogen ion activity), the glass electrode
was calibrated in standard pH 7 buffer (National Bureau of Standards) by applying the appropriate temperature correction. Then
the pH of a standard pH 4 buffer was checked. The obtained
reading differed by less than 0.02 units from the expected value.
At the conclusion of an $MnCO_3$ solubility run, during which the
electrodes had been continuously immersed in a $MnCO_3$ suspension for several hours, the electrodes were rinsed and immersed
in reference solution to check calibration. In all instances the

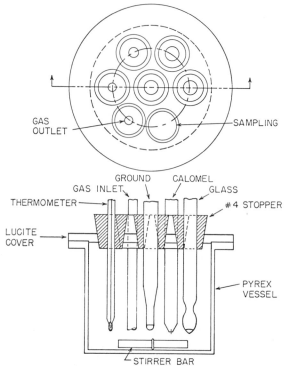

GAS
OUTLET

SAMPLING

GROUND   CALOMEL
GAS INLET
GLASS
THERMOMETER

#4 STOPPER

LUCITE
COVER

PYREX
VESSEL

STIRRER BAR

FIGURE 2   VESSEL USED FOR MnCO$_3$ SOLUBILITY
                EXPERIMENTS UNDER CONSTANT PARTIAL
                PRESSURE.

reading was within 0.01 pH unit of the expected value.

Neutral solutions of $Mn(ClO_4)_2 \cdot 6H_2O$ and $MnCl_2 \cdot 4H_2O$ were prepared by dissolving weighed portions of these salts in twice-distilled water. The solutions were standardized by the method of Lingane and Karplus (59).

The precipitated MnCO$_3$ used in the experiments was Fisher "Certified". Ionic strength was controlled by addition of appropriate volumes of 2M NaNO$_3$. All solutions and suspensions were prepared with twice-distilled water. Analyzed CO_2-N_2 gas mixtures and pure CO_2 were washed with distilled water before being introduced into the equilibration vessel.

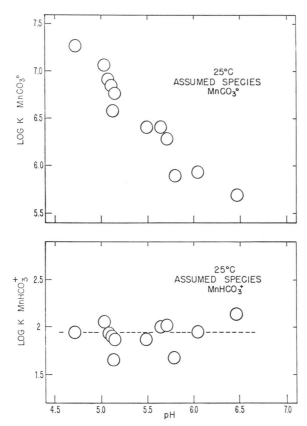

FIGURE 3   COMPUTED STABILITY CONSTANTS AS A
              FUNCTION OF pH FOR TWO ASSUMED
              MANGANESE-CARBONATE SPECIES.

EXPERIMENTAL RESULTS

Homogeneous Equilibria Experiments
    Experimental results of twelve determinations of $K_{MnHCO_3^+}$
and $K_{MnCO_{3(aq)}}$ from potentiometric pH determinations are
presented in Tables II and III, repectively. The following equilibrium constants have been employed in calculating these results:
(a) 4.16×10^{-7} for the first acidity constant of H_2CO_3 and 4.84
$\times 10^{-11}$ for the second acidity constant (15); (b) 3.16×10^{-2} for the

TABLE II   RESULTS OF DETERMINATIONS OF A STABILITY CONSTANT FOR THE SPECIES $MnHCO_3^+$ BASED ON POTENTIOMETRIC pH DETERMINATION 25^oC

(1) pH	(2) [ALK] x10^3	(3) [Mn(II)]_t x10^3	(4) I x10^3	(5) $f_{Mn^{+2}}$	(6) $f_{HCO_3^-}$	(7) [HCO_3^-] x10^3	(8) [MnHCO_3^+] x10^4	(9) [Mn^{+2}] x10^3	(10) log $K_{MnHCO_3^+}$
4.74	0.87	1.74	13.9	0.64	0.89	0.813	0.77	1.67	1.95
5.03	1.76	1.76	13.8	0.64	0.89	1.58	1.80	1.58	2.05
5.08	1.91	1.89	7.2	0.71	0.92	1.73	1.80	1.71	1.93
5.10	2.04	2.43	8.9	0.69	0.91	1.82	2.20	2.21	1.90
5.12	2.04	2.31 (a)	8.7	0.69	0.91	1.91	1.30	2.18	1.65
5.14	2.11	1.25	5.7	0.73	0.92	1.98	1.20	1.13	1.86
5.48	4.77	2.08 (a)	10.3	0.67	0.91	4.40	3.70	1.71	1.86
5.64(b)	0.87	1.74	13.8	0.64	0.89	0.786	0.84	1.65	2.00
5.70	8.17	2.31 (a)	13.6	0.64	0.89	7.41	7.60	1.55	2.01
5.78	9.09	1.28 (a)	12.4	0.64	0.90	8.82	2.70	1.01	1.67
6.05(b)	2.11	1.25	5.5	0.74	0.92	1.96	1.45	1.11	1.95
6.46(c)	2.04	2.43	8.7	0.69	0.91	1.71	3.30	2.10	2.13

(a) $Mn(ClO_4)_2$ used; $MnCl_2$ used in other experiments.   (b) $P_{CO_2} = 0.12$.
(c) $P_{CO_2} = 0.04$; $P_{CO_2} = 1$ for all other experiments.

TABLE III   RESULTS OF DETERMINATIONS OF A STABILITY CONSTANT FOR THE SPECIES $MnCO_3$(aq) BASED ON POTENTIOMETRIC pH DETERMINATION

25°C

(1) pH	(2) $[ALK]$ x10^3	(3) $[Mn\{II\}]_t$ x10^3	(4) I x10^3	(5) $[HCO_3^-]$ x10^3	(6) $[MnCO_3^0]$ x10^5	(7) $[Mn^{+2}]$ x10^3	(8) (CO_3^{-2}) x10^8	(9) $\log K_{MnCO_3^0}$
4.74	0.87	1.74	13.9	0.813	3.85	1.09	0.193	7.27
5.03	1.76	1.76	13.8	1.58	9.00	1.06	0.732	7.06
5.08	1.91	1.89	7.2	1.73	9.00	1.28	0.92	6.90
5.10	2.04	2.43	8.9	1.82	11.00	1.59	1.01	6.83
5.12	2.04	2.31 (a)	8.7	1.91	6.50	1.55	1.11	6.58
5.14	2.11	1.25	5.7	1.98	6.00	0.88	1.22	6.75
5.48	4.77	2.08 (a)	10.3	4.40	18.5	1.27	5.82	6.40
6.64(b)	0.87	1.74	13.8	0.786	4.20	1.09	1.49	6.42
5.70	8.17	2.31 (a)	13.6	7.41	38.0	1.24	16.02	6.28
5.78	9.09	1.28 (a)	12.4	8.82	13.5	0.75	23.10	5.89
6.05(b)	2.11	1.25	5.5	1.96	7.25	0.87	9.85	5.93
6.46(c)	2.04	2.43	8.7	1.71	16.5	1.56	21.65	5.69

(a) $Mn(ClO_4)_2$ used; $MnCl_2$ used in other experiments.   (b) P_{CO_2} = 0.12.

(c) P_{CO_2} = 0.04; P_{CO_2} = 1 for other experiments.

equilibrium $CO_{2(g)} + H_2O = H_2CO_{3(aq)}$ (22). The constants computed for each of the two assumed species, $MnHCO_3^+$ and $MnCO_3^0$, are plotted against pH in Figure 3. The values of $K_{MnHCO_3^+}$ are essentially independent of pH while the values of $K_{MnCO_3^0}$ decrease with increasing pH. The decrease is approximately one log unit per pH unit. These results support the hypothesis that $MnHCO_3^+$ is the soluble complex species in the pH and concentration range investigated.

Heterogeneous Equilibria Experiments

Three different experiments in which samples of precipitated $MnCO_3$ were dissolved in distilled water under a CO_2 partial pressure of 1 atm yielded the same equilibrium pH value, 5.37. For the assumption of no complexing of Mn(II) by carbonic species, the calculated thermodynamic constant for $MnCO_{3(c)}$ from equation 22-24 is 4.35×10^{-11}. If the same data are interpreted by considering the existence of $MnHCO_3^+$ then the calculated solubility product of $MnCO_{3(c)}$ is 3.92×10^{-11}. These results are summarized in Table IV.

Two experiments were performed in which $MnCO_3$ was equilibrated with dilute Na_2CO_3 solutions under a CO_2 partial pressure of 1 atm. The equilibrium pH thus was shifted into the range 6 to 7. Soluble Mn was estimated by pipetting samples, filtering rapidly through a millipore filter, and reacting the filtrate solution with formaldoxime (25). The solubility product was assumed to be 3.92×10^{-11}, as determined above, and the stability constant for $MnHCO_3^+$ was evaluated by applying the pertinent equilibrium constant and electroneutrality expressions. The results are presented in Table V.

Polarographic Evaluation of $MnHCO_3^+$ Stability

Application of the polargraphic technique to a study of complex metal ions in aqueous solution has been discussed in detail by Lingane (26). A study of the influence of bicarbonate ion upon the potential of reduction to the metallic state was attempted with the objective of confirming the magnitude of the $MnHCO_3^+$ stability constant obtained by potentiometric methods. The dissociation constant of the metal ion complex is related to the shift in half-wave potential by the approximation:

$$E_{1/2} = \frac{0.0591}{n} K_c' - p \frac{0.0591}{n} \log [X] \qquad (22-33)$$

TABLE IV SOLUBILITY OF $MnCO_{3(c)}$ IN DISTILLED WATER

$$P_{CO_2} = 1 \text{ atm}$$

25°C

Assumed Condition	pH	$\begin{bmatrix} HCO_3^- \end{bmatrix}$ x10^3	$\begin{bmatrix} MnHCO_3^+ \end{bmatrix}$ x10^4	$\begin{bmatrix} Mn^{+2} \end{bmatrix}$ x10^3	(CO_3^{-2}) x 10^8	$K_{MnCO_{3(c)}}$ x10^{11}
No complex	5.37(a)	3.33	0	1.66	3.51	4.99	4.35
$MnHCO_3^+$	5.37(a)	3.32	3.34	1.49	3.50	4.81	3.92

(a) Three determinations

TABLE V $MnHCO_3^+$ STABILITY CONSTANT ESTIMATED BY
ANALYSIS OF $MnCO_3$ SUSPENSION

$$P_{CO_2} = 1 \text{ atm}$$

25°C

$$K_{MnCO_{3(c)}} = 3.92 \times 10^{-11}$$

pH	(CO_3^{-2}) x10^6	$\begin{bmatrix} Mn(II) \end{bmatrix}_{anal}$ x10^4	$\begin{bmatrix} Mn^{+2} \end{bmatrix}_{calc}$ x10^5	$\begin{bmatrix} MnHCO_3^+ \end{bmatrix}$ x10^5	I x10^2	$K_{MnHCO_3^+}$
6.14	1.187	1.352	5.67	7.85	2.2	110
6.58	9.18	0.210	0.94	1.16	6.4	50

where n is the number of electrons involved in the reduction, K_c' is the dissociation constant under actual solution conditions, p is the number of the complexing species bound per metal ion, and X is the molar concentration of the complexing species (26).

Polarograms were run on solutions at $22^\circ C$ that were prepared by dissolving weighed quantities of analytical grade chemicals in water redistilled from glass. A polarographic electrolysis vessel (H form) was used for the reduction. A saturated KCl bridge was used in the horizontal member of the cell. A saturated calomel half cell was contained in the reference arm of the cell. Prepurified N_2 washed with distilled water was used to purge solutions of oxygen before running each polarogram.

Perchlorate ion is not reduced at the dropping mercury electrode. Thus it was possible to use a $Mn(ClO_4)_2$ solution as the source of Mn^{+2} ions and $NaClO_4$ solution as background electrolyte. A 0.6 I medium, prepared by mixing the required quantities of $NaClO_4$ and $NaHCO_3$ solutions, was used for obtaining all of the Mn(II) reduction waves. Reversibility of the reduction was tested by measuring values of $\dfrac{i}{id-i}$ from the polarograms and plotting the logs of these values against the applied voltage. Typical results obtained in the absence and presence of $NaHCO_3$ are presented in Figure 4. The values for the slope appear to be in sufficient agreement with the expected slope of 29 mv for reversible reduction from the (II) state of Mn to the metal amalgam. The half-wave potential in the presence of HCO_3^- is observed. An evaluation of the coordination number of $MnHCO_3^+$ complex was made by plotting the shift in half-wave potential as a function of log $[HCO_3^-]$. The plotted data shown in Figure 5 suggest that one HCO_3^- is bound per Mn^{+2}, the slope being close to 29 mv, in agreement with a value of 1 for p in equation 22-33.

The dissociation constant for the $MnHCO_3^+$ species was evaluated by applying equation 22-33 to the data for half-wave potential as a function of $[HCO_3^-]$. Six determinations of the instability constant in 0.6 I medium were made. The values obtained for K_c' were: 2.73×10^{-2}; 2.70×10^{-2}; 2.61×10^{-2}; 2.86×10^{-2}; 3.25×10^{-2}; and 2.98×10^{-2}. The arithmetic mean of these six values is 2.85×10^{-2}. Expressed as a stability constant for the equilibrium from equation 22-9 the mean value is 35.1 in 0.6 I medium. If it is assumed that the activity coefficients of $MnHCO_3^+$ and HCO_3^- are approximately equal in the experimental environment and if it is assumed further that the

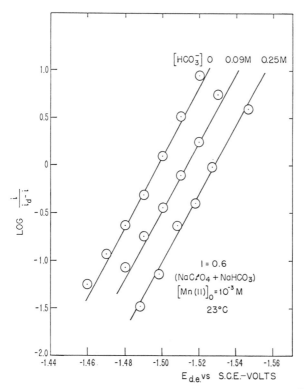

FIGURE 4   POLAROGRAPHIC DATA FOR Mn^{+2}
             REDUCTION IN PRESENCE OF BICARBONATE.

activity coefficient of the Mn^{+2} ion can be approximated from
Figure 1, a value of $K_{MnHCO_3^+}$ = 115 is obtained.   The stability
constant estimated by potentiometric procedures was 90, at 25°C.

Stability of $MnSO_4$ (aq)
     A brief polarographic study was made of the half-wave poten-
tial of Mn(II) reductions in the presence of difference concentrations of SO_4^{-2}.   The experimental procedure was, in general,
the same as that employed in the polarographic study of the HCO_3^-
complex. Na_2SO_4 and $NaClO_4$ solutions were mixed in required
amounts to obtain different SO_4^{-2} concentrations and constant I.
Figure 6 shows log plots obtained from polarograms of Mn(II)

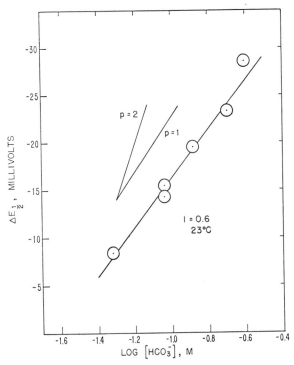

FIGURE 5   HALF-WAVE POTENTIAL OF Mn IN
              BICARBONATE SOLUTION AS A FUNCTION
              OF BICARBONATE CONCENTRATION.

reductions run in the absence and in the presence of SO_4^{-2}. The
equilibrium constant for the reaction:

$$Mn^{+2} + SO_4^{-2} = MnSO_4 \text{ (aq)} \qquad\qquad (22\text{-}34)$$

in 0.5 I medium was estimated at 30 and 27 in two experiments.
If activities of 0.3 are taken for both the Mn^{+2} and SO_4^{-2} ions,
and if the activity coefficient of $MnSO_4$ (aq) is assumed to be
close to unity, the K_{MnSO_4} is estimated to be in order of 3×10^2.
A value of 1.9×10^2 has been determined by conductivity measurements (2).

Solubility Product of $Mn(OH)_2$
          Three determinations of the solubility product of $Mn(OH)_2$

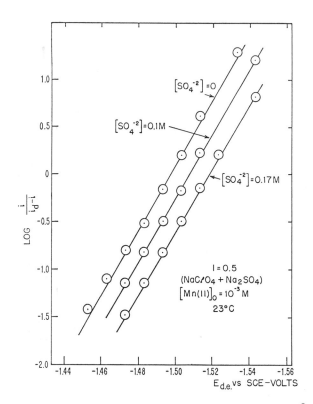

FIGURE 6   POLAROGRAPHIC DATA FOR Mn^{+2}
                REDUCTION IN PRESENCE OF SULFATE.

were made at $25^{\circ}C$. Known quantities of the Mn(II) salt were
added to deoxygenated, distilled water that was maintained under
a N_2 atmosphere. A measured quantity of standardized, deaerated NaOH was added to the system was observed with its equilibrium value recorded. The glass electrode was calibrated
against standard buffers at pH values in neighborhood of 7 and 9.
The soluble [Mn] of the system was estimated by rapidly with-
drawing an aliquot, filtering through a $0.22\,\mu$ membrane filter,
and oxidizing the filtrate Mn to MnO_4^{-}.
    These expressions represent the equilibrium relationships
existing in $Mn(OH)_2$ suspensions:

$$K_{Mn(OH)_{2(c)}} = (Mn^{+2})\,(OH^{-})^2 \qquad\qquad (22\text{-}35)$$

$$K_W = (H^+) \ (OH^-) \tag{22-20}$$

$$2[Mn^{+2}] + [MnOH^+] + [Na^+] + [H^+] = [OH^-] + [ClO_4^-] \tag{22-36}$$

$$K_H = \frac{(MnOH^+) \ (H^+)}{(Mn^{+2})} \tag{22-37}$$

The value of the acidity or hydrolysis constant for Mn(II) ion has been determined recently by Perrin (27). The value is too small to have any appreciable effect in the pH range involved. Calculation of the Mn(II) ion activity was made with equation 22-32. Table VI summarizes the data and calculated pK values for three determinations of the $Mn(OH)_2$ solubility product.

Summary of Manganese Thermodynamic Data

Table VII lists the values of free energies of formation of many of the species considered in this paper. These data were drawn from the compilations of Latimer (15) and Mah (23), from the general chemical literature, and from the present study. It needs to be emphasized again that knowledge of the thermodynamic properties of Mn probably is still rather incomplete with respect to species actually existing in aqueous systems at low temperature. For example, a variety of so-called non-stoichiometric oxides and hydroxides of Mn have been observed by various workers. Such species may be metastable.

TABLE VI DETERMINATION OF $Mn(OH)_2$ SOLUBILITY PRODUCT
25°C

pH	I	$f_{Mn^{+2}}$	Mn^{+2} calc $\times 10^4$	Mn^{+2} anal $\times 10^4$	pK
9.10	0.0065	0.721	9.17	8.95	12.98
9.15	0.0085	0.693	10.69	10.80	12.83
9.28	0.0025	0.808	2.87	2.98	13.07

TABLE VII STANDARD FREE ENERGIES OF FORMATION OF SOME SPECIES CONSIDERED IN THE PRESENT STUDY

$$(kcal/mole, \text{ at } 25^{O}C)$$

SPECIES	ΔF^{O}	LITERATURE CITED
Mn (c)	0.0	(15)
Mn^{+2} (aq)	-54.4	(15)
$MnOH^{+}$(aq)	-96.63	(27)
$Mn(OH)_3^{-}$ (aq)	-177.59	(15)
$MnHCO_3^{+}$ (aq)	-197.4	This study
$MnSO_4$ (aq)	-234.8	(2)
MnO (c)	-86.8	(15)
$Mn(OH)_2$ (c)	-147.3	This study
$MnCO_3$ (c)	-194.8	This study
MnS (c)	-53.0	(15)
Mn_3O_4 (c)	-306.0	(15)
Mn_2O_3 (c)	-209.85	(28)
$MnOOH$ (c)	-133.9	Estimated
$Mn(OH)_3$ (c)	-181.0	(15)
MnO_2 (c)	-111.3	(28)
MnO_4^{-2} (aq)	-120.4	(15)
MnO_4^{-} (aq)	-107.4	"
H_2O (l)	-56.690	"
H^{+} (aq)	0.00	"
OH^{-} (aq)	-37.595	"
HCO_3^{-} (aq)	-140.31	"
CO_3^{-2} (aq)	-126.22	"
SO_4^{-2} (aq)	-177.34	"
S^{-2} (aq)	+22.1	"
H_2O_2 (aq)	-31.470	"
HO_2^{-} (aq)	-15.610	"
HO_2 (aq)	+3.0	"
O_2^{-} (aq)	+13.0	"

THE SOLUBILITY OF MANGANOUS MANGANESE (II)

In the absence of dissolved oxygen or other strong oxidizing agents the stable form of manganese in aqueous systems is the (II) oxidation state. The thermodynamic stability of the (II) state with respect to other oxidation states is discussed later. The principal equilibria which control the concentrations of total soluble Mn(II) in water involve $Mn(OH)_2$, $MnCO_3$, and MnS as the pure solid phases. The presumed major soluble species of Mn(II) are: $[Mn(H_2O)_6]^{+2}$; $[Mn(H_2O)_5OH]^+$; $[Mn(H_2O)_3(OH)_3]^-$; $[Mn(H_2O)_5(HCO_3)]^+$; and $[Mn(H_2O)_5(SO_4)]$. In addition to these, a variety of soluble complex species must be anticipated that involve various ligands. Such ligands might include amino acids, hydroxy acids, and various carboxylic acids as well as a number of inorganic species, e.g., phosphate. Sufficient quantitative information about the properties of such complexes and the presence of organic complexing species in natural waters is not available. Table VIII lists the equilibria which can be considered now in evaluation of Mn(II) solubility in the three simple cases of carbonate-free, carbonate-containing, and sulfide-containing waters.

Manganous Hydroxide

In solutions which contain neither CO_2 nor H_2S constituents, the solubility of Mn(II) is limited by the solubility equilibria of $Mn(OH)_2$ (c). Because soluble hydroxo complexes ($MnOH^+$, $Mn(OH)_3^-$) exist, the solubility product (equilibrium 1, Table VIII) is not sufficient to define the total soluble Mn(II) concentration that can exist in aqueous solutions. The equilibria represented by 2 and 3 in Table VIII must be considered also. Simultaneous application of the equilibrium expressions 1, 2, and 3 leads to the solubility relations represented in Figure 7. The total solubility of Mn(II) cannot exceed the limits of the boundary defined by the shaded area in this figure. The explicit statement of the maximum possible equilibrium concentration of Mn(II), $[Mn(II)]_t$, as a function of $[H^+]$ is:

$$[Mn(II)]_t = \frac{K_1}{K_w}[H^+]^2 + \frac{K_2}{K_w}[H^+] + \frac{K_3 K_w}{[H^+]} \qquad (22\text{-}38)$$

in which K_w is the ion product of water, and K_1, K_2, and K_3 are the equilibrium constants of reactions 1, 2, and 3, respectively, in Table VIII.

TABLE VIII MANGANESE (II) SOLUBILITY, ACIDITY, AND COMPLEX EQUILIBRIA

No.	Equilibrium	Log K (25°C)	Literature Cited
1	$Mn(OH)_2(c) = Mn^{+2} + 2\ OH^-$	-12.96	This study
2	$Mn(OH)_2(c) = MnOH^+ + OH^-$	-9.55	calc
3	$Mn(OH)_2(c) + OH^- = Mn(OH)_3^-$	-5.35	(29)
4	$MnCO_3(c) = Mn^{+2} + CO_3^{-2}$	-10.41	This study
5	$MnCO_3(c) + OH^- = MnOH^+ + CO_3^{-2}$	-7.00	calc
6	$MnCO_3(c) + 3\ OH^- = Mn(OH)_3^- + CO_3^{-2}$	-2.80	calc
7	$MnCO_3(c) + H^+ = MnHCO_3^+$	+1.91	calc
8	$MnS(c) = Mn^{+2} + S^{-2}$	-15.16	(30)
9	$MnS(c) + OH^- = MnOH^+ + S^{-2}$	-11.74	calc
10	$MnS(c) + 3\ OH^- = Mn(OH)_3^- + S^{-2}$	-7.54	calc
11	$Mn^{+2} + H_2O = MnOH^+ + H^+$	-10.59	(27)
12	$H_2CO_3 = HCO_3^- + H^+$	-6.38	(15)
13	$HCO_3^- = CO_3^{-2} + H^+$	-10.32	(15)
14	$H_2S(aq) = H^+ + HS^-$	-6.96	(30)
15	$HS^- = H^+ + S^{-2}$	-14.00	(30)
16	$Mn^{+2} + HCO_3^- = MnHCO_3^+$	+1.95	This study

Manganous Carbonate

The solubility of $MnCO_3$ has been studied experimentally, with the results presented above. The pertinent Mn solubility equilibria for carbonate-containing waters are contained in Table VIII. Graphical representations of the controlling equilibria are shown in Figure 8 for a total carbonic species concentration of 2×10^{-3}M. The distribution of the carbonic species as a function of pH is shown in Figure 8a, while Figure 8b presents $[Mn(II)]_t$ as a function of pH.

A comparison of Figures 7 and 8b shows that up to a pH of about 10, Mn(II) is considerably less soluble in a HCO_3^-

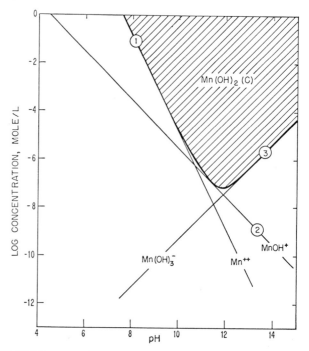

FIGURE 7   SOLUBILITY OF MANGANOUS HYDROXIDE.

containing water than in one free of HCO$_3^-$. For example, at
pH 8, more than 10^3 times as much Mn^{+2} can be retained in a
carbonate-free solution as in a water containing 2×10^{-3}M total
carbonic species. In the pH range from about 7.0 to 9.5, the
total carbonic species, C_t, is approximately equal to $[HCO_3^-]$.
The soluble Mn can be estimated by:

$$[Mn(II)]_t = \frac{(H^+)}{C_t K_{13}} \quad K_4 + \frac{K_5 K_w}{(H^+)} + K_7 (H^+) \quad (22\text{-}39)$$

where the subscripts refer to the numbered reactions in Table VIII
In terms of alkalinity, the soluble manganese may be estimated by

$$[Mn(II)]_t = \frac{(H^+) + 2K_{13}}{[ALK] K_{13}} \quad K_{14} + \frac{K_5 K_w}{(H^+)} + K_7 (H^+) \quad (22\text{-}40)$$

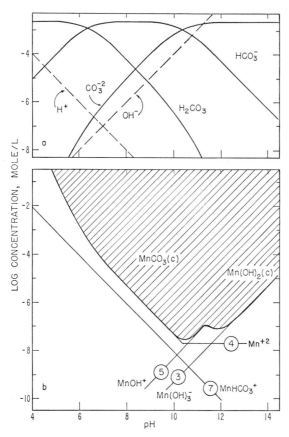

FIGURE 8   SOLUBILITY OF Mn(II) IN WATER
                CONTAINING 2 x 10⁻³M TOTAL
                CARBONIC SPECIES.

Equations 22-39 and 22-40 are valid for waters containing at
least 1×10^{-4}M total carbonic species. It can be seen from
Figure 8b that the $MnHCO_3^+$ complex or ion-pair has a relatively
small influence on the total solubility of Mn(II) under the conditions considered. At much higher concentrations of HCO_3^- the
existence of the complex would exert a proportionately greater
influence but the absolute solubility would apparently not be

greatly affected.   The equilibrium for $MnHCO_3^+$ formation establishes a lower limit for soluble Mn in HCO_3^- containing waters.

Manganous Sulfide

The presence of S(II) components (H_2S, HS^-, and S^{-2}) in the
hypolimnetic waters of lakes and reservoirs and in certain ground
waters is not unusual. Sulfide species may be produced in bottom
waters through biological reduction of SO_4^{-2}. It is, therefore,
necessary to direct some attention to the solubility relations of
Mn(II) and sulfides.

The published thermodynamic data on MnS provides a rather
wide range of solubility product values and standard free energies
The volume "Stability Constants" lists solubility products ranging from 10^{-10} to 10^{-20} (2).   Ringbom gave log K=- 9.6 for pink
MnS and log K = -12.6 for the green form (31).   Recently, a
NMR study of MnS precipitation from homogeneous solution concluded that the maximum value of the solubility product is 6 x
10^{-12} (32).   The solubility product given by Latimer, 7 x 10^{-16},
has been selected for the calculations made here.   The free
energy of formation listed in Table VII, -53.0 kcal, is consistent with this value of K.

Equilibria 8, 9, 10, 14, and 15 in Table VIII can be invoked
to describe the solubility of Mn(II) in an aqueous system containing a fixed level of total sulfide.   Whether or not $MnS_{(c)}$ controls
the solubility of Mn(II) depends upon the ratio of sulfide of carbonic species and upon the pH.   The total solubility of Mn(II) as
a function of pH is depicted in Figure 9b for a system containing
10^{-4}M total sulfide and 2 x 10^{-3}M total carbonic species.   Under
these conditions, solubility is controlled by the existence of
$MnS_{(c)}$ only in the pH range ca 10 to 12.   However, the line describing soluble Mn^{+2} as governed by equilibrium 8 (Table VIII)
lies rather close (about 0.2 units) to line 4 on Figure 9b.   Thus,
for a significantly smaller ratio of carbonic species to sulfide
species, the solubility of $MnS_{(c)}$ could become controlling.   This
situation might possibly develop in waters of low alkalinity and
intense biological activity producing high sulfide concentrations.
It must be emphasized that the description of sulfide solubility
presented here may be much simplified in comparison to real
situations, where polysulfide phases may actually exercise a
strong influence upon Mn(II) solubility in sulfide-containing
waters.

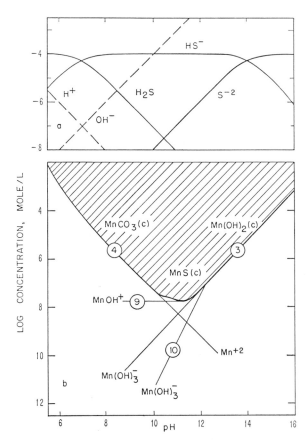

FIGURE 9   SOLUBILITY OF Mn(II) IN WATER
             CONTAINING 1 x 10^{-4}M TOTAL SULFIDE
             AND 2 x 10^{-3}M TOTAL CARBONIC SPECIES.

STABILITIES OF THE DIFFERENT OXIDATION STATES OF MANGANESE

The relative stabilities of a number of Mn species in different states of oxidation can be represented by means of potential-pH diagrams. These diagrams depict the equivalent free energies of various half reactions as functions of pH under specified conditions. The equivalent free energy variable is computed for each half reaction by employing the standard free energies of formation listed in Table VII. The conceptual meaning of the potential, in the thermodynamic sense, is that it is the equivalent free energy, i.e., the free energy change per mole of electrons associated with a particular oxidation or reduction process. This potential has been represented by the symbol U_e. It is equal to $\Delta F/n\mathcal{F}$, and has the dimensions of volts.

Together with the solubility diagrams presented above, the oxidation-reduction diagrams constitute a valuable summary of limiting relations in the light of presently available thermodynamic information. These relations are for 1 atm and 25°C, and such other solution conditions as may be specified, e.g., concentration of carbonic species.

The System Mn-H_2O

Oxidation-reduction equilibria in the simple system consisting only of Mn in its various oxidation states, and water, will be considered first. The oxidation states for which stable species exist in some zone in the pH range 0 to 14 in the system are: metallic Mn; II; IV; VI; and VII. Certain mixtures of the II and IV states are included.

Equivalent free energy -pH functions have been computed for the pertinent equilibria involved in the Mn-H_2O system. These equilibria and their associated mathematical functions are presented in Table IX. These functions were computed with the standard free energy values of Table VII and the relations:

$$\frac{\Delta F}{n} = \frac{\Delta F^O}{n} + \frac{RT}{n} \ln Q \tag{22-41}$$

$$U_e{}^O = \frac{\Delta F^O}{n\mathcal{F}} \tag{22-42}$$

$$U_e = U_e{}^O + \frac{RT}{n} \ln Q \tag{22-43}$$

where U_e is the oxidation potential, $U_e{}^O$ is the standard oxidation potential, and Q is the activity quotient of the reaction.

The free energy relations for the different oxidation states of aqueous Mn are depicted in Figure 10. Also shown are the relations of the reactions corresponding to the oxidation and reduction of water (lines 1 and 2) and the reduction of oxygen to peroxide (line 1a). Figure 10 has been prepared for the condition that soluble Mn is equal to 10^{-6}M, and for the assumption that activities are essentially equal to concentrations. Also shown is a partial description of the relations for 10^{-4}M soluble Mn(II).

TABLE IX OXIDATION POTENTIAL OR EQUIVALENT FREE ENERGY FUNCTIONS FOR THE SYSTEM Mn-H$_2$O
25°C, 1 atm

No.	Equilibrium	Function
1	$2H_2O = O_2 + 4H^+ + 4e^-$	$U_e = 1.229 + 0.01479 \log P_{O_2} - 0.05916\ pH$
1a	$H_2O_2 = O_2 + 2H^+ + 2e^-$	$U_e = 0.682 + 0.02958 \log P_{O_2} - 0.02958 \log (H_2O_2) - 0.05916\ pH$
2	$H_2 = 2H^+ + 2e^-$	$U_e = 0.000 - 0.02958 \log P_{H_2} - 0.05916\ pH$
3	$Mn = Mn^{+2} + 2e^-$	$U_e = 1.18 + 0.02958 \log (Mn^{+2})$
4	$Mn + 2H_2O = Mn(OH)_2 + 2H^+ + 2e^-$	$U_e = 0.734 - 0.05916\ pH$
5	$Mn + 3H_2O = Mn(OH)_3^- + 3H^+ + 2e^-$	$U_e = -0.163 + 0.02958 \log (Mn(OH)_3^-) - 0.08874\ pH$
6	$3Mn(OH)_2 = Mn_3O_4 + 2H_2O + 2H^+ + 2e^-$	$U_e = 0.448 - 0.05915\ pH$
7	$3Mn(OH)_3^- + H^+ = Mn_3O_4 + 5H_2O + 2e^-$	$U_e = -1.228 - 0.08874 \log (Mn(OH)_3^-) + 0.02958\ pH$
8	$3Mn^{+2} + 4H_2O = Mn_3O_4 + 8H^+ + 2e^-$	$U_e = 1.1818 - 0.08874 \log (Mn^{+2}) - 0.2364\ pH$
9	$Mn^{+2} + 2H_2O = MnOOH + 3H^+ + e^-$	$U_e = 1.468 - 0.05916 \log (Mn^{+2}) - 0.17748\ pH$
10	$Mn_3O_4 + 2H_2O = 3MnOOH + H^+ + e^-$	$U_e = 0.767 - 0.05916\ pH$
11	$MnOOH = MnO_2 + H^+ + e^-$	$U_e = 0.978 - 0.05916\ pH$
12	$Mn^{+2} + 2H_2O = MnO_2 + 4H^+ + 2e^-$	$U_e = 1.225 - 0.02958 \log (Mn^{+2}) - 0.11832\ pH$
13	$MnO_2 + 2H_2O = MnO_4^- + 4H^+ + 3e^-$	$U_e = 1.693 + 0.01972 \log (MnO_4^-) - 0.0788\ pH$
14	$MnO_2 + 2H_2O = MnO_4^{-2} + 4H^+ + 2e^-$	$U_e = 2.26 + 0.02958 \log (MnO_4^{-2}) - 0.11832\ pH$
15	$MnO_4^{-2} = MnO_4^- + e^-$	$U_e = 0.563 + 0.05916 \log (MnO_4^{-2})/(MnO_4^-)$
16	$Mn(OH)_2 + 2H^+ = Mn^{+2} + 2H_2O$	$\log (Mn^{+2}) = 15.04 - 2\ pH$
17	$Mn(OH)_2 + H_2O = Mn(OH)_3^- + H^+$	$\log (Mn(OH)_3^-) = -19.36 + pH$

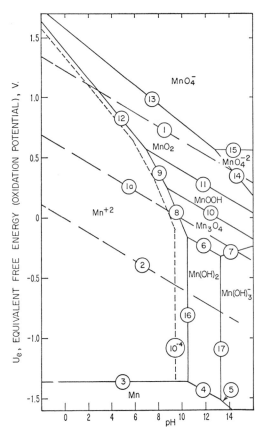

FIGURE 10   MANGANESE POTENTIAL DIAGRAM
FOR $Mn-O_2-H_2O$, 25°C, $10^{-6}M$.

The System $Mn-H_2O-CO_2$

     In the presence of carbonic species, it is necessary to con-
sider additional oxidation-reduction equilibria in order to describe the stabilities of the different Mn oxidation states. Specifically, $MnCO_{3(c)}$ and $MnHCO_3^+{}_{(aq)}$ must be considered. Table X
contains the additional half reactions and coordinative equilibria
which are required to describe the stabilities of different Mn
species in carbonate-containing waters. An equivalent free
energy vs pH diagram for a $Mn-H_2O-CO_2$ system containing
$2 \times 10^{-3}M$ total dissolved carbonic species and $1 \times 10^{-6}M$ total

TABLE X   OXIDATION POTENTIAL OR EQUIVALENT FREE ENERGY FUNCTIONS FOR THE SYSTEM Mn-H$_2$O-CO$_2$

25°C, 1 atm

No.	Equilibrium	Function
18	$Mn + HCO_3^- = MnCO_3 + H^+ + 2e^-$	$U_e = -1.18 - 0.02958 \log (HCO_3^-) - 0.02958$ pH
19	$MnCO_3 + H^+ = Mn^{+2} + HCO_3^-$	$\log (Mn^{+2}) = -0.09 \log (HCO_3^-) -$ pH
20	$MnCO_3 + H^+ = MnHCO_3^+$	$\log (MnHCO_3^+) = 1.91 -$ pH
21	$MnCO_3 + 2H_2O = Mn(OH)_2 + HCO_3^- + H^+$	pH $= \log (HCO_3^-) + 15.13$
22	$3MnCO_3 + 4H_2O = Mn_3O_4 + 3HCO_3^- + 5H^+ + 2e^-$	$U_e = 1.825 + 0.08874 \log (HCO_3^-) - 0.1479$ pH
23	$MnCO_3 + 2H_2O = MnOOH + HCO_3^- + 2H^+ + e^-$	$U_e = 1.475 + 0.05916 \log (HCO_3^-) - 0.11812$ pH

dissolved Mn species has been prepared by simultaneously considering the equilibria in Tables IX and X. The result is shown
in Figure 11. The effect of the presence of carbonic species on
the system is readily seen by a comparison of Figures 10 and 11.
$MnCO_{3(c)}$ is stable from a pH of about 8.5 to 11.5. The pH region
in which Mn^{+2}(aq) is stable, therefore, is reduced considerably
in comparison to the region of stability in the absence of carbonate.
The region of $Mn(OH)_{2(c)}$ stability is diminished also. The field
of stability of $Mn_3O_{4(c)}$ has been slightly reduced at the expense
of $MnCO_{3(c)}$. With respect to oxidation of Mn(II), the effect of
the carbonate is thus to make it less favorable, in the thermodynamic sense, in the pH range 8.5 to 11.5.

Potential diagrams reveal the region of stability of a particular oxidation state. For example, it is clear from Figure 11
that, for systems no more oxidizing than ca 0.4 v, the Mn species
in the II state are stable with respect to oxidation. When this
fact has been established, it is advantageous to make use of the
concentration-pH diagram in order to identify the fields of stability of the different solid phases and to describe the concentrations
of soluble Mn and other species as a function of pH. For this
reason it is not necessary to show a large number of concentration
contours on the potential-pH diagrams.

Some Oxidation-Reduction Equilibria for Other Aqueous Systems
Because of their significance with respect to the behavior of
Mn in analytical chemistry, in nature, and in treatment processes,
additional oxidation reduction equilibria are considered briefly.
Of interest are half reactions involving various sulfur species,
chlorine, organic systems, and some well-known oxidizing and
reducing agents. With respect to possible Mn-S interactions, in
addition to the formation of Mn(II)-S(II) compounds, the reduction
of higher oxides of Mn by sulfide, for example:

$$8\ MnOOH\ +\ S^{-2}\ +\ 16\ H^+\ =\ 8\ Mn^{+2}\ +\ SO_4^{-2}\ +\ 12\ H_2O \quad (22\text{-}4)$$

are generally spontaneous. A list of some oxidation-reduction
equilibria of interest in relation to the chemistry of aqueous Mn
is presented in Table XI.

In Figure 12 an attempt is made to depict potential-pH relations for several important aqueous Mn forms and certain other
species of natural and analytical chemical interest. The Mn^{+2} -
MnO_x boundaries (lower cross-hatched lines) are drawn for
10^{-6}M soluble Mn, the MnO_4^- - MnO_2 boundary (upper cross-

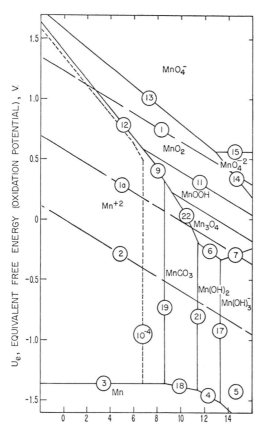

FIGURE 11   MANGANESE POTENTIAL DIAGRAM FOR
Mn-O_2-CO_2-H_2O, 25°C, 10^{-6}M.

hatched line) is drawn also for 10^{-6}M soluble Mn. Details are
omitted for the different oxides; Mn_3O_4, MnOOH, and MnO_2.
   From the relative position of the MnO_2 - Mn^{+2} and the
O_2 - H_2O (No. 1) lines it is apparent that, at pH values somewhat below 3, MnO_2 becomes unstable with respect to the oxidation of water. In the pH range of oxygen-containing natural
waters, MnO_2 appears to be the only stable form. From the
free energies of the MnO_4^- - MnO_2 and MnO_2 - Mn^{+2} half-
reactions in comparison to that of the hypochlorite-chloride

TABLE XI SOME ADDITIONAL REDUCTION-OXIDATION EQUILIBRIA OF SIGNIFICANCE IN MANGANESE CHEMISTRY
25°C

No.	Equilibrium	Standard Potential v	Literature Cited
24	$H_2S + 4H_2O = HSO_4^- + 9H^+ + 8e^-$	0.290	computed
25	$H_2S + 4H_2O = SO_4^{-2} + 10H^+ + 8e^-$	0.303	computed
26	$HS^- + 4H_2O = SO_4^{-2} + 9H^+ + 8e^-$	0.250	computed
27	$H_2S = S^0 + 2H^+ + 2e^-$	0.142	computed
28	2 cysteine=cystine $+ 2H^+ + 2e^-$	0.074	(33)
29	Ascorbate= Dehydroascorbate $+ 2H^+ + 2e^-$	0.40	(33)
30	Gallic Acid (red) = Gallic Acid (ox) $+ 2H^+ + 2e^-$	0.80	(33)
31	o-Tolidine (red) = o-Tolidine (ox)$+ 2H^+ + 2e^-$	0.88	(33)
32	$Fe^{+2} = Fe^{+3} + e^-$	0.77	(15)
33	$\left[Mn(II) (P_2O_7)\right]_n = \left[Mn(III) (P_2O_7)\right]_n + e^-$	1.15	(34)
34	$2 Cl^- = Cl_2 + 2e^-$	1.36	(15)
35	$Cl^- + H_2O = HOCl + H^+ + 2e^-$	1.55	(15)
36	$Ag(I) = Ag(II) + e^-$ $(HNO_3$ medium)	1.93	(35)

half reaction, it is apparent that Cl_2 might be expected to serve
as an oxidant for Mn(II) and Mn(IV) species in the neutral and
alkaline range. In fact OCl^- is employed to oxidize MnO_4^{-2} to
MnO_4^-.

Benzidine, o-tolidine, and a variety of related organic
reagents are useful in detecting higher Mn oxides, e.g., MnO_2.
The reason may be seen by comparing the position of the
MnO_2^- Mn^{+2} boundary with that for reaction 31 which represents
the oxidation of o-tolidine in acid solution. The oxidized form
of the o-tolidinium couple is colored intensely. The change in
slope of line number at approximately pH 3 corresponds to a
change in predominant species because of acid-base equilibria.

It may be noted that the oxidation of o-tolidine by Fe(III),
line 32 on the diagram, appears to be possible at pH values
greater than ca 2. However, the hydrolysis of Fe(III) species
causes a change in the formal potential of the Fe(III)-Fe(II)
system, also at about pH 2, so that it may be that o-tolidine
is not oxidized by Fe(III) even above pH 2. Agents which would
tend to stabilize Mn(III) could shift the potential of the Mn(III)-
Mn(II) couple to a value at which o-tolidine and similar compounds would not be oxidized. For example, in the presence
of cyanide, the half reaction:

$$Mn(CN)_6^{-4} = Mn(CN)_6^{-3} + e^- \qquad\qquad (22\text{-}45)$$

has a standard potential of -0.22 v.

The possible significance of sulfide species as reductants
of Mn oxides has been mentioned already. Lines 23, 26, and 27
in Figure 12 indicate the reducing strengths of the $S(II)\text{-}SO_4^{-2}$
and $S(II)\text{-}S^0$ couples, respectively. MnO_2 is definitely unstable
with respect to reduction by sulfide. In fact, reaction of
$\partial\text{-}MnO_2$ and aqueous H_2S can be observed readily by mixing
the two at room temperature.

The thermodynamic tendencies of three other reducing
systems to react with MnO_2 and lower Mn oxides can be seen
from Figure 12. The systems cysteine-cystine (line 28), ascor-
bate-dehydroascorbate (line 29), and the reduced and oxidized
forms of gallic acid (line 30) are pertinent. For a detailed
discussion of the potentials of different classes of organic
substances in solution the reader is referred to the text by
Clark (33). The potential of the cysteine-cystine couple indicates
a strong tendency to reduce higher oxides of Mn in acid, neutral,
and alkaline solutions. The potentials of the cysteine-cystine

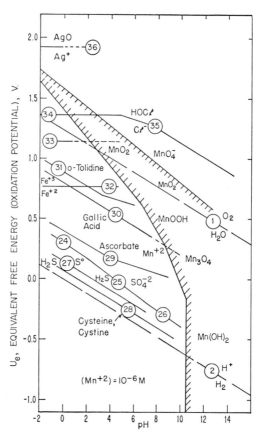

FIGURE 12   POTENTIAL DIAGRAM SHOWING THE
                 RELATION OF A NUMBER OF OXIDATION-
                 REDUCTION REACTIONS TO MAJOR
                 MANGANESE SPECIES.

system as a function of pH are fairly representative of those of
other sulphydryl compounds, i.e., the compounds are all quite
strongly reducing. Ascorbic acid has strong reducing tendencies
over a large pH range. The actual reduction of MnO_2 by both
cysteine and ascorbic acid in H_2CO_3 solutions has been demonstrated by Hochster and Quastel (36).
     Gallic acid (3, 4, 5-trihydroxy benzoic acid) is found in
sumach, tea, and many other plants. It may be prepared by

hydrolysis of tannic acid. The potential for gallic acid oxidation given in Table XI is an estimate based on the compilation prepared by Clark for the benzoquinone compounds (33). It may be compared with the standard potential reported for pyrogallol (the decarboxylation product of gallic acid), 0.71 v (33). From the relative positions of the MnO_2 line and the gallic acid line it might predict that the oxide would be reduced by gallic acid, at least, when $Mn(II)$ is present in low concentration. This prediction is confirmed by mixing a ∂-MnO_2 with a tannic acid solution indicates a high concentration of Mn. The reducing properties of such materials as tannic and gallic acids suggest that considerable caution is necessary in interpreting the chemical behavior of Mn, Fe, and similar elements even in relatively simple organic systems. In the case of Mn, it seems clear that organic substances are involved as reducing agents. They may also play a significant role as complexing agents as mentioned earlier.

PRODUCTS OF MANGANESE (II) OXIDATION BY OXYGEN

In the foregoing sections several equilibrium properties of aqueous Mn have been considered that include those relating to the relative stabilities of such pure phases as $Mn(OH)_2$, Mn_3O_4, MnOOH, and MnO_2. However, research by a number of workers seems to indicate that when $Mn(II)$ is oxidized by oxygen the products are frequently not characterizable in terms of simple stoichiometries. While the existence of the pure phases mentioned above is well established by crystallography and, often, by chemical analysis, it is still pertinent to inquire about the nature of the oxygenation products of $Mn(II)$ under various solution conditions (e.g., pH, alkalinity). The products initially obtained in nature and in laboratory experiments on the kinetics of oxygenation may not represent well-defined phases, i.e., they may be nonstoichiometric and metastable.

Table XII lists well-defined oxides of Mn which have been observed previously as products of oxygenation in aqueous systems at ordinary temperature and pressure. Laboratory preparations of hausmannite and manganite have been reported recently by Bricker (45).

Experiments on Mn(II) Oxygenation Stoichiometry and Products

In considering available information concerning the stoichiometric aspects of $Mn(II)$ oxygenation in aqueous systems, a need for additional data about the kind of products obtained under

TABLE XII SOME OXIDES OF MANGANESE FORMED
BY OXYGENATION

Formula	Mineralogical Name	X (MnO_x)	Literature Cited
$Mn(OH)_2$	pyrochroite	1.00 - 1.15	(37)
Mn_3O_4	hausmannite	1.33 - 1.42	(38,39)
$Mn_3O_4 \cdot nH_2O$	(a)hydrohausmannite	1.15 - 1.45	(40)
β-MnOOH		1.25 - 1.50	(40)
δ-MnOOH	manganite	1.50	(38)
Manganous Manganite		1.7 - 1.9	(40,41)
∂-MnO_2$	(birnessite)	1.90	(42,43,41)

(a) Recently shown to be a non-stoichiometric mixture
   of Mn_3O_4 and Mn_2O_3 (44).

conditions of more dilute Mn concentrations was evident. Since previous investigations on the reaction stoichiometry have not included experiments on oxygen used over a wide range of base to Mn(II) ratios (and pH values), such experiments were included in the work described herein.

A convenient means of determining the amount of O_2 required to oxidize Mn(II) is afforded by the conventional Warburg constant volume manometer apparatus. The reaction between a Mn(II) salt solution and O_2 in air can be initiated by tipping in the solution from the side arm of a Warburg flask whose main compartment contains a base, e.g., NaOH solution. The course of oxygen uptake with time and the final extent of the reaction is followed then by observing the decrease in pressure. When X-ray data are to be obtained, the flask contents can be filtered through a membrane filter wherefrom the oxide is removed and the sample mounted for the diffraction patterns. Some results obtained by the manometric technique are presented herein.

When the quantity of strong base added is insufficient to precipitate (as Mn(OH))) all or nearly all the Mn(II) present in

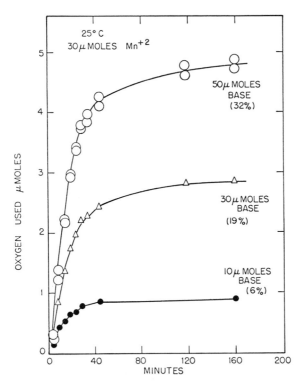

FIGURE 13   MANOMETRIC MEASUREMENT OF O_2
                 USED IN AIR OXIDATION OF Mn^{+2}
                 IN VARYING DEFICIENCIES OF BASE.

an oxygenating system, the extent of oxygen uptake is found to
be significantly less than that required for formation of Mn_3O_4,
Mn_2O_3, or MnO_2. Results of experiments, in which varying
amount of base were all less than equivalent to the Mn, are
shown in Figure 13. The [Mn] is rather high, $8.6 \times 10^{-3}M$.
It is seen that O_2 uptake in these systems depends upon the
relative deficiency of base. The initial pH of a few parallel
reaction systems was between 9 and 10 whereupon the pH value
dropped sharply and was near neutral at the end of the experiments.

Amounts of oxygen utilized per mole of Mn present during
air oxidation in three different buffering media, borax, CO_3^{-2}
$-HCO_3^-$, and $Ca(OH)_2$ are shown in Figure 14. These results

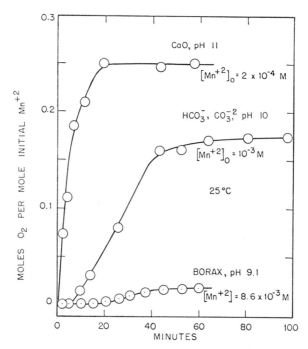

FIGURE 14   MANOMETRIC MEASUREMENT OF O_2
               USED IN AIR OXIDATION OF Mn^{+2}
               AT THREE pH VALUES.

also give a qualitative impression of the dependence of the
oxygenation rate upon pH. The buffer capacity of the borax
solution was actually rather small with respect to the [Mn]
present. The extent of the oxygen uptake, therefore, may have
been limited by pH depression occurring after the onset of
oxidation at about the 20 minute time. In the case of CO_3^{-2}
-HCO_3^- system, the higher concentration of buffering species
relative to Mn would be expected to provide a more nearly
constant pH. The amount of O_2 utilization corresponds to an
average degree of oxidation of about 1.3 to 1.4 since, essentially,
all Mn was removed from the solution phase.

    Three experimental systems were used in order to relate
the O_2 uptake during air oxidation of Mn with the X-ray patterns
of the products. The oxygen uptake curves for 2.3×10^{-3}M
$Mn(ClO_4)_2$ in presence of 0.7, 1.1, and 18 equivalents of

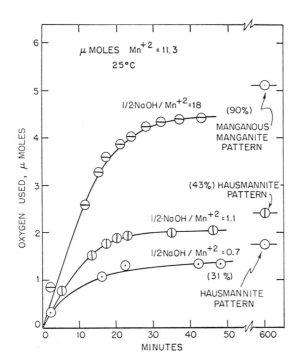

FIGURE 15   MANOMETRIC MEASUREMENT OF O_2
USED IN AIR OXIDATION OF Mn^{+2}
IN PRESENCE OF VARYING AMOUNTS
OF NaOH.

NaOH per Mn(II) equivalent are shown in Figure 15.   The
manometric systems were allowed to run for about ten hours.
In these experiments a rapid consumption of O_2 is followed by
an extended period of very slow oxygen uptake. After about
ten hours of oxygenation, the oxidation products were removed
for X-ray analysis.   For the systems with equivalent ratios of
0.7 and 1.1, each of the oxygenation products showed patterns
strongly similar to the pattern exhibited by hausmannite, Mn_3O_4.
Thus, there is general agreement between the X-ray data
and the O_2 consumption. The oxygenation product for the system
with a base to Mn(II) equivalent ratio of 18 yielded a X-ray pattern
which was closely similar to that which has been obtained for
manganous-manganite and ∂-MnO_2 by several investigators
(4, 8, 22).   The maximum oxygen uptake per Mn indicates that the

average degree of oxidation may be represented by $MnO_{1.90}$.
This formulation is within the range of compounds for which
the manganous-manganite pattern has been reported previously.

In addition to manometric observations of oxygen uptake as
a measure of oxygenation stoichiometry, available analytical
methods have been employed to determine the principal composition of hydrous Mn oxides formed by air oxidation in dilute
solutions (10^{-5} to 10^{-4}M) (25). These results have recently been
reported (46). In the pH range 9 - 10, compositions of the oxidation products ranged from $MnO_{1.24}$ to $MnO_{1.43}$.

KINETICS OF MANGANESE (II) OXYGENATION

It has been noted above on the basis of the thermodynamic
data that Mn(II) is unstable with respect to oxidation by O_2 over
the entire pH range of natural water. Oxidation potentials,
however, give no information about either the rate or the nature
of the oxygenation reactions.

Only a few experimental studies on the kinetics of the
reaction between Mn(II) and dissolved oxygen have been reported
(47, 48). Nichols and Walton measured the consumption of oxygen
as a function of time at 25°C in systems containing concentrated
solutions of $MnCl_2$, NH_3, and varying amounts of NH_4Cl (47).
Their data indicated a strong effect of initial pH on the reaction
rate in the range 8.6 to 9.6. The ultimate amounts of O_2 consumed were 67 to 77% of that required for MnO_2. The kinetic
data were considered to be indicative of autocatalysis. It was
noted also that autoxidation by air is much slower than that by
pure O_2.

Experiments with air oxidation of Mn have recently been
reported by Hem (48). The disappearance of Mn from dilute
$NaHCO_3$ or NaOH solutions was followed at room temperature
by filtering suspensions of oxidized Mn and measuring the Mn
content of the filtrates. The principal conclusions reached by
Hem are: (a) that the rate of Mn oxidation and precipitation by
aeration is affected by pH with an increase in pH causing an
increase in rate; (b) that the rate is significantly decreased by
the presence of HCO_3^- and SO_4^{-2}; and (c) that the form of the
rate curves for the oxidations in HCO_3^- solutions suggests
autocatalysis.

Kinetic Experiments

An extensive experimental study of Mn oxygenation kinetics

was conducted in order to attain a more quantitative understanding of the nature of the oxygenation reaction and to examine the effect of concentration, pH, oxygen, HCO_3^-, SO_4^{-2}, and temperature upon the kinetics. The processes of Mn(II) oxidation and removal from solution have been examined independently by the use of appropriate analytical techniques. Some of the pertinent findings of this study herein are presented. An extensive description of the experimental procedures and a discussion of experimental results are available elsewhere (49, 50).

General Procedure for Kinetic Experiments
     Oxygen at a known partial pressure (O_2-N_2 gas mixtures) was bubbled through a buffer solution of the desired pH, in a 1500-ml pyrex beaker that was kept in a constant temperature water bath. After a sufficient time had elapsed for the system to become saturated with oxygen, a measured volume of standardized $Mn(ClO_4)_2$ was added rapidly, and a stopwatch started. The contents of the beaker were mixed vigorously and continuously by means of a propeller stirrer. At suitable times aliquots of the oxygenating mixture were withdrawn with a pipet and analyzed for either soluble Mn or oxidized Mn according to methods described previously (25).

Results of Kinetic Experiments
     In an initial series of experiments oxygenation was studied over a wide pH range, 6 to 12, and in various media. In several hours, no oxidation was observed at pH values less than 8.6 at Mn(II) concentrations of 2×10^{-4}M and an O_2 partial pressure of 1.0. Detectable (ca 2%) oxidation was observable in 3 hours at pH 9.0 under these conditions. At pH 12, oxidation is apparently complete with formation of $MnO_{1.75}$ in less than one minute.
     In long-term experiments in the slightly alkaline pH range, these observations were typical: (a) The pH of a distilled water solution saturated with oxygen was adjusted to 8.5 by adding a small amount of NaOH. A quantity of neutral Mn solution was added to a concentration of 2×10^{-4}M. The one-liter solution was stored for two weeks in a stoppered Pyrex bottle. The amount of oxidation was found to be 0.013 eq/mole, i.e., 2.6×10^{-6} total equivalent of oxidized Mn; (b) An oxygen-saturated solution containing 2×10^{-3}M $NaHCO_3$ and 2×10^{-4}M $Mn(ClO_4)_2$, pH 8.5, was stored in a stoppered Pyrex reagent bottle for six days. A yellow color developed slowly in the solution and on the glass surface during this time. Analysis revealed 3.3×10^{-5}

equivalent of oxidized Mn or roughly 5% oxidation; and (c) A crystal of calcite was suspended in a 1 x 10^{-4}M neutral $Mn(ClO_4)$ solution. Over a period of two months coatings of oxidized Mn appeared at the edges of the calcite crystal. No oxide appeared on the smooth surfaces. The total equivalent of oxidized Mn on the calcite was 1.4 x 10^{-6} or roughly 3% of the original Mn in solution.

Experiments in Borate Solutions

A few oxygenation experiments were made in which a 1.2 x 10^{-2}M $Na_2B_4O_7$ buffer controlled pH during the reaction. Results are presented in Figures 16a and 16b. Figure 16a shows $Mn(II)$ oxidation obtained from three experiments at pH 9.8 and from one experiment at pH 9.2. An autocatalytic pattern is observed for the reaction of pH 9.8. In Figure 16b, soluble Mn concentrations are plotted as a function of time at both pH values. Similar patterns of $Mn(II)$ oxidation and removal are evident in comparing Figures 16a and 16b. The average oxidation state of the solid product at pH 9.8 after ca. 40 min of reaction can be represented by $MnO_{1.28}$.

Experiments in Bicarbonate-Carbonate Solutions

Because of the importance of HCO_3^- and CO_3^{-2} solutions in the chemistry of natural waters, emphasis has been given to studies of $Mn(II)$ oxygenation in these systems. Figure 17 shows results from kinetic experiments in $HCO_3^--CO_3^{-2}$ buffer solutions at pH 9.5. Two Mn concentrations were employed in a 2:1 ratio. These observations are in qualitative agreement with a second-order autocatalytic rate law as discussed below.

Rates of oxygenation in systems containing 2.25 x 10^{-4}M $Mn(II)$ were observed in total carbonic species concentrations (C_t) of 4 x 10^{-3}M and 6 x 10^{-3}M, at pH 9.7, and in C_t concentrations of 2 x 10^{-3}M and 6 x 10^{-3}M, at pH 9.5. The temperature was 22°C. The kinetic data are shown in Figure 18. Under conditions of these experiments, the total carbonate concentration is seen to exert a definite influence on the rate of $Mn(II)$ oxidation. A possible insight into the reason for the marked effect of carbonic species concentration upon the kinetics of oxidation may be gained by considering the $MnCO_3$ solubility equilibria discussed earlier. The systems studied in these experiments are initially supersaturated with respect to $MnCO_3$ precipitation. Evidence for the existence of $MnCO_{3(c)}$ in these oxygenated systems is

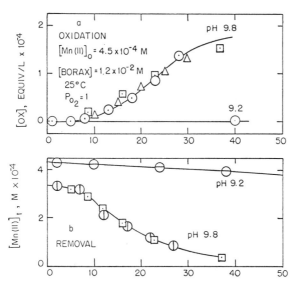

FIGURE 16   OXIDATION AND REMOVAL OF Mn(II)
IN BORAX SOLUTIONS.

provided by the X-ray diffraction pattern of the solid product
obtained upon prolonged oxygenation of $5 \times 10^{-4}M$ Mn(II) in a
$2 \times 10^{-3}M$ NaHCO$_3$ solution whose initial pH was adjusted to
pH 9.5. Observed diffraction spacings (14 lines) for the filtered
solid agree quite well with published ASTM spacings for synthetic rhodochrosite (51). Although the system also contained
considerable oxidized material no strong lines attributable to
known Mn oxides could be found in the X-ray patterns. Apparently
the oxides present were amorphous. In addition to MnCO$_3$ precipitation, the possible significance of the ion-pair MnHCO$_3^+$
must be considered also. The relative importance of this
species is considered in the concluding discussion.

Oxygen Partial Pressure
     The influence of oxygen partial pressure upon the rate of
Mn(II) oxidation in carbonic systems was observed at pH 9.7
and 22°C in HCO$_3^-$ solutions. The results are shown in Figure 19.
The specific rates of the reaction under the two different partial
pressures were found to be approximately in the ratio 5:1 as

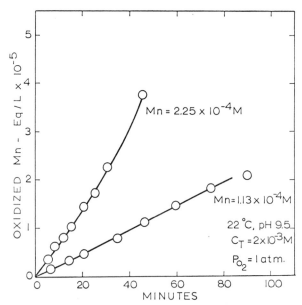

FIGURE 17   INFLUENCE OF Mn(II) CONCENTRATION
             ON OXYGENATION RATE IN BICARBONATE-
             CARBONATE SOLUTION.

expected. A similar dependence of Fe(II) oxidation rate upon
oxygen partial pressure has been noted also (52, 53).

Temperature
    The rate of the Mn(II) oxygenation reaction is influenced by
temperature which affects the various acid-base and solubility
equilibria involved in the reaction solution. The solubility of
O_2 under a given partial pressure also depends upon temperature.
Reaction rate constants are, in general, influenced by temperature.
    Experiments were conducted at $22^{O}C$ and $11^{O}C$ in solutions
containing $4.0 \times 10^{-3}M$ total carbonic species (C_t) and $2.25 \times$
$10^{-4}M$ Mn(II). The oxygen partial pressure was 1 atm. The
data on Mn(II) oxidation are presented in Figure 20. By considering the effects of temperature of the ion-product of water
and on the solubility of O_2 in water, it is estimated that the
reaction rate itself is decreased by a factor of two in lowering
the temperature from $22^{O}C$ to $11^{O}C$.

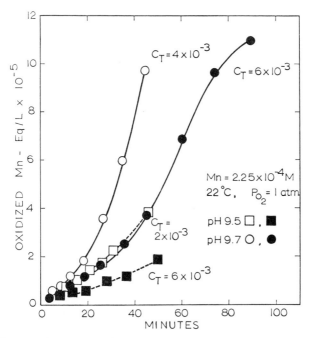

FIGURE 18   INFLUENCE OF TOTAL CARBONIC
               SPECIES ON RATE OF Mn(II) OXYGENATION.

Sulfate
        Experiments were conducted in order to determine whether
the presence of sulfate exerts a strong influence on the oxygenation of Mn in carbonate solution. In one experiment, a solution
containing 1 x 10^{-2}M total carbonic species and 2 x 10^{-2}M
Na_2SO_4 was employed. The oxygen partial pressure was 1 atm
and the temperature was 25°C. The pH of the solution with
sulfate was depressed below the value of 9.5 for the corresponding sulfate-free solution. The pH depression was close to 0.3
units.
        In another experiment, 0.01M sulfate was added to a carbon-
ate buffer and the pH was adjusted to 9.7. This is the same pH
existing in a corresponding sulfate-free buffer. Results of these
experiments are presented in Figure 21. While there may be
some slight kinetic influence on the part of sulfate, these experiments indicate that it is minor. The principal effect of the high

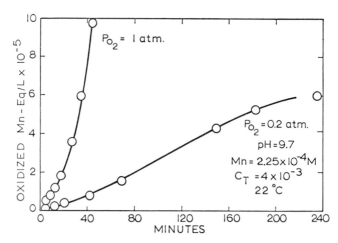

FIGURE 19   INFLUENCE OF OXYGEN PARTIAL PRESSURE
                 ON RATE OF Mn(II) OXYGENATION.

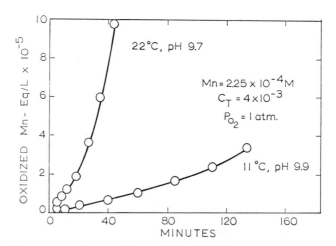

FIGURE 20   INFLUENCE OF TEMPERATURE ON RATE
                 OF Mn(II) OXYGENATION.

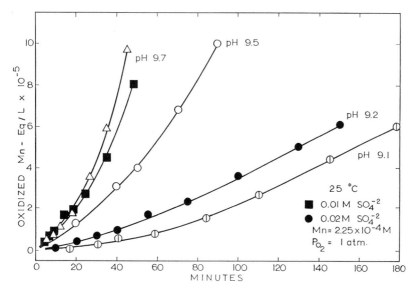

FIGURE 21   OXYGENATION OF Mn(II) IN PRESENCE
              AND ABSENCE OF SULFATE.

concentrations of SO_4^{-2} would seem to be to depress the pH of
the $HCO_3^- - CO_3^{-2}$ solution of pH 9.5. This impression is in
accord with the results noted when the pH was adjusted to the
same value in the presence and absence of 0.01M sulfate. No
pronounced influence upon the oxygenation rate is evident.

Autocatalytic Reaction Model
        The rate at which Mn(II) is removed from oxygen saturated
solutions containing 1.6×10^{-3}M $NaHCO_3$ was observed at three
different pH values; 9.0, 9.3, and 9.5. The conditions of Mn
concentration and alkalinity chosen for these particular experiments are approximately those employed by Hem (48). Small
changes in pH accompanying the oxidation reaction were compensated by using an automatic titrator. The anticipation control of the titrator was adjusted to minimize deviations from
the set pH.
        Experimental results on Mn removal from the oxygenated
$HCO_3^- - CO_3^{-2}$ systems are shown in Figure 22 in which log
soluble Mn is plotted as a function of reaction time. Rates of

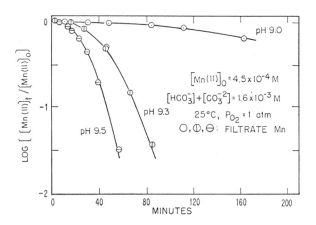

FIGURE 22   REMOVAL OF Mn^{+2} BY OXYGENATION IN
CARBONATE SOLUTIONS.

oxidative removal are seen to be strongly dependent upon pH as
observed by others. The reaction does not follow a first-order
rate law with respect to Mn. If the rate law were:

$$-\frac{[d\ Mn(II)]}{dt} = k_o\,[Mn(II)] + k\,[Mn(II)]\,[MnO_x] \qquad (22\text{-}46)$$

it would be expected that kinetic data for the Mn(II) oxygenation
and removal process could be linearized by plotting $\log\left(\frac{[Mn(II)]_o}{[Mn(II)]_t}\right)$
against t, the reaction time (49). In Figure 23 the rate data
have been replotted according to this interpretation. The reasonably good fit lends support to the autocatalytic model. Similar
results have been obtained for the oxidation process in carbonic
solutions and for the removal and oxidation processes in ammon-
iacal solutions (49, 50). The results are in agreement with a
second-order dependence of the rate upon [OH] (50, 54).

DISCUSSION
     From a thermodynamic viewpoint, Mn(II) is unstable with
respect to air oxidation to MnO_2 or to other of the Mn oxides.
However, oxygen is essentially absent in a number of aqueous
environments wherein equilibria among the various solid and
soluble species of Mn(II) determine total Mn solubility. Further,
as has been seen, even in the presence of oxygen rates of

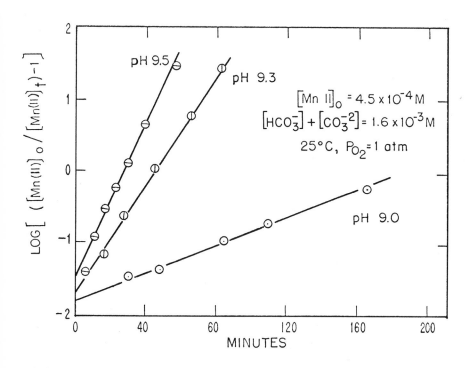

FIGURE 23   DATA OF FIGURE 22 PLOTTED ACCORDING
              TO AUTOCATALYTIC EXPRESSION.

oxidation can be extremely slow. The maximum concentration
of Mn^{+2} in many natural waters is limited by the solubility product of $MnCO_3$ (compare Figures 7 and 8). Thus, in fresh waters
with alkalinities on the order of 100 mg/l, the maximum $[Mn^{+2}]$
at pH 8.0 is about $5 \times 10^{-6}M$. In sea waters, the corresponding
limiting value is about $2 \times 10^{-5}M$. The actual Mn concentrations
of sea water, 10^{-8} to $10^{-7}M$, are considerably below this level.
With low alkalinities and reducing conditions in fresh waters,
solubility may be restricted by high sulfide concentrations.
      It is necessary to consider such species as $MnHCO_3^+$ and

$MnSO_4$ in evaluating total solubility or the distribution of soluble
$Mn(II)$. For example, consider the relative equilibrium concentrations of Mn^{+2}, $MnHCO_3^+$, $MnSO_4$, and $Mn(II)$ - chloro complexes
in sea water by making use of the stability constants for $MnHCO_3^+$
and $MnSO_4$ determined above and recently reported constants
for the species $MnCl^+$, $MnCl_2$, and $MnCl_3^-$ (55). The total soluble
manganese, Mn_t, is approximated by:

$$Mn_t \approx \left[Mn^{+2}\right] + \left[MnCl^+\right] + \left[MnCl_2\right] + \left[MnCl_3^-\right] + \left[MnSO_4\right] + \left[MnHCO_3^+\right]$$

neglecting possible organic complexes for which data are not
available at present. The approximate percentages for the major
species are computed to be:

Mn^{+2}, 21%; $MnCl^+$, 47%, $MnCl_2$, 12%; $MnSO_4$, 18%, and
$MnHCO_3^+$, 2%.

Estimated activity coefficients and a typical sea water composition have been employed in the approximate calculation. Consideration of the reduced activities of HCO_3^- and SO_4^{-2}, because of ion
pair formation (58), has been omitted. Correction for these effects
would reduce the estimated concentrations of $MnSO_4$ and $MnHCO_3^+$.

In contrast, a fresh water of $2 \times 10^{-3}M$ total carbonic species
and 100 mg/l sulfate is estimated to contain the following relative
soluble species at equilibrium: Mn^{+2}, 67%; $MnSO_4$, 20%; and
$MnHCO_3^+$, 13%. For negligible sulfate and chloride, with $2 \times 10^{-3}M$
carbonic species, approximately 85% Mn^{+2} and 15% $MnHCO_3^+$ can
be estimated. For an alkalinity of 300 mg/l, the simple metal
ion would represent about 60% and the complex 40% of the soluble
$Mn(II)$. Hydrolysis of the $Mn(II)$ ion has only relatively small
influence for pH values below 10. The foregoing estimates may
be viewed as merely first approximations in that they reflect only
the available equilibrium data.

In the presence of dissolved O_2 and at sufficiently high pH
values, the products of air oxidation are found to resemble
Mn_3O_4 more nearly than MnO_2. As reported by Drotschmann
and others (39), oxides, such as Mn_3O_4, can release Mn^{+2} upon
even slight acidification. The effect of this release is to increase
the average oxidation state of the solid-phase Mn. As reported
previously, $Mn(II)$ ions can participate in pH-dependent exchange
or sorption reactions on solid MnO_2 (or other metal oxides) (56).
Thus, the intermediate-oxidation-state products of air oxidation

of Mn(II) have been considered as Mn(IV)-Mn(II) combinations.
They can exchange soluble Mn with the solution phase without
involvement in reduction-oxidation reactions. On the other
hand, of course, reduction of these oxides by a number of agents
is thermodynamically possible (compare Figure 12). Actual data
on the oxidation state composition of the Mn oxides found in
different aquatic environments would be useful in obtaining a
better understanding of the relative roles of exchange and reduction phenomena.

The oxygenation of soluble Mn(II) in simple media is autocatalytic and heterogeneous in nature resulting in solid oxidation
products ($MnO_{1.2}$-$MnO_{1.5}$) which are variable in composition and
frequently are colloidal. The principal environmental parameters
for the reaction have been described. They are oxygen concentration, pH, and temperature. In addition, carbonate species concentration influencesthe reaction velocity when Mn concentrations
are sufficiently high.

An important consequence of the autocatalytic character of
Mn oxygenation is that rates of initially homogeneous reaction
must be extremely slow at the typically small concentration of
Mn found in nature. Further, the strong pH dependence leads to
the prediction that the reaction rate must be particularly slow
under the pH conditions found in most natural waters.

As an example of the possible implications of the kinetic
data, a rough estimate of the order of magnitude of the time
required for ca. 90% oxidation of the Mn in sea water has been
made. Calculations indicate an estimated oxidation time on the
order of somewhat more than 10^3 years at the pH and temperature
of sea water and a Mn content of $10^{-7}M$. While Sillen has indicated
that it seems dubious that Mn^{+2} could exist for long periods at
concentrations some 10^9 times the oxidation-reduction equilibrium
value, the kinetics are indeed quite unfavorable and steady-state
levels of Mn^{+2} and MnO_x of the order of 10^{-7} may not appear
unreasonable (14).

The kinetic results suggest the importance of sorption or
exchange processes for establishing the distribution of Mn in
natural waters. This aspect has been investigated recently in
some detail by Hem (57). Goldberg (7) as well as Hem has
suggested a possibly quite important role for sand surfaces and
metal oxide surfaces in catalyzing Mn(II) oxidation by O_2. It
is reasonable to expect that the sorptive properties of clays,
sand, ferric oxides, and other substances might lead to catalyzed

oxidation in addition to the removal of Mn(II) ions from the solution phase.

The influence of $HCO_3^- - CO_3^{-2}$ on oxygenation rates has been demonstrated in the kinetic experiments. In experiments at, e.g, pH 9.5, $2 \times 10^{-3}M$ C_t, and Mn(II) concentrations of $2 \times 10^{-4}M$, such systems are more than a thousand-fold supersaturated with respect to maximum soluble Mn(II) for $MnCO_{3(c)}$. It obviously is difficult to assess the role of $MnHCO_3^+$ formation in the reaction since it would amount to only about 15% of the initially soluble Mn(II). In the case of sulfate, previous calculations have indicated that appreciable concentrations of $MnSO_4$ should be present at equilibrium. The possibly slight influence of sulfate of Mn(II) oxygenation rate (Figure 21) might be the result of an estimated 30-35% of the soluble Mn present as $MnSO_4$.

There is a need for more adequate data on the forms of Mn in surface waters. The available thermodynamic data enable computations of the distribution of Mn(II) among the hexaquo species, chloro complexes, and the sulfate and HCO_3^- complexes. There seems to be few data describing the total soluble Mn in the bivalent form in natural waters. Also, as emphasized by Hutchinson, almost nothing whatever is known of the identity of the solid oxidized Mn components in lakes (7). Evaluation of thermodynamic and kinetic models will require such information.

ACKNOWLEDGEMENTS

The work was supported by Research Grants WP-00013 and WP-00732 from the Public Health Service, USDHEW, Washington, D.C. The author wishes to thank Jessie Lee and Joel Gordon for excellent technical assistance.

LITERATURE CITED

1. Cotton, F.A. and G. Wilkinson, Advanced Inorganic Chemistry, p694, Interscience, New York, N.Y., (1962).

2. Bjerrum, J., et al, Stability Constants, Parts I and II, Chem Soc Special Publ 7, London, England,(1958).

3. Martell, A.E. and M. Calvin, Chemistry of the Metal Chelate Compounds, Prentice-Hall, New York, N.Y., (1953).

4. Charlot G. and D. Bezler, Quantitative Inorganic Analysis, John Wiley and Sons, New York, N.Y. (1957).

5. Mellor, J.W., A Comprehensive Treatise on Inorganic and Theoretical Chemistry, 12, p139, Longmans, Green, and Co., New York, N.Y., (1932).

6. Anderson, A. and E.J. Underwood, Sci Am, 200, 97 (1959).

7. Goldberg, E.D., The Oceans as a Chemical System in The Sea, M.N. Hill, Ed., 2, 4, Interscience, New York, N.Y., (1963).

8. Buser, W. and A. Grutter, Schweiz Mineral Petrog Mitt, 36, 49 (1956).

9. Goldberg, E.D., Chemistry in the Oceans, Proc Inter Oceanog Cong Publ No. 67, pp589-594, Am Assoc Advan Sci, Washington, D.C., (1961).

10. Mero, J.L., Sci Am, 203, 64 (1960).

11. Graham, J.W., Science, 129, 1428 (1959).

12. Drinking Water Standards Revised 1962, PHS Publ No. 956 pp46-47, USDHEW, Washington, D.C. (1962).

13. Meyers, H.C., J Am Water Works Assoc, 53, 579 (1961).

14. Sillen, L.G., The Physical Chemistry of Sea Water, Proc Intern Oceanog Congress, Publ No. 67, pp549-81, Am Assoc Advan Sci, Washington, D.C., (1961).

15. Latimer, W.M., Oxidation Potentials, 2nd Ed., Prentice-Hall, New York, N.Y., (1952).

16. Mellor, J.W., Inorganic and Theoretical Chemistry, 12, p437, Longmans, Green, and Co., New York, N.Y., (1932).

17. Garrels, R.M., et al, Am J Sci, 258, 402 (1960).

18. Nasanen, R., Z Phys Chem, A191, 54 (1942).

19. Hem, J.D., J Chem Eng Data, 8, 99 (1963).

20. Klotz, I., Chemical Thermodynamics, Prentice-Hall, New York, N.Y., (1950).

21. Robinson, R.A. and R.H. Stokes, Electrolyte Solutions, Academic Press, New York, N.Y., (1955).

22. Garrels, R.M., Mineral Equilibria at Low Temperature and Pressure, Harper and Brothers, New York, N.Y., (1960).

23. Walker, A.C., et al, J Am Chem Soc, 49, 1235 (1927).

24. Harned, H.S. and B.B. Owen, The Physical Chemistry of Electrolytic Solutions, 3rd Ed., Reinhold, New York, N.Y., (19

25. Morgan, J.J. and W. Stumm, J Am Water Works Assoc, 57, 107 (1965).

26. Lingane, J.J., Chem Revs, 29, 1 (1941).

27. Perrin, D.D., J Chem Soc, p2197 (1962).

28. Mah, A.D., Thermodynamic Properties of Manganese and Its Compounds, U S Bur Mines, Report of Investigations, 5600 (1960).

29. Fox, R.K., et al, J Am Chem Soc, 63, 1779 (1 941).

30. Kolthoff, I.M., J Phys Cheml,35, 2711 (1931).

31. Ringbom, A., Solubilities of Sulfides, Report to Analytical Section, IUPAC (1953).

32. Causey, R.L. and R.M. Mazo, Anal Chem, 34, 1930 (1962).

33. Clark, W.M., Oxidation-Reduction Potentials of Organic Systems, Williams and Wilkins, Baltimore, Md (1960).

34. Watters, J.J. and I.M. Kolthoff, J Am Chem Soc, 70, 2455 (1948).

35. Lingane, J.J. and D.G. Davis, Anal Chim Acta, 15, 201 (1956).

36. Hochster, R.M. and J.H. Quastel, Arch Biochem Biophys, 136, 132 (1952).

37. Simon, A. and A. Frolich, Z Anorg Allgem Chem, 232, 369 (1937).

38. Moore, T.E., et al, J Am Chem Soc, 72, 856 (1950).

39. Drotschmann, C., Batterien, 14, 128 (1961).

40. Feitknecht, W. and W. Marti, Helv Chim Acta, 28, 129 (1945).

41. Buser, W., et al, Helv Chim Acta, 37, 2322 (1954).

42. Jones, L.H.P. and A.A. Milne, Scotland Min Mag, 31, 283 (1956).

43. Frondel, E., et al, Am Mineralogist, 45, 871 (1960).

44. Feitkneicht, W., et al, Z Anorg Allgem Chem, 316, 154 (1962).

45. Bricker, O.P., PhD Thesis, Harvard University, Cambridge, Mass.,(1964).

46. Morgan, J.J. and J.J. Smith, 14th Southern Water Resources and Pollution Control Conf, pp 148-164, Chapel Hill, N.C., (1965).

47. Nichols, A.R. and J.H. Walton, J Am Chem Soc, 64, 1866 (1942).

48. Hem, J.D., U S Geol Survey Water Supply Paper 1667-A, pp 52-59 (1963).

49. Morgan, J.J., PhD Thesis, Harvard University, Cambridge, Mass., (1964).

50. Morgan J.J. and W. Stumm, Oxygenation of Aqueous Manganese (II), Div Water Waste Chem, Am Chem Soc, 145th Meeting, New York, N.Y., (1963).

51. Joint Committee on Chemical Analysis by Powder Diffraction Methods, X-ray Powder Data File, Am Soc Test Materials, Philadelphia, Penna., (1962).

52. Huffman, R.E. and N. Davidson, J Am Chem Soc, 78, 4836 (1956).

53. Stumm, W. and G. F. Lee, Ind Eng Chem, 53, 143 (1961).

54. Morgan, J. J. and W. Stumm, Proc Second Intern Conf
    Water Pollution Res, pp 103-131, Pergamon Press, New York,
    N. Y., (1965).

55. Morris, D. F. C. and E. L. Short, J Chem Soc, p 5148 (1961).

56. Morgan J. J. and W. Stumm, J Colloid Sci, 19, 347 (1964).

57. Hem, J. D. , U S Geol Survey Water Supply Paper 1667-B,
    pp 14-33 (1964).

58. Garrels, R. M. and M. E. Thompson, Am J Sci, 260, 57 (1962).

59. Lingane, J. J. and R. Karplus, Anal Chem, 18, 191 (1946).

DISCUSSION
      DR. RIEMAN: May we have some discussion of this paper ?
      MR. J. D. HEM (U S Geological Survey): It is gratifying to
me to be in agreement with most of these values that you had in
your paper. Incidentally, I was very much interested in it
throughout. The question I had was when you were conducting
your studies of the effect of sulfate on the oxidation rate, whether
these solutions contained bicarbonate also.
      DR. MORGAN: The experiments on the effects of other ions
are carried out in carbonate, bicarbonate buffer, usually $2 \times 10^{-3}M$
sometimes higher. One experimental difficulty is that when you
use the carbonate buffer system you may precipitate $MnCO_3$. We
have actually observed this.
      MR. HEM: I don't remember what conditions in my solutions
were any more, but they may not have had bicarbonate in them.
      DR. MORGAN: One thing concerns me. Our results are in
better agreement when we talk about experiments which you have
made in bicarbonate systems and in poorer agreement when we
talk about experiments which you have made in the absence of
bicarbonate. The explanation, we believe , is that you adjusted
pH by the addition of KOH. We tried this and found it most fru-
strating, because the pH fluctuated from about 6 to 12, and we
observed oxidation. This may be part of the explanation.
      MR. G. J. CRITS (Crane Company): Messrs. Gurney and
West at Lake Charles, Louisiana, at a water treatment plant
where iron is being removed from a well water, show that the

reaction time is cut down by about a half when 1 mg/l copper sulfate is added. Did you try this catalytic effect by copper?

DR. MORGAN: They oxidized Mn with Cl_2 in the paper you are talking about and observed the strong influence of copper on the oxidation rate. We made experiments at pH conditions where we observed slow air oxidation in the absence of copper and equally slow oxidation in the presence of copper. We tried to use concentrations truly catalytic in nature.

One trouble you run into is the formation of copper hydroxides. There may be precipitation. When we begin to do our work on chlorine we are anxious to look at the effect of copper, because all indications show there should be a catalytic effect. Stumm and Lee noticed it very clearly for ferrous iron oxygenation.

It may be we didn't push the copper concentration far enough and these are inconclusive experiments. The Mn was $10^{-4}M$, and we used copper (II) concentrations of no larger than $10^{-5}M$ with copper nitrate as the salt.

DR. HEALY (University of California): I am delighted about that thousand years you mentioned, but there is a question I still have. Were you able to satisfactorily incorporate CO_2 equilibria in the ocean?

DR. MORGAN: No.

DR. HEALY: What effect will that have and what measures of oxygen pressures at depth were you able to use? I don't know how people measure these. And finally, what [Mn] would you expect in river water as it goes into the ocean? How is that related to Mn(II) concentrations you actually find in the ocean?

DR. MORGAN: The concentration of Mn in river water is variable. I show this in the paper. It can be as low as far below the limit of detection or it can be as high as a few mg/l or $10^{-5}M$ range.

What you observe in the ocean can be justified in terms of available data on Mn. There are all sorts of complexities. One, upon entering the sea, soluble Mn may become greater as it is desorbed from clays. There is a nice piece of work done on this 30 years ago, where it was shown that as fresh waters mixed with those of the estuary sea water the Mn increased because of the competition between high concentrations of Ca and Mg in the ocean and the change in the environment.

As far as oxygen partial pressure is concerned, you can formulate the appropriate kinetic rate expression; oxygen concentration data in the ocean are variable. But if we take on the order of 0.2 atm for the oxygen partial pressure, we can make a rough calculation.

The third thing is the most troublesome. I am not very well informed about the effects of pressures on carbonate equilibria. I made some calculations of whether or not there would be much Mn in the form of $MnCO_3$, and I concluded that since the carbonate is so well complexed, there is very little carbonate left over to complex the small concentrations of total Mn; that is one thing.

The second is even if there were much carbonate, the Mn would be small. The chloride complex appears to be predominant. I don't know what the effect of these complexes would be on the rate law.

And the last factor is that Mn in sea water is very much below the $MnCO_3$ solubility limit. If my calculations are correct or close to correct, you should have 10^{-5} or 10^{-6} in sea water. Where you have less than this there would be no $MnCO_3$ expected.

Taking all of these things into consideration, it looks as though something between 500 and 5000 years might not be too far off.

John D. Hem
U. S. Geological Survey
Menlo Park, California

EQUILIBRIUM CHEMISTRY OF IRON IN GROUND WATER

Differences in solid mineral assemblages and impaired circulation of water often bring about chemical variation in ground water. The solution of iron may be favored at some places whereas the precipitation of iron may be favored at other places. Mixing of water from all the water saturated material to which a well is open may yield a water that is objectionably high in dissolved iron. At the same time, encrustation in the well may interfere with water movement. Exposure of reduced iron minerals, such as pyrite, to an oxidizing condition or of oxidized iron minerals, such as limonite, to reducing conditions, brings large amounts of iron into solution. If bicarbonate species are present, the solubility of iron may be controlled by the solubility of siderite under conditions where both pyrite and limonite are unstable. Large amounts of iron can be present in solution at equilibrium with siderite.

Equilibrium relations have explained the occurrence of iron in ground waters in portions of the Atlantic Coastal Plain and Mississippi Embayment geologic regions of the United States. These relations also aid in explaining encrustation of wells with siderite in certain irrigated areas of West Pakistan. Proper well construction and operation techniques may aid in avoiding problems resulting from iron-bearing ground water.

APPLICABILITY OF EQUILIBRIUM CONCEPTS
The chemical behavior of iron in underground waters often seems complex and puzzling. For example, two adjacent wells may yield water of similar composition except that one is high in iron content whereas the other is low or the iron content may fluctuate with time in an apparently irrational way. Besides the problem of treatment of the pumped water to decrease the iron content, some wells present additional problems of declining yields caused by encrustation of iron compounds on well screens or at other openings where water enters the well.

A sufficient understanding to explain the observed behavior of iron in ground water and to predict its occurrence can be obtained from suitable applications of principles of chemical equilibrium. Difficulties in sampling and in extrapolating laboratory results to field conditions prevent completely rigorous application of the equilibrium model but it has been generally useful in explaining field observations.

In this discussion the physical and chemical features of ground-water systems will be outlined in a general way and illustrated with specific examples. Wider application of chemical principles in planning well construction and operation offers promise of coping more effectively with problems related to the high iron content of some ground water.

GROUND-WATER CIRCULATION
Water at and near the land surface flows in response to imposed energy potentials. That portion of the circulating water which is present in the zone where interconnected pores and other openings of rock strata are saturated completely, is commonly termed ground water. It moves from areas of recharge or replenishment toward areas of discharge in response to hydraulic head or potential. The bodies of rock capable of transmitting and yielding water are termed aquifers. That portion of the ground-water body which extends to a depth of a few thousand feet is of greatest interest to man as a source of readily recoverable water although locally it contains undesirable quantities of dissolved ions.

In general, recharge to the ground-water body represents water from precipitation moving downward through the soil and subsoil or rock to the saturated zone. Ground water moves at a relatively slow rate through the saturated section following

a pattern that often is represented oy a simple flow net. When
this general picture is examined in more detail, however, it
becomes evident that water-bearing rocks transmit water in
a non-uniform way. Flow is more rapid through the coarse-
grained, well-sorted detrital sediments and slower where the
grains are fine or where interstices are partly closed as by
cementation. Movement of water generally occurs more freely
along the bedding surfaces of rocks than across them. Crystalline rocks may transmit water only along fractures whereas
carbonate rocks may transmit water principally through channels
enlarged by solution. Vertical circulation of ground water
often is considerably impaired. In an artesian system, the
drastic impairment of vertical movement confines ground water
and causes development of the pressure that is the distinguishing
feature of the artesian aquifer.

Ground water may discharge naturally where the zone of
saturation intersects the land surface. It may be withdrawn
at a well where the hydraulic potential is artificially lowered
and water movement toward the well thereby is induced.

A well generally penetrates a considerable distance into
the aquifer wherefrom the water represents a mixture of that
moving in various parts of the adjacent saturated zone. The
mixture will contain a larger portion of water from the more
permeable zones than from the less permeable ones. As the
head around the well declines with continued pumping, movements
of water considerably different from the initial natural flow
patterns will take place.

Operation of the pump may change conditions in the water
in the well bore by introducing air or by causing dissolved gases
to be released. The latter effect could cause an increase in
pH of the solution when CO_2 is released. Even when it is not
being pumped, the well bore provides a short circuit through
which waters from different zones that do not naturally contact
each other, may have opportunity for intimate mixing.

GEOCHEMICAL SYSTEMS IN GROUND-WATER AQUIFERS

In the usual ground-water system a relatively large
surface area of solid minerals is exposed to slowly circulating
water. A tendency toward establishment of an equilibrium
between dissolved ions and solid minerals is promoted by
these conditions. Non-homogeneous composition of the aquifer,
however, can be expected to influence the chemical composition
of the circulating water as well as the flow patterns that control

with aquifer materials. The nature of solid mineral alteration products and the composition of the solution in an aquifer are controlled by the total environment. For example, near sources of recharge the ground water contains dissolved oxygen and CO_2 replenished by contact with the atmosphere and soil air. Under these conditions carbonates tend to dissolve and oxidized iron minerals are generally stable. In sections of the saturated zone far separated from the air, especially where organic matter may be present to consume any dissolved oxygen, reducing conditions are to be expected wherein reduced iron minerals will be stable. Transitional zones and the seasonal rise and fall of the water table impose oxidizing conditions on reduced minerals and vice versa. Thus, iron-bearing minerals are attacked and parts of the saturated zone may at times contain water high in dissolved iron.

Wells obviously may penetrate strata containing water of differing composition. Solutions entering the well bore, however, are mixed together in the water discharged through the pump. Hence, composition of water samples from a well that withdraws water from two or more zones of differing chemical composition may not help much in understanding the geochemistry of the ground water. Usually, in studying an area, wells can be found which are constructed so that they intercept only shallow or only deep ground water. In such places, some insight into the changes in composition with depth can be obtained.

THE Eh- pH DIAGRAM

The actual solubility of iron under different conditions at equilibrium can be calculated conveniently with the results shown graphically by means of the Eh-pH or stability-field diagram. Such diagrams are prepared using the Nernst equation and other chemical thermodynamic relationships and data. The procedures are described by Garrels (1) and have been used by the writer in other reports. The two variables, Eh and pH, can be used to define areas of "stability" for compounds whose free energies are known if other pertinent conditions are specified. For iron oxide or hydroxide species, the only other variable is the dissolved iron activity. It is assumed the conditions of significance are those in which water itself is stable at 25°C and 1 atm pressure.

A diagram of iron-species stability fields for a total dissolved iron activity of 2×10^{-7} molal was given by Hem and Cropper (2). If additional concentration lines are shown, the diagram can be

used as an indication of the solubility of iron in the presence
of the assumed solids. The indicated solids are those stable
under the specified conditions of pH and Eh.

Natural waters contain other solutes, notably dissolved
CO_2 and S species, which are involved in precipitation or
solution of other solid forms of iron. To represent clearly
the effects of these solutes in a two-dimensional diagram,
however, requires that a constant single activity for each be
used. The results of different amounts of dissolved CO_2 and S
species can be represented by using different diagrams each
with a single activity of these constituents.

To demonstrate the principal factors involved in establishing equilibrium iron solubility, three Eh-pH diagrams have
been prepared and are shown in Figures 1, 2, and 3. A constant
activity of 10^{-4} molal of sulfur was used (equivalent to about
9.6 mg/l SO_4^{-2}). One diagram is for a total dissolved CO_2
species activity of 10^{-4} molal, one for 10^{-3} molal, and one for
10^{-2} molal. These are equivalent to HCO_3^- activities at pH 8.2
of 6.1, 61, and 610 mg/l, respectively. Iron solubility lines
were drawn for each at molalities of 10^{-5}, 10^{-4}, 10^{-3}, 10^{-2},
10^{-1}, 10^0, and 10^1. The areas on the diagram where iron solubility is below 10 molal were identified by using distinctive
patterns for the species $Fe(OH)_3$ (representing limonite or
other hydrated ferric oxide minerals), $FeCO_3$ (siderite),
$Fe(OH)_2$, and FeS_2 (pyrite). Increasing or decreasing the
sulfur activity would have relatively little effect on the positions
of the pyrite boundaries. (See equations 23-1 to 23-18).

The positions of the boundaries were determined from the
Nernst Equation and the mass law. Equilibrium constants and
standard potentials were calculated from standard free-energy
values for the species considered. The free-energy data were
obtained from Latimer (3).

The fundamental equations are:

$$\ln K = \frac{-\Delta F^O}{RT} \qquad\qquad (23-19)$$

$$E^O = \frac{-\Delta F^O}{n\,\mathcal{F}} \qquad\qquad (23-20)$$

$$Eh = E^O + \frac{RT}{n\,\mathcal{F}} \ln \frac{oxid}{red} \qquad\qquad (23-21)$$

where $\ln K$ = natural log of equilibrium constant

ΔF^O = standard free-energy change in reaction

R = gas constant
T = temperature in degrees Kelvin
E^O = standard potential
n = number of electrons exchanged per ion of reactant
     reduced
$\not{F}$ = Faraday constant
Eh = redox potential
$\ln \dfrac{oxid}{red}$ = natural log of mass-law statement of the activities of
     reactants and products

The European sign convention is used in these calculations;
that is, increasingly positive potentials are considered to
represent increasingly oxidizing conditions.

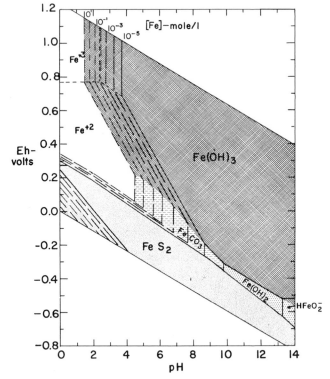

FIGURE 1   SOLUBILITY OF IRON IN RELATION TO
                  pH AND Eh AT 25°C AND 1 ATM. TOTAL
                  DISSOLVED SULFUR 10^{-4}M; BICARBONATE
                  SPECIES 10^{-4}M.

Chemical equilibria considered in making the diagrams include:

$$Fe^{+3} + e^- = Fe^{+2} \qquad (23\text{-}1)$$

$$Fe^{+3} + H_2O = FeOH^{+2} + H^+ \qquad (23\text{-}2)$$

$$Fe(OH)_{3(c)} + 2H^+ = FeOH^{+2} + 2H_2O \qquad (23\text{-}3)$$

$$Fe(OH)_{3(c)} + 3H^+ = Fe^{+3} + 3H_2O \qquad (23\text{-}4)$$

$$Fe(OH)_{3(c)} + 3H^+ + e^- = Fe^{+2} + 3H_2O \qquad (23\text{-}5)$$

$$Fe(OH)_{3(c)} + HCO_3^- + 2H^+ + e^- = FeCO_{3(c)} + 3H_2O \qquad (23\text{-}6)$$

$$Fe(OH)_{3(c)} + H^+ + e^- = Fe(OH)_{2(c)} + H_2O \qquad (23\text{-}7)$$

$$Fe(OH)_{3(c)} + e^- = HFeO_2^- + H_2O \qquad (23\text{-}8)$$

$$FeCO_{3(c)} + H^+ = Fe^{+2} + HCO_3^- \qquad (23\text{-}9)$$

$$FeCO_{3(c)} + 2H_2O = Fe(OH)_{2(c)} + CO_3^{-2} + 2H^+ \qquad (23\text{-}10)$$

$$FeCO_{3(c)} + 2SO_4^{-2} + 17H^+ + 14e^- = FeS_{2(c)} + 8H_2O + HCO_3^- \qquad (23\text{-}11)$$

$$Fe(OH)_{2(c)} = HFeO_2^- + H^+ \qquad (23\text{-}12)$$

$$Fe(OH)_{2(c)} + 2SO_4^{-2} + 18H^+ + 14e^- = FeS_{2(c)} + 10H_2O \qquad (23\text{-}13)$$

$$Fe^{+2} + 2SO_4^{-2} + 16H^+ + 14e^- = FeS_{2(c)} + 8H_2O \qquad (23\text{-}14)$$

$$Fe^{+2} + 2HSO_4^- + 14H^+ + 14e^- = FeS_{2(c)} + 8H_2O \qquad (23\text{-}15)$$

$$FeS_{2(c)} + 4H^+ + 2e^- = Fe^{+2} + 2H_2S \text{ (aq)} \qquad (23\text{-}16)$$

$$Fe^{+2} + 2S_{(c)} + 2e^- = FeS_{2(c)} \qquad (23\text{-}17)$$

$$HFeO_2^- + 2SO_4^{-2} + 19H^+ + 14e^- = FeS_{2(c)} + 10H_2O \qquad (23\text{-}18)$$

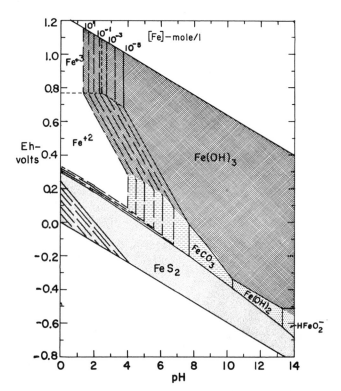

FIGURE 2   SOLUBILITY OF IRON IN RELATION TO
                pH AND Eh AT 25°C AND 1 ATM. TOTAL
                DISSOLVED SULFUR 10^{-4}M; BICARBONATE
                SPECIES 10^{-3}M.

From Figure 1 it can be seen that iron concentrations below
0.5 mg/l are to be expected over a wide area of the $Fe(OH)_3$
and FeS_2 regions. The conditions in an aerated water or a
water in a strongly reduced environment, near neutral pH, are
favorable for only very small dissolved-iron contents. Within
the siderite region of the diagram, however, iron becomes
relatively soluble at pH values between 5.0 and 9.0.

Figure 1 indicates that the solubility of iron at pH 7.0 is a
little less than 10^{-3}M (around 50 mg/l) between Eh values of
- 0.14 and +0.03. The HCO_3^- activity assumed for this diagram
is 10^{-4}M or about 6 mg/l.

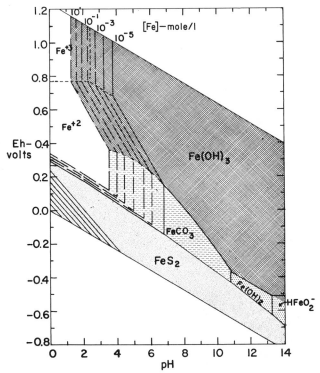

FIGURE 3   SOLUBILITY OF IRON IN RELATION TO
             pH AND Eh AT 25°C AND 1 ATM. TOTAL
             DISSOLVED SULFUR 10^{-4}M; BICARBONATE
             SPECIES 10^{-2}M.

Figure 2 shows what happens when all other parameters
remain constant but HCO_3^- activity becomes 10^{-3}M (61 mg/l).
Here the solubility of iron at pH 7.0 is decreased 10-fold to
near 5 mg/l, but the Eh range over which this value would occur
is widened from -0.15 to +0.08 v. In Figure 3 where the HCO_3^-
activity is 610 mg/l, a little less than 0.5 mg/l of iron could
remain in solution at pH 7.0 whereas Eh values range still more
widely from -0.16 to -0.12 v. Between the stability regions for
Fe(OH)$_3$ and pyrite there lies an area of relatively high iron
solubility. This area may be reached either by reduction of
ferric species or oxidation of pyrite. Within this region iron
solubility is controlled only by pH and HCO_3^- activity and is

independent of Eh because the iron is in the same oxidation state in solution, Fe^{+2}, as in the solid. If CO_2 is absent or present in very small amounts, the solubility of iron in the region between the pryite and $Fe(OH)_3$ fields is even higher than in Figure 1.

APPLICATIONS TO NATURAL CONDITIONS

The specific capacity of a well, that is, the rate at which water can be pumped per foot of lowering of the head often tends to decrease with increasing length of service. In many areas the relative shortness of the useful life of wells is a significant economic problem. The decline in yield commonly results from deposits of $CaCO_3$, iron oxide, and sometimes other materials around screen openings, in the gravel pack, or on the surface of water-yielding rock if the well is uncased. Specific instances of encrustation have been described for wells in New Jersey by Linn (4) and at Lansing, Michigan, by Erickson and Wright (5). A study of well stimulation by Koenig gives some idea as to the widespread nature of the problem and methods used for coping with it (6).

Precipitates containing iron could form in wells through mixing of waters having incompatible chemical characteristics or as a result of changes in pH or Eh resulting from the act of pumping. These precipitates may be associated also with growth of microbiota occurring in the well.

The mass-law statement of the solubility equilibrium for siderite is:

$$\frac{\left[H\bar{C}O_3 \right]\left[Fe^{+2} \right]}{\left[H^+ \right]} = K = 0.46 \qquad (23\text{-}22)$$

In the solubility equilibrium for calcite, the equilibrium constant is considerably greater:

$$\frac{\left[H\bar{C}O_3 \right]\left[Ca^{+2} \right]}{\left[H^+ \right]} = K = 97 \qquad (23\text{-}23)$$

A solution at equilibrium with both solids simultaneously would have an activity of Ca^{+2} about 200 times that of Fe^{+2}. Two solutions which started with an equal supply of dissolved CO_2 and reached equilibrium in separate environments, one where siderite was present and one where calcite was present, would have very different pH values. When the two waters were mixed,

a solution strongly supersaturated with respect to siderite
would generally result.

To demonstrate, assume solutions I and II both of which are
continually exposed to a gas phase with a partial pressure of
CO_2 of 10^{-2} atm. Solution I enters a stratum containing siderite
and no calcite. By means of simultaneous equations for siderite
solubility, CO_2 dissociation, and ionic balance it can be calculated
that, at equilibrium, the pH value would be 6.57, activity of
$H\bar{C}O_3$ $10^{-3.28}$ molal or 32 mg/l, and activity of Fe^{+2}, $10^{-3.64}$
molal or 13 mg/l. Figure 4 is a graphical representation of
conditions which will occur at equilibrium in the presence of
siderite.

Solution II, exposed to the same partial pressure of CO_2,
enters a stratum in which calcite is plentiful. Using similar
calculations it can be shown that at equilibrium the pH value
of this solution would be 7.37, activity of $H\bar{C}O_3$, $10^{-2.48}$ molal
or 202 mg/l, and activity of Ca^{+2}, $10^{-2.90}$ molal or 50 mg/l.

In calculations of this type, the mass-law equations are
based on thermodynamic concentrations and the ionic balance
equations are based on stoichiometric concentrations. The
activity coefficients for the ions were assumed as a first
approximation to be unity from which the calculated results
were used to compute an ionic strength of the solution. This
value in turn was used with the Debye-Hückel equation to calculate approximate activity coefficients for the ions. The equilibrium calculation was repeated with these approximate coefficients to obtain a more exact set of values. The process was
repeated until final values of satisfactory accuracy were obtained.
This recycling calculation procedure is described by Garrels (1).

If now solutions I and II are intercepted by a well and
thereby are mixed in equal proportions, the stoichiometric concentrations (calculated from the activity values) are:

Solution	$H\bar{C}O_3$	Fe^{+2}	Ca^{+2}	I
I	33	15	-	0.00097
II	215	-	68	0.0051
Mixture	124	7.5	34	0.003

The final activities of the mixture, before any chemical
reaction occurs, are $[H\bar{C}O_3]$ = 118 mg/l or $10^{-2.71}$ molal,
and $[Fe]$ = 6.0 mg/l or $10^{-3.97}$ molal. In the partial pressure
of CO_2 remains constant, the mixture will still be $10^{-3.50}$ molal
with respect to H_2CO_3. The pH values of the mixture can be

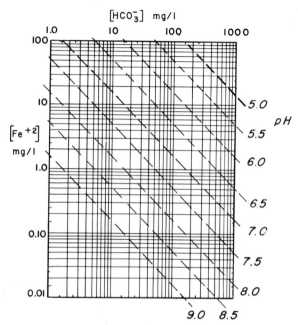

FIGURE 4   EQUILIBRIUM SOLUBILITY OF FERROUS
              IRON IN THE PRESENCE OF SIDERITE;
              25°C, 1 ATM.

calculated from the dissociation constant for H_2CO_3 and the
activities which equals 7.14.

From Figure 4 it is evident that this mixture will be unstable
with respect to siderite at pH 7.14. In the presence of 118 mg/l
HCO_3^- activity, only about 1.0 mg/l of iron can be retained in
solution at equilibrium rather than the 6.0 mg/l present.

The conditions assumed for this calculation were simplified
to include an assumption of constant partial pressure for CO_2.
In ground-water systems such a condition is probably not usually
attained. If no gas phase is present, however, the components
of the mixture would probably differ more widely from each
other and produce a still more unstable combination.

Of course, if the redox potential rises owing to aeration,
the stable solid will be the even less soluble $Fe(OH)_3$. Both
the carbonate precipitation and oxidation reactions are slow
compared with reactions that can be conveniently studied in the

laboratory unless the solutions are grossly out of equilibrium.
It should be borne in mind, however, that the encrustation builds
up over months and years and in the course of time may effectively seal the well.

Besides effects of mixing, the act of pumping itself may tend
to change the composition of water in and around a well. As a
result of turbulence and head losses, some CO_2 may be released
from solution, which tends to raise the pH of the effluent above
the level it would otherwise have had. This release of CO_2
implies the generation of bubbles of gas at precipitation sites.
Positive evidence that this is occurring is difficult to obtain.
Probably the release of CO_2 during pumping is seldom an
important effect insofar as the behavior of iron is concerned.
An effect of greater potential importance is the tendency for
O_2 to be introduced from the air thus bringing about a higher
Eh in the upper part of the saturated zone near the well, and
especially in the dewatered zone, than would normally occur.

Construction and Operation of Wells

In regions where iron-bearing ground waters occur some
of the foregoing principles possibly can be applied to construct
and operate wells in such a way as to minimize the problem.
For example, in Camp, Morris, Titus, and Franklin counties
in northeast Texas, the sedimentary rocks can be considered
to comprise three layers with each having characteristic geochemical conditions with respect to iron (13). The uppermost
layer extends from the land surface to a depth of 50' to 100' in
most places but generally does not extend much below the
lowest seasonal position of the water table. In this zone the
water is oxygenated and essentially all the iron minerals are
oxidized species such as limonite. Wells ending in this zone
yield water low in iron, pH, and dissolved solids. In the deepest
layer, extending downward from a depth of about 200' below
land surface, the redox potentials evidently are very low wherein
reduced iron minerals, such as pyrite, are stable. The water
from this zone generally is low in dissolved iron and may give
other evidence of reducing conditions, such as low sulfate
content or presence of H_2S. Between the oxidized and reduced
layers is a third layer which is an intermediate zone within
which oxidation of the reduced iron minerals is occurring now.
Water from this zone commonly is high in dissolved iron.

Although in some places these layers or zones may be
related to the stratigraphy, they are essentially of geochemical

origin. They are related to currently existing patterns of
weathering, erosion, and ground-water circulation as well as
to the texture and other characteristics of the rocks.

Thus, a well which is drilled deeply enough and screened
only opposite the reduced portion of the aquifer can obtain
water low in iron where wells of intermediate depth or those
screened at all depths obtain water high in iron. Wells in the
oxidized zone also obtain water low in iron but yields are
generally small and fluctuate seasonally. Figure 5 shows by
means of bar diagrams the chemical composition of water
from the 3 zones in this area.

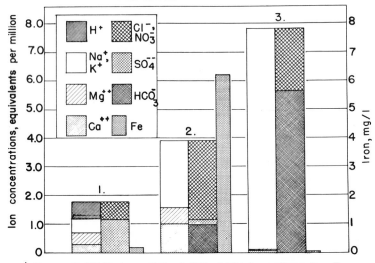

I. Dug well 23 ft. deep, 8.5 mi. SE of Pittsburg, Camp Co., Tex.

2. Well 90 ft. deep, 1 mi. south of Mt. Vernon, Franklin Co., Tex.

3. City well no. 4, 670 ft. deep, Pittsburg, Camp Co., Tex.

FIGURE 5   CHEMICAL ANALYSES OF GROUND WATER
                  FROM DIFFERENT DEPTHS, CAMP AND
                  FRANKLIN COUNTIES, TEXAS.

From the Eh-pH diagrams it is evident that an intermediate
region of high solubility of iron exists between the domains of
pyrite and $Fe(OH)_2$. This region corresponds to the depths
within which active oxidation of reduced iron species occurs
in ground water environments of northeastern Texas.

The degree to which stratification in Eh might take place
in an aquifer system would be dependent on many factors. It
would seem, therefore, that there might be more tendency for
stratification where the circulation of water is slow, especially
in a vertical direction. The extent to which conditions like
those in northeastern Texas might occur elsewhere is unknown,
but there are somewhat similar sediments over wide areas of
the Mississippi Embayment geologic province.

In the Gulf Coastal Plain, at Lafayette, La., Turcan and
Fader reported that ground water at depths less than 300' was
high in iron (7 to 9 mg/l) but that deeper water had considerably
less iron, in some places less than 1.0 mg/l (7). Jones and
others reported that reduced iron minerals including pyrite,
marcasite, and siderite were common in the deeper sediments
of southwestern Louisiana (8).

Occurrence of iron in ground waters of the Atlantic Coastal
Plain in Maryland has been studied by Barnes and Back (9).
They reported limonite to be the principal iron mineral in all
the sediments of their area and attributed high iron contents to
the contact of $Fe(OH)_3$ with relatively reducing ground water.
Iron concentrations do not systematically decrease with depth
in that area.

The sediments of all these areas contain considerable
amounts of glauconite. The absence of thermodynamic data,
however, precludes systematic consideration of glauconite as
a possible source of iron in ground water.

In general, troublesome concentrations of iron in ground
water can be expected to occur when either oxidizing water
circulates in contact with reduced iron minerals (especially
pyrite) or when reducing water circulates through strata containing oxidized iron minerals. Both conditions can occur
naturally. Where evidence, such as drill cores or cuttings,
provides information on aquifer mineralogy, iron-bearing
waters may be avoided by placement or performation of well
casing so as to avoid zones of iron-mineral instability.

The operation of a pump may induce considerable vertical
movement of water in the vicinity of the well. Thus, a well
could yield water nearly free of iron when first placed in use
but increasing iron concentrations might develop with time.
Such behavior can be explained as a result of changing redox
potentials in solutions in the aquifer in contact with iron-
bearing minerals. If water levels are drawn down excessively
during pumping, air and oxidizing conditions may be imposed

on the sediments near the well screen. Large fluctuations in water level, resulting from heavy pumping alternating with periods of shutdowns, can cause oxidation of iron minerals followed by reduction and solution in reducing water as the partly dewatered cone around the well expands and contracts. Some of these effects perhaps can be minimized by proper pumping regimes which avoid large fluctuations in withdrawal rates.

Problems of well encrustation might be anticipated, as pointed out earlier, when a well intercepts water of different composition from different depths. The city of Wichita, Kansas has given some consideration to avoiding this problem by screening supply wells at only one horizon (10). Although precipitation may not be quantitative when waters are mixed in a well, the large supply of a supersaturated solution per unit area screen may still result in a troublesome encrustation. In wells where there are encrustation problems, some benefit might be obtained by continuous pump operation so that the unstable mixture is removed before chemical reactions have time to occur.

Rather severe cases of corrosion and encrustation have been experienced in wells in certain areas of West Pakistan. The wells in question are located in the irrigated Indus Plains and penetrate several hundred feet of saturated alluvium. They are pumped at high discharge rates. The composition of the ground water is non-uniform both areally and with depth. In one well, the discharge declined to only about one-fourth of its original value during a two-year period. Slotted steel well casings removed from certain wells gave evidence of deposition of siderite, some calcite, and other materials as well as considerable corrosion.

More information has been obtained on the nature of chemical equilibria in water from the problem areas of West Pakistan than has been available in most places. A preliminary report has been prepared by Clarke and Barnes and more detailed computations and a more complete report are being prepared by these investigators (11). The brief discussion here is based on the preliminary report.

Field measurements of pH in discharges of 6 wells of one area gave values ranging from 7.6 to 7.7. Measurements of Eh gave values ranging from 0.03 to 0.08 v. These points fall in the siderite fields of Figures 2 and 3. Determinations of HCO_3 gave activities ranging from about $10^{-2.5}$ to $10^{-2.2}$ molal.

Iron contents generally were between 10^{-5} and 10^{-4} molal. The water of 4 of the 6 wells was supersaturated with respect to siderite. In all the wells, the water also was supersaturated with respect to calcite. If the water is corrosive, some iron is derived from the well casing wherein activities of dissolved iron thereby may be increased near the casing surfaces and even more favorable conditions for siderite precipitation established. The complexity of the chemical relations is indicated by the presence of small amounts of sulfide, copper, and manganese in solution in the water. Calculations show that supersaturation with respect to Cu_2O, CuO, malachite, and various sulfide phases also needs consideration (14).

Calcite and iron minerals commonly occur naturally as a result of mixing of ground waters of differing composition, or other processes affecting pH and Eh. That mixing which takes place in or around a well should give rise to such deposits is, of course, not particularly surprising.

Microbiologic Factors

Deposition of $Fe(OH)_3$ and solution of iron often are associated with the activities of bacteria. Members of genera Crenothrix and Leptothrix are found in deposits of $Fe(OH)_3$ in wells. The role of these bacteria probably lies in promoting the oxidation of ferrous iron in an oxygenated environment. This reaction is slow enough that it does not normally reach equilibrium within the time mixed components remain within a flowing or pumping well. Bacteria may speed the reaction to the extent that a greater part of the iron is precipitated in the well.

Suter has indicated that Crenothrix can exist only in water where dissolved-oxygen concentrations range from 1 mg/l to 4 mg/l (12). Leptothrix is tolerant of higher oxygen content but both species require some oxygen.

Deposits of $Fe(OH)_3$ in drainage-tile lines laid to lower the water table in agricultural lands have been described as containing evidence of bacterial colonies (13). The solutions intercepted by such drain structures may resemble in some of their properties, the stratified iron-bearing waters that are intercepted at depth in some water wells.

Reduction and oxidation of sulfur species also are associated with bacteria. Some of these reactions remove iron from solution or release it to solution.

In general, the reactions in which bacteria are involved are those which are thermodynamically possible in the environments where they take place. The behavior of iron in ground water, therefore, can be indicated by means of an equilibrium model despite the influence of biota. Biologic agencies operating in natural systems should then conform more closely to the equilibrium condition.

Economic Implications
    The expenses of coping with excessive iron in water obtained from wells, with losses in well yield resulting from encrustation and corrosion, and with the resulting costs of well-renovation or replacement are substantial. Additional efforts to understand the hydrochemistry of iron-bearing water would seem to be amply justified.
    Particularly, further studies of geochemical relations between ground water and iron-bearing minerals should be made to attain a more widespread working grasp of the chemical equilibria and reaction rates involved in iron solution and deposition in ground-water systems. Ultimately, this information will aid in improving the efficiency of well construction and operation.

ACKNOWLEDGEMENT
    Publication was authorized by the Director, U.S. Geological Survey, Washington, D.C.

LITERATURE CITED
1. Garrels, R.M., Mineral Equilibria, Harper and Bros, New York, N.Y., (1960).

2. Hem, J.D. and W.H. Cropper, U S Geol Survey Water-Supply Paper 1459-A, (1959).

3. Latimer, W.M., Oxidation Potentials, 2nd Ed, Prentice-Hall, New York, N.Y., (1952).

4. Linn, G.L.E., J Am Water Works Assoc, 46, 534 (1954).

5. Erickson, C.R. and R.C. Wright, J Am Water Works Assoc, 49, 817 (1957).

6. Koenig, L., J Am Water Works Assoc, 52, 333 (1960).

7. Turcan, A.N., Jr. and S.W. Fader, Louisiana Dept of Pub Works, Water Resources Pamphlet 6, (1959).

8. Jones, P.H., et al, U S Geol Survey Water-Supply Paper 1364, (1956).

9. Barnes, I. and W. Back, J Geol, 72, 435 (1964).

10. Lawrence, R.E. and R.H. Hess, J Am Water Works Assoc, 55, 1081 (1963).

11. Clarke, F.E. and I. Barnes, Preliminary Evaluation of Corrosion and Encrustation Mechanisms in Tube Wells of Indus Plains, West Pakistan, U S Geol Survey Open-File Report (1964).

12. Suter, M., J Am Water Works Assoc, 54, 371 (1962).

13. Broom, M.E., Personal Communication.

14. Barnes, I., Personal Communication.

DISCUSSION
DR. RIEMAN: We will discuss this briefly if there are questions or comments.
DR. MORGAN: I wonder if one of the geochemists present would like to comment on the possible accuracy of the free energy value for siderite? Some have been concerned with that.
MR. HEM: This is an old value.
DR. D. LANGMUIR (U. S. Geological Survey): The siderite free energy value quoted by Latimer is based on a 1918 solubility study. A comparison of the activity product of ferrous iron times bicarbonate for a number of New Jersey Coastal Plain ground waters flowing in aquifers which contain recent siderite, suggests at least the approximate validity of Latimer's free energy value. However, another experimental determination of siderite stability in the laboratory would be highly desirable. In any case a slight revision of the free energy value for siderite probably won't affect Mr. Hem's over-all picture significantly.